TIME FOR FAIRY TALES

compiled by May Hill Arbuthnot

Illustrated by John Averill, Wade Ray,
Seymour Rosofsky, and Debi Sussman

A representative collection of folk tales, myths, epics,

fables, and modern fanciful tales for children, to be used

in the classroom, home, or camp; especially planned for college classes

in children's literature; with a general introduction, four section

introductions, and headnotes for the individual stories

Scott, Foresman and Company

Revised Edition

TIME FOR FAIRY TALES

OLD AND NEW

To my university students, wherever they are,

in their homes or classrooms,

and to young teachers-in-training

who like to read and tell stories to children,

this book is affectionately dedicated.

Library of Congress catalog card number 61–5726

CONTENTS

PREFACE

TO THE REVISED EDITION

This book begins with folk tales from various peoples scattered over our earth. There would seem to be no reason to add to such a collection of ancient and traditional tales—tales which have been passed on by word of mouth for years and often centuries before being set down in print. Interestingly enough, however, in this last decade of space travel and moon-circling, many new collections of folk tales from both old and new sources have appeared. Publishing houses have seemed to vie with each other in issuing such collections, as well as many single tales, handsomely illustrated, including many of the children's old favorites from "Sleeping Beauty" to Andersen's "Swineherd." One of the chief reasons, then, for this revised edition of *Time for Fairy Tales* was the desire to present some of this wealth of new material, first by adding tales to national groups already included—one new Russian and two new French tales—and second by presenting tales from countries previously not represented—Scottish, Italian, Korean, Turkish, Polish, Costa Rican, and Canadian tales.

In the modern fanciful tales less change was necessary or possible. Some of the best recent examples of fanciful stories (for example, *Charlotte's Web,* a modern classic) are closely knit, book-length works and therefore do not lend themselves to excerpting. The two new examples from *The Borrowers* and *The Children of Green Knowe* are delightful exceptions. These two books and *Charlotte's Web* have such distinction that they may well take their places with *Alice's Adventures in Wonderland* and *The Wind in the Willows* as classics in everything except years.

Another important reason for this revision was the need to bring the bibliography up to date. Indeed, the number of folk tales and modern fanciful tales published in the last ten years is amazing. Adults who guide children's reading are continually astonished at the popularity of fantasy. Is the children's love of fantasy a reaction to the pressure of grim and menacing facts in this age of violence? Whatever the cause, it is a matter for rejoicing that so many gay, poignant, and well-written books are appearing in this field. Such literature keeps alive children's imaginations and helps their young spirits to escape, now and then, from the forebodings of the present into a world of beauty, laughter, and nobility.

May Hill Arbuthnot

Cleveland, 1960

TELLING STORIES AND
READING ALOUD TO CHILDREN

The principal of an elementary school paused in the hall, as a burst of contagious laughter rang out suddenly from the children in a second-grade room. Smiling involuntarily, the principal stepped into the room to see what had occasioned the merriment. The teacher was comfortably seated, reading aloud to her children, who were sitting, not with folded hands, but in a variety of relaxed positions. Their eyes were shining, their faces alive with interest as they anticipated the next ludicrous mishap that would overtake "Sonny-Boy Sim" in the forest. The principal remained to hear the hilarious conclusion of the story and the children's chuckles and comments. Then she went on her way thoughtfully. The children in that second-grade room were good readers. Why was the teacher spending time reading aloud? But come to think of it, that teacher always read aloud to her children and told stories, too. And whether she had a bright group or dull, her children were invariably interested in books and tackled their own reading activities with enthusiasm. Was there any connection between the children's interest in reading and the teacher's policy of telling stories and reading aloud? Perhaps so, but what could it be?

Why tell stories and read aloud to children?

There are many reasons why a program of telling stories and reading aloud to children is favorable to their own learning-to-read program. First, all normal children, bright or dull, good readers or poor, *need to have their reading interests expanded.* They get into a rut. Some children demand fairy tales and more fairy tales or horse stories and more horse stories. A grownup can introduce them to better examples of their favorite sort of reading and gradually lead them into other fields and other subjects. One teacher whose children were sure they disliked biography began to tell them exciting or poignant episodes from some of the new biographies. She soon had her children reading that form of literature avidly. Many a mother has made poetry lovers of her children because she liked to read it aloud and shared her pleasure with her children. It is the business of adults in homes as well as schools to expand children's reading interests by exposing them to a variety of literature.

This sounds like a dangerous reduction of effort the child should make for himself. And it is dangerous if it is used to the point where it becomes a substitute for the child's own reading. But if storytelling and reading aloud are used now and then, as special treats, they serve as incomparable baits to an expanded experience with books.

The second reason why reading aloud and telling stories to children are desirable practices is that *they help reduce the lag between the child's ability to read for himself and his capacity to understand and enjoy literature.* Such a lag exists for all except a few older children who are superior readers. For most children there is a difference of from one to three years (and even more in exceptional cases) between their reading skill and their level of appreciation. This becomes evident to the most casual observer if he follows the stories the child enjoys in the moving pictures and on radio or television and compares them with the necessarily limited content of the materials with which the child is learning to read. Until a child acquires an easy fluency in reading, this discrepancy is bound to exist. An eight-year-old may enjoy listening to a story which he will not be able to read independently for another year or two. And the poorer or more limited the child's reading skill, the more irksome this difference is apt to be. So, to keep the child's reading limitations from discouraging him and to keep him interested in making an effort to learn to read, it is highly desirable to read to him poetry and stories which captivate him although they are beyond his reading ability at present.

There is an amusing by-product of the adult's fluent, effortless reading aloud. *It makes reading seem easy.* The child unconsciously gets the impression that if dad or teacher or mother can read like that, and have so much fun doing it, it can't be so hard after all. Reading begins to seem a simple and an enviable skill.

A fourth virtue of storytelling and reading aloud is that the listening children *develop a growing power of aural comprehension.* Their ears and minds are focused on the spoken word, without any extraneous aids to understanding. In this age, when there are immensely expanded opportunities for listening, the ability to hear, comprehend, and react intelligently to the spoken word is of great importance. But it is not easy. In a university nursery school it was found that the children were so used to stories with copious illustrations that they could not attend to or readily comprehend a story which was told without benefit of pictures. This is a serious limitation in learning a language. The ear must be trained, not merely to hear sound, but to make those appropriate connections within the brain which result in understanding. Picture clues are invaluable first aids to reading in the early years. But parallel with the use of pictures to aid word meaning, children should have practice in hearing poetry and stories which are not illustrated in picture-story style. With such practice, their vocabularies will grow and so will their ability to understand and react intelligently to the spoken word.

Incidentally, *a word which has been heard and understood is easier to recognize in print.* So, actually, this reading aloud policy, used in moderation, is just one more useful device for promoting word recognition on the printed page. It

widens children's familiarity with words. It may increase their speaking vocabularies. It should train their ears for the music of language and their feeling for the beauty and power of words.

Finally, *storytelling and reading aloud make it easier for children to understand and enjoy certain types of literature which they might never try to read for themselves.* Probably no average American child will read *The Wind in the Willows* for himself. Does that mean that it should be removed from lists of books recommended for children's reading? The answer is No, and the justification for this answer is to be found in the example of the music groups in our schools. If they find most of their children are in the tin-pan-alley level of music enjoyment, do they say, "Ah, this means that there is no use in trying to give them Chopin, Schubert, and Beethoven. They could not understand them"? Indeed, they say nothing of the kind. Instead, they may begin where the child is, but they lead him to better music by daily and continuous exposure to it. Over and over, he hears simple, melodious selections from the classics until his ear is trained to these and he enjoys them. Then, he is ready to hear the themes of great symphonies in all their variations. Selections are discussed, replayed, and discussed again. The result of this music program in our schools is that young America today is listening to and enjoying better music than ever before.

Have we done as well for literature? Probably not, but we can if we go at it as systematically as the music people have. Such a program is immensely aided by teachers and parents who are themselves lovers of good literature. Books of quality and variety should be available to children both in their schools and their homes. And children should have a daily exposure to stories and poetry read aloud by adults who enjoy them and like to talk them over, informally, just for fun, as they read. A child who has grown up in a school or a home where someone reads aloud well and discusses as he reads is a lucky child because he acquires a homey approach to reading. He laughs or weeps or protests as the book progresses. He is used to talking books as some people talk baseball, with ardor and bias, because the people and situations in books seem as real as his baseball heroes. And children should, of course, develop their own point of view about their favorite and their not-so-favorite stories and characters.

When is there school time for reading aloud?

Teachers rightly raise the question about the time element in their already overcrowded curriculum. How can they possibly take a period to tell stories or read poetry and stories to the children? The general answer is that where there is a will to do it there will be time, but practically, it takes a little planning. Sometimes, stories in the children's readers suggest another story similar to or with a different slant on the same theme. Let the children conclude their reading period with a good stretch, and then read them the related story or poems. Good reader manuals list such materials and their sources. Sometimes, a social studies period finishes sooner than planned, or the nurse or the doctor keeps the children waiting. For such times have a book of stories on hand to read from. These are the casual, on-the-spur-of-the-moment periods which occur almost daily and may be utilized if you are prepared for them. But a planned period for reading aloud and storytelling, some three or four times a week, is also highly desirable. The last period either in the morning or the afternoon is particularly effective. A fascinating story, well read or told at the end of a school day, can unite teacher and children in a common interest. Small frictions and anxieties are forgotten in the pleasure of a shared interest. Children and teacher go home relaxed, buoyant, and secure in the feeling that school is a good place to be.

Camp councilors know the values of story hours round the campfire just before bedtime. Playground directors like to quiet the children down after strenuous activities by a story hour. In the home, the hour before dinner is ideal for stories if mother does not have to be too strenuously engaged in the kitchen. When she does, then just before bedtime for the children seems to be the favored period for reading or storytelling, and either mother or father may be pressed into service. This period has one disadvantage. Too much excitement is fatal to falling asleep; so, it means picking out poetry and stories of a quiet nature or at least tapering off with them.

If you know stories and poems to tell or say without benefit of books, your children are really in luck. A walk, a picnic, an ironing job, a too long automobile ride are all good occasions for the gentle arts of telling stories or saying poetry together.

You, who have children on playgrounds, in schools, camps, or your own homes, remember that the stories which you tell or read to your children you make memorable. They will associate those periods of enjoyment with you. Try, then, to conclude each day with the beauty, the fun, the thrill, and the nobility of fine literature.

Telling stories to children

Storytelling is the oldest, the least formal, and one of the most effective of the arts. It is the art not of the stage but of the fireside. When "peevish, won't-be-comforted, little bairns" have to wait for their suppers, or to have their curls brushed, or their playtime ended, mothers and nurses have always known the efficacy of storytelling. Many a father has discovered how close it brings him to his child to take him on his lap and tell him a tale, half remembered, half improvised, but wholly intimate and entertaining. Camp councilors can testify to the magic of storytelling around the glowing embers of a campfire. And both playground directors and teachers have seen a well-told story transform a group of belligerent young pugilists, at war with each other and the world, into a serene and united group. It is the intimate, personal quality of storytelling as well as the power of the story itself that accomplishes these minor miracles. Yet in order to work this spell, a story must be learned, remembered, and so delightfully told that it catches and holds the attention of the most inveterate wrigglers. And because this process of mastering a story requires laborious preparation and self-discipline, busy people ask quite reasonably, "But why not read a story? Why isn't reading just as effective as storytelling?"

The first answer to this question is that storytelling is more direct than reading. There is no book between you and your children. You can watch their faces and sense their reactions much more quickly than you can when you are cribbed and confined by an author's exact words and the physical presence of the book. The children watch your face and respond to the twinkle in your eye. They share with you anticipation of the joke that is just ahead. They also get the story plus your enjoyment of it. On your side, you watch the children, and their enjoyment heightens your own. Or you see Tommy begin to yawn or to tweak his neighbor's braid, and you call him back, not by speaking his name, but by intensifying the drama of the story. This close rapport between the storyteller and his audience makes it easier to see the blank look that an unfamiliar word or situation arouses. Immediately, the narrator paraphrases the strange word or amplifies the baffling situation until he sees comprehension replace confusion on the faces of his audience. In short, storytelling is direct communication between a grownup and children, almost as intimate as conversation. It creates a kind of homey "just-between-ourselves" atmosphere that makes it easy for children to accept and understand.

When to tell and when to read a story

The younger children are, the more they need the informal approach to literature that the storyteller brings. But even big boys and girls who read well are charmed by a storyteller who can relate, in folksy style, a tall tale, a folk story of wit and maturity, or an epic of heroic proportions. Folk tales were created orally and told over the years with many variations. They are infinitely more convincing to children today if they are told rather than read. Of course, it is better to read a story than to mangle it by poor storytelling. But anyone with any gift for spontaneous narration should tell and not read the folk tales. There is a unique satisfaction in making them come vividly to life for the children, just as the ancient storytellers made them live for their audiences long ago.

Stories which are better read, with book in hand, are of two varieties—the picture-stories for the youngest children and any story where the charm of the tale depends upon the exact words of the author. By picture-stories are meant such books as Marjorie Flack's *Angus* books or Beatrix Potter's *Tale of Peter Rabbit,* in which the pictures are an integral part of the text. Such

stories lose much of their charm when they are used without their pictures. They should be read to the children and the pictures shown along with the text. Stories that are distinguished for their literary style or ones in which the text would suffer from any alterations in the wording should be read and not told. Kipling's *Just So Stories* (see "The Elephant's Child," p. 336) is a good example of both. To tell one of these stories, taking any liberties with the text, destroys the quality of the story which depends for its subtle humor upon the author's play with words. When someone elects to "tell" these stories, it is not really storytelling but pure recitation. The two are vastly different. The recitation is a memorized performance; storytelling is intimate and partially spontaneous communication. Kenneth Grahame's *Wind in the Willows* and Andersen's *Fairy Tales* may be cut, here and there, but not otherwise altered. Both demand reading rather than telling if the children are to catch their unusual beauty of style and spirit. Even Wanda Gág's little picture-stories, in which the illustrations are often too small for a whole group of children to see as they are read, have a precise wording that suffers from telling and should, therefore, be read. In general, it is safe to say that folk tales should be told, in so far as it is possible, and picture-stories and all stories which demand the precise words of the author, should be read.

How to tell stories

For a decade or so, storytelling seemed to be a lost art, but a new interest in the folklore of our own United States has brought with it a renewed appreciation of this ancient art. It is good to hear men's voices again among the storytellers today, for fathers and grandfathers and now brothers returned from the wars have always been able to enthrall children with their tales. One of the virtues of masculine storytelling is the lack of expurgation. Men are less afraid of gory or violent action or the colorful language of stories than women are; so their tales have a robust quality that has sometimes been lacking in feminine storytelling. However, if you listen to a number of good storytellers, you discover that their styles are as individual as their personalities and only certain general qualities are common to all of them.

The first of these qualities is basic. *The storyteller must enjoy his story and the telling of it.* He must have fallen in love with its sly humor, its beauty, or its exciting action to the point where he wants to share it with others. Its style must have captivated him so that he wants to get the hang of it and be able to use it as easily as if its vernacular were his own native language. To hear Richard Chase tell a "Jack" tale, in the laconic drawl of the mountain man, or Mrs. Gudrun Thorne-Thomsen tell "Gudbrand on the Hill-Side," with tender sympathy for the folly and the loyalty of the old couple, is to feel at once the storyteller's love for his tale and his complete identification with its characters and its style. These are essential. No one can tell a story without a genuine unforced delight in the story and emotional identification with its characters and situations.

It is desirable also to have *an agreeable voice and pure diction.* No story can survive slovenly, obscure speech nor a voice that fades away or is unpleasantly harsh, loud, or nasal. But certainly no special voice is needed for storytelling. The saccharine voices and unctuous tones of some of the radio storytellers should be a warning to all who essay the art. Children can sense the artificial in a flash, and there is nothing they resent more than the tone of patronage, the "dee-ah children" approach. Speak naturally, but be sure that your natural voice is pleasing. Don't overarticulate, but use your everyday diction if that is crisp, good diction. It will improve both your voice and diction to read poetry aloud or practice your storytelling orally, listening critically to yourself as you do so. Is your voice pleasant to hear and varied? Can you suggest in the dialogue of a story the cockiness of the Pancake, the sorrow of the Goose Girl, the sternness of the princess' royal father in "The Frog-King"? It will help you to hear yourself objectively, if you can obtain a tape recorder. Or have someone with a good ear listen to you and evaluate your voice and diction. Speak naturally, but be sure that your speech is the best there is for your locale. The West does not speak like New England nor New England like the South. Every part of this broad country of ours has its impure and its good

speech. Try for the best diction indigenous to your part of the country.

The language of a story must be characteristic of the particular type of tale you are telling and it must be understood by your audience. This is easier said than done. Folk tales, because they grew up in certain countries and were told chiefly by rural people of long ago, have a distinct vocabulary and style. An Irish folk tale differs from a Norwegian, and both have a vocabulary and phrasing that would be completely foreign to an English folk tale, an East Indian story, or an American tall tale. A good storyteller must absorb this unique style of the story and he must also make it understandable to his audience. In spite of this latter requirement, a sensitivity to words should prevent you from interjecting any modern phrases or colloquialisms. "Boots got real mad" does not belong to a Norwegian folk tale, although it might fit a "Jack" tale. "Cinderella had a swell time at the dance" may be clear to the children, but it breaks the spell of the courtly French tale and turns Cinderella into a bobbysoxer out for "a good time." Read your story aloud until you catch its word patterns, and then, as you practice it orally, listen to yourself and see that the words fit the story.

To make the unfamiliar words clear to children is not always easy. Obsolete, rural, or little used words and phrases are common in folk tales. What, for instance, does a child get from such words as "lassie," "lad," "noodle," "goody," "steed," "mare," "foal," "tapers," or such phrases as "put the spade in his wallet," "laced her stays," "threw his tinder over the steed"? And these are just a few of the baffling words and phrases children hear in these folk tales. Don't drop the old words. They are part of the flavor of the story, but paraphrase them as briefly and unobtrusively as possible, "And the goody, the good wife, said—" or "So, he threw his tinder over the steed because he knew there was magic in his tinder." Such interjections clarify meaning without interrupting the flow of the story. But this practice can be carried to extremes. For instance, Sleeping Beauty's "spindle" does not call for an elaborate dissertation on spinning. It is merely a magic object (like the "tinder") which the fairy said would cause the spell to fall on Beauty. And it did. Sometimes, if a strange word is essential to knowing what the story is about, clear it up before you tell the tale. Sometimes talk about the spindle or tinder after the story is finished. Actually, these queer magic objects seldom bother the children. If they accept a fairy godmother or a magic horse, what is a spindle or a tinder more or less? In short, be clear but don't feel that you must turn lecturer in the middle of a story.

Your appearance while you tell a story is important in general, but the particulars of your style of beauty or plainness are of no consequence. What children look for are the twinkle in your eye and the relaxed air of leisure that promise a good time ahead. Sit down to tell your story, if possible, but if there is no corner in your classroom where you and your children can sit together, then stand, as comfortably as possible, and get on with the story. Perhaps you tell stories sitting in front of a fire with your child on your lap or on the ground by a campfire with children around you or by your child's bed or in a shady corner of a hot playground. It does not matter where you sit or stand just so that you create an atmosphere of easy enjoyment which storytelling should always carry with it.

Keep your hands free of handkerchiefs, pencils, or any other impedimenta which may cramp some of the small, natural gestures most storytellers use. But even to this rule there may be exceptions. A mother used to pacify her children, waiting impatiently for their supper, by telling them some of their favorite stories. It was funny to see her gesticulating like the goody in "The Pancake" with "the frying-pan in one hand and the ladle in the other." But she was satisfactorily dramatic and the children loved it, even if her "frying pan" was more hygienically the lid of a double boiler.

Practice your storytelling in front of a mirror to begin with, and watch your posture. Informality and ease do not mean sitting or standing sloppily. Watch yourself until you know how you should look, sitting or standing, so that you make an alert but an easy and agreeable picture. If you are telling to large groups, your clothes should be the kind the audience forgets the moment the tale begins. If you are a woman, don't wear a hat; it will give you a formal air. Beware of chains or dangles, which you may be tempted to finger

or, if you are a man, the inevitable pockets from which a hand can seldom be recalled once it has disappeared therein. These are all details of the general admonition—present to your audience an agreeable picture of relaxed enjoyment and the audience will relax too.

Finally, there is the matter of *learning to tell a story*, about which no two people are ever in complete agreement. Some visualize the characters and scenes in a story in considerable detail. They see the long bleak road down which the Lad travels to the North Wind's house. They see Tattercoats, advancing bravely to meet her handsome prince across the ballroom floor, with the geese hissing and waddling absurdly beside her to the tune of the herd boy's piping. When a narrator sees his story unfolding before his inner eye, he feels a great urgency to make his audience see it too and he relates it with conviction. But other storytellers are not conscious of this visualizing process, or feel that it comes only in flashes. The action of the story, the dramatic dialogue, the flow and cadence of word patterns, catch their imagination and remain in their memories.

Whatever your approach to a story may be, one thing is essential. *A story must be learned to the point where forgetting is impossible.* To learn a story to this degree would seem to imply exact memorizing and reciting, but that is not storytelling. The form of the folk tale was always fluid and varied with the teller. Even today, when words are learned from the printed page and not from the lips of another storyteller, no two students in a class in children's literature will tell a story alike. It becomes uniquely the story of each one who tells it. Exact memorizing of the printed text is not only out of key with folk tale tradition, but it is dangerous. A single slip of the memory will throw the teller completely off her narrative so that she has to start over, repeat phrases, or stop entirely while she racks her brain for the missing words. This is fatal to storytelling. If, instead of precise memorizing of every word, the story is thoroughly learned, in flexible form, it will remain in the memory for years.

The learning process goes something like this. Read your story carefully enough to know that you like it and would enjoy telling it. Then, read it aloud at a leisurely pace, noting the special vocabulary, the unusual turn of a phrase, the dialogue, and any repetitional refrains there may be. Then, begin to tell the story aloud, book in hand, from the beginning to the end. It will be a slow process, with constant reference to the book, but never mind, keep at it. Polish the beginning and the end until they are smooth and sure. Repeat dialogue over and over until you speak it fluently and are able to characterize the bully or the modest lad or the haughty sisters as you speak their words. Repeat the rough spots until you are sure of them but go through the whole story every time. Then, begin to live with your story. Tell it in bed, just before you fall asleep and in the morning, when you are getting dressed. Tell it on the bus or street car or while you are walking. When you reach the point where interruptions and distractions may stop your story but never cause you to forget it, when the language is flexible, fluent, and in character, when the whole creation seems to be a part of you, then you are ready to tell your story and you will be able to tell it years hence.

Storytelling is the art of the fireside, the campfire, the classroom, and the cribside but never the stage. It should remain as natural and sometimes as dramatic as everyday talk, but it is not drama. Small children like action and it is natural when you are telling them stories to make some of the large gestures that suggest the action of the tale, as making a big circular motion with the arm when the pancake rolls out of the door "like a wheel." But these imitative action-gestures should diminish to the vanishing point in stories for older children. With them, only the small gestures of everyday talk remain. Do not dramatize in storytelling. "The lassie made a low bow" is not accompanied by a bow. Instead, when you speak these words, your voice suggests the humility or fear of the lassie. Mockery, impudence, a tossing head or a hanging head are never acted literally, but merely suggested in voice and manner. The moment such restraint is forgotten, something stagy and foreign to the forthright simplicity of the folk tale creeps in.

How to read aloud

Most of the suggestions for telling stories apply to reading them aloud. A good voice and diction, sincerity, simplicity, a contagious enjoyment of the tale—these are as essential to reading as to telling a story. Reading may seem much easier than telling a story, but actually, with the exception of gaining complete independence of the text, the preparation is similar and it offers certain complications not found in storytelling. You have, for instance, the handicap of a book between you and your children. You look more at the book and less at the children. If there are pictures with the text, as in picture-stories, you have the added complication of showing the illustrations and satisfying the children's clamor to see them better. All this means that it is actually easier to lose your children when you are reading to them than it is when you tell them a story. To guard against this, be so familiar with the story you are going to read that you know just how and when to show the pictures and you can anticipate the suspense and build up to the climax most effectively.

Content and purpose of this book

This collection of stories has been assembled for grownups to tell or to read to children. It is designed for use in the home, around the campfire, with playground groups, and in the classroom, and its content will appeal to children from four-years-old to fourteen. Ideally, such a collection should contain only short stories, each one a complete unit in itself. But, unfortunately, some worth-while authors write only books and no short stories. It is possible that if a child encounters a portion of a fine book, presented with the contagious enthusiasm and prestige of grownup enjoyment, he may wish to read the whole book. It is, for instance, hard to imagine a child listening to the excerpt from *Robin Hood* or *Elmer and the Dragon* or *Pinocchio* without demanding the rest of the story. For this reason a few excerpts from books are included in this collection. They are in the minority, but they do occur with the hope that the adult who reads them will so spellbind the children that they will promptly demand the whole book.

This particular volume is devoted to tales of magic, old and new, grave and hilarious, fantastic nonsense and pseudoscientific. If a child does not like one story, he will probably be enthusiastic about another one. But it is well to be warned in advance that in the field of imaginative fiction there is a greater difference in children's tastes than in any other field. All you can do is to expose children to a variety of stories and be prepared to abide by their preferences.

Of course, you won't give children an unadulterated dose of these folk and fairy tales but will intersperse them with poetry, realistic fiction, and biography. Folk tales and myths may be used in connection with the study of a people; or you may just slip them in now and then for their entertainment values. The modern fanciful stories, in all their fascinating variety, can be used almost anytime as a special treat or as a change from a too intensive pursuit of the factual. All these imaginative stories are a wholesome antidote for the necessarily heavy emphasis upon facts which school and, indeed, our whole modern world entails. These tales, old and new, are imaginative play. They are dreams of a daft world where two and two may sometimes make five, or a tender world where a plain little princess becomes beautiful, but in any case, a world of wish fulfillment and fun.

Most of the stories in this collection will bear repetition, and the younger the children, the more they need such repetition. Perhaps the older children will come to love some of these stories to the point where they wish to take the book and read for themselves. This is greatly to be desired. But essentially, the collection is planned for grownups to use with children. What stories they are, sometimes full of beauty or sly humor, sometimes with a hint of tragedy or a burst of sheer nonsense. One quality they have in common, and that is imagination. They stretch the mind and spirit with their dreams. It is this quality of wonder and speculation that makes them worth using with children.

It is curious in an age as realistic and mechanized as ours that the magic of the folk tales still casts its spell on modern children. Witches and dragons, talking beasts and rebellious pancakes, flying carpets and cloaks of darkness, fairies and wise women, spells and enchantments are accepted as casually by children as airplanes and television.

It is true that the modern child becomes interested in fairy tales later than people used to think, and perhaps he wears them out a little sooner. Except for a few of the simplest nursery tales of "The Little Red Hen" and "The Story of the Three Little Pigs" variety, the peak of

OLD MAGIC: THE FOLK TALES

children's interest in tales of magic seems to fall somewhere around eight- or nine-years-old and not earlier. After nine there is a continued but steadily diminishing interest in such stories through the ages of ten, eleven, and twelve years. There are many reasons why the modern child still enjoys these tales, as we shall see, and why it is well to delay his exposure to any great number of them until sometime after the six-year-old period.

In the first place, most of these old stories were created by adults for the entertainment of other adults. Only a small fraction of them were composed for and told to children. A majority of the tales mirrors the mature lives, customs, beliefs, and emotions of peoples all over the world, and their adult themes make large numbers of them totally unsuited to children. There still remain, however, enough stories with lively plots, plenty of action, and conclusions which satisfy children's liking for justice and successful achievement, to account for their continued popularity with young people.

Origins of the folk tales[1]

The problem of why and how the folk tales originated has given rise to many conflicting theories. Some of these are now completely discredited, others are considered partially applicable, and new explanations have developed from the studies which psychologists and anthropologists have made of peoples all over the world, their motives and drives, customs and beliefs.

One of the earliest theories of folk tale origin stemmed from the belief that a language-group known as Aryan was a pure racial strain and that all of the folk tales sprang from this one source. This theory of *single origin* or *monogenesis* is now discredited because we know that there is no such thing as a pure racial strain, and that the Aryan group consisted of many strains.

The theory of *many origins* or *polygenesis* grew out of the belief that human beings are basically alike in their reactions, and would therefore make up the same kind of stories. This would seem to account for the 345 variants of "Cinderella" which have been discovered. But anthropological studies of different peoples show that human beings differ too widely in their customs and emotional reactions to explain such story similarities. Although stepmothers may be a problem in one group, they may not be in another.

The "Aryan myth" gave rise to another theory, namely, that the folk tales preserved *remnants of the nature myths* of that single racial strain. Perhaps Red Riding Hood may have symbolized the setting sun swallowed up by the darkness of the night, the wolf. But certainly no large num-

[1] For an expanded discussion of origins see May Hill Arbuthnot, *Children and Books,* pp. 231–234.

ber of the stories could be accounted for in this way. Nor could masses of them be explained on the grounds that they preserved *remnants of religious beliefs and rituals.* It is true that some evidence of early religions, charms, and incantations is to be found in a number of the tales, but the bulk of them contain no such traces.

Some of the recent psychological explanations of folk tale origins are interesting speculations. The idea that the tales were all *symbols of emotional fantasy,* unconscious sexual love for the parent, for example, has been refuted by anthropology's discovery that peoples differ in their emotional reactions and would also differ in their symbols. More plausible is the suggestion that the tales grew out of the *dreams and nightmares* of the storytellers. When the night turns cold, or the blanket slips off, we sometimes dream of being abroad with few or no clothes on. So, perhaps, tales developed of poor lassies out in the snow, clad only in paper dresses. And, perhaps, the descriptions of fine foods and rich feasts, so common in the fairy tales, may have grown from the hunger of the dreamer.

This theory suggests still another psychological interpretation of folk tale origin, namely that the old storytellers created in these tales a *satisfaction for their own unconscious frustrations and drives.* This is a fertile suggestion. The poor, the obscure, or the oppressed dream of riches, achievement, and power; so, they make up tales about the goose-girl who marries a prince and a cat that turns his master into the Lord Mayor of London—splendid dreams which symbolize *wish fulfillment* for each succeeding generation.

The most conclusive explanation of folk tale origin has grown out of the findings of social anthropology. In the light of their studies of modern folk societies, many anthropologists conclude that folk tales were the *cement of society,* the carriers of the moral code. The folk tales taught kindness, industry, and courage by dramatic stories revealing the rewards of these virtues. They showed meanness, laziness, and deceit exposed at last, and well punished. By creating these dramatic examples of good and bad behavior, properly rewarded or punished, they helped to cement society together with a common body of social and moral standards.

Modern children learn from these old tales

something about their own behavior in relation to other people. They learn that it's well to use your head. Henny Penny was punished for her gullibility, but the third little pig prospered because he had courage and used his wits. Children learn that you must look beyond appearances which do not always reveal character. The prince discovered this to his sorrow when he accepted the false maid as his princess, in "The Goose-Girl." Beauty found her true love because she looked beyond the ugliness of the poor beast to his kindness. And Boots accomplished the impossible because he had the courage to wonder, to investigate, and to tackle things for himself. To the sophisticated, such philosophy may not seem to be borne out by the hard facts of modern life. But actually, gangsters and dictators are still coming to bad ends. Children are going to inherit plenty of dragons, ogres, and giants to be exterminated. They need some of the cement of society to be found in the folk tales, a belief in the moral code of decency, courage, and goodness.

Wide diffusion of the folk tales

Folk tales are a legacy from anonymous artists of the past, the old wives and grannies as well as the professional storytellers. They were first created orally and passed on by word of mouth for generations before the printing press caught up with them. Soldiers, sailors, slaves, traders, monks, and scholars carried these stories from one country to another and, of course, the stories were changed in the process. A story passed on orally, from memory, is bound to vary with each new telling. This collecting of stories from the oral tradition of old storytellers is still going on today. Missionaries, marines, teachers, and scholars are still finding and preserving the old tales.

Written versions of some of the folk tales began to circulate in Europe in the twelfth century. Merchants and crusaders brought the talking beast tales from India, in Arabic or Persian translations, and these were soon turned into Latin. The great Celtic manuscripts introduced stories of witchcraft and enchantment that are said to go back to 400 B.C. The world of fairy which these remarkable vellum manuscripts recorded brought to the folk tales many of those elements which make the children call them "fairy tales." In the sixteenth century, Caxton's fine translations of Aesop's fables, the King Arthur legends, and the Homeric epics appeared. Although these are not folk tales, they are, like the ballads, a part of the rich stream of literature we know as folklore. In France, in the seventeenth century, Charles Perrault lent his name to a collection of eight famous folk tales which delighted the French court in Perrault's time.

Perrault's eight tales marked the beginning of a great interest in folklore collecting which has gone on ever since. The eighteenth century saw the appearance of some of the major collections. The Grimm brothers made scrupulous records of German tales from the lips of old storytellers, not for children's entertainment but as a serious study of the German language. Children soon appropriated them, however. In Norway, Peter Christian Asbjörnsen, a zoologist, and Jörgen E. Moe, a theologian and poet, collected the Norwegian folk tales. Since Sir George Webbe Dasent translated these into English, under the title *East o' the Sun and West o' the Moon,* they have become almost as familiar to American children as Grimm's "Hansel and Gretel." The English tales were edited by Joseph Jacobs, who was himself an authority on folklore. However, Jacobs had children definitely in mind in his collection and said frankly that he omitted episodes which were unduly coarse or brutal and made some changes in the language. However, when you study his changes they are not too heinous even to folklore scholars, and the full flavor of ancient storytelling is still there. Since Jacobs' time, printed collections of folk tales have multiplied until now there are collections from all the major countries of the world.[2]

Of special interest to the children of the United States is a newly inspired enthusiasm for American folk tales. Joel Chandler Harris' *Uncle Remus* tales of the American Negro have long delighted children and grownups. The so-called "tall tales" are favorites. Stories from the various tribes of the American Indian have been known but have never been popular, because they are not, on the whole, well constructed. But the new

[2] For further discussion of national collections see May Hill Arbuthnot, *Children and Books,* pp. 235–254.

enthusiasm is for the American variants of the old European folk tales which are now appearing in large numbers and which show a fresh turn of phrase and a humor that is characteristically American. Richard Chase is an enthusiastic collector of these tales, and his storytelling is doing much to popularize them all over the country.

Predominant types of folk tales

The stories in this collection are a sampling from important national and racial collections and from most of the types of stories which occur in folklore in general. Not all children will like every story, but most children will like a goodly number of them.

Accumulative or repetitional stories appeal to children four- to six-years-old or even seven. In these stories, plot is at a minimum and action takes its place. The episodes follow each other in logical order and are related in a repetitional cadence that is almost like a patter-song. It swings the listener along until the spiral action ends abruptly or runs backwards to its beginning. "The Old Woman and Her Pig" is an example of running up the spiral and back, but "Henny Penny" and "The Pancake" come to a sudden and surprising end at the top of the spiral. These stories grow imperceptibly, from mere chants to such plot stories as "The Four Musicians."

Talking beast stories are usually prime favorites. Sometimes the animals talk with human beings, as in "Puss in Boots" or "The Fox and His Travels," and sometimes they just converse with other animals. Their talk betrays their folly or wisdom even as human talk betrays it. Children feel superior when they sense the absurdity of Henny Penny's ruminations, and they identify themselves with the wise and witty remarks of Padre Porko. Occasionally there is a talking beast who is no beast at all but an unhappy prince or princess under a wicked spell. That is, of course, quite a different matter. But the talk of the three Billy Goats Gruff, Brer Rabbit, the clever jackal, and all the pigs, bears, and foxes of the folk tales is quite as understandable and perhaps a shade more reasonable to the child than much of the talking-to he receives from grownups.

The drolls or humorous stories were obviously told for sheer entertainment. Stories of the sillies

and the numskulls are ancestors of *The Peterkin Papers* and the modern moron tales. Fortunately, the humor of the folk tales is not confined to such foolish ones as "Clever Elsie" but progresses to the gaieties of "King O'Toole and His Goose," and "Tom Tit Tot," and the subtle humor of "Clever Manka" and "The Most Obedient Wife." The last two stories should always be used as a pair, with the elevens and twelves. Read them "The Most Obedient Wife" and hear the boys chuckle and the girls fume over the ignominious taming of the Wife. Then, the next day perhaps, read them "Clever Manka" and turn the tables, to the delight of the girls.

Realistic stories, wherein everything that happens might conceivably be so, are few and far between in the folk tales. The old storytellers seemed to have little use for the here-and-now stuff of everyday living. Even when they told a story that was possible, it was likely to be fabulous. "Clever Elsie" is the extreme of silliness. Dick Whittington, on the other hand, is a very possible hero of flesh-and-blood proportions and Manka and the obedient wife are possible, too. Perhaps the prettiest of the realistic stories is "Gudbrand on the Hill-Side," which is a tender version of "Mr. Vinegar," with a loving wife instead of a shrew. But, on the whole, folk tales pay scant attention to the laws of probability and are far happier and more numerous in the field of the impossible.

Some *religious tales* of long ago have been appropriated by the children. In the Middle Ages the stories which grew out of the morality plays often included the devil, the saints, or occasionally the Virgin or the Christ Child. The devil stories were invariably humorous with the devil getting the worst of it at the hands of resourceful human beings, especially scolding wives. The stories of the saints were generally grave, although this collection includes one that is broadly comic, "King O'Toole and His Goose."

Tales of magic are the heart of the folk tales. Fairies and fairy godmothers, giants, water nixies, lads who ride up glass hills, impossible tasks which are nonchalantly performed, three wishes, three trials, enchanted men or maidens, these are just a suggestion of fairy tale motifs and atmosphere. These give the tales an unearthly quality, often so beautiful that it comes close to poetry.

Actually, fairy folk are a remarkably varied lot as you will discover even in this selection of tales. Wise women, witches, and wizards may be either helpful or ruthless. Sometimes they serve as fairy godmothers and sometimes they lure children with gingerbread houses, for wicked reasons of their own. There are trooping fairies, with a queen, who live in underground halls of great magnificence. They sometimes steal children or bewitch handsome young men, but generally they are gay and kindly.

The Norse hill folk and the German dwarfs live underground also, but they are the humble workers of the fairy world. There are pixies who ride across moors on fairy steeds, water sprites and nixies who haunt wells and rivers, elves or brownies who sometimes abide in a house and make themselves useful, and an occasional imp, like Tom Tit Tot, who bobs up unexpectedly and invariably yearns for a human child to cheer his old age. Giants and ogres may be good or bad. Some are bloodthirsty and cruel and feast on their enemies. But others swallow oceans or stride over mountains in their seven-league boots on behalf of some cinderlad who shared his crust of bread with them.

Fairy animals not only aid discouraged heroes but, like Puss in Boots or the Horse of Power, are actually the brains of the enterprise. What a picturesque and unforgettable lot are these fairy beasts—Dapplegrim, sly old Lishka, the Flounder, the Three Bears, and the Three Pigs. And picturesque, too, are the magic objects in the tales—Aladdin's lamp, Boots' ram that coins money, and Freddy's merry fiddle.

Enchanted people are often a piteous group— the poor frog-king so rudely treated by the princess, Beauty's Beast, Little Burnt-Face, and the great White Bear, all waiting for someone to break their unhappy spells. And it can't be just anyone, either, because fairies and fairy spells work by definite laws. No magic ever ultimately succeeds for the mean or cowardly or cruel. But for kind souls, who are also courageous, help comes in time of need, and magic is always waiting for him who knows how to use it. Dark spells can only be broken by love and self-sacrifice and it takes a brave lassie to save her prince from the hags and witches who have ensnared him. The youngest son must first brave lions before magic reveals to him the water of life. Through all this fairy world the child hears over and over again that grace and strength are bestowed upon those who strive mightily and keep an honest, kindly heart.

Using the tales with children

On the whole the selections in this book are the simpler, merrier tales from the great collections. Each of the large groups begins with easier stories, most of them with nursery tales for the youngest children. They progress through tales of magic for the sevens, eights, and nines to the more mature stories which will command the respect of the elevens and twelves. Grownups will discover likenesses in some of the stories from the different national and racial groups, and these likenesses sometimes interest children. See "Tom Tit Tot" and "Rumpelstiltskin," "Mr. Vinegar" and "Gudbrand," "Cinderella," "Tattercoats," and "Little Burnt-Face," "Beauty and the Beast" and "East o' the Sun and West o' the Moon," "Sadko" and "Urashimo Taro and the Princess of the Sea." Remember that the folk tales were created and kept alive by the oral tradition of gifted storytellers. Read them aloud if you must, but tell them if you can, for in the spontaneity of good storytelling, these tales come most vividly to life for you and your children.

Finally, tales of magic should never be used exclusively or in too great numbers, but in balanced proportion to realistic fiction and informational reading. Use the folk tales in connection with the study of a people—the Chinese, English, or East Indian, for example. Use them to stimulate the children's creative urge to paint or dramatize or write. The tall tales have often set children to creating their own "whoppers." Above all, use these stories for sheer delight. They have humor, nonsense, romance, and poetic beauty. They will help to break up the tight literalness that overtakes some children. They also reiterate moral truths that are important for children to know. "Be of good cheer," these stories seem to say. "Use your head, keep a kindly heart, a civil tongue, and a fearless spirit and you will surely find the water of life and your heart's desire."

British folk tales

Joseph Jacobs, the folklorist, collected many of the English tales. He had a child audience in mind and intended, he said, "to write as a good old nurse will speak when she tells Fairy Tales." And he succeeded. Here in the British collections, you find the favorites of the nursery—the accumulative, the humorous, and the simple talking beast stories. What fun to share with small children—"The Three Little Pigs," "Henny-Penny," "The Three Bears" and all the others! The British folk tales are also notable for their giant-killers, which are not included in this book, for their humor, and for the songs and cadenced repetition that swing the stories along with a contagious rhythm. Of the stories included here, only "The Black Bull of Norroway" and "Whippety Stourie" are for the oldest children—the elevens and twelves. The others will be loved from four-years-old to ten or more.

THE OLD WOMAN AND HER PIG

This accumulative tale falls naturally into a kind of humorous chant, which the children like to try with you. It is funnier if you speed up the returning sequence a bit.

An old woman was sweeping her house, and she found a little crooked sixpence. "What," said she, "shall I do with this little sixpence? I will go to market, and buy a little pig."

As she was coming home, she came to a stile: but the piggy wouldn't go over the stile.

She went a little further, and she met a dog. So she said to him: "Dog! dog! bite pig; piggy won't go over the stile; and I shan't get home to-night." But the dog wouldn't.

She went a little further, and she met a stick. So she said: "Stick! stick! beat dog! dog won't bite pig; piggy won't get over the stile; and I shan't get home to-night." But the stick wouldn't.

She went a little further, and she met a fire. So she said: "Fire! fire! burn stick; stick won't beat dog; dog won't bite pig; piggy won't get over the stile; and I shan't get home to-night." But the fire wouldn't.

She went a little further, and she met some water. So she said: "Water! water! quench fire; fire won't burn stick; stick won't beat dog; dog won't bite pig; piggy won't get over the stile; and I shan't get home to-night." But the water wouldn't.

She went a little further, and she met an ox. So she said: "Ox! ox! drink water; water won't quench fire; fire won't burn stick; stick won't beat dog; dog won't bite pig; piggy won't get over the stile; and I shan't get home to-night." But the ox wouldn't.

She went a little further, and she met a butcher. So she said: "Butcher! butcher! kill ox; ox won't drink water; water won't quench fire; fire won't burn stick; stick won't beat dog; dog won't bite pig; piggy won't get over the stile; and I shan't get home to-night." But the butcher wouldn't.

She went a little further, and she met a rope. So she said: "Rope! rope! hang butcher; butcher won't kill ox; ox won't drink water; water won't quench fire; fire won't burn stick; stick won't beat dog; dog won't bite pig; piggy won't get over the stile; and I shan't get home to-night." But the rope wouldn't.

She went a little further, and she met a rat. So she said: "Rat! rat! gnaw rope; rope won't hang butcher; butcher won't kill ox; ox won't drink

"The Old Woman and Her Pig." From *English Fairy Tales*, edited by Joseph Jacobs. Selections from *English Fairy Tales* are used by permission of G. P. Putnam's Sons and Frederick Muller Ltd., London

water; water won't quench fire; fire won't burn stick; stick won't beat dog; dog won't bite pig; piggy won't get over the stile; and I shan't get home to-night." But the rat wouldn't.

She went a little further, and she met a cat. So she said: "Cat! cat! kill rat; rat won't gnaw rope; rope won't hang butcher; butcher won't kill ox; ox won't drink water; water won't quench fire; fire won't burn stick; stick won't beat dog; dog won't bite pig; piggy won't get over the stile; and I shan't get home to-night." But the cat said to her, "If you will go to yonder cow, and fetch me a saucer of milk, I will kill the rat." So away went the old woman to the cow.

But the cow said to her: "If you will go to yonder hay-stack, and fetch me a handful of hay, I'll give you the milk." So away went the old woman to the hay-stack; and she brought the hay to the cow.

As soon as the cow had eaten the hay, she gave the old woman the milk; and away she went with it in a saucer to the cat.

As soon as the cat had lapped up the milk, the cat began to kill the rat; the rat began to gnaw the rope; the rope began to hang the butcher; the butcher began to kill the ox; the ox began to drink the water; the water began to quench the fire; the fire began to burn the stick; the stick began to beat the dog; the dog began to bite the pig; the little pig in a fright jumped over the stile; and so the old woman got home that night.

THE STORY

OF THE THREE BEARS

This is the version of "The Three Bears" that the children like best. They will expect the traditional variations in the voices of the bears, from the deep, gruff voice of the Big Bear to the high, squeaky voice of the Little Wee Bear.

Once upon a time there were three Bears, who lived together in a house of their own, in a wood. One of them was a Little Wee Bear, and one was

"The Story of the Three Bears." From *English Fairy Tales* retold by Flora Annie Steel. By permission of The Macmillan Company, New York and Macmillan & Co. Ltd., London

a Middle-sized Bear, and the other was a Great Big Bear. They had each a bowl for their porridge: a little bowl for the Little Wee Bear; and a middle-sized bowl for the Middle-sized Bear; and a great bowl for the Great Big Bear. And they had each a chair to sit in: a little chair for the Little Wee Bear; and a middle-sized chair for the Middle-sized Bear; and a great chair for the Great Big Bear. And they had each a bed to sleep in: a little bed for the Little Wee Bear; and a middle-sized bed for the Middle-sized Bear; and a great bed for the Great Big Bear.

One day, after they had made the porridge for their breakfast, and poured it into their porridge-bowls, they walked out into the wood while the porridge was cooling, that they might not burn their mouths by beginning too soon, for they were polite, well-brought-up Bears.

And while they were away a little girl called Goldilocks, who lived at the other side of the wood and had been sent on an errand by her mother, passed by the house, and looked in at the window. And then she peeped in at the keyhole, for she was not at all a well-brought-up little girl. Then seeing nobody in the house she lifted the latch. The door was not fastened, because the Bears were good Bears, who did nobody any harm, and never suspected that anybody would harm them. So Goldilocks opened the door and went in; and well pleased was she when she saw the porridge on the table. If she had been a well-brought-up little girl she would have waited till the Bears came home, and then, perhaps, they would have asked her to breakfast; for they were good Bears—a little rough or so, as the manner of Bears is, but for all that very good-natured and hospitable. But she was an impudent, rude little girl and so she set about helping herself.

First she tasted the porridge of the Great Big Bear, and that was too hot for her. Next she tasted the porridge of the Middle-sized Bear, but that was too cold for her. And then she went to the porridge of the Little Wee Bear, and tasted it, and that was neither too hot nor too cold, but just right, and she liked it so well, that she ate it all up, every bit!

Then Goldilocks, who was tired, for she had been catching butterflies instead of running on her errand, sat down in the chair of the Great Big Bear, but that was too hard for her. And then she sat down in the chair of the Middle-sized Bear, and that was too soft for her. But when she sat down in the chair of the Little Wee Bear, that was neither too hard, nor too soft, but just right. So she seated herself in it, and there she sat till the bottom of the chair came out, and down she came, plump upon the ground; and that made her very cross, for she was a bad-tempered little girl.

Now, being determined to rest, Goldilocks went upstairs into the bedchamber in which the Three Bears slept. And first she lay down upon the bed of the Great Big Bear, but that was too high at the head for her. And next she lay down upon the bed of the Middle-sized Bear, and that was too high at the foot for her. And then she lay down upon the bed of the Little Wee Bear, and that was neither too high at the head, nor at the foot, but just right. So she covered herself up comfortably, and lay there till she fell fast asleep.

By this time the Three Bears thought their porridge would be cool enough for them to eat it properly; so they came home to breakfast. Now careless Goldilocks had left the spoon of the Great Big Bear standing in his porridge.

"SOMEBODY HAS BEEN AT MY PORRIDGE!" said the Great Big Bear in his great, rough, gruff voice.

Then the Middle-sized Bear looked at his porridge and saw the spoon was standing in it too.

"SOMEBODY HAS BEEN AT MY PORRIDGE!" said the Middle-sized Bear in his middle-sized voice.

Then the Little Wee Bear looked at his, and there was the spoon in the porridge-bowl, but the porridge was all gone!

"SOMEBODY HAS BEEN AT MY PORRIDGE, AND HAS EATEN IT ALL UP!" said the Little Wee Bear in his little wee voice.

Upon this the Three Bears, seeing that someone had entered their house, and eaten up the Little Wee Bear's breakfast, began to look about them. Now the careless Goldilocks had not put the hard cushion straight when she rose from the chair of the Great Big Bear.

"SOMEBODY HAS BEEN SITTING IN MY CHAIR!" said the Great Big Bear in his great, rough, gruff voice.

And the careless Goldilocks had squatted down the soft cushion of the Middle-sized Bear.

"SOMEBODY HAS BEEN SITTING IN MY CHAIR!" said the Middle-sized Bear in his middle-sized voice.

"SOMEBODY HAS BEEN SITTING IN MY CHAIR, AND HAS SAT THE BOTTOM THROUGH!" said the Little Wee Bear in his little wee voice.

Then the Three Bears thought they had better make further search in case it was a burglar, so they went upstairs into their bedchamber. Now Goldilocks had pulled the pillow of the Great Big Bear out of its place.

"SOMEBODY HAS BEEN LYING IN MY BED!" said the Great Big Bear in his great, rough, gruff voice.

And Goldilocks had pulled the bolster of the Middle-sized Bear out of its place.

"SOMEBODY HAS BEEN LYING IN MY BED!" said the Middle-sized Bear in his middle-sized voice.

But when the Little Wee Bear came to look at his bed, there was the bolster in its place!

And the pillow was in its place upon the bolster!

And upon the pillow——? There was Goldilocks' yellow head—which was not in its place, for she had no business there.

"SOMEBODY HAS BEEN LYING IN MY BED—AND HERE SHE IS STILL!" said the Little Wee Bear in his little wee voice.

Now Goldilocks had heard in her sleep the great, rough, gruff voice of the Great Big Bear; but she was so fast asleep that it was no more to her than the roaring of wind, or the rumbling of thunder. And she had heard the middle-sized voice of the Middle-sized Bear, but it was only as if she had heard someone speaking in a dream. But when she heard the little wee voice of the Little Wee Bear, it was so sharp and so shrill, that it awakened her at once. Up she started, and when she saw the Three Bears on one side of the bed, she tumbled herself out at the other, and ran to the window. Now the window was open, because the Bears, like good, tidy Bears, as they were, always opened their bedchamber window when they got up in the morning. So naughty, frightened little Goldilocks jumped; and whether she broke her neck in the fall, or ran into the wood and was lost there, or found her way out of the wood and got whipped for being a bad girl and playing truant, no one can say. But the Three Bears never saw anything more of her.

THE STORY
OF THE THREE LITTLE PIGS

It is likely that this story is the top favorite of all five-year-olds who know it.

Once upon a time when pigs spoke rhyme,
And monkeys chewed tobacco,
And hens took snuff to make them tough,
And ducks went quack, quack, quack, O!

There was an old sow with three little pigs, and as she had not enough to keep them, she sent them out to seek their fortune. The first that went off met a man with a bundle of straw, and said to him:

"Please, man, give me that straw to build me a house."

Which the man did, and the little pig built a house with it. Presently came along a wolf, and knocked at the door, and said:

"Little pig, little pig, let me come in."

To which the pig answered:

"No, no, by the hair of my chinny chin chin."

The wolf then answered to that:

"Then I'll huff, and I'll puff, and I'll blow your house in."

So he huffed, and he puffed, and he blew his house in, and ate up the little pig.

The second little pig met a man with a bundle of furze and said:

"Please, man, give me that furze to build a house."

Which the man did, and the pig built his house. Then along came the wolf, and said:

"Little pig, little pig, let me come in."

"No, no, by the hair of my chinny chin chin."

"Then I'll puff, and I'll huff, and I'll blow your house in."

So he huffed, and he puffed, and he puffed and he huffed, and at last he blew the house down, and he ate up the little pig.

The third little pig met a man with a load of bricks, and said:

"Please, man, give me those bricks to build a house with."

So the man gave him the bricks, and he built his house with them. So the wolf came, as he did to the other little pigs, and said:

"Little pig, little pig, let me come in."

"No, no, by the hair of my chinny chin chin."

"Then I'll huff, and I'll puff, and I'll blow your house in."

"The Story of the Three Little Pigs." From *English Fairy Tales*, edited by Joseph Jacobs. Used by permission of G. P. Putnam's Sons and Frederick Muller Ltd., London

Well, he huffed, and he puffed, and he huffed and he puffed, and he puffed and huffed; but he could *not* get the house down. When he found that he could not, with all his huffing and puffing, blow the house down, he said:

"Little pig, I know where there is a nice field of turnips."

"Where?" said the little pig.

"Oh, in Mr. Smith's home-field, and if you will be ready to-morrow morning I will call for you, and we will go together, and get some for dinner."

"Very well," said the little pig, "I will be ready. What time do you mean to go?"

"Oh, at six o'clock."

Well, the little pig got up at five and got the turnips before the wolf came (which he did about six), who said:

"Little pig, are you ready?"

The little pig said, "Ready! I have been and come back again and got a nice potful for dinner."

The wolf felt very angry at this, but thought that he would be up to the little pig somehow or other, so he said:

"Little pig, I know where there is a nice apple-tree."

"Where?" said the pig.

"Down at Merry-Garden," replied the wolf, "and if you will not deceive me, I will come for you at five o'clock to-morrow and get some apples."

Well, the little pig bustled up the next morning at four o'clock, and went off for the apples, hoping to get back before the wolf came; but he had further to go and had to climb the tree, so that just as he was coming down from it, he saw the wolf coming, which, as you may suppose,

frightened him very much. When the wolf came up he said:

"Little pig, what! are you here before me? Are they nice apples?"

"Yes, very," said the little pig. "I will throw you down one."

And he threw it so far, that, while the wolf was gone to pick it up, the little pig jumped down and ran home. The next day the wolf came again and said to the little pig:

"Little pig, there is a fair at Shanklin this afternoon; will you go?"

"Oh, yes," said the pig, "I will go; what time shall you be ready?"

"At three," said the wolf. So the little pig went off before the time as usual and got to the fair and bought a butter-churn, which he was going home with, when he saw the wolf coming. Then he could not tell what to do. So he got into the churn to hide, and by so doing turned it round, and it rolled down the hill with the pig in it, which frightened the wolf so much, that he ran home without going to the fair. He went to the little pig's house and told him how frightened he had been by a great round thing which came down the hill past him. Then the little pig said:

"Hah, I frightened you then. I had been to the fair and bought a butter-churn; and when I saw you, I got into it, and rolled down the hill."

Then the wolf was very angry indeed and declared he *would* eat up the little pig, and that he would get down the chimney after him. When the little pig saw what he was about, he hung on the pot full of water and made up a blazing fire, and, just as the wolf was coming down, took off the cover, and in fell the wolf; so the little pig put on the cover again in an instant, boiled him up, and ate him for supper and lived happy ever afterwards.

HENNY-PENNY

Perhaps the East Indian "The Hare That Ran Away" is the ancestor of this story, "The Pancake," "The Gingerbread Boy," and all the other runaways.

One day Henny-Penny was picking up corn in the cornyard when—whack!—something hit her upon the head. "Goodness gracious me!" said Henny-Penny; "the sky's a-going to fall; I must go and tell the king."

So she went along, and she went along, and she went along till she met Cocky-Locky. "Where are you going, Henny-Penny?" says Cocky-Locky. "Oh! I'm going to tell the king the sky's a-falling," says Henny-Penny. "May I come with you?" says Cocky-Locky. "Certainly," says Henny-Penny. So Henny-Penny and Cocky-Locky went to tell the king the sky was falling.

They went along, and they went along, and they went along till they met Ducky-Daddles. "Where are you going to, Henny-Penny and Cocky-Locky?" says Ducky-Daddles. "Oh! we're going to tell the king the sky's a-falling," said Henny-Penny and Cocky-Locky. "May I come with you?" says Ducky-Daddles. "Certainly," said Henny-Penny and Cocky-Locky. So Henny-Penny, Cocky-Locky, and Ducky-Daddles went to tell the king the sky was a-falling.

So they went along, and they went along, and they went along, till they met Goosey-Poosey. "Where are you going to, Henny-Penny, Cocky-Locky, and Ducky-Daddles?" said Goosey-Poosey. "Oh! we're going to tell the king the sky's a-falling," said Henny-Penny and Cocky-Locky and Ducky-Daddles. "May I come with you?" said Goosey-Poosey. "Certainly," said Henny-Penny, Cocky-Locky, and Ducky-Daddles. So Henny-Penny, Cocky-Locky, Ducky-Daddles, and Goosey-Poosey went to tell the king the sky was a-falling.

So they went along, and they went along, and they went along, till they met Turkey-Lurkey. "Where are you going, Henny-Penny, Cocky-Locky, Ducky-Daddles, and Goosey-Poosey?" says Turkey-Lurkey. "Oh! we're going to tell the king

"Henny-Penny." From *English Fairy Tales*, edited by Joseph Jacobs. Used by permission of G. P. Putnam's Sons and Frederick Muller Ltd., London

the sky's a-falling," said Henny-Penny, Cocky-Locky, Ducky-Daddles, and Goosey-Poosey. "May I come with you, Henny-Penny, Cocky-Locky, Ducky-Daddles, and Goosey-Poosey?" said Turkey-Lurkey. "Oh, certainly, Turkey-Lurkey," said Henny-Penny, Cocky-Locky, Ducky-Daddles, and Goosey-Poosey. So Henny-Penny, Cocky-Locky, Ducky-Daddles, Goosey-Poosey, and Turkey-Lurkey all went to tell the king the sky was a-falling.

So they went along, and they went along, and they went along, till they met Foxy-Woxy, and Foxy-Woxy said to Henny-Penny, Cocky-Locky, Ducky-Daddles, Goosey-Poosey, and Turkey-Lurkey: "Where are you going, Henny-Penny, Cocky-Locky, Ducky-Daddles, Goosey-Poosey, and Turkey-Lurkey?" And Henny-Penny, Cocky-Locky, Ducky-Daddles, Goosey-Poosey, and Turkey-Lurkey said to Foxy-Woxy: "We're going to tell the king the sky's a-falling." "Oh! but this is not the way to the king, Henny-Penny, Cocky-Locky, Ducky-Daddles, Goosey-Poosey, and Turkey-Lurkey," says Foxy-Woxy; "I know the proper way; shall I show it you?" "Oh, certainly, Foxy-Woxy," said Henny-Penny, Cocky-Locky, Ducky-Daddles, Goosey-Poosey, and Turkey-Lurkey. So Henny-Penny, Cocky-Locky, Ducky-Daddles, Goosey-Poosey, Turkey-Lurkey, and Foxy-Woxy all went to tell the king the sky was a-falling. So they went along, and they went along, and they went along, till they came to a narrow and dark hole. Now this was the door of Foxy-Woxy's cave. But Foxy-Woxy said to Henny-Penny, Cocky-Locky, Ducky-Daddles, Goosey-Poosey, and Turkey-Lurkey: "This is the short way to the king's palace; you'll soon get there if you follow me. I will go first and you come after, Henny-Penny, Cocky-Locky, Ducky-Daddles, Goosey-Poosey, and Turkey-Lurkey." "Why of course, certainly, without doubt, why not?" said Henny-Penny, Cocky-Locky, Ducky-Daddles, Goosey-Poosey, and Turkey-Lurkey.

So Foxy-Woxy went into his cave, and he didn't go very far, but turned round to wait for Henny-Penny, Cocky-Locky, Ducky-Daddles, Goosey-Poosey, and Turkey-Lurkey. So at last at first Turkey-Lurkey went through the dark hole into the cave. He hadn't got far when "Hrumph," Foxy-Woxy snapped off Turkey-Lurkey's head and threw his body over his left shoulder. Then Goosey-Poosey went in, and "Hrumph," off went her head and Goosey-Poosey was thrown beside Turkey-Lurkey. Then Ducky-Daddles waddled down, and "Hrumph," snapped Foxy-Woxy, and Ducky-Daddles' head was off and Ducky-Daddles was thrown alongside Turkey-Lurkey and Goosey-Poosey. Then Cocky-Locky strutted down into the cave, and he hadn't gone far when "Snap, Hrumph!" went Foxy-Woxy and Cocky-Locky was thrown alongside of Turkey-Lurkey, Goosey-Poosey, and Ducky-Daddles.

But Foxy-Woxy had made two bites at Cocky-Locky; and when the first snap only hurt Cocky-Locky, but didn't kill him, he called out to Henny-Penny. But she turned tail and off she ran home; so she never told the king the sky was a-falling.

THE COCK, THE MOUSE, AND THE LITTLE RED HEN

Once upon a time there was a hill, and on the hill there was a pretty little house.

It had one little green door, and four little windows with green shutters, and in it there lived A COCK, and A MOUSE, and A LITTLE RED HEN. On another hill close by, there was another little house. It was very ugly. It had a door that wouldn't shut, and two broken windows, and all the paint was off the shutters. And in this house there lived A BOLD BAD FOX and FOUR BAD LITTLE FOXES.

One morning these four bad little foxes came to the big bad Fox and said:

"Oh, Father, we're so hungry!"

"We had nothing to eat yesterday," said one.

"And scarcely anything the day before," said another.

The big bad Fox shook his head, for he was thinking. At last he said in a big gruff voice:

"On the hill over there I see a house. And in that house there lives a Cock."

"And a Mouse!" screamed two of the little foxes.

"The Cock, the Mouse, and the Little Red Hen." By Félicité LeFèvre

"And a little Red Hen," screamed the other two.

"And they are nice and fat," went on the big bad Fox. "This very day I'll take my sack and I will go up that hill and in at that door, and into my sack I will put the Cock, and the Mouse, and the little Red Hen."

So the four little foxes jumped for joy, and the big bad Fox went to get his sack ready to start upon his journey.

But what was happening to the Cock, and the Mouse, and the little Red Hen, all this time?

Well, sad to say, the Cock and the Mouse had both got out of bed on the wrong side that morning. The Cock said the day was too hot, and the Mouse grumbled because it was too cold.

They came grumbling down to the kitchen, where the good little Red Hen, looking as bright as a sunbeam, was bustling about.

"Who'll get some sticks to light the fire with?" she asked.

"I shan't," said the Cock.

"I shan't," said the Mouse.

"Then I'll do it myself," said the little Red Hen.

So off she ran to get the sticks. "And now, who'll fill the kettle from the spring?" she asked.

"I shan't," said the Cock.

"I shan't," said the Mouse.

"Then I'll do it myself," said the little Red Hen.

And off she ran to fill the kettle.

"And who'll get the breakfast ready?" she asked, as she put the kettle on to boil.

"I shan't," said the Cock.

"I shan't," said the Mouse.

"I'll do it myself," said the little Red Hen.

All breakfast time the Cock and the Mouse quarrelled and grumbled. The Cock upset the milk jug, and the Mouse scattered crumbs upon the floor.

"Who'll clear away the breakfast?" asked the poor little Red Hen, hoping they would soon leave off being cross.

"I shan't," said the Cock.

"I shan't," said the Mouse.

"Then I'll do it myself," said the little Red Hen.

So she cleared everything away, swept up the crumbs and brushed up the fireplace.

"And now, who'll help me to make the beds?"

"I shan't," said the Cock.

"I shan't," said the Mouse.

"Then I'll do it myself," said the little Red Hen.

And she tripped away upstairs.

But the lazy Cock and Mouse each sat down in a comfortable arm-chair by the fire, and soon fell fast asleep.

Now the bad Fox had crept up the hill and into the garden, and if the Cock and Mouse hadn't been asleep, they would have seen his sharp eyes peeping in at the window.

"Rat tat tat! Rat tat tat!" the Fox knocked at the door.

"Who can that be?" said the Mouse, half opening his eyes.

"Go and look for yourself, if you want to know," said the rude Cock.

"It's the postman perhaps," thought the Mouse to himself, "and he may have a letter for me." So without waiting to see who it was, he lifted the latch and opened the door.

As soon as he opened it, in jumped the big Fox.

"Oh! oh! oh!" squeaked the Mouse, as he tried to run up the chimney.

"Doodle doodle do!" screamed the Cock, as he jumped on the back of the biggest arm-chair.

But the Fox only laughed, and without more ado he took the little Mouse by the tail, and popped him into the sack, and seized the Cock by the neck and popped him in too.

Then the poor little Red Hen came running downstairs to see what all the noise was about, and the Fox caught her and put her into the sack with the others.

Then he took a long piece of string out of his pocket, wound it round, and round, and round the mouth of the sack, and tied it very tight indeed. After that he threw the sack over his back, and off he set down the hill, chuckling to himself.

"Oh, I wish I hadn't been so cross," said the Cock, as they went bumping about.

"Oh! I wish I hadn't been so lazy," said the Mouse, wiping his eyes with the tip of his tail.

"It's never too late to mend," said the little Red Hen. "And don't be too sad. See, here I have my little work-bag, and in it there is a pair of scissors, and a little thimble, and a needle and

thread. Very soon you will see what I am going to do."

Now the sun was very hot, and soon Mr. Fox began to feel his sack was heavy, and at last he thought he would lie down under a tree and go to sleep for a little while. So he threw the sack down with a big bump, and very soon fell fast asleep.

Snore, snore, snore, went the Fox.

As soon as the little Red Hen heard this, she took out her scissors, and began to snip a hole in the sack just large enough for the Mouse to creep through.

"Quick," she whispered to the Mouse, "run as fast as you can and bring back a stone just as large as yourself."

Out scampered the Mouse, and soon came back, dragging the stone after him.

"Push it in here," said the little Red Hen, and he pushed it in, in a twinkling.

Then the little Red Hen snipped away at the hole, till it was large enough for the Cock to get through.

"Quick," she said, "run and get a stone as big as yourself."

Out flew the Cock, and soon came back quite out of breath, with a big stone, which he pushed into the sack too.

Then the little Red Hen popped out, got a stone as big as herself, and pushed it in. Next she put on her thimble, took out her needle and thread, and sewed up the hole as quickly as ever she could.

When it was done, the Cock, and the Mouse and the little Red Hen ran home very fast, shut the door after them, drew the bolts, shut the shutters, and drew down the blinds and felt quite safe.

The bad Fox lay fast asleep under the tree for some time, but at last he awoke.

"Dear, dear," he said, rubbing his eyes and then looking at the long shadows on the grass, "how late it is getting. I must hurry home."

So the bad Fox went grumbling and groaning down the hill, till he came to the stream. Splash! In went one foot. Splash! In went the other, but the stones in the sack were so heavy that at the very next step, down tumbled Mr. Fox into a deep pool. And then the fishes carried him off to their fairy caves and kept him a prisoner there, so he was never seen again. And the four greedy little foxes had to go to bed without any supper.

But the Cock and the Mouse never grumbled again. They lit the fire, filled the kettle, laid the breakfast, and did all the work, while the good little Red Hen had a holiday, and sat resting in the big arm-chair.

No foxes ever troubled them again, and for all I know they are still living happily in the little house with the green door and green shutters, which stands on the hill.

THE TRAVELS OF A FOX

There are some amusing phrases in this story which you must make the most of—"while I go to Squintum's," for example. The children like to roll that one under their tongues.

One day a fox was digging behind a stump and he found a bumblebee; and the fox put the bumblebee in a bag and took the bag over his shoulder and travelled.

At the first house he came to, he went in and said to the mistress of the house, "Can I leave my bag here while I go to Squintum's?"

"Yes," said the woman.

"Then be careful not to open the bag," said the fox.

But as soon as he was out of sight the woman said to herself, "Well, I wonder what the fellow has in his bag that he is so careful about. I will look and see. It can't do any harm, for I shall tie the bag right up again."

However, the moment she unloosed the string, out flew the bumblebee, and the rooster caught him and ate him all up.

After a while the fox came back. He took up his bag and knew at once that his bumblebee was gone, and he said to the woman, "Where is my bumblebee?"

And the woman said, "I untied the string just to take a little peep to find out what was in your bag, and the bumblebee flew out and the rooster ate him."

"The Travels of a Fox." From *The Oak Tree Fairy Book*, edited by Clifton Johnson, copyright 1933. With the kind permission of Mrs. Clifton Johnson

"Very well," said the fox; "I must have the rooster, then."

So he caught the rooster and put him in his bag and travelled.

At the next house he came to, he went in and said to the mistress of the house, "Can I leave my bag here while I go to Squintum's?"

"Yes," said the woman.

"Then be careful not to open the bag," said the fox.

But as soon as he was out of sight the woman said to herself, "Well, I wonder what the fellow has in his bag that he is so careful about. I will look and see. It can't do any harm, for I shall tie the bag right up again."

However, the moment she unloosed the string the rooster flew out and the pig caught him and ate him all up.

After a while the fox came back. He took up his bag and knew at once that his rooster was gone, and he said to the woman, "Where is my rooster?"

And the woman said, "I untied the string just to take a little peep to find out what was in your bag, and the rooster flew out and the pig ate him."

"Very well," said the fox, "I must have the pig, then."

So he caught the pig and put him in his bag and travelled.

At the next house he came to, he went in and said to the mistress of the house, "Can I leave my bag here while I go to Squintum's?"

"Yes," said the woman.

"Then be careful not to open the bag," said the fox.

But as soon as he was out of sight the woman said to herself, "Well, I wonder what the fellow has in his bag that he is so careful about. I will look and see. It can't do any harm, for I shall tie the bag right up again."

However, the moment she unloosed the string, the pig jumped out and the ox gored him.

After a while the fox came back. He took up his bag and knew at once that his pig was gone, and he said to the woman, "Where is my pig?"

And the woman said, "I untied the string just to take a little peep to find out what was in your bag, and the pig jumped out and the ox gored him."

And the woman said, "I untied the string just to take a little peep to find out what was in your bag, and the ox got out and my little boy chased him out of the house and across a meadow and over a hill, clear out of sight."

"Very well," said the fox, "I must have the little boy, then."

So he caught the little boy and put him in his bag and travelled.

At the next house he came to, he went in and said to the mistress of the house, "Can I leave my bag here while I go to Squintum's?"

"Yes," said the woman.

"Then be careful not to open the bag," said the fox.

The woman had been making cake, and when it was baked she took it from the oven, and her children gathered around her teasing for some of it.

"Oh, ma, give me a piece!" said one, and "Oh, ma, give me a piece!" said each of the others.

And the smell of the cake came to the little boy in the bag, and he heard the children beg for the cake, and he said, "Oh, mammy, give me a piece!"

"Very well," said the fox, "I must have the ox, then."

So he caught the ox and put him in his bag and travelled.

At the next house he came to, he went in and said to the mistress of the house, "Can I leave my bag here while I go to Squintum's?"

"Yes," said the woman.

"Then be careful not to open the bag," said the fox.

But as soon as he was out of sight the woman said to herself, "Well, I wonder what the fellow has in his bag that he is so careful about. I will look and see. It can't do any harm, for I shall tie the bag right up again."

However, the moment she unloosed the string, the ox got out, and the woman's little boy chased the ox out of the house and across a meadow and over a hill, clear out of sight.

After a while the fox came back. He took up his bag and knew at once that his ox was gone, and he said to the woman, "Where is my ox?"

Then the woman opened the bag and took the little boy out; and she put the house-dog in the bag in the little boy's place, and the little boy joined the other children.

After a while the fox came back. He took up his bag and he saw that it was tied fast and he thought that the little boy was safe inside. "I have been all day on the road," said he, "without a thing to eat, and I am getting hungry. I will just step off into the woods now and see how this little boy I have in my bag tastes."

So he put the bag on his back and travelled deep into the woods. Then he sat down and untied the bag, and if the little boy had been in there things would have gone badly with him.

But the little boy was at the house of the woman who made the cake, and when the fox untied the bag the house-dog jumped out and killed him.

MASTER OF ALL MASTERS

A girl once went to the fair to hire herself for servant. At last a funny-looking old gentleman engaged her, and took her home to his house. When she got there, he told her that he had something to teach her, for that in his house he had his own names for things.

He said to her: "What will you call me?"

"Master or mister, or whatever you please, sir," says she.

He said: "You must call me 'master of all masters.' And what would you call this?" pointing to his bed.

"Bed or couch, or whatever you please, sir."

"No, that's my 'barnacle.' And what do you call these?" said he pointing to his pantaloons.

"Breeches or trousers, or whatever you please, sir."

"You must call them 'squibs and crackers.' And what would you call her?" pointing to the cat.

"Cat or kit, or whatever you please, sir."

"You must call her 'white-faced simminy.' And this now," showing the fire, "what would you call this?"

"Fire or flame, or whatever you please, sir."

"You must call it 'hot cockalorum,' and what this?" he went on, pointing to the water.

"Water or wet, or whatever you please, sir."

"No, 'pondalorum' is its name. And what do you call all this?" asked he as he pointed to the house.

"House or cottage, or whatever you please, sir."

"You must call it 'high topper mountain.'"

That very night the servant woke her master up in a fright and said: "Master of all masters, get out of your barnacle and put on your squibs and crackers. For white-faced simminy has got a spark of hot cockalorum on its tail, and unless you get some pondalorum, high topper mountain will be all on hot cockalorum". . . .
. . . . That's all.

MR. VINEGAR

Gudbrand in the Scandinavian version of this tale was a luckier man than Mr. Vinegar, for in spite of Gudbrand's follies his wife remained loyal and loving and his foolish adventures had a happy conclusion.

Mr. and Mrs. Vinegar were very poor, and they lived in a shabby little house that they had built with their own hands. It was made of old boards and other rubbish which they had picked up, and it rattled and shook in every high wind. One morning, Mrs. Vinegar, who was a very good housewife, was busily sweeping her kitchen floor when an unlucky thump of the broom against the walls brought down the whole house, clitter-clatter about her ears. Mr. Vinegar had gone to a neighboring thicket to gather some fagots, and she hurried off with much weeping and wailing to tell him of the disaster.

When she found him she exclaimed, "Oh, Mr. Vinegar! Mr. Vinegar! we are ruined, we are ruined! I have knocked the house down and it is all to pieces!"

"My dear," said Mr. Vinegar, "pray do not

"Master of All Masters." From *English Fairy Tales*, edited by Joseph Jacobs. Used by permission of G. P. Putnam's Sons and Frederick Muller Ltd., London

"Mr. Vinegar." From *The Oak Tree Fairy Book*, edited by Clifton Johnson, copyright 1933. With the kind permission of Mrs. Clifton Johnson

weep any more. I will go back with you and see what can be done."

So they returned, and Mr. Vinegar said, "Yes, wife, the house is all in bits and we can never live in it again; but here is the door. I will take that on my back and we will go forth to seek our fortune."

With his wife's help he got the door on his back, and off they started. They walked all that day, and by nightfall they were both very tired. They had now come to a thick forest and Mr. Vinegar said, "My love, I will climb up into a tree with this door and you shall follow after."

So he climbed up among the branches of a great tree, and when he had adjusted the door at a level Mrs. Vinegar climbed up also, and they stretched their weary limbs on it and were soon fast asleep.

But in the middle of the night Mr. Vinegar was awakened by the sound of voices directly below him. He looked down and, to his dismay, saw that a party of robbers were met under the tree to divide some money they had stolen.

"Jack," said one, "here's five pounds for you; and Bill, here's ten pounds for you; and Bob, here's three pounds for you."

Mr. Vinegar was so frightened he could listen no longer, and he trembled so violently that he shook the door off the branches on which it lay, and he and Mrs. Vinegar had to cling to the tree to save themselves from a bad tumble. When the door began to drop, the noise it made startled the robbers and they looked up to learn the cause, but no sooner did they do this than the door came down on their heads and they all ran away greatly terrified.

Mr. and Mrs. Vinegar, however, dared not quit their tree till broad daylight. Then Mr. Vinegar scrambled down.

"I hope the door was not broken by its fall," said he as he lifted it.

Just then he espied a number of golden guineas that had been beneath the door where they had been dropped on the ground by the robbers in their haste to get away.

"Come down, Mrs. Vinegar!" he cried, "come down, I say! Our fortune is made! Come down, I say!"

Mrs. Vinegar came down as quickly as she could and saw the money with great delight, and when they counted it they found they were the possessors of forty guineas. "Now, my dear," said she, "I'll tell you what you shall do. You must take these forty guineas and go to the nearest town and buy a cow. I can make butter and cheese which you shall sell at market, and we shall then be able to live very comfortably."

"I will do as you say," replied Mr. Vinegar, "and you can stay here till I return."

So he took the money and went off to the nearest town; and there was a fair in the town, and crowds of people. When he arrived he walked about until he saw a beautiful red cow that he thought would just suit him.

"Oh, if I only had that cow," said Mr. Vinegar, "I should be the happiest man alive."

Then he offered the forty guineas for the cow and the owner was quite ready to part with it at that price, and the bargain was made. Mr. Vinegar was proud of his purchase, and he led the cow backwards and forwards to show it. But by and by he saw a man playing some bagpipes—tweedledum, tweedledee. The children followed after the bagpipe man, and he appeared to be pocketing a great deal of money.

"What a pleasant and profitable life that musician must lead," said Mr. Vinegar. "If I had that instrument I should be the happiest man alive, and I could earn far more than with this cow."

So he went up to the man and said, "Friend, what a charming instrument that is, and what a deal of money you must make!"

"Why, yes," said the man; "I make a great deal of money, to be sure, and it is a wonderful instrument."

"Oh!" cried Mr. Vinegar, "how I should like to possess it!"

"Well," said the man, "I will exchange it for your red cow."

"Done!" said the delighted Mr. Vinegar.

So the beautiful red cow was given for the bagpipes. Mr. Vinegar walked up and down with his purchase, but in vain he attempted to play a tune, and the children, instead of giving him pennies, hooted and laughed at him. The day was chilly and poor Mr. Vinegar's fingers grew very cold. At last, heartily ashamed and mortified, he was leaving the town when he met a man wearing a fine, thick pair of gloves.

"Oh, my fingers are so very cold!" said Mr.

Vinegar to himself. "If I had those warm gloves I should be the happiest man alive."

Then he went up to the man and said to him, "Friend, you seem to have a capital pair of gloves there."

"Yes, truly," replied the man, "these are excellent gloves."

"Well," said Mr. Vinegar, "I should like to have them. I will give you these bagpipes for them."

"All right," said the man, and he took the bagpipes and Mr. Vinegar put on the gloves and felt entirely contented as he trudged along toward the forest.

But the farther he walked the more tired he became, until presently he saw a man coming toward him with a good stout cane in his hand. "Oh!" said Mr. Vinegar, "if I had that cane I should be the happiest man alive."

Then he said to the man, "Friend, what a rare good cane you have."

"Yes," the man responded, "I have used it for many a mile and it has been a great help."

"How would it suit you to give it to me in exchange for these gloves?" asked Mr. Vinegar.

"I will do so willingly," replied the man.

"My hands had become perfectly warm," said Mr. Vinegar as he went on with his cane, "and my legs were very weary. I could not have done better."

As he drew near to the forest where he had left his wife he heard an owl on a tree laughing, "Hoo, hoo, hoo!" Then it called out his name and he stopped to ask what it wanted.

"Mr. Vinegar," said the owl, "you foolish man, you blockhead, you simpleton! you went to the fair and laid out all your money in buying a cow. Not content with that, you changed the cow for some bagpipes on which you could not play and which were not worth one tenth as much as the cow. Ah, foolish, foolish man! Then you no sooner had the bagpipes than you changed them for the gloves that were worth not one quarter as much as the bagpipes; and when you got the gloves you exchanged them for a cane, and now for your forty guineas you have nothing to show but that poor miserable stick which you might have cut in any hedge. Hoo, hoo, hoo, hoo, hoo!"

The bird laughed loud and long, and Mr. Vinegar became very angry and threw his cane at its head. The cane lodged in the tree, and Mr. Vinegar returned to his wife without money, cow, bagpipes, gloves, or stick, and she said things to him that he liked even less than what the bird had said.

TATTERCOATS

This is one of the prettiest of the 345 variants of the "Cinderella" theme.

In a great Palace by the sea there once dwelt a very rich old lord, who had neither wife nor children living, only one little granddaughter, whose face he had never seen in all her life. He hated her bitterly, because at her birth his favourite daughter died; and when the old nurse brought him the baby, he swore that it might live or die as it liked, but he would never look on its face as long as it lived.

So he turned his back, and sat by his window looking out over the sea, and weeping great tears for his lost daughter, till his white hair and beard grew down over his shoulders and twined round his chair and crept into the chinks of the floor, and his tears, dropping on to the window-ledge, wore a channel through the stone, and ran away in a little river to the great sea. And, meanwhile, his granddaughter grew up with no one to care for her, or clothe her; only the old nurse, when no one was by, would sometimes give her a dish of scraps from the kitchen, or a torn petticoat from the rag-bag; while the other servants of the Palace would drive her from the house with blows and mocking words, calling her "Tattercoats," and pointing at her bare feet and shoulders, till she ran away crying, to hide among the bushes.

And so she grew up, with little to eat or wear, spending her days in the fields and lanes, with only the gooseherd for a companion, who would play to her so merrily on his little pipe, when she was hungry, or cold, or tired, that she forgot all her troubles, and fell to dancing, with his flock of noisy geese for partners.

"Tattercoats." From *More English Fairy Tales*, edited by Joseph Jacobs. By permission of G. P. Putnam's Sons and Frederick Muller Ltd., London

But, one day, people told each other that the King was travelling through the land, and in the town near by was to give a great ball to all the lords and ladies of the country, when the Prince, his only son, was to choose a wife.

One of the royal invitations was brought to the Palace by the sea, and the servants carried it up to the old lord who still sat by his window, wrapped in his long white hair and weeping into the little river that was fed by his tears.

But when he heard the King's command, he dried his eyes and bade them bring shears to cut him loose, for his hair had bound him a fast prisoner and he could not move. And then he sent them for rich clothes, and jewels, which he put on; and he ordered them to saddle the white horse, with gold and silk, that he might ride to meet the King.

Meanwhile Tattercoats had heard of the great doings in the town, and she sat by the kitchen-door weeping because she could not go to see them. And when the old nurse heard her crying she went to the Lord of the Palace, and begged him to take his granddaughter with him to the King's ball.

But he only frowned and told her to be silent, while the servants laughed and said: "Tattercoats is happy in her rags, playing with the gooseherd, let her be—it is all she is fit for."

A second, and then a third time, the old nurse begged him to let the girl go with him, but she

was answered only by black looks and fierce words, till she was driven from the room by the jeering servants, with blows and mocking words.

Weeping over her ill-success, the old nurse went to look for Tattercoats; but the girl had been turned from the door by the cook, and had run away to tell her friend the gooseherd how unhappy she was because she could not go to the King's ball.

But when the gooseherd had listened to her story, he bade her cheer up, and proposed that they should go together into the town to see the King, and all the fine things; and when she looked sorrowfully down at her rags and bare feet, he played a note or two upon his pipe, so gay and merry, that she forgot all about her tears and her troubles, and before she well knew, the herdboy had taken her by the hand, and she, and he, and the geese before them, were dancing down the road towards the town.

Before they had gone very far, a handsome young man, splendidly dressed, rode up and stopped to ask the way to the castle where the King was staying; and when he found that they too were going thither, he got off his horse and walked beside them along the road.

The herdboy pulled out his pipe and played a low sweet tune, and the stranger looked again and again at Tattercoats' lovely face till he fell deeply in love with her, and begged her to marry him.

But she only laughed, and shook her golden head.

"You would be finely put to shame if you had a goosegirl for your wife!" said she; "go and ask one of the great ladies you will see to-night at the King's ball, and do not flout poor Tattercoats."

But the more she refused him the sweeter the pipe played, and the deeper the young man fell in love; till at last he begged her, as a proof of his sincerity, to come that night at twelve to the King's ball, just as she was, with the herdboy and his geese, and in her torn petticoat and bare feet, and he would dance with her before the King and the lords and ladies, and present her to them all, as his dear and honoured bride.

So when night came, and the hall in the castle was full of light and music, and the lords and ladies were dancing before the King, just as the clock struck twelve, Tattercoats and the herdboy, followed by his flock of noisy geese, entered at the great doors, and walked straight up the ballroom, while on either side the ladies whispered, the lords laughed, and the King seated at the far end stared in amazement.

But as they came in front of the throne, Tattercoats' lover rose from beside the King, and came to meet her. Taking her by the hand, he kissed her thrice before them all, and turned to the King.

"Father!" he said, for it was the Prince himself, "I have made my choice, and here is my bride, the loveliest girl in all the land, and the sweetest as well!"

Before he had finished speaking, the herdboy put his pipe to his lips and played a few low notes that sounded like a bird singing far off in the woods; and as he played, Tattercoats' rags were changed to shining robes sewn with glittering jewels, a golden crown lay upon her golden hair, and the flock of geese behind her became a crowd of dainty pages, bearing her long train.

And as the King rose to greet her as his daughter, the trumpets sounded loudly in honour of the new Princess, and the people outside in the street said to each other:

"Ah! now the Prince has chosen for his wife the loveliest girl in all the land!"

But the gooseherd was never seen again, and no one knew what became of him; while the old

lord went home once more to his Palace by the sea, for he could not stay at Court, when he had sworn never to look on his granddaughter's face.

So there he still sits by his window, if you could only see him, as you some day may, weeping more bitterly than ever, as he looks out over the sea.

TOM TIT TOT

This is a humorous variant of the German "Rumpelstiltskin." No one knows which came first.

Once upon a time there was a woman, and she baked five pies. And when they came out of the oven, they were that overbaked the crusts were too hard to eat. So she says to her daughter:

"Darter," says she, "put you them there pies on the shelf, and leave 'em there a little, and they'll come again."—She meant, you know, the crust would get soft.

But the girl, she says to herself: "Well, if they'll come again, I'll eat 'em now." And she set to work and ate 'em all, first and last.

Well, come supper-time the woman said: "Go you, and get one o' them there pies. I dare say they've come again now."

The girl went and she looked, and there was nothing but the dishes. So back she came and says she:

"Noo, they ain't come again."

"Not one of 'em?" says the mother.

"Not one of 'em," says she.

"Well, come again, or not come again," said the woman, "I'll have one for supper."

"But you can't, if they ain't come," said the girl.

"But I can," says she. "Go you, and bring the best of 'em."

"Best or worst," says the girl, "I've ate 'em all, and you can't have one till that's come again."

Well, the woman she was done, and she took her spinning to the door to spin, and as she span she sang:

"Tom Tit Tot." From *English Fairy Tales,* edited by Joseph Jacobs. Used by permission of G. P. Putnam's Sons and Frederick Muller Ltd., London

"My darter ha' ate five, five pies to-day.
My darter ha' ate five, five pies to-day."

The king was coming down the street, and he heard her sing, but what she sang he couldn't hear, so he stopped and said:

"What was that you were singing, my good woman?"

The woman was ashamed to let him hear what her daughter had been doing, so she sang, instead of that:

"My darter ha' spun five, five skeins to-day.
My darter ha' spun five, five skeins to-day."

"Stars o' mine!" said the king. "I never heard tell of any one that could do that."

Then he said: "Look you here, I want a wife, and I'll marry your daughter. But look you here," says he, "eleven months out of the year she shall have all she likes to eat, and all the gowns she likes to get, and all the company she likes to keep; but the last month of the year she'll have to spin five skeins every day, and if she don't, I shall kill her."

"All right," says the woman; for she thought what a grand marriage that was. And as for the five skeins, when the time came, there'd be plenty of ways of getting out of it, and likeliest, he'd have forgotten all about it.

Well, so they were married. And for eleven months the girl had all she liked to eat, and all the gowns she liked to get, and all the company she liked to keep.

But when the time was getting over, she began to think about the skeins and to wonder if he had 'em in mind. But not one word did he say about 'em, and she thought he's wholly forgotten 'em.

However, the last day of the last month he takes her to a room she'd never set eyes on before. There was nothing in it but a spinning-wheel and a stool. And says he:

"Now, my dear, here you'll be shut in to-morrow with some victuals and some flax, and if you haven't spun five skeins by night, your head'll go off."

And away he went about his business.

Well, she was that frightened, she'd always been such a gatless girl, that she didn't so much

as know how to spin, and what was she to do to-morrow with no one to come nigh her to help her? She sat down on a stool in the kitchen, and law! how she did cry!

However, all of a sudden she heard a sort of a knocking low down on the door. She upped and oped it, and what should she see but a small little black thing with a long tail. That looked up at her right curious, and that said:

"What are you a-crying for?"

"What's that to you?" says she.

"Never you mind," that said, "but tell me what you're a-crying for."

"That won't do me no good if I do," says she.

"You don't know that," that said, and twirled that's tail round.

"Well," says she, "that won't do no harm, if that don't do no good," and she upped and told about the pies, and the skeins, and everything.

"This is what I'll do," says the little black thing, "I'll come to your window every morning and take the flax and bring it spun at night."

"What's your pay?" says she.

That looked out of the corner of that's eyes, and that said: "I'll give you three guesses every night to guess my name, and if you haven't guessed it before the month's up you shall be mine."

Well, she thought she'd be sure to guess that's name before the month was up. "All right," says she, "I agree."

"All right," that says, and law! how that twirled that's tail.

Well, the next day, her husband took her into the room, and there was the flax and the day's food.

"Now, there's the flax," says he, "and if that ain't spun up this night, off goes your head." then he went out and locked the door.

He'd hardly gone, when there was a knocking against the window.

She upped and she oped it, and there sure enough was the little old thing sitting on the ledge.

"Where's the flax?" says he.

"Here it be," says she. And she gave it to him.

Well, come the evening a knocking came again to the window. She upped and she oped it, and there was the little old thing with five skeins of flax on his arm.

"Here it be," says he, and he gave it to her.

"Now, what's my name?" says he.

"What, is that Bill?" says she.

"Noo, that ain't," says he, and he twirled his tail.

"Is that Ned?" says she.

"Noo, that ain't," says he, and he twirled his tail.

"Well, is that Mark?" says she.

"Noo, that ain't," says he, and he twirled his tail harder, and away he flew.

Well, when her husband came in, there were the five skeins ready for him. "I see I shan't have to kill you to-night, my dear," says he; "you'll have your food and your flax in the morning," says he, and away he goes.

Well, every day the flax and the food were brought, and every day that there little black impet used to come mornings and evenings. And all the day the girl sat trying to think of names to say to it when it came at night. But she never hit on the right one.

And as it got toward the end of the month, the impet began to look so maliceful, and that twirled that's tail faster and faster each time she gave a guess.

At last it came to the last day but one. The impet came at night along with the five skeins, and that said:

"What, ain't you got my name yet?"

"Is that Nicodemus?" says she.

"Noo, 't ain't," that says.

"Is that Sammle?" says she.

"Noo, 't ain't," that says.

"A-well, is that Methusalem?" says she.

"Noo, 't ain't that neither," that says.

Then that looks at her with that's eyes like a coal o' fire, and that says: "Woman, there's only to-morrow night, and then you'll be mine!" And away it flew.

Well, she felt that horrid. However, she heard the king coming along the passage.

In he came, and when he sees the five skeins, he says, says he:

"Well, my dear," says he. "I don't see but what you'll have your skeins ready to-morrow night as well, and as I reckon I shan't have to kill you, I'll have supper in here to-night." So they brought supper, and another stool for him, and down the two sat.

Well, he hadn't eaten but a mouthful or so, when he stops and begins to laugh.

"What is it?" says she.

"A-why," says he, "I was out a-hunting today, and I got away to a place in the wood I'd never seen before. And there was an old chalk-pit. And I heard a kind of a sort of humming. So I got off my hobby, and I went right quiet to the pit, and I looked down. Well, what should there be but the funniest little black thing you ever set eyes on. And what was that doing, but that had a little spinning-wheel, and that was spinning wonderful fast, and twirling that's tail. And as that span that sang:

> "Nimmy nimmy not
> My name's Tom Tit Tot."

Well, when the girl heard this, she felt as if she could have jumped out of her skin for joy, but she didn't say a word.

Next day that there little thing looked so maliceful when he came for the flax. And when the night came she heard that knocking against the window panes. She oped the window, and that come right in on the ledge. That was grinning from ear to ear, and Oo! that's tail was twirling round so fast.

"What's my name?" that says, as that gave her the skeins.

"Is that Solomon?" she says, pretending to be afeard.

"Noo, 't ain't," that says, and that came further into the room.

"Well, is that Zebedee?" says she again.

"Noo, 't ain't," says the impet. And then that laughed and twirled that's tail till you couldn't hardly see it.

"Take time, woman," that says; "next guess, and you're mine." And that stretched out that's black hands at her.

Well, she backed a step or two, and she looked at it, and then she laughed out, and says she, pointing her finger at it:

> "Nimmy nimmy not
> Your name's Tom Tit Tot."

Well, when that heard her, that gave an awful shriek and away that flew into the dark, and she never saw it any more.

THE BLACK
BULL OF NORROWAY

Here is a somber and beautiful story of a black spell which is broken at last by the faithful love of a girl. The rhymes add much to its charm.

Long ago in Norroway there lived a lady who had three daughters. Now they were all pretty, and one night they fell a-talking of whom they meant to marry.

And the eldest said, "I will have no one lower than an Earl."

And the second said, "I will have no one lower than a Lord."

But the third, the prettiest and the merriest, tossed her head and said, with a twinkle in her eye, "Why so proud? As for me I would be content with the Black Bull of Norroway."

At that the other sisters bade her be silent and not talk lightly of such a monster. For, see you, is it not written:

> To wilder measures now they turn,
> The black black Bull of Norroway;
> Sudden the tapers cease to burn,
> The minstrels cease to play.

So, no doubt, the Black Bull of Norroway was held to be a horrid monster.

But the youngest daughter would have her laugh, so she said three times that she would be content with the Black Bull of Norroway.

Well! It so happened that the very next morning a coach-and-six came swinging along the road, and in it sat an Earl who had come to ask the hand of the eldest daughter in marriage. So there were great rejoicings over the wedding, and the bride and bridegroom drove away in the coach-and-six.

Then the next thing that happened was that a coach-and-four with a Lord in it came swinging along the road; and he wanted to marry the second daughter. So they were wed, and there were great rejoicings, and the bride and bridegroom drove away in the coach-and-four.

"The Black Bull of Norroway." From *English Fairy Tales* retold by Flora Annie Steel. By permission of The Macmillan Company, New York and Macmillan & Co. Ltd., London

Now after this there was only the youngest, the prettiest and the merriest, of the sisters left, and she became the apple of her mother's eye. So you may imagine how the mother felt when one morning a terrible bellowing was heard at the door, and there was a great big Black Bull waiting for his bride.

She wept and she wailed, and at first the girl ran away and hid herself in the cellar for fear, but there the Bull stood waiting, and at last the girl came up and said:

"I promised I would be content with the Black Bull of Norroway, and I must keep my word. Farewell, mother, you will not see me again."

Then she mounted on the Black Bull's back, and it walked away with her quite quietly. And ever it chose the smoothest paths and the easiest roads, so that at last the girl grew less afraid. But she became very hungry and was nigh to faint when the Black Bull said to her, in quite a soft voice that wasn't a bellow at all:

> "Eat out of my left ear,
> Drink out of my right,
> And set by what you leave
> To serve the morrow's night."

So she did as she was bid, and, lo and behold! the left ear was full of delicious things to eat, and the right was full of the most delicious drinks, and there was plenty left over for several days.

Thus they journeyed on, and they journeyed on, through many dreadful forests and many lonely wastes, and the Black Bull never paused for bite or sup, but ever the girl he carried ate out of his left ear and drank out of his right, and set by what she left to serve the morrow's night. And she slept soft and warm on his broad back.

Now at last they reached a noble castle where a large company of lords and ladies were assembled, and greatly the company wondered at the sight of these strange companions. And they invited the girl to supper, but the Black Bull they turned into the field, and left to spend the night after his kind.

But when the next morning came, there he was ready for his burden again. Now, though the girl was loth to leave her pleasant companions, she remembered her promise, and mounted on his back, so they journeyed on, and journeyed on, and journeyed on, through many tangled woods and over many high mountains. And ever the Black Bull chose the smoothest paths for her and set aside the briars and brambles, while she ate out of his left ear and drank out of his right.

So at last they came to a magnificent mansion where Dukes and Duchesses and Earls and Countesses were enjoying themselves. Now the company, though much surprised at the strange companions, asked the girl in to supper; and the Black Bull they would have turned into the park for the night, but that the girl, remembering how well he had cared for her, asked them to put him into the stable and give him a good feed.

So this was done, and the next morning he was waiting before the hall-door for his burden; and she, though somewhat loth at leaving the fine company, mounted him cheerfully enough, and they rode away, and they rode away, and they rode away, through thick briar brakes and up fearsome cliffs. But ever the Black Bull trod the brambles underfoot and chose the easiest paths, while she ate out of his left ear and drank out of his right, and wanted for nothing, though he had neither bite nor sup. So it came to pass that he grew tired and was limping with one foot when, just as the sun was setting, they came to a beautiful palace where Princes and Princesses were disporting themselves with ball on the green grass. Now, though the company greatly wondered at the strange companions, they asked the girl to join them, and ordered the grooms to lead away the Black Bull to a field.

But she, remembering all he had done for her, said, "Not so! He will stay with me!" Then seeing a large thorn in the foot with which he had been limping, she stooped down and pulled it out.

And, lo and behold! in an instant, to every one's surprise, there appeared, not a frightful monstrous bull, but one of the most beautiful Princes ever beheld, who fell at his deliverer's feet, thanking her for having broken his cruel enchantment.

A wicked witch-woman who wanted to marry him had, he said, spelled him until a beautiful maiden of her own free will should do him a favour.

"But," he said, "the danger is not all over. You have broken the enchantment by night; that by day has yet to be overcome."

So the next morning the Prince had to resume the form of a bull, and they set out together; and they rode, and they rode, and they rode, till they came to a dark and ugsome glen. And here he bade her dismount and sit on a great rock.

"Here you must stay," he said, "while I go yonder and fight the Old One. And mind! move neither hand nor foot whilst I am away, else I shall never find you again. If everything around you turns blue, I shall have beaten the Old One; but if everything turns red, he will have conquered me."

And with that, and a tremendous roaring bellow, he set off to find his foe.

Well, she sat as still as a mouse, moving neither hand nor foot, nor even her eyes, and waited, and waited, and waited. Then at last everything turned blue. But she was so overcome with joy to think that her lover was victorious that she forgot to keep still, and lifting one of her feet, crossed it over the other!

So she waited, and waited, and waited. Long she sat, and aye she wearied; and all the time he was seeking for her, but he never found her.

At last she rose and went she knew not whither, determined to seek for her lover through the whole wide world. So she journeyed on, and she journeyed on, and she journeyed on, until one day in a dark wood she came to a little hut where lived an old, old woman who gave her food and shelter, and bid her Godspeed on her errand, giving her three nuts, a walnut, a filbert, and a hazel nut, with these words:

"When your heart is like to break,
   And once again is like to break,
Crack a nut and in its shell
   That will be that suits you well."

After this she felt heartened up, and wandered on till her road was blocked by a great hill of glass; and though she tried all she could to climb it, she could not; for aye she slipped back, and slipped back, and slipped back; for it was like ice.

Then she sought a passage elsewhere, and round and about the foot of the hill she went sobbing and wailing, but ne'er a foothold could she find. At last she came to a smithy; and the smith promised if she would serve him faithfully for seven years and seven days, that he would make her iron shoon wherewith to climb the hill of glass.

So for seven long years and seven short days she toiled, and span, and swept, and washed in the smith's house. And for wage he gave her a pair of iron shoon, and with them she clomb the glassy hill and went on her way.

Now she had not gone far before a company of fine lords and ladies rode past her talking of all the grand doings that were to be done at the young Duke of Norroway's wedding. Then she passed a number of people carrying all sorts of good things which they told her were for the Duke's wedding. And at last she came to a palace castle where the courtyards were full of cooks and bakers, some running this way, some running that, and all so busy that they did not know what to do first.

Then she heard the horns of hunters and cries of "Room! Room for the Duke of Norroway and his bride!"

And who should ride past but the beautiful Prince she had but half unspelled, and by his side was the witch-woman who was determined to marry him that very day.

Well! at the sight she felt that her heart was indeed like to break, and over again was like to break, so that the time had come for her to crack one of the nuts. So she broke the walnut, as it was the biggest, and out of it came a wonderful wee woman carding wool as fast as ever she could card.

Now when the witch-woman saw this wonderful thing she offered the girl her choice of anything in the castle for it.

"If you will put off your wedding with the Duke for a day, and let me watch in his room tonight," said the girl, "you shall have it."

Now, like all witch-women, the bride wanted everything her own way, and she was so sure she had her groom safe, that she consented; but before the Duke went to rest she gave him, with her own hands, a posset so made that any one who drank it would sleep till morning.

Thus, though the girl was allowed alone into the Duke's chamber, and though she spent the livelong night sighing and singing:

"Far have I sought for thee,
Long have I wrought for thee,
Near am I brought to thee,
Dear Duke o' Norroway;
Wilt thou say naught to me?"

The Duke never wakened, but slept on. So when day came the girl had to leave him without his ever knowing she had been there.

Then once again her heart was like to break, and over and over again like to break, and she cracked the filbert nut, because it was the next biggest. And out of it came a wonderful wee, wee woman spinning away as fast as ever she could spin. Now when the witch-bride saw this wonderful thing she once again put off her wedding so that she might possess it. And once again the girl spent the livelong night in the Duke's chamber sighing and singing:

"Far have I sought for thee,
Long have I wrought for thee,
Near am I brought to thee,
Dear Duke o' Norroway;
Wilt thou say naught to me?"

But the Duke, who had drunk the sleeping-draught from the hands of his witch-bride, never stirred, and when dawn came the girl had to leave him without his ever knowing she had been there.

Then, indeed, the girl's heart was like to break, and over and over and over again like to break, so she cracked the last nut—the hazel nut—and out of it came the most wonderful wee, wee, wee-est woman reeling away at yarn as fast as she could reel.

And this marvel so delighted the witch-bride that once again she consented to put off her wedding for a day, and allow the girl to watch in the Duke's chamber the night through, in order to possess it.

Now it so happened that when the Duke was dressing that morning he heard his pages talking amongst themselves of the strange sighing and singing they had heard in the night; and he said to his faithful old valet, "What do the pages mean?"

And the old valet, who hated the witch-bride, said:

"If the master will take no sleeping-draught to-night, mayhap he may also hear what for two nights has kept me awake."

At this the Duke marvelled greatly, and when the witch-bride brought him his evening posset, he made excuse it was not sweet enough, and while she went away to get honey to sweeten it withal, he poured away the posset and made believe he had swallowed it.

So that night when dark had come, and the girl stole in to his chamber with a heavy heart thinking it would be the very last time she would ever see him, the Duke was really broad awake. And when she sat down by his bedside and began to sing:

"Far have I sought for thee,"

he knew her voice at once, and clasped her in his arms.

Then he told her how he had been in the power of the witch-woman and had forgotten everything, but that now he remembered all and that the spell was broken for ever and aye.

So the wedding feast served for their marriage, since the witch-bride, seeing her power was gone, quickly fled the country and was never heard of again.

WHITTINGTON AND HIS CAT

The story of Dick Whittington is a popular legend, a hero tale and a success story! It is overlong and will be improved by a free telling of the main incidents, cutting the details. The children will enjoy Marcia Brown's picture-story of Dick.

In the reign of the famous King Edward III there was a little boy called Dick Whittington, whose father and mother died when he was very young. As poor Dick was not old enough to work, he was very badly off; he got but little for his dinner, and sometimes nothing at all for his breakfast; for the people who lived in the village

"Whittington and His Cat." From *English Fairy Tales*, edited by Joseph Jacobs. Used by permission of G. P. Putnam's Sons and Frederick Muller Ltd., London

were very poor indeed, and could not spare him much more than the parings of potatoes, and now and then a hard crust of bread.

Now Dick had heard many, many very strange things about the great city called London; for the country people at that time thought that folks in London were all fine gentlemen and ladies; and that there was singing and music there all day long; and that the streets were all paved with gold.

One day a large waggon and eight horses, all with bells at their heads, drove through the village while Dick was standing by the sign-post. He thought that this waggon must be going to the fine town of London; so he took courage, and asked the waggoner to let him walk with him by the side of the waggon. As soon as the waggoner heard that poor Dick had no father or mother, and saw by his ragged clothes that he could not be worse off than he was, he told him he might go if he would, so off they set together.

So Dick got safe to London, and was in such a hurry to see the fine streets paved all over with gold, that he did not even stay to thank the kind waggoner; but ran off as fast as his legs would carry him, through many of the streets, thinking every moment to come to those that were paved with gold; for Dick had seen a guinea three times in his own little village, and remembered what a deal of money it brought in change; so he thought he had nothing to do but to take up some little bits of the pavement, and should then have as much money as he could wish for.

Poor Dick ran till he was tired, and had quite forgot his friend the waggoner; but at last, finding it grow dark, and that every way he turned he saw nothing but dirt instead of gold, he sat down in a dark corner and cried himself to sleep.

Little Dick was all night in the streets; and next morning, being very hungry, he got up and walked about, and asked everybody he met to give him a halfpenny to keep him from starving; but nobody stayed to answer him, and only two or three gave him a halfpenny; so that the poor boy was soon quite weak and faint for the want of victuals.

In this distress he asked charity of several people and one of them said crossly: "Go to work for an idle rogue." "That I will," said Dick, "I will go to work for you, if you will let me." But the man only cursed at him and went on.

At last a good-natured looking gentleman saw how hungry he looked. "Why don't you go to work, my lad?" said he to Dick. "That I would, but I do not know how to get any," answered Dick. "If you are willing, come along with me," said the gentleman, and took him to a hay-field, where Dick worked briskly, and lived merrily till the hay was made.

After this he found himself as badly off as before; and being almost starved again, he laid himself down at the door of Mr. Fitzwarren, a rich merchant. Here he was soon seen by the cook-maid, who was an ill-tempered creature, and happened just then to be very busy dressing dinner for her master and mistress; so she called out to poor Dick: "What business have you there, you lazy rogue? there is nothing else but beggars; if you do not take yourself away, we will see how you will like a sousing of some dish-water; I have some here hot enough to make you jump."

Just at that time Mr. Fitzwarren himself came home to dinner; and when he saw a dirty ragged boy lying at the door, he said to him: "Why do you lie there, my boy? You seem old enough to work; I am afraid you are inclined to be lazy."

"No, indeed, sir," said Dick to him, "that is not the case, for I would work with all my heart, but I do not know anybody, and I believe I am very sick for the want of food."

"Poor fellow, get up; let me see what ails you."

Dick now tried to rise, but was obliged to lie down again, being too weak to stand, for he had not eaten any food for three days, and was no longer able to run about and beg a halfpenny of people in the street. So the kind merchant ordered him to be taken into the house, and have a good dinner given him, and be kept to do what work he was able to do for the cook.

Little Dick would have lived very happy in this good family if it had not been for the ill-natured cook. She used to say: "You are under me, so look sharp; clean the spit and the dripping-pan, make the fires, wind up the jack, and do all the scullery work nimbly, or——" and she would shake the ladle at him. Besides, she was so fond of basting, that when she had no meat to baste, she would baste poor Dick's head and shoulders with a broom, or anything else that happened to fall in her way. At last her ill-usage of him was told to Alice, Mr. Fitzwarren's daughter, who told the cook she should be turned away if she did not treat him kinder.

The behaviour of the cook was now a little better; but besides this, Dick had another hardship to get over. His bed stood in a garret, where there were so many holes in the floor and the walls that every night he was tormented with rats and mice. A gentleman having given Dick a penny for cleaning his shoes, he thought he would buy a cat with it. The next day he saw a girl with a cat, and asked her, "Will you let me have that cat for a penny?" The girl said: "Yes, that I will, master, though she is an excellent mouser."

Dick hid his cat in the garret, and always took care to carry a part of his dinner to her; and in a short time he had no more trouble with the rats and mice, but slept quite sound every night.

Soon after this, his master had a ship ready to sail; and as it was the custom that all his servants should have some chance for good fortune as well as himself, he called them all into the parlour and asked them what they would send out.

They all had something that they were willing to venture except poor Dick, who had neither money nor goods, and therefore could send nothing. For this reason he did not come into the parlour with the rest; but Miss Alice guessed what was the matter and ordered him to be called in. She then said: "I will lay down some money for him, from my own purse"; but her father told her: "This will not do, for it must be something of his own."

When poor Dick heard this, he said: "I have nothing but a cat which I bought for a penny some time since of a little girl."

"Fetch your cat then, my lad," said Mr. Fitzwarren, "and let her go."

Dick went upstairs and brought down poor puss, with tears in his eyes, and gave her to the captain; "For," he said, "I shall now be kept awake all night by the rats and mice." All the company laughed at Dick's odd venture; and Miss Alice, who felt pity for him, gave him some money to buy another cat.

This, and many other marks of kindness shown him by Miss Alice, made the ill-tempered cook jealous of poor Dick, and she began to use him more cruelly than ever, and always made game of him for sending his cat to sea. She asked him. "Do you think your cat will sell for as much money as would buy a stick to beat you?"

At last poor Dick could not bear this usage any longer, and he thought he would run away from his place; so he packed up his few things, and started very early in the morning, on All-hallows Day, the first of November. He walked as far as Halloway, and there sat down on a stone, which to this day is called "Whittington's Stone," and began to think to himself which road he should take.

While he was thinking what he should do, the Bells of Bow Church, which at that time were only six, began to ring, and at their sound seemed to say to him:

"Turn again, Whittington,
Thrice Lord Mayor of London."

"Lord Mayor of London!" said he to himself. "Why, to be sure, I would put up with almost anything now, to be Lord Mayor of London, and ride in a fine coach, when I grow to be a man! Well, I will go back, and think nothing of the cuffing and scolding of the old cook, if I am to be Lord Mayor of London at last."

Dick went back, and was lucky enough to get into the house, and set about his work, before the old cook came downstairs.

We must now follow Miss Puss to the coast of Africa. The ship with the cat on board was a long time at sea; and was at last driven by the winds on a part of the coast of Barbary, where the only people were the Moors, unknown to the English. The people came in great numbers to see the sailors, because they were of different colour to themselves, and treated them civilly; and, when they became better acquainted, were very eager to buy the fine things that the ship was loaded with.

When the captain saw this, he sent patterns of the best things he had to the king of the country; who was so much pleased with them, that he sent for the captain to the palace. Here they were placed, as it is the custom of the country, on rich carpets flowered with gold and silver. The king and queen were seated at the upper end of the room; and a number of dishes were brought in for dinner. They had not sat long, when a vast number of rats and mice rushed in, and devoured all the meat in an instant. The captain wondered at this, and asked if these vermin were not unpleasant.

"Oh yes," said they, "very offensive; and the king would give half his treasure to be freed of them, for they not only destroy his dinner, as you see, but they assault him in his chamber, and even in bed, so that he is obliged to be watched while he is sleeping, for fear of them."

The captain jumped for joy; he remembered poor Whittington and his cat, and told the king he had a creature on board the ship that would despatch all these vermin immediately. The king jumped so high at the joy which the news gave him, that his turban dropped off his head. "Bring this creature to me," says he; "vermin are dreadful in a court, and if she will perform what you say, I will load your ship with gold and jewels in exchange for her."

The captain, who knew his business, took this opportunity to set forth the merits of Mrs. Puss. He told his majesty: "It is not very convenient to part with her, as, when she is gone, the rats and mice may destroy the goods in the ship—but to oblige your majesty, I will fetch her."

"Run, run!" said the queen; "I am impatient to see the dear creature."

Away went the captain to the ship, while another dinner was got ready. He put Puss under his arm, and arrived at the place just in time to see the table full of rats. When the cat saw them,

rats, bargained with the captain for the whole ship's cargo, and then gave him ten times as much for the cat as all the rest amounted to.

The captain then took leave of the royal party, and set sail with a fair wind for England, and after a happy voyage arrived safe in London.

One morning, early, Mr. Fitzwarren had just come to his counting-house and seated himself at the desk to count over the cash, and settle the business for the day, when somebody came tap, tap, at the door. "Who's there?" said Mr. Fitzwarren. "A friend," answered the other; "I come to bring you good news of your ship *Unicorn*." The merchant, bustling up in such a hurry that he forgot his gout, opened the door, and who should he see waiting but the captain and factor, with a cabinet of jewels and a bill of lading; when he looked at this the merchant lifted up his eyes and thanked Heaven for sending him such a prosperous voyage.

They then told the story of the cat, and showed the rich present that the king and queen had sent for her to poor Dick. As soon as the merchant heard this, he called out to his servants:

"Go send him in, and tell him of
    his fame;
Pray call him Mr. Whittington
    by name."

Mr. Fitzwarren now showed himself to be a good man; for when some of his servants said so great a treasure was too much for him, he answered: "God forbid I should deprive him of the value of a single penny; it is his own, and he shall have it to a farthing."

He then sent for Dick, who at that time was scouring pots for the cook, and was quite dirty. He would have excused himself from coming into the counting-house, saying, "The room is swept, and my shoes are

she did not wait for bidding, but jumped out of the captain's arms, and in a few minutes laid almost all the rats and mice dead at her feet. The rest of them in their fright scampered away to their holes.

The king was quite charmed to get rid so easily of such plagues, and the queen desired that the creature who had done them so great a kindness might be brought to her, that she might look at her. Upon which the captain called: "Pussy, pussy, pussy!" and she came to him. He then presented her to the queen, who started back, and was afraid to touch a creature who had made such a havoc among the rats and mice. However, when the captain stroked the cat and called: "Pussy, pussy," the queen also touched her and cried: "Putty, putty," for she had not learned English. He then put her down on the queen's lap, where she purred and played with her majesty's hand, and then purred herself to sleep.

The king, having seen the exploits of Mrs. Puss, and being informed that her kittens would stock the whole country, and keep it free from

dirty and full of hobnails." But the merchant ordered him to come in.

Mr. Fitzwarren ordered a chair to be set for him, and so he began to think they were making game of him, and at the same time said to them: "Do not play tricks with a poor simple boy, but let me go down again, if you please, to my work."

"Indeed, Mr. Whittington," said the merchant, "we are all quite in earnest with you, and I most heartily rejoice in the news that these gentlemen have brought you; for the captain has sold your cat to the King of Barbary, and brought you in return for her more riches than I possess in the whole world; and I wish you may long enjoy them!"

Mr. Fitzwarren then told the men to open the great treasure they had brought with them, and said: "Mr. Whittington has nothing to do but to put it in some place of safety."

Poor Dick hardly knew how to behave himself for joy. He begged his master to take what part of it he pleased, since he owed it all to his kindness. "No, no," answered Mr. Fitzwarren, "this is all your own; and I have no doubt but you will use it well."

Dick next asked his mistress, and then Miss Alice, to accept a part of his good fortune; but they would not, and at the same time told him they felt great joy at his good success. But this poor fellow was too kind-hearted to keep it all to himself; so he made a present to the captain, the mate, and the rest of Mr. Fitzwarren's servants; and even to the ill-natured old cook.

After this Mr. Fitzwarren advised him to send for a proper tailor, and get himself dressed like a gentleman; and told him he was welcome to live in his house till he could provide himself with a better.

When Whittington's face was washed, his hair curled, his hat cocked, and he was dressed in a nice suit of clothes, he was as handsome and genteel as any young man who visited at Mr. Fitzwarren's; so that Miss Alice, who had once been so kind to him, and thought of him with pity, now looked upon him as fit to be her sweetheart; and the more so, no doubt, because Whittington was now always thinking what he could do to oblige her, and making her the prettiest presents that could be.

Mr. Fitzwarren soon saw their love for each

other, and proposed to join them in marriage; and to this they both readily agreed. A day for the wedding was soon fixed; and they were attended to church by the Lord Mayor, the court of aldermen, the sheriffs, and a great number of the richest merchants in London, whom they afterwards treated with a very rich feast.

History tells us that Mr. Whittington and his lady lived in great splendour, and were very happy. They had several children. He was Sheriff of London, thrice Lord Mayor, and received the honour of knighthood by Henry V.

He entertained his king and his queen at dinner, after his conquest of France, so grandly, that the king said: "Never had prince such a subject"; when Sir Richard heard this, he said: "Never had subject such a prince."

The figure of Sir Richard Whittington with his cat in his arms, carved in stone, was to be seen till the year 1780 over the archway of the old prison at Newgate, which he built for criminals.

WHIPPETY STOURIE

This queer Scottish tale of the wee ladies with the lopsided mouths begins like a variant of "Tom Tit Tot," but the conclusion is amusingly different.

On a day long ago, when the bracken sprang green and tender on the hills, a fine gentleman rode over the braeside to woo a fair lady. As the summer passed the lady came to love her suitor very dearly; and by the time that the bracken

"Whippety Stourie." From *Scottish Folk-Tales and Legends* by Barbara Ker Wilson. Reprinted by permission of Henry Z. Walck, Inc.

hung crisp and golden on the hills they were married with great rejoicing, and he took her away from her father's home to live in his own house.

The lady thought she had never been happier in all her life, for she had all that her heart desired: a great house, rich velvet gowns, and beautiful jewels. But one day her husband came to her and said:

"Now, wife, it is time you put your fair hand to the spinning-wheel; for a home is no home without the clack of a shuttle within its walls; and a wife is no wife unless she can spin fine thread for her husband's shirts."

The lady looked downcast at these words, and she displayed her hands imploringly.

"Alas," she said, "I have never spun a single thread in all my life, husband, for in my father's house it was not thought fitting that a maid of high degree should learn such a lowly occupation."

Then her husband's face grew dark and he replied:

"To sit by the spinning-wheel and spin fine thread is a womanly task that all good wives should perform. From now on you must spin me twelve hanks of thread each day—or, dear as you are to my heart, it will be the worse for you."

"Truly, husband," his lady wept, "I am not too proud to do your bidding, for I would willingly obey your slightest wish. But I fear I shall never be able to spin one good hank of thread, let alone twelve. For how shall I set about my spinning, with no one to show me the way it should be done?"

But her husband would not listen to her pleading, and only replied that she must find out for herself how to spin. Then he ordered the servants to bring a spinning-wheel to his lady's room, and to provide her each day with sufficient flax to spin twelve hanks of thread.

During the week that followed, the lady rose early each morning and sat herself down before the spinning-wheel, with a heap of shining flax by her side. But though she turned the wheel from the time the sunlight first struck the heather on the hills until it grew dusk, she did not spin one good hank of thread. Every night when her husband came to her room, he would

find her resting wearily on her stool and weeping bitterly. Then he would pick up the shuttle and see perhaps half a hank of ravelled and knotted thread.

"This is not the fine thread I want," he said, "but coarse stuff, fit for a crofter's garments. You must do better than this, wife—or, dear as you are to my heart, it will be the worse for you."

On the last night of the week he came to her and announced that he was going away on a journey.

"And when I come back," he said, "you must have spun a hundred hanks of fine thread. If you have not, then, dear as you are to my heart, I must surely cast you aside and find a new wife to spin for me."

(For you must know that in those days if a man was not satisfied with his first wife, he could cast her aside just so and get himself another instead.)

And he kissed his wife farewell and rode away.

"Alas, alas," the lady grieved, "what shall I do now? For I well know that I shall never manage to spin a hundred hanks of fine thread before my husband returns; and he will surely cast me aside and find a new wife."

She left her room and went out to the braeside to wander among the bracken and the heather, full of sorrowful thoughts. She had not gone far when she felt weary, and sat down on a flat grey stone in the shade of a scarlet-berried rowan-tree. By and by she heard a faint sound of music; and to her amazement it seemed to be coming from underneath the very stone where she sat.

"Now surely it is faery music I can hear," she thought. "For I never heard a mortal piper play such a bonny tune."

And plucking a twig of the rowan-tree to protect herself, she jumped up and rolled away the stone, to find that it had concealed the entrance to a green cave in the hill-side. Peering inside the cave, she was surprised to see six wee ladies in green gowns, all sitting round in a circle. One of them had a little spinning-wheel before her, and as the shuttle clacked busily to and fro she sang:

"Little kens my dame at hame
That Whippety Stourie is my name."

Without taking a second thought, the lady stepped into the cave and greeted the Little Folk pleasantly. They nodded to her in reply; and she noticed that all their six mouths were as lop-sided as a fir-tree leaning against the wind. Now as soon as she saw the fine, fine thread that the wee lady called Whippety Stourie was spinning, the lady was reminded of all her troubles, and she could not stop the tears from trickling down her cheeks.

"Why do you weep?" one of the Little Folk asked her out of the side of her mouth. "For you seem a fine lady in your rich velvet gown and beautiful jewels, and should have nothing to weep for."

"Alas, good folk, my husband has gone away on a journey, and when he comes back I must have spun for him a hundred hanks of fine thread—or, dear as I am to his heart, he will surely kill me and find another wife. And I weep because I am not able to spin one good hank of thread, let alone a hundred; and so I cannot do his bidding."

Then the six wee ladies looked at one another out of their sharp bright eyes, and they all burst into lop-sided laughter.

"Och, is that all your trouble?" said Whippety Stourie. "You can forget your sorrow, fair lady, for we will help you. If you ask us to take supper with you in your fine house on the day appointed for your husband's return, you will find that you will have nothing more to worry about."

The lady looked at the six wee folk in their gowns of green, and she felt an upspringing of hope.

"Indeed, you are welcome to take supper in our house on the day that my husband returns," she said. "And if only you can help me, I will be grateful to you as long as I live."

Then she took her leave of them and rolled back the flat grey stone so that it once more concealed the entrance to their green cave in the hill-side. When she returned to her house, she sat no more at her spinning-wheel, and left untouched the heap of shining flax that lay in her room—for she knew that the Little Folk would keep their word and come to help her.

Her husband came riding home in the evening of the day appointed for his return. He greeted his wife fondly and seemed to have left his grouchy humour behind him on his travels. At every moment his lady was expecting him to ask her about her spinning; but he did not have time to do so before the servants announced that supper was ready.

"Why are there six more places made ready at the table, and six wee stools drawn up beside them?" her husband asked as they sat down.

"Och, I asked six wee ladies to come and take supper with us tonight, for I thought the company would cheer you on your return," the lady replied.

She had no sooner spoken than there was a scuttering of feet in the passage outside, and in came the six wee ladies in their gowns of green. The husband greeted them courteously, and bade them be seated. During the meal he talked and joked with them in high good humour, and his wife was pleased to see how well they agreed. Then there was a pause in their talk, and the husband looked at the six wee ladies curiously.

"Would you mind telling me," he asked them, "why it is that your mouths are all as lop-sided as a fir-tree leaning against the wind?"

Then the six wee ladies burst into loud, lop-sided laughter, and Whippety Stourie herself replied:

"Och, it's with our constant spin-spin-spinning. For we're all of us great ones for the spinning, and there's no surer way to a lop-sided mouth."

At these words the husband grew pale. He looked at his fair wife, and he glanced at the wee ladies, and his alarm was plain to see.

And when their six wee guests had taken their leave and departed, he put his arm round his lady's shoulders and called the servants to him.

"Burn the spinning-wheel that is in my wife's room," he told them, "and see that it perishes on a bright flame. I would not have my fair lady spin one more inch of thread, for fear she should spoil her bonny face. For there's no surer way to a lop-sided mouth than a constant spin-spin-spinning."

The lady's heart leapt for joy at her husband's words; and from that day onwards the two of them lived contentedly for the rest of their days, with never the clack of a shuttle to disturb their happiness.

German folk tales

The German folk tales were known to English children in translation long before their own stories were collected. Since their first translation into English, the Grimm Fairy Tales *have been translated into most of the languages of the civilized world and are the beloved heritage of children everywhere. Because Jacob and Wilhelm Grimm were students of the German language, they collected their stories from the lips of old storytellers and recorded them faithfully. The result is that these German stories, even in translation, have the authentic spellbinding quality of great storytelling. The plots range from stories for the nursery to mature themes for older children and even adults. The tales are dramatic, exciting, full of suspense and smashing climaxes that make children eager to hear more of them. "Snow-White and the Seven Dwarfs," "Mother Holle," and a lot of others are still among the best known and the most continuously popular fairy tales ever told to children.*

THE WOLF AND THE SEVEN LITTLE KIDS

"The Story of the Three Little Pigs" can be used with five-year-olds but this similar tale is a bit more alarming and is better for the sevens. The joyful conclusion makes everything all right.

There was once on a time an old goat who had seven little kids and loved them with all the love of a mother for her children. One day she wanted to go into the forest and fetch some food. So she called all seven to her and said, "Dear children, I have to go into the forest; be on your guard against the wolf; if he comes in, he will devour you all—skin, hair, and all. The wretch often disguises himself, but you will know him at once by his rough voice and his black feet." The kids said, "Dear mother, we will take good care of ourselves; you may go away without any anxiety." Then the old one bleated, and went on her way with an easy mind.

It was not long before some one knocked at the house-door and cried, "Open the door, dear children; your mother is here, and has brought something back with her for each of you." But the little kids knew that it was the wolf, by the rough voice. "We will not open the door," cried

"The Wolf and the Seven Little Kids." From *Grimm's Household Tales,* translated by Margaret Hunt

they, "You are not our mother. She has a soft, pleasant voice, but your voice is rough; you are the wolf!" Then the wolf went away to a shopkeeper and bought himself a great lump of chalk, ate this and made his voice soft with it. Then he came back, knocked at the door of the house, and cried, "Open the door, dear children, your mother is here and has brought something back with her for each of you." But the wolf had laid his black paws against the window, and the children saw them and cried, "We will not open the door; our mother has not black feet like you: you are the wolf!" Then the wolf ran to a baker and said, "I have hurt my feet, rub some dough over them for me." And when the baker had rubbed his feet over, he ran to the miller and said, "Strew some white meal over my feet for me." The miller thought to himself, "The wolf wants to deceive some one," and refused; but the wolf said, "If you will not do it, I will devour you." Then the miller was afraid and made his paws white for him. Truly men are like that.

So now the wretch went for the third time to the house-door, knocked at it, and said, "Open the door for me, children, your dear little mother has come home and has brought every one of you something back from the forest with her." The little kids cried, "First show us your paws that we may know if you are our dear little mother." Then he put his paws in through the window, and when the kids saw that they were white, they believed that all he said was true, and opened the door. But who should come in but the wolf! They were terrified and wanted to hide themselves. One sprang under the table, the second into the bed, the third into the stove, the fourth into the kitchen, the fifth into the cupboard, the sixth under the washing-bowl, and the seventh into the clock-case. But the wolf found them all and used no great ceremony; one after the other he swallowed them down his throat. The youngest in the clock-case was the only one he did not find. When the wolf had satisfied his appetite, he took himself off, laid himself down under a tree in the green meadow outside, and began to sleep. Soon afterwards the old goat came home again from the forest. Ah! what a sight she saw there! The house-door stood wide open. The table, chairs, and benches were thrown down, the washing-bowl lay broken to pieces, and the quilts and pillows were pulled off the bed. She sought her children, but they were nowhere to be found. She called them one after another by name, but no one answered. At last, when she came to the youngest, a soft voice cried, "Dear mother, I am in the clock-case." She took the kid out, and it told her that the wolf had come and had eaten all the others. Then you may imagine how she wept over her poor children.

At length in her grief she went out, and the youngest kid ran with her. When they came to the meadow, there lay the wolf by the tree and snored so loud that the branches shook. She looked at him on every side and saw that something was moving and struggling in his gorged body. "Ah, heavens," said she, "is it possible that my poor children whom he has swallowed down for his supper can be still alive?" Then the kid had to run home and fetch scissors, and a needle and thread, and the goat cut open the monster's stomach, and hardly had she made one cut, than one little kid thrust its head out, and when she had cut farther, all six sprang out one after another, and were all still alive, and had suffered no injury whatever, for in his greediness the monster had swallowed them down whole. What rejoicing there was! Then they embraced their dear mother, and jumped like a tailor at his wedding. The mother, however, said, "Now go and look for some big stones, and we will fill the wicked beast's stomach with them while he is still asleep." Then the seven kids dragged the stones thither with all speed, and put as many of them into his stomach as they could get in; and the mother sewed him up again in the greatest haste, so that he was not aware of anything and never once stirred.

When the wolf at length had had his sleep out, he got on his legs, and as the stones in his stomach made him very thirsty, he wanted to go to a well to drink. But when he began to walk and to move about, the stones in his stomach knocked against each other and rattled. Then cried he,

> "What rumbles and tumbles
> Against my poor bones?
> I thought 'twas six kids,
> But it's naught but big stones."

And when he got to the well and stooped over the water and was just about to drink, the heavy stones made him fall in and there was no help, but he had to drown miserably. When the seven kids saw that, they came running to the spot and cried aloud, "The wolf is dead! The wolf is dead!" and danced for joy round about the well with their mother.

THE ELVES
AND THE SHOEMAKER

This story has an excellent plot but dull style. Try turning the narrative into direct conversation here and there; for example, let the shoemaker say, "Good wife, good wife, see what has happened this night. Someone has stitched my leather into shoes." Then have the good wife reply, "And they are perfectly made. They should sell for a good price."

There was once a shoemaker who worked very hard and was very honest; but still he could not earn enough to live upon, and at last all he had in the world was gone, except just leather enough to make one pair of shoes.

"The Elves and the Shoemaker." From *Grimm's Popular Stories*, translated by Edgar Taylor

Then he cut them all ready to make up the next day, meaning to get up early in the morning to work. His conscience was clear and his heart light amidst all his troubles; so he went peaceably to bed, left all his cares to heaven, and fell asleep.

In the morning, after he had said his prayers, he set himself down to his work, when to his great wonder, there stood the shoes, all ready made, upon the table. The good man knew not what to say or think of this strange event. He looked at the workmanship; there was not one false stitch in the whole job, and all was so neat and true that it was a complete masterpiece.

That same day a customer came in, and the shoes pleased him so well that he willingly paid a price higher than usual for them; and the poor shoemaker with the money bought leather enough to make two pairs more. In the evening he cut out the work, and went to bed early that he might get up and begin betimes next day. But he was saved all the trouble, for when he got up in the morning the work was finished ready to his hand.

Presently in came buyers, who paid him handsomely for his goods, so that he bought leather enough for four pairs more. He cut out the work again over night, and found it finished in the morning as before; and so it went on for some time; what was got ready in the evening was always done by daybreak, and the good man soon became thriving and prosperous again.

One evening about Christmas time, as he and his wife were sitting over the fire chatting together, he said to her, "I should like to sit up and watch to-night, that we may see who it is that comes and does my work for me." The wife liked the thought; so they left a light burning, and hid themselves in the corner of the room behind a curtain and watched to see what would happen.

As soon as it was midnight, there came two little naked dwarfs; and they sat themselves upon the shoemaker's bench, took up all the work that was cut out, and began to ply with their little fingers, stitching and rapping and tapping away at such a rate that the shoemaker was all amazement, and could not take his eyes off for a moment. And on they went till the job was quite finished, and the shoes stood ready for use upon the table. This was long before day-break; and then they bustled away as quick as lightning.

The next day the wife said to the shoemaker, "These little wights have made us rich, and we ought to be thankful to them, and do them a good office in return. I am quite vexed to see them run about as they do; they have nothing upon their backs to keep off the cold. I'll tell you what, I will make each of them a shirt, and a coat and waistcoat, and a pair of pantaloons into the bargain; do you make each of them a little pair of shoes."

The thought pleased the good shoemaker very much; and one evening, when all the things were ready, they laid them on the table instead of the work that they used to cut out, and then went and hid themselves to watch what the little elves would do.

About midnight the elves came in and were going to sit down to their work as usual; but when they saw the clothes lying for them, they laughed and were greatly delighted. Then they dressed themselves in the twinkling of an eye, and danced and capered and sprang about as merry as could be, till at last they danced out at the door and over the green; and the shoemaker saw them no more; but everything went well with him from that time forward, as long as he lived.

THE FOUR MUSICIANS

This story is wonderful to tell, to illustrate, and to dramatize! In another amusing version of the rhyme the cock crows, "Cuck, cuck, cuck, cucdoo-oo!" and the robber thinks a fellow is calling, "Cut the man in two-oo!" The story lends itself to simple dramatization by six- or seven-year-olds in a classroom, playroom, or yard. A few bandannas will make the robbers and the animals may be costumed or not depending upon the formality or spontaneity of the occasion.

There was once a donkey who had worked for his master faithfully many years, but his strength at last began to fail, and every day he became more and more unfit for work. Finally his master concluded it was no longer worth while to keep him and was thinking of putting an end to him. But the donkey saw that mischief was brewing and he ran away.

"I will go to the city," said he, "and like enough I can get an engagement there as a musician; for though my body has grown weak, my voice is as strong as ever."

So the donkey hobbled along toward the city, but he had not gone far when he spied a dog lying by the roadside and panting as if he had run a long way. "What makes you pant so, my friend?" asked the donkey.

"Alas!" replied the dog, "my master was going to knock me on the head because I am old and weak and can no longer make myself useful to him in hunting. So I ran away; but how am I to gain a living now, I wonder?"

"Hark ye!" said the donkey. "I am going to the city to be a musician. You may as well keep company with me and try what you can do in the same line."

The dog said he was willing, and they went on together. Pretty soon they came to a cat sitting in the middle of the road and looking as dismal as three wet days. "Pray, my good lady," said the donkey, "what is the matter with you, for you seem quite out of spirits?"

"Ah me!" responded the cat, "how can I be

"The Four Musicians." From *The Oak Tree Fairy Book*, edited by Clifton Johnson, copyright 1933. With the kind permission of Mrs. Clifton Johnson

cheerful when my life is in danger? I am getting old, my teeth are blunt, and I like sitting by the fire and purring better than chasing the mice about. So this morning my mistress laid hold of me and was going to drown me. I was lucky enough to get away from her; but I do not know what is to become of me, and I'm likely to starve."

"Come with us to the city," said the donkey, "and be a musician. You understand serenading, and with your talent for that you ought to be able to make a very good living."

The cat was pleased with the idea and went along with the donkey and the dog. Soon afterward, as they were passing a farmyard, a rooster flew up on the gate and screamed out with all his might, "Cock-a-doodle-doo!"

"Bravo!" said the donkey, "upon my word you make a famous noise; what is it all about?"

"Oh," replied the rooster, "I was only foretelling fine weather for our washing-day; and that I do every week. But would you believe it! My mistress doesn't thank me for my pains, and she has told the cook that I must be made into broth for the guests that are coming next Sunday."

"Heaven forbid!" exclaimed the donkey; "come with us, Master Chanticleer. It will be better, at any rate, than staying here to have your head cut off. We are going to the city to be musicians; and—who knows?—perhaps the four of us can get up some kind of a concert. You have a good voice, and if we all make music together, it will be something striking. So come along."

"With all my heart," said the cock; and the four went on together.

The city was, however, too far away for them to reach it on the first day of their travelling, and when, toward night, they came to a thick woods, they decided to turn aside from the highway and pass the night among the trees. So they found a dry, sheltered spot at the foot of a great oak and the donkey and dog lay down on the ground beneath it; but the cat climbed up among the branches, and the rooster, thinking the higher he sat the safer he would be, flew up to the very top. Before he went to sleep the rooster looked around him to the four points of the compass to make sure that everything was all right. In so doing he saw in the distance a little light shining, and he called out to his companions, "There must be a house no great way off, for I can see a light."

"If that be the case," said the donkey, "let us get up and go there. Our lodging here is not what I am used to, and the sooner we change it for better the more pleased I shall be."

"Yes," said the dog, "and perhaps I might be able to get a few bones with a little meat on them at that house."

"And very likely I might get some milk," said the cat.

"And there ought to be some scraps of food for me," said the rooster.

So the cat and the rooster came down out of the tree and they all walked off with Chanticleer in the lead toward the spot where he had seen the light.

At length they drew near the house, and the donkey, being the tallest of the company, went up to the lighted window and looked in.

"Well, what do you see?" asked the dog.

"What do I see?" answered the donkey. "I see that this is a robber's house. There are swords and pistols and blunderbusses on the walls, and there are chests of money on the floor, and all sorts of other plunder lying about. The robbers are sitting at a table that is loaded with the best of eatables and drinkables, and they are making themselves very comfortable and merry."

"Those eatables and drinkables would just suit us," declared the rooster.

"Yes, indeed they would," said the donkey, "if we could only get at them; but that will never be, unless we can contrive to drive away the robbers first."

Then they consulted together and at last hit on a plan. The donkey stood on his hind legs with his forefeet on the window-sill, the dog got on the donkey's shoulders, the cat mounted the back of the dog, and the rooster flew up and perched on the back of the cat. When all was ready they began their music.

"Hehaw! hehaw! hehaw!" brayed the donkey.

"Bow-wow! bow-wow!" barked the dog.

"Meow! meow!" said the cat.

"Cock-a-doodle-doo!" crowed the rooster.

Then they all burst through the window into the room, breaking the glass with a frightful clatter. The robbers, not doubting that some hideous hobgoblin was about to devour them, fled to the woods in great terror.

The donkey and his comrades now sat down at the table and made free with the food the robbers had left, and feasted as if they had been hungry for a month. When they had finished they put out the lights and each sought a sleeping-place to his own liking. The donkey laid himself down on some straw in the yard, the dog stretched himself on a mat just inside the door, the cat curled up on the hearth near the warm ashes, and the rooster flew up on the roof and settled himself on the ridge beside the chimney. They were all tired and soon fell fast asleep.

About midnight the robbers came creeping back to the house. They saw that no lights were burning and everything seemed quiet. "Well, well," said the robber captain, "we need not have been so hasty. I think we ran away without reason. But we will be cautious. The rest of you stay here while I go and find out if we are likely to have any more trouble."

So he stepped softly along to the house and entered the kitchen. There he groped about until he found a candle and some matches on the mantel over the fireplace. The cat had now waked up and stood on the hearth watching the robber with shining eyes. He mistook those eyes for two live coals and reached down to get a light by touching a match to them. The cat did not fancy that sort of thing and flew into his face, spitting and scratching. Then he cried out in fright and ran toward the door, and the dog, who was lying there, bit the robber's leg. He managed, however, to get out in the yard, and there the donkey struck out with a hind foot and gave him a kick that knocked him down, and Chanticleer who had been roused by the noise, cried out "Cock-a-doodle-doo! Cock-a-doodle-doo!"

The robber captain had barely strength to crawl away to the other robbers. "We cannot live at that house any more," said he. "In the kitchen is a grewsome witch, and I felt her hot breath and her long nails on my face, and by the door there stood a man who stabbed me in the leg, and in the yard is a black giant who beat me with a club, and on the roof is a little fellow who kept shouting, 'Chuck him up to me! Chuck him up to me!'"

So the robbers went away and never came back, and the four musicians found themselves so well pleased with their new quarters that they did not go to the city, but stayed where they were; and I dare say you would find them there at this very day.

MOTHER HOLLE

One little girl approved the justice of the conclusion of this tale by remarking sternly, "It served that girl right to get pitch on her. She was a real mean girl."

There was once a widow who had two daughters—one of whom was pretty and industrious, whilst the other was ugly and idle. But she was much fonder of the ugly and idle one, because she was her own daughter; and the other, who was a step-daughter, was obliged to do all the work, and be the Cinderella of the house. Every day the poor girl had to sit by a well, in the highway, and spin and spin till her fingers bled.

Now it happened that one day the shuttle was marked with her blood, so she dipped it in the well, to wash the mark off; but it dropped out of her hand and fell to the bottom. She began to weep, and ran to her step-mother and told her of the mishap. But she scolded her sharply, and was so merciless as to say, "Since you have let the shuttle fall in, you must fetch it out again."

So the girl went back to the well, and did not know what to do; and in the sorrow of her heart she jumped into the well to get the shuttle. She lost her senses; and when she awoke and came to herself again, she was in a lovely meadow where the sun was shining and many thousands of flowers were growing. Across this meadow she went, and at last came to a baker's oven full of bread, and the bread cried out, "Oh, take me out! take me out! or I shall burn; I have been baked a long time!" So she went up to it, and took out all the loaves one after another with the bread-shovel. After that she went on till she

"Mother Holle." From *Grimm's Household Tales*, translated by Margaret Hunt

came to a tree covered with apples, which called out to her, "Oh, shake me! shake me! we apples are all ripe!" So she shook the tree till the apples fell like rain, and went on shaking till they were all down, and when she had gathered them into a heap, she went on her way.

At last she came to a little house, out of which an old woman peeped; but she had such large teeth that the girl was frightened, and was about to run away. But the old woman called out to her, "What are you afraid of, dear child? Stay with me; if you will do all the work in the house properly, you shall be the better for it. Only you must take care to make my bed well, and to shake it thoroughly till the feathers fly—for then there is snow on the earth. I am Mother Holle."

As the old woman spoke so kindly to her, the girl took courage and agreed to enter her service. She attended to everything to the satisfaction of her mistress, and always shook her bed so vigorously that the feathers flew about like snow-flakes. So she had a pleasant life with her; never an angry word; and to eat she had boiled or roast meat every day.

She stayed some time with Mother Holle, before she became sad. At first she did not know what was the matter with her, but found at length that it was home-sickness: although she was many thousand times better off here than at home, still she had a longing to be there. At last she said to the old woman: "I have a longing for home; and however well off I am down here, I cannot stay any longer; I must go up again to my own people." Mother Holle said, "I am pleased that you long for your home again, and as you have served me so truly, I myself will take you up again." Thereupon she took her by the hand, and led her to a large door. The door was opened, and just as the maiden was standing beneath the doorway, a heavy shower of golden rain fell, and all the gold remained sticking to her, so that she was completely covered over with it.

"You shall have that because you have been so industrious," said Mother Holle; and at the same time she gave her back the shuttle which she had let fall into the well. Thereupon the door closed, and the maiden found herself up above upon the earth, not far from her mother's house.

And as she went into the yard the cock was sitting on the well, and cried——

"Cock-a-doodle-doo!
Your golden girl's come back to you!"

So she went in to her mother, and as she arrived thus covered with gold, she was well received, both by her and her sister.

The girl told all that had happened to her; and as soon as the mother heard how she had come by so much wealth, she was very anxious to obtain the same good luck for the ugly and lazy daughter. She had to seat herself by the well and spin; and in order that her shuttle might be stained with blood, she stuck her hand into a thorn bush and pricked her finger. Then she threw her shuttle into the well, and jumped in after it.

She came, like the other, to the beautiful meadow and walked along the very same path. When she got to the oven the bread again cried, "Oh, take me out! take me out! or I shall burn; I have been baked a long time!" But the lazy thing answered, "As if I had any wish to make myself dirty!" and on she went. Soon she came to the apple-tree, which cried, "Oh, shake me! shake me! we apples are all ripe!" But she answered, "I like that! one of you might fall on my head," and so went on.

When she came to Mother Holle's house she **was not afraid,** for she had already heard of her big teeth, and she hired herself to her immediately.

The first day she forced herself to work diligently, and obeyed Mother Holle when she told her to do anything, for she was thinking of all the gold that she would give her. But on the second day she began to be lazy, and on the third day still more so, and then she would not get up in the morning at all. Neither did she make Mother Holle's bed as she ought, and did not shake it so as to make the feathers fly up. Mother Holle was soon tired of this, and gave her notice to leave. The lazy girl was willing enough to go, and thought that now the golden rain would come. Mother Holle led her also to the great door; but while she was standing beneath it, instead of the gold a big kettleful of pitch was emptied over her. "That is the reward for your service," said Mother Holle, and shut the door.

So the lazy girl went home; but she was quite covered with pitch, and the cock by the well-side, as soon as he saw her, cried out——

"Cock-a-doodle-doo!
Your pitchy girl's come back to you!"

But the pitch stuck fast to her, and could not be got off as long as she lived.

THE HUT IN THE FOREST

A poor wood-cutter lived with his wife and three daughters in a little hut on the edge of a lonely forest. One morning as he was about to go to his work, he said to his wife, "Let my dinner be brought into the forest to me by my eldest daughter, or I shall never get my work done, and in order that she may not miss her way," he added, "I will take a bag of millet with me and strew the seeds on the path." When, therefore, the sun was just above the centre of the forest, the girl set out on her way with a bowl of soup, but the field-sparrows, and wood-sparrows, larks and finches, blackbirds and siskins had picked up the millet long before, and the girl could not find the track. Then trusting to

"The Hut in the Forest." From *Grimm's Household Tales,* translated by Margaret Hunt

chance, she went on and on, until the sun sank and night began to fall. The trees rustled in the darkness, the owls hooted, and she began to be afraid. Then in the distance she perceived a light which glimmered between the trees. "There ought to be some people living there, who can take me in for the night," thought she, and went up to the light. It was not long before she came to a house the windows of which were all lighted up. She knocked, and a rough voice from the inside cried, "Come in." The girl stepped into the dark entrance and knocked at the door of the room. "Just come in," cried the voice, and when she opened the door, an old grey-haired man was sitting at the table, supporting his face with both hands, and his white beard fell down over the table almost as far as the ground. By the stove lay three animals, a hen, a cock, and a brindled cow. The girl told her story to the old man, and begged for shelter for the night. The man said,

> "Pretty little hen,
> Pretty little cock,
> And pretty brindled cow,
> What say ye to that?"

"Duks," answered the animals, and that must have meant, "We are willing," for the old man said, "Here you shall have shelter and food; go to the fire, and cook us our supper." The girl found in the kitchen abundance of everything, and cooked a good supper, but had no thought of the animals. She carried the full dishes to the table, seated herself by the grey-haired man, ate and satisfied her hunger. When she had had enough, she said, "But now I am tired, where is there a bed in which I can lie down, and sleep?" The animals replied,

> "Thou hast eaten with him,
> Thou hast drunk with him,
> Thou hast had no thought for us,
> So find out for thyself where thou canst pass the
> night."

Then said the old man, "Just go upstairs, and thou wilt find a room with two beds; shake them up, and put white linen on them, and then I, too, will come and lie down to sleep." The girl went up, and when she had shaken the beds and

put clean sheets on, she lay down in one of them without waiting any longer for the old man. After some time, however, the grey-haired man came, took his candle, looked at the girl and shook his head. When he saw that she had fallen into a sound sleep, he opened a trap-door, and let her down into the cellar.

Late at night the wood-cutter came home and reproached his wife for leaving him to hunger all day. "It is not my fault," she replied, "the girl went out with your dinner, and must have lost herself, but she is sure to come back to-morrow." The wood-cutter, however, arose before dawn to go into the forest, and requested that the second daughter should take him his dinner that day. "I will take a bag with lentils," said he; "the seeds are larger than millet; the girl will see them better, and can't lose her way." At dinner-time, therefore, the girl took out the food, but the lentils had disappeared. The birds of the forest had picked them up as they had done the day before, and had left none. The girl wandered about in the forest until night, and then she too reached the house of the old man, was told to go in, and begged for food and a bed. The man with the white beard again asked the animals,

> "Pretty little hen,
> Pretty little cock,
> And pretty brindled cow,
> What say ye to that?"

The animals again replied "Duks," and everything happened just as it had happened the day before. The girl cooked a good meal, ate and drank with the old man, and did not concern herself about the animals, and when she inquired about her bed they answered,

> "Thou hast eaten with him,
> Thou hast drunk with him,
> Thou hast had no thought for us,
> So find out for thyself where thou canst pass the
> night."

When she was asleep the old man came, looked at her, shook his head, and let her down into the cellar.

On the third morning the wood-cutter said

to his wife, "Send our youngest child out with my dinner today, she has always been good and obedient, and will stay in the right path, and not run about after every wild humble-bee, as her sisters did." The mother did not want to do it, and said, "Am I to lose my dearest child, as well?"

"Have no fear," he replied, "the girl will not go astray; she is too prudent and sensible; besides I will take some peas with me, and strew them about. They are still larger than lentils, and will show her the way." But when the girl went out with her basket on her arm, the wood-pigeons had already got all the peas in their crops, and she did not know which way she was to turn. She was full of sorrow and never ceased to think how hungry her father would be, and how her good mother would grieve, if she did not go home.

At length when it grew dark, she saw the light and came to the house in the forest. She begged quite prettily to be allowed to spend the night there, and the man with the white beard once more asked his animals,

> "Pretty little hen,
> Pretty little cock,
> And beautiful brindled cow,
> What say ye to that?"

"Duks," said they. Then the girl went to the stove where the animals were lying, and petted the cock and hen, and stroked their smooth feathers with her hand, and caressed the brindled cow between her horns; and when, in obedience to the old man's orders, she had made ready some good soup, and the bowl was placed upon the table, she said, "Am I to eat as much as I want, and the good animals to have nothing? Outside is food in plenty, I will look after them first."

So she went and brought some barley and strewed it for the cock and hen, and a whole armful of sweet-smelling hay for the cow. "I hope you will like it, dear animals," said she, "and you shall have a refreshing draught in case you are thirsty." Then she fetched in a bucketful of water, and the cock and hen jumped on to the edge of it and dipped their beaks in, and then held up their heads as the birds do when they drink, and the brindled cow also took a hearty draught. When the animals were fed, the girl seated herself at the table by the old man and ate what he had left. It was not long before the cock and the hen began to thrust their heads beneath their wings, and the eyes of the cow likewise began to blink. Then said the girl, "Ought we not to go to bed?"

> "Pretty little hen,
> Pretty little cock,
> And pretty brindled cow,
> What say ye to that?"

The animals answered "Duks,"

> "Thou hast eaten with us,
> Thou hast drunk with us,
> Thou hast had kind thought for all of us,
> We wish thee good-night."

Then the maiden went upstairs, shook the feather-beds, and laid clean sheets on them, and when she had done it the old man came and lay down on one of the beds, and his white beard reached down to his feet. The girl lay down on the other, said her prayers, and fell asleep.

She slept quietly till midnight, and then there was such a noise in the house that she awoke. There was a sound of cracking and splitting in every corner, and the doors sprang open, and beat against the walls. The beams groaned as if they were being torn out of their joints, it seemed as if the staircase were falling down, and at length there was a crash as if the entire roof had fallen in. As, however, all grew quiet once more, and the girl was not hurt, she stayed quietly lying where she was, and fell asleep again.

But when she woke up in the morning with the brilliancy of the sunshine, what did her eyes behold? She was lying in a vast hall, and everything around her shone with royal splendour; on the walls, golden flowers grew up on a ground of green silk, the bed was of ivory, and the canopy of red velvet, and on a chair close by, was a pair of shoes embroidered with pearls. The girl believed that she was in a dream, but three richly clad attendants came in, and asked what orders she would like to give? "If you will go," she replied, "I will get up at once and make ready some soup for the old man, and then I will feed the pretty little hen, and the cock, and the beautiful brindled cow." She thought the old man was up already, and looked round at his bed; he, however, was not lying in it, but a stranger.

And while she was looking at him, and becoming aware that he was young and handsome, he awoke, sat up in bed, and said, "I am a King's son, and was bewitched by a wicked witch, and made to live in this forest, as an old grey-haired man; no one was allowed to be with me but my three attendants in the form of a cock, a hen, and a brindled cow. The spell was not to be broken until a girl came to us whose heart was so good that she showed herself full of love, not only towards mankind, but towards animals—and that you have done, and by you at midnight we were set free, and the old hut in the forest was changed back again into my royal palace."

And when they had arisen, the king's son ordered the three attendants to set out and fetch the father and mother of the girl to the marriage feast. "But where are my two sisters?" inquired the maiden. "I have locked them in the cellar, and to-morrow they shall be led into the forest, and shall live as servants to a charcoal-burner, until they have grown kinder, and do not leave poor animals to suffer hunger."

THE FROG-KING

Here is an enchantment not broken by the love of the princess but by the king's stern insistence that what she has promised she must perform. Faithful Henry is a curious addition to the story which really ends with the transformation of the Frog into a prince.

In olden times when wishing still helped one, there lived a king whose daughters were all beautiful, but the youngest was so beautiful that the sun itself, which has seen so much, was astonished whenever it shone in her face. Close by the King's castle lay a great dark forest, and

"The Frog-King." From *Grimm's Household Tales,* translated by Margaret Hunt

under an old lime-tree in the forest was a well, and when the day was very warm, the King's child went out into the forest and sat down by the side of the cool fountain; and when she was bored she took a golden ball, and threw it up on high and caught it; and this ball was her favourite plaything.

Now it so happened that on one occasion the princess's golden ball did not fall into the little hand which she was holding up for it, but on to the ground beyond, and rolled straight into the water. The King's daughter followed it with her eyes, but it vanished, and the well was deep, so deep that the bottom could not be seen. At this she began to cry, and cried louder and louder, and could not be comforted. And as she thus lamented, some one said to her, "What ails you, King's daughter? You weep so that even a stone would show pity." She looked round to the side from whence the voice came, and saw a frog stretching forth its thick, ugly head from the water. "Ah! old water-splasher, is it you?" said she; "I am weeping for my golden ball, which has fallen into the well."

"Be quiet, and do not weep," answered the frog, "I can help you, but what will you give me if I bring your plaything up again?" "Whatever you will have, dear frog," said she—"my clothes, my pearls and jewels, and even the golden crown which I am wearing."

The frog answered: "I do not care for your clothes, your pearls and jewels, nor for your golden crown; but if you will love me and let me be your companion and play-fellow, and sit by you at your little table, and eat off your little golden plate, and drink out of your little cup, and sleep in your little bed—if you will promise me this I will go down below, and bring your golden ball up again."

"Oh, yes," said she, "I promise you all you wish, if you will but bring me my ball back again." But she thought: "How the silly frog does talk! He lives in the water with the other frogs, and croaks, and can be no companion to any human being!"

But the frog when he had received this promise, put his head into the water and sank down, and in a short while came swimming up again with the ball in his mouth, and threw it on the grass. The King's daughter was delighted to see her pretty plaything once more, and picked it up, and ran away with it. "Wait, wait," said the frog. "Take me with you. I can't run as you can." But what did it avail him to scream his croak, croak, after her, as loudly as he could? She did not listen to it, but ran home and soon forgot the poor frog, who was forced to go back into his well again.

The next day when she had seated herself at table with the King and all the courtiers, and was eating from her little golden plate, something came creeping splish splash, splish splash, up the marble staircase, and when it had got to the top, it knocked at the door and cried, "Princess, youngest princess, open the door for me." She ran to see who was outside, but when she opened the door, there sat the frog in front of it. Then she slammed the door to, in great haste, sat down to dinner again, and was quite frightened. The King saw plainly that her heart was beating violently, and said, "My child, what are you so afraid of? Is there perchance a giant outside who wants to carry you away?" "Ah, no," replied she, "it is no giant, but a disgusting frog."

"What does the frog want with you?" "Ah, dear father, yesterday when I was in the forest sitting by the well, playing, my golden ball fell into the water. And because I cried so, the frog brought it out again for me; and because he insisted so on it, I promised him he should be my companion, but I never thought he would be able to come out of his water! And now he is outside there, and wants to come in to me."

In the meantime it knocked a second time, and cried:

"Princess! youngest princess!
Open the door for me!
Do you not know what you said to me
Yesterday by the cool waters of the fountain?
Princess, youngest princess!
Open the door for me!"

Then said the King, "That which you have promised must you perform. Go and let him in." She went and opened the door, and the frog hopped in and followed her, step by step, to her chair. There he sat still and cried: "Lift me up beside you." She delayed, until at last the King

commanded her to do it. Once the frog was on the chair he wanted to be on the table, and when he was on the table he said: "Now, push your little golden plate nearer to me that we may eat together." She did this, but it was easy to see that she did not do it willingly. The frog enjoyed what he ate, but almost every mouthful she took choked her. At length he said, "I have eaten and am satisfied; now I am tired, carry me into your little room and make your little silken bed ready, and we will both lie down and go to sleep."

The King's daughter began to cry, for she was afraid of the cold frog which she did not like to touch, and which was now to sleep in her pretty, clean little bed. But the King grew angry and said, "He who helped you when you were in trouble ought not afterwards to be despised by you." So she took hold of the frog with two fingers, carried him upstairs, and put him in a corner.

But when she was in bed he crept to her and said: "I am tired, I want to sleep as well as you, lift me up or I will tell your father." Then she was terribly angry, and took him up and threw him with all her might against the wall. "Now, you will be quiet, odious frog," said she. But when he fell down he was no frog but a king's son with kind and beautiful eyes. He by her father's will was now her dear companion and husband. Then he told her how he had been bewitched by a wicked witch, and how no one could have delivered him from the well but herself, and that to-morrow they would go together into his kingdom.

Then they went to sleep, and next morning when the sun awoke them, a carriage came driving up with eight white horses, which had white ostrich feathers on their heads, and were harnessed with golden chains, and behind stood the young King's servant, faithful Henry. Faithful Henry had been so unhappy when his master was changed into a frog, that he had caused three iron bands to be laid round his heart, lest it should burst with grief and sadness. The carriage was to conduct the young King into his kingdom. Faithful Henry helped them both in, and placed himself behind again, and was full of joy because of this deliverance. And when they had driven a part of the way, the King's son heard a cracking behind him as if something had broken. So he turned round and cried: "Henry, the carriage is breaking."

"No, master, it is not the carriage. It is a band from my heart, which was put there in my great pain when you were a frog and imprisoned in the well." Again and once again while they were on their way something cracked, and each time the King's son thought the carriage was breaking; but it was only the bands which were springing from the heart of faithful Henry because his master was set free and was happy.

HANSEL AND GRETEL

This is a favorite story to illustrate and dramatize. Humperdinck added a fence of gingerbread children which came joyously to life when the wicked witch was dead.

Near a great forest there lived a poor woodcutter and his wife, and his two children; the boy's name was Hansel and the girl's, Gretel. They had very little to bite or to sup, and once, when there was great dearth in the land, the man could not even gain the daily bread.

As he lay in bed one night thinking of this, and turning and tossing, he sighed heavily, and said to his wife, who was the children's stepmother,

"What will become of us? We cannot even

"Hansel and Gretel." From *Household Stories from the Brothers Grimm*, translated by Lucy Crane. By permission of The Macmillan Company, publishers

feed our children; there is nothing left for ourselves."

"I will tell you what, husband," answered the wife; "we will take the children early in the morning into the forest, where it is thickest; we will make them a fire, and we will give each of them a piece of bread, then we will go to our work and leave them alone; they will never find the way home again, and we shall be quit of them."

"No, wife," said the man, "I cannot do that; I cannot find it in my heart to take my children into the forest and to leave them there alone; the wild animals would soon come and devour them."

"O you fool," said she, "then we will all four starve; you had better get the coffins ready," and she left him no peace until he consented.

The two children had not been able to sleep for hunger, and had heard what their stepmother had said to their father. Gretel wept bitterly, and said to Hansel,

"It is all over with us."

"Do be quiet, Gretel," said Hansel, "and do not fret; I will manage something." When the parents had gone to sleep, Hansel got up, put on his little coat, opened the back door, and slipped out. The moon was shining brightly, and the white pebbles that lay in front of the house glistened like pieces of silver. Hansel stooped and filled the little pocket of his coat as full as it would hold. Then he went back again, and said to Gretel,

"Be easy, dear little sister, and go to sleep quietly; God will not forsake us," and laid himself down again in his bed.

When the day was breaking, and before the sun had risen, the wife came and awakened the two children, saying,

"Get up, you lazy bones! We are going into the forest to cut wood."

Then she gave each of them a piece of bread, and said,

"That is for dinner, and you must not eat it before then, for you will get no more."

Gretel carried the bread under her apron, for Hansel had his pockets full of pebbles. Then they set off all together on their way to the forest. When they had gone a little way Hansel stood still and looked back towards the house, and this he did again and again, till his father said to him,

"Hansel, what are you looking at? Take care not to forget your legs."

"O father," said Hansel, "I am looking at my little white kitten, who is sitting up on the roof to bid me good-bye."

"You foolish boy," said the woman, "that is not your kitten, but the sunshine on the chimney pot."

Of course Hansel had not been looking at his kitten, but had been taking every now and then a pebble from his pocket and dropping it on the road.

When they reached the middle of the forest the father told the children to collect wood to make a fire to keep them warm; and Hansel and Gretel gathered brushwood enough for a little mountain; and it was set on fire, and when the flame was burning quite high the wife said,

"Now lie down by the fire and rest yourselves, you children, and we will go and cut wood; and when we are ready we will come and fetch you."

So Hansel and Gretel sat by the fire, and at noon they each ate their pieces of bread. They thought their father was in the wood all the time, as they seemed to hear the strokes of the axe, but really it was only a dry branch hanging to a withered tree that the wind moved to and fro.

So when they had stayed there a long time their eyelids closed with weariness, and they fell fast asleep. When at last they woke it was night, and Gretel began to cry, and said,

"How shall we ever get out of this wood?" But Hansel comforted her, saying,

"Wait a little while longer, until the moon rises, and then we can easily find the way home."

And when the full moon came up, Hansel took his little sister by the hand, and followed the way where the pebbles shone like silver, and showed them the road. They walked on the whole night through, and at the break of day they came to their father's house. They knocked at the door, and when their stepmother opened it and saw that it was Hansel and Gretel she said,

"You naughty children, why did you sleep so long in the wood? We thought you were never coming home again!"

But the father was glad, for it had gone to his heart to leave them both in the woods alone.

Not very long after that there was again great scarcity in those parts, and the children heard their stepmother say to their father,

"Everything is finished up; we have only half a loaf, and after that the tale comes to an end. The children must be off; we will take them farther into the wood this time, so that they shall not be able to find the way back again; there is no other way to manage."

The man felt sad at heart, and he thought,

"It would be better to share one's last morsel with one's children."

But the wife would listen to nothing that he said, but scolded and reproached him.

But the children were not asleep, and had heard all the talk. When the parents had gone to sleep, Hansel got up to go out and get more pebbles as he did before, but the stepmother had locked the door, and Hansel could not get out; but he comforted his little sister, and said,

"Don't cry, Gretel, and go to sleep quietly, and God will help us."

Early the next morning the wife came and pulled the children out of bed. She gave them each a little piece of bread—less than before; and on the way to the wood Hansel crumbled the bread in his pocket, and often stopped to throw a crumb on the ground.

"Hansel, what are you stopping behind and staring for?" said the father.

"I am looking at my little pigeon sitting on the roof, to say good-bye to me," answered Hansel.

"You foolish boy," said the wife, "that is no pigeon, but the morning sun shining on the chimney pots."

Hansel went on as before, and strewed bread crumbs all along the road.

The woman led the children far into the wood, where they had never been before in all their lives. And again there was a large fire made, and the stepmother said,

"Sit still there, you children, and when you are tired you can go to sleep; we are going into the forest to cut wood, and in the evening, when we are ready to go home we will come and fetch you."

So when noon came Gretel shared her bread with Hansel, who had strewed his along the road.

Then they went to sleep, and the evening passed, and no one came for the poor children. When they awoke it was dark night, and Hansel comforted his little sister, and said,

"Wait a little, Gretel, until the moon gets up, then we shall be able to see our way home by the crumbs of bread that I have scattered along the road."

So when the moon rose they got up, but they could find no crumbs of bread, for the birds of the woods and of the fields had come and picked them up. Hansel thought they might find the way all the same, but they could not.

They went on all that night, and the next day from the morning until the evening, but they could not find the way out of the wood, and they were very hungry, for they had nothing to eat but the few berries they could pick up. And when they were so tired that they could no longer drag themselves along, they lay down under a tree and fell asleep.

It was now the third morning since they had left their father's house. They were always trying to get back to it, but instead of that they only found themselves farther in the wood, and if help had not soon come they would have been starved. About noon they saw a pretty snow-white bird sitting on a bough, and singing so sweetly that they stopped to listen. And when he had finished, the bird spread his wings and flew before them, and they followed after him until they came to a little house, and the bird perched on the roof, and when they came nearer they saw that the house was built of gingerbread, and roofed with cakes; and the window was of transparent sugar.

"We will have some of this," said Hansel, "and make a fine meal. I will eat a piece of the roof, Gretel, and you can have some of the window—that will taste sweet."

So Hansel reached up and broke off a bit of the roof, just to see how it tasted, and Gretel stood by the window and gnawed at it. Then they heard a thin voice call out from inside,

"Nibble, nibble, like a mouse,
Who is nibbling at my house?"

And the children answered,

"Never mind,
It is the wind."

And they went on eating, never disturbing themselves. Hansel, who found that the roof tasted very nice, took down a great piece of it, and Gretel pulled out a large round window-pane, and sat her down and began upon it. Then the door opened, and an aged woman came out, leaning upon a crutch. Hansel and Gretel felt very frightened, and let fall what they had in their hands. The old woman, however, nodded her head, and said,

"Ah, my dear children, how come you here? You must come indoors and stay with me, you will be no trouble."

So she took them each by the hand, and led them into her little house. And there they found a good meal laid out, of milk and pancakes, with sugar, apples, and nuts. After that she showed them two little white beds, and Hansel and Gretel laid themselves down on them, and thought they were in heaven.

The old woman, although her behavior was so kind, was a wicked witch, who lay in wait for children, and had built the little house on purpose to entice them. When they were once inside she used to kill them, cook them, and eat them, and then it was a feast-day with her. The witch's eyes were red, and she could not see very far, but she had a keen scent, like the beasts, and knew very well when human creatures were near. When she knew that Hansel and Gretel were coming, she gave a spiteful laugh, and said triumphantly,

"I have them, and they shall not escape me!"

Early in the morning, before the children were awake, she got up to look at them, and as they lay sleeping so peacefully with round rosy cheeks, she said to herself,

"What a fine feast I shall have!"

She grasped Hansel with her withered hand, and led him into a little stable, and shut him up behind a grating; and call and scream as he might, it was no good. Then she went back to Gretel and shook her, crying,

"Get up, lazy bones! Fetch water, and cook something nice for your brother; he is outside in the stable, and must be fattened up. And when he is fat enough, I will eat him."

Gretel began to weep bitterly, but it was of no use, she had to do what the wicked witch bade her.

And so the best kind of victuals was cooked for poor Hansel, while Gretel got nothing but crab-shells. Each morning the old woman visited the little stable, and cried,

"Hansel, stretch out your finger, that I may tell if you will soon be fat enough."

Hansel, however, held out a little bone, and the old woman, who had weak eyes, could not see what it was, and supposing it to be Hansel's finger, wondered very much that it was not getting fatter. When four weeks had passed and Hansel seemed to remain so thin, she lost patience and could wait no longer.

"Now then, Gretel," cried she to the little girl, "be quick and draw water. Be Hansel fat or be he lean, to-morrow I must kill and cook him."

Oh, what a grief for the poor little sister to have to fetch water, and how the tears flowed down over her cheeks!

"Dear God, pray help us!" cried she. "If we had been devoured by wild beasts in the wood, at least we should have died together."

"Spare me your lamentations," said the old woman. "They are of no avail."

Early next morning Gretel had to get up, make the fire, and fill the kettle.

"First we will do the baking," said the old woman. "I have heated the oven already, and kneaded the dough."

She pushed poor Gretel towards the oven, out of which the flames were already shining.

"Creep in," said the witch, "and see if it is properly hot so that the bread may be baked."

And Gretel once in, she meant to shut the door upon her and let her be baked, and then she would have eaten her. But Gretel perceived her intention, and said,

"I don't know how to do it. How shall I get in?"

"Stupid goose," said the old woman, "the opening is big enough, do you see? I could get in myself!" and she stooped down and put her head in the oven's mouth. Then Gretel gave her a push, so that she went in farther, and she shut the iron door upon her, and put up the bar. Oh, how frightfully she howled! But Gretel ran away, and left her in the oven. Then Gretel went straight to Hansel, opened the stable door and cried,

"Hansel, we are free! The old witch is dead!"

Then out flew Hansel like a bird from its cage as soon as the door is opened. How rejoiced they both were! How they fell each on the other's neck! And danced about, and kissed each other! And as they had nothing more to fear, they went over all the old witch's house, and in every corner there stood chests of pearls and precious stones.

"This is something better than pebbles," said Hansel, as he filled his pockets. And Gretel, thinking she also would like to carry something home with her, filled her apron full.

"Now, away we go," said Hansel, "if we only can get out of the witch's wood!"

When they had journeyed a few hours they came to a great piece of water.

"We can never get across this," said Hansel. "I see no stepping-stones and no bridge."

"And there is no boat either," said Gretel. "But here comes a white duck; if I ask her, she will help us over." So she cried,

"Duck, duck, here we stand,
  Hansel and Gretel, on the land,
  Stepping-stones and bridge we lack,
  Carry us over on your nice white back."

And the duck came accordingly, and Hansel got upon her and told his sister to come too.

"No," answered Gretel, "that would be too hard upon the duck; we can go separately, one after the other."

And that was how it was managed, and after that they went on happily, until they came to the wood, and the way grew more and more familiar, till at last they saw in the distance their father's house. Then they ran till they came up to it, rushed in at the door, and fell on their father's neck. The man had not had a quiet hour since he left his children in the wood; but his wife was dead. And when Gretel opened her apron, the pearls and precious stones were scattered all over the room, and Hansel took one handful after another out of his pocket. Then was all care at an end, and they lived in great joy together.

SNOW-WHITE AND ROSE-RED

There was once a poor widow who lived in a lonely cottage. In front of the cottage was a garden wherein stood two rose-trees, one of which bore white and the other red roses. She had two children who were like the two rose-trees, and one was called Snow-White, and the other Rose-Red. They were as good and happy, as busy and cheerful as ever two children in the world were, only Snow-White was more quiet and gentle than Rose-Red. Rose-Red liked better to run about in the meadows and fields seeking flowers and catching butterflies; but Snow-White sat at home with her mother, and helped her with her house-work, or read to her when there was nothing to do.

The two children were so fond of each other that they always held each other by the hand when they went out together, and when Snow-White said, "We will not leave each other," Rose-Red answered, "Never so long as we live," and their mother would add, "What one has she must share with the other."

They often ran about the forest alone and gathered red berries, and no beasts did them any harm, but came close to them trustfully. The little hare would eat a cabbage-leaf out of their hands, the roe grazed by their side, the stag leapt merrily by them, and the birds sat still upon the boughs, and sang whatever they knew.

No mishap overtook them; if they had stayed too late in the forest, and night came on, they laid themselves down near one another upon the moss, and slept until morning came, and their mother knew this and had no distress on their account.

Once when they had spent the night in the wood and the dawn had roused them, they saw a beautiful child in a shining white dress sitting near their bed. He got up and looked quite kindly at them, but said nothing and went away into the forest. And when they looked round they found that they had been sleeping quite close to a precipice, and would certainly have fallen into it in the darkness if they had gone only a few paces further. And their mother told

"Snow-White and Rose-Red." From *Grimm's Household Tales*, translated by Margaret Hunt

them that it must have been the angel who watches over good children.

Snow-White and Rose-Red kept their mother's little cottage so neat that it was a pleasure to look inside it. In the summer Rose-Red took care of the house, and every morning laid a wreath of flowers by her mother's bed before she awoke, in which was a rose from each tree. In the winter Snow-White lit the fire and hung the kettle on the wrekin. The kettle was of copper and shone like gold, so brightly was it polished. In the evening, when the snowflakes fell, the mother said, "Go, Snow-White, and bolt the door," and then they sat round the hearth, and the mother took her spectacles and read aloud out of a large book, and the two girls listened as they sat and span. And close by them lay a lamb upon the floor, and behind them upon a perch sat a white dove with its head hidden beneath its wings.

One evening, as they were thus sitting comfortably together, some one knocked at the door as if he wished to be let in. The mother said, "Quick, Rose-Red, open the door, it must be a traveller who is seeking shelter." Rose-Red went and pushed back the bolt, thinking that it was a poor man, but it was not; it was a bear that stretched his broad, black head within the door.

Rose-Red screamed and sprang back, the lamb bleated, the dove fluttered, and Snow-White hid herself behind her mother's bed. But the bear began to speak and said, "Do not be afraid, I will do you no harm! I am half-frozen, and only want to warm myself a little beside you."

"Poor bear," said the mother, "lie down by the fire, only take care that you do not burn your coat." Then she cried, "Snow-White, Rose-Red, come out, the bear will do you no harm, he means well." So they both came out, and by-and-by the lamb and dove came nearer, and were not afraid of him. The bear said, "Here, children, knock the snow out of my coat a little;" so they brought the broom and swept the bear's hide clean; and he stretched himself by the fire and growled contentedly and comfortably. It was not long before they grew quite at home, and played tricks with their clumsy guest. They tugged his hair with their hands, put their feet upon his back and rolled him about, or they took a hazel-switch and beat him, and when he growled they laughed. But the bear took it all in good part, only when they were too rough he called out, "Leave me alive, children,

> "Snowy-White, Rosy-Red,
> Will you beat your lover dead?"

When it was bed-time, and the others went to bed, the mother said to the bear, "You can lie there by the hearth, and then you will be safe from the cold and the bad weather." As soon as day dawned the two children let him out, and he trotted across the snow into the forest.

Henceforth the bear came every evening at the same time, laid himself down by the hearth, and let the children amuse themselves with him as much as they liked; and they got so used to him that the doors were never fastened until their black friend had arrived.

When spring had come and all outside was green, the bear said one morning to Snow-White, "Now I must go away, and cannot come back for the whole summer." "Where are you going, then, dear bear?" asked Snow-White. "I must go into the forest and guard my treasures from the wicked dwarfs. In the winter, when the earth is frozen hard, they are obliged to stay below and cannot work their way through; but now, when the sun has thawed and warmed the earth, they break through it, and come out to pry and steal; and what once gets into their hands, and in their caves, does not easily see daylight again."

Snow-White was quite sorry for his going away, and as she unbolted the door for him, and the bear was hurrying out, he caught against the bolt and a piece of his hairy coat was torn off, and it seemed to Snow-White as if she had seen gold shining through it, but she was not sure about it. The bear ran away quickly, and was soon out of sight behind the trees.

A short time afterwards the mother sent her children into the forest to get fire-wood. There they found a big tree which lay felled on the ground, and close by the trunk something was jumping backwards and forwards in the grass, but they could not make out what it was. When they came nearer they saw a dwarf with an old withered face and a snow-white beard a yard long. The end of the beard was caught in a crevice of the tree, and the little fellow was

jumping backwards and forwards like a dog tied to a rope, and did not know what to do.

He glared at the girls with his fiery red eyes and cried, "Why do you stand there? Can you not come here and help me?" "What are you about there, little man?" asked Rose-Red. "You stupid, prying goose!" answered the dwarf; "I was going to split the tree to get a little wood for cooking. The little bit of food that one of us wants gets burnt up directly with thick logs; we do not swallow so much as you coarse, greedy folk. I had just driven the wedge safely in, and everything was going as I wished; but the wretched wood was too smooth and suddenly sprang asunder, and the tree closed so quickly that I could not pull out my beautiful white beard; so now it is tight in and I cannot get away, and the silly, sleek, milk-faced things laugh! Ugh! how odious you are!"

The children tried very hard, but they could not pull the beard out, it was caught too fast. "I will run and fetch some one," said Rose-Red. "You senseless goose!" snarled the dwarf; "why should you fetch some one? You are already two too many for me; can you not think of something better?" "Don't be impatient," said Snow-White, "I will help you," and she pulled her scissors out of her pocket, and cut off the end of the beard.

As soon as the dwarf felt himself free he laid hold of a bag which lay amongst the roots of the tree, and which was full of gold, and lifted it up, grumbling to himself, "Uncouth people, to cut off a piece of my fine beard. Bad luck to you!" and then he swung the bag upon his back, and went off without even once looking at the children.

Some time after that Snow-White and Rose-Red went to catch a dish of fish. As they came near the brook they saw something like a large grasshopper jumping towards the water, as if it were going to leap in. They ran to it and found it was the dwarf. "Where are you going?" said Rose-Red; "you surely don't want to go into the water?" "I am not such a fool!" cried the dwarf; "don't you see that the accursed fish wants to pull me in?" The little man had been sitting there fishing, and unluckily the wind had twisted his beard with the fishing-line; just then a big fish bit, and the feeble creature had not strength to pull it out; the fish kept the upper hand and pulled the dwarf towards him. He held on to all the reeds and rushes, but it was of little good, he was forced to follow the movements of the fish, and was in urgent danger of being dragged into the water.

The girls came just in time; they held him fast and tried to free his beard from the line, but all in vain, beard and line were entangled fast together. Nothing was left but to bring out the scissors and cut the beard, whereby a small part of it was lost. When the dwarf saw that he screamed out, "Is that civil, you toad-stool, to disfigure one's face? Was it not enough to clip off the end of my beard? Now you have cut off the best part of it. I cannot let myself be seen by my people. I wish you had been made to run the soles off your shoes!" Then he took out a sack of pearls which lay in the rushes, and without saying a word more he dragged it away and disappeared behind a stone.

It happened that soon afterwards the mother sent the two children to the town to buy needles and thread, and laces and ribbons. The road led them across a heath upon which huge pieces of rock lay strewn here and there. Now they noticed a large bird hovering in the air, flying slowly round and round above them; it sank lower and lower, and at last settled near a rock not far off. Directly afterwards they heard a loud, piteous cry. They ran up and saw with horror that the eagle had seized their old acquaintance the dwarf, and was going to carry him off.

The children, full of pity, at once took tight hold of the little man, and pulled against the eagle so long that at last he let his booty go. As soon as the dwarf had recovered from his first fright he cried with his shrill voice, "Could you not have done it more carefully! You dragged at my brown coat so that it is all torn and full of holes, you helpless clumsy creatures!" Then he took up a sack full of precious stones, and slipped away again under the rock into his hole. The girls, who by this time were used to his thanklessness, went on their way and did their business in the town.

As they crossed the heath again on their way home they surprised the dwarf, who had emptied out his bag of precious stones in a clean spot, and had not thought that any one would come there

so late. The evening sun shone upon the brilliant stones; they glittered and sparkled with all colours so beautifully that the children stood still and looked at them. "Why do you stand gaping there?" cried the dwarf, and his ashen-grey face became copper-red with rage. He was going on with his bad words when a loud growling was heard, and a black bear came trotting towards them out of the forest. The dwarf sprang up in a fright, but he could not get to his cave, for the bear was already close. Then in the dread of his heart he cried, "Dear Mr. Bear, spare me, I will give you all my treasures; look, the beautiful jewels lying there! Grant me my life; what do you want with such a slender little fellow as I? You would not feel me between your teeth. Come, take these two wicked girls, they are tender morsels for you, fat as young quails; for mercy's sake eat them!" The bear took no heed of his words, but gave the wicked creature a single blow with his paw, and he did not move again.

The girls had run away, but the bear called to them, "Snow-White and Rose-Red, do not be afraid; wait, I will come with you." Then they knew his voice and waited, and when he came up to them suddenly his bearskin fell off, and he stood there a handsome man, clothed all in gold. "I am a King's son," he said, "and I was bewitched by that wicked dwarf, who had stolen my treasures; I have had to run about the forest as a savage bear until I was freed by his death. Now he has got his well-deserved punishment."

Snow-White was married to him, and Rose-Red to his brother, and they divided between them the great treasure which the dwarf had gathered together in his cave. The old mother lived peacefully and happily with her children for many years. She took the two rose-trees with her, and they stood before her window, and every year bore the most beautiful roses, white and red.

CLEVER ELSIE

There was once a man who had a daughter who was called Clever Elsie. And when she had grown up her father said, "We will get her

"Clever Elsie." From *Grimm's Household Tales*, translated by Margaret Hunt married." "Yes," said the mother, "if only any one would come who would have her." At length a man came from a distance and wooed her, who was called Hans; but he stipulated that Clever Elsie should be really wise. "Oh," said the father, "she's sharp enough"; and the mother said, "Oh, she can see the wind coming up the street, and hear the flies coughing." "Well," said Hans, "if she is not really wise, I won't have her." When they were sitting at dinner and had eaten, the mother said, "Elsie, go into the cellar and fetch some beer."

Then Clever Elsie took the pitcher from the wall, went into the cellar, and tapped the lid briskly as she went, so that the time might not appear long. When she was below she fetched herself a chair, and set it before the barrel so that she had no need to stoop, and did not hurt her back or do herself any unexpected injury. Then she placed the can before her, and turned the tap, and while the beer was running she would not let her eyes be idle, but looked up at the wall, and after much peering here and there, saw a pick-axe exactly above her, which the masons had accidently left there.

Then Clever Elsie began to weep and said, "If I get Hans, and we have a child, and he grows big, and we send him into the cellar here to draw beer, then the pick-axe will fall on his head and kill him." Then she sat and wept and screamed with all the strength of her body, over the misfortune which lay before her. Those upstairs waited for the drink, but Clever Elsie still did not come. Then the woman said to the servant, "Just go down into the cellar and see where Elsie is." The maid went and found her sitting in front of the barrel, screaming loudly. "Elsie, why do you weep?" asked the maid. "Ah," she answered, "have I not reason to weep? If I get Hans, and we have a child, and he grows big, and has to draw beer here, the pick-axe will perhaps fall on his head, and kill him." Then said the maid, "What a clever Elsie we have!" and sat down beside her and began loudly to weep over the misfortune.

After a while, as the maid did not come back, and those upstairs were thirsty for the beer, the man said to the boy, "Just go down into the cellar and see where Elsie and the girl are." The boy went down, and there sat Clever Elsie and the girl both weeping together. Then he asked, "Why are you weeping?" "Ah," said Elsie, "have I not reason to weep? If I get Hans, and we have a child, and he grows big, and has to draw beer here, the pick-axe will fall on his head and kill him." Then said the boy, "What a clever Elsie we have!" and sat down by her, and likewise began to howl loudly.

Upstairs they waited for the boy, but as he still did not return, the man said to the woman, "Just go down into the cellar and see where Elsie is!" The woman went down, and found all three in the midst of their lamentations, and inquired what was the cause; then Elsie told her also that her future child was to be killed by the pick-axe, when it grew big and had to draw beer, and the pick-axe fell down. Then said the mother likewise, "What a clever Elsie we have!" and sat down and wept with them.

The man upstairs waited a short time, but as his wife did not come back and his thirst grew ever greater, he said, "I must go into the cellar myself and see where Elsie is." But when he got into the cellar, and they were all sitting together crying, and he heard the reason, and that Elsie's child was the cause, and that Elsie might perhaps bring one into the world some day, and that he might be killed by the pick-axe, if he should happen to be sitting beneath it, drawing beer just at the very time when it fell down, he cried, "Oh, what a clever Elsie!" and sat down, and likewise wept with them.

The bridegroom stayed upstairs alone for a long time; then as no one would come back he thought, "They must be waiting for me below: I too must go there and see what they are about." When he got down, the five of them were sitting screaming and lamenting quite piteously, each out-doing the other. "What misfortune has happened then?" asked he. "Ah, dear Hans," said Elsie, "if we marry each other and have a child, and he is big, and we perhaps send him here to draw something to drink, then the pick-axe which has been left up there might dash his brains out if it were to fall down, so have we not reason to weep?" "Come," said Hans, "more understanding than that is not needed for my household, as you are such a clever Elsie, I will have you," and he seized her hand, took her upstairs with him, and married her.

After Hans had had her some time, he said, "Wife, I am going out to work and earn some money for us; go into the field and cut the corn that we may have some bread." "Yes, dear Hans, I will do that." After Hans had gone away, she cooked herself some good broth and took it into the field with her. When she came to the field she said to herself, "What shall I do; shall I cut first, or shall I eat first? Oh, I will eat first." Then she drank her cup of broth, and when she was fully satisfied, she once more said, "What shall I do? Shall I cut first, or shall I sleep first? I will sleep first." Then she lay down among the corn and fell asleep. Hans had been at home for a long time, but Elsie did not come; then said he, "What a clever Elsie I have; she is so industrious that she does not even come home to eat."

But when evening came and she still stayed away, Hans went out to see what she had cut, but nothing was cut, and she was lying among the corn asleep. Then Hans hastened home and brought a fowler's net with little bells and hung it round about her, and she still went on sleeping. Then he ran home, shut the house-door, and sat down in his chair and worked.

At length, when it was quite dark, Clever Elsie awoke and when she got up there was a jingling all round about her, and the bells rang at each step which she took. Then she was alarmed, and became uncertain whether she really was Clever Elsie or not, and said, "Is it I, or is it not I?" But she knew not what answer to make to this, and stood for a time in doubt; at length she thought: "I will go home and ask if it be I, or if it be not I, they will be sure to know." She ran to the door of her own house, but it was shut; then she knocked at the window and cried, "Hans, is Elsie within?" "Yes," answered Hans, "she is within." Hereupon she was terrified, and said, "Ah, heavens! Then it is not I," and went to another door; but when the people heard the jingling of the bells they would not open it, and she could get in nowhere. Then she ran out of the village, and no one has seen her since.

SNOW-WHITE AND THE SEVEN DWARFS

It was in the middle of winter, when the broad flakes of snow were falling around, that a certain queen sat working at a window, the frame of which was made of fine black ebony; and as she was looking out upon the snow, she pricked her finger, and three drops of blood fell upon it. Then she gazed thoughtfully upon the red drops which sprinkled the white snow, and said, "Would that my little daughter may be as white as that snow, as red as the blood, and as black as the ebony window-frame!"

And so the little girl grew up. Her skin was as white as snow, her cheeks as rosy as blood, and her hair as black as ebony; and she was called Snow-White.

But this queen died; and the king soon married another wife, who was very beautiful, but so proud that she could not bear to think that any one could surpass her. She had a magical mirror, to which she used to go and gaze upon herself in it, and say,

"Mirror, Mirror on the wall
Who is fairest of us all?"

"Snow-White and the Seven Dwarfs." From *Grimm's Popular Stories*, translated by Edgar Taylor (slightly adapted)

And the glass answered,

"Thou, queen, art fairest of them all."

But Snow-White grew more and more beautiful; and when she was seven years old, she was as bright as the day, and fairer than the queen herself. Then the glass one day answered the queen, when she went to consult it as usual,

"Queen, you are full fair, 'tis true,
But Snow-White fairer is than you."

When the queen heard this she turned pale with rage and envy; and called to one of her servants and said, "Take Snow-White away into the wide wood, that I may never see her more." Then the servant led Snow-White away; but his heart melted when she begged him to spare her life, and he said, "I will not hurt thee, thou pretty child." So he left her by herself, and though he thought it most likely that the wild beasts would tear her in pieces, he felt as if a great weight were taken off his heart when he had made up his mind not to kill her, but leave her to her fate.

Then poor Snow-White wandered along through the wood in great fear; and the wild beasts roared about her, but none did her any harm. In the evening she came to a little cottage, and went in there to rest herself, for her little feet would carry her no further. Every thing was spruce and neat in the cottage. On the table was spread a white cloth, and there were seven little plates with seven little loaves, and seven little glasses, and knives and forks laid in order; and by the wall stood seven little beds. Then, as she was very hungry, she picked a little piece off each loaf, and drank a very little from each glass; and after that she thought she would lie down and rest. So she tried all the little beds; and one was too long, and another was too short, till at last the seventh suited her; and there she laid herself down, and went to sleep.

Presently in came the masters of the cottage, who were seven little dwarfs that lived among the mountains, and dug and searched about for gold. They lighted up their seven lamps, and saw directly that all was not right. The first said, "Who has been sitting on my stool?" The second, "Who has been eating off my plate?" The third, "Who has been picking my bread?" The fourth, "Who has been meddling with my spoon?" The fifth, "Who has been handling my fork?" The sixth, "Who has been cutting with my knife?" The seventh, "Who has been drinking from my glass?" Then the first looked round and said, "Who has been lying on my bed?" And the rest came running to him, and every one cried out that somebody had been upon his bed. But the seventh saw Snow-White, and called all his brethren to come and see her; and they cried out with wonder and astonishment, and brought their lamps to look at her, and said, "Oh, what a lovely child she is!" And they were delighted to see her, and took care not to wake her; and the seventh dwarf slept an hour with each of the other dwarfs in turn, till the night was gone.

In the morning Snow-White told them all her story; and they pitied her, and said if she would keep all things in order, and cook and wash, and knit and spin for them, she might stay where she was, and they would take good care of her. Then they went out all day long to their work, seeking for gold and silver in the mountains; and Snow-White remained at home; and they warned her, and said, "The queen will soon find out where you are, so take care and let no one in."

But the queen, now that she thought Snow-White was dead, believed that she was certainly the handsomest lady in the land; and she went to her mirror and said,

"Mirror, Mirror on the wall
Who is fairest of us all?"

And the mirror answered,

"Queen, thou art of beauty rare,
But Snow-White living in the glen
With the seven little men,
Is a thousand times more fair."

Then the queen was very much alarmed; for she knew that the glass always spoke the truth, and was sure that the servant had betrayed her. And she could not bear to think that any one lived who was more beautiful than she was; so she disguised herself as an old pedlar and went her way over the hills to the place where the dwarfs dwelt. Then she knocked at the door, and cried, "Fine wares to sell!" Snow-White looked out at the window, and said, "Good-day, good-woman; what have you to sell?" "Good wares, fine wares," said she; "laces and bobbins of all colors." "I will let the old lady in; she seems to be a very good sort of body," thought Snow-White; so she ran down, and unbolted the door. "Bless me!" said the old woman, "how badly your stays are laced! Let me lace them up with one of my nice new laces." Snow-White did not dream of any mischief; so she stood up before the old woman, who set to work so nimbly, and pulled the lace so tight, that Snow-White lost her breath, and fell down as if she were dead. "There's an end of all thy beauty," said the spiteful queen, and went away home.

In the evening the seven dwarfs returned; and I need not say how grieved they were to see their faithful Snow-White stretched upon the ground motionless, as if she were quite dead. However, they lifted her up, and when they found what was the matter, they cut the lace; and in a little time she began to breathe, and soon came to life again. Then they said, "The old woman was the queen herself; take care another time, and let no one in when we are away."

When the queen got home, she went straight to her glass, and spoke to it as usual; but to her great surprise it still said,

"Queen, thou art of beauty rare,
But Snow-White living in the glen
With the seven little men,
Is a thousand times more fair."

Then the blood ran cold in her heart with spite and malice to see that Snow-White still lived; and she dressed herself up again in a disguise, but very different from the one she wore before, and took with her a poisoned comb. When she reached the dwarfs' cottage, she knocked at the door, and cried, "Fine wares to sell!" But Snow-White said, "I dare not let any one in." Then the queen said, "Only look at my beautiful combs"; and gave her the poisoned one. And it looked so pretty that Snow-White took it up and put it into her hair to try it. But the moment it touched her head the poison was so powerful that she fell down senseless. "There you may lie," said the queen, and went her way. But by good luck the dwarfs returned very early that evening, and when they saw Snow-White lying on the ground, they guessed what had happened, and soon found the poisoned comb. When they took it away, she recovered, and told them all that had passed; and they warned her once more not to open the door to any one.

Meantime the queen went home to her glass, and trembled with rage when she received exactly the same answer as before; and she said, "Snow-White shall die, if it costs me my life." So she went secretly into a chamber, and prepared a poisoned apple. The outside looked very rosy and tempting, but whoever tasted it was sure to die. Then she dressed herself up as a peasant's wife, and travelled over the hills to the dwarfs' cottage, and knocked at the door; but Snow-White put her head out of the window and said, "I dare not let any one in, for the dwarfs have told me not." "Do as you please," said the old woman, "but at any rate take this pretty apple; I will make you a present of it." "No," said Snow-White, "I dare not take it." "You silly girl!" answered the other, "what are you afraid of? Do you think it is poisoned? Come! Do you eat one part, and I will eat the other." Now the apple was so prepared that one side was good, though the other side was poisoned. Then Snow-White was very much tempted to taste, for the apple looked exceedingly nice; and when she saw the old woman eat, she could refrain no longer. But she had scarcely put the piece into her mouth, when she fell down dead upon the ground. "This time nothing will save you," said the queen; and she went home to her glass and at last it said,

"Thou, queen, art the fairest of them all."

And then her envious heart was glad, and as happy as such a heart could be.

When evening came, and the dwarfs returned home, they found Snow-White lying on the ground. No breath passed her lips, and they were afraid that she was quite dead. They lifted her up, and combed her hair, and washed her face with water; but all was in vain, for the little girl seemed quite dead. So they laid her down upon a bier, and all seven watched and bewailed her three whole days; and then they proposed to bury her; but her cheeks were still rosy, and her face looked just as it did while she was alive; so they said, "We will never bury her in the cold ground." And they made a coffin of glass, so that they might still look at her, and wrote her name upon it, in golden letters, and that she was a king's daughter. And the coffin was placed upon the hill, and one of the dwarfs always sat by it and watched. And the birds of the air came too, and bemoaned Snow-White; first of all came an owl, and then a raven, but at last came a dove.

And thus Snow-White lay for a long, long time, and still looked as though she were only asleep; for she was even now as white as snow, and as red as blood, and as black as ebony. At last a prince came and called at the dwarfs' house; and he saw Snow-White, and read what was written in golden letters. Then he offered the dwarfs money, and earnestly prayed them to let him take her away; but they said, "We will not part with her for all the gold in the world." At last, however, they had pity on him, and gave him the coffin; but the moment he lifted it up to carry it home with him, the piece of apple fell from between her lips, and Snow-White awoke, and said, "Where am I?" And the prince answered, "Thou art safe with me." Then he told her all that had happened, and said, "I love you better than all the world. Come with me to my father's palace, and you shall be my wife." And Snow-White consented, and went home with the prince; and every thing was prepared with great pomp and splendour for their wedding.

To the feast was invited, among the rest, Snow-White's old enemy, the queen; and as she was dressing herself in fine rich clothes, she looked in the glass, and said,

"Mirror, Mirror on the wall,
Who is fairest of us all?"

And the glass answered,

"O Queen, although you are of beauty rare
The young queen is a thousand times more fair."

When she heard this, she started with rage; but her envy and curiosity were so great, that she could not help setting out to see the bride. And when she arrived, and saw that it was no other than Snow-White, who, as she thought, had been dead a long while, she choked with passion, and fell ill and died. But Snow-White and the prince lived and reigned happily over that land many, many years.

THE FISHERMAN AND HIS WIFE

There is another version of the rhyme that goes, "Oh, fish of the sea,/Come listen to me,/ For, Isabel, my wife,/The plague of my life,/ Has sent me to beg a boon of thee." Because this story is unduly long, it is wise to cut one or two of the episodes.

There was once upon a time a Fisherman who lived with his wife in a miserable hovel close by the sea, and every day he went out fishing. And once as he was sitting with his rod, looking at the clear water, his line suddenly went down, far

"The Fisherman and His Wife." From *Grimm's House-hold Tales*, translated by Margaret Hunt

down below, and when he drew it up again, he brought out a large Flounder. Then the Flounder said to him, "Hark, you Fisherman, I pray you, let me live, I am no Flounder really, but an enchanted prince. What good will it do you to kill me? I should not be good to eat, put me in the water again, and let me go." "Come," said the Fisherman, "there is no need for so many words about it—a fish that can talk I should certainly let go, anyhow," with that he put him back again into the clear water, and the Flounder went to the bottom, leaving a long streak of blood behind him. Then the Fisherman got up and went home to his wife in the hovel.

"Husband," said the woman, "have you caught nothing to-day?" "No," said the man, "I did catch a Flounder, who said he was an enchanted prince, so I let him go again." "Did you not wish for anything first?" said the woman. "No," said the man; "what should I wish for?" "Ah," said the woman, "it is surely hard to have to live always in this dirty hovel; you might have wished for a small cottage for us. Go back and call him. Tell him we want to have a small cottage, he will certainly give us that." "Ah," said the man, "why should I go there again?" "Why," said the woman, "you did catch him, and you let him go again; he is sure to do it. Go at once." The man still did not quite like to go, but did not like to oppose his wife either, and went to the sea.

When he got there the sea was all green and yellow, and no longer so smooth; so he stood and said,

> "Flounder, flounder in the sea,
> Come, I pray thee, here to me;
> For my wife, good Ilsabil,
> Wills not as I'd have her will."

Then the Flounder came swimming to him and said: "Well, what does she want then?" "Ah," said the man, "I did catch you, and my wife says I really ought to have wished for something. She does not like to live in a wretched hovel any longer; she would like to have a cottage." "Go, then," said the Flounder, "she has it already."

When the man went home, his wife was no longer in the hovel, but instead of it there stood a small cottage, and she was sitting on a bench before the door. Then she took him by the hand and said to him, "Just come inside. Look, now isn't this a great deal better?" So they went in, and there was a small porch, and a pretty little parlour and bedroom, and a kitchen and pantry, with the best of furniture, and fitted up with the most beautiful things made of tin and brass, whatsoever was wanted. And behind the cottage there was a small yard, with hens and ducks, and a little garden with flowers and fruit. "Look," said the wife, "is not that nice!" "Yes," said the husband, "and so we must always think it—now we will live quite contented." "We will think about that," said the wife. With that they ate something and went to bed.

Everything went well for a week or a fortnight, and then the woman said, "Hark you, husband, this cottage is far too small for us, and the garden and yard are little; the Flounder might just as well have given us a larger house. I should like to live in a great stone castle; go to the Flounder, and tell him to give us a castle." "Ah, wife," said the man, "the cottage is quite good enough; why should we live in a castle?" "What!" said the woman; "just go there, the Flounder can always do that." "No, wife," said the man, "the Flounder has just given us the cottage, I do not like to go back so soon, it might make him angry." "Go," said the woman, "he can do it quite easily, and will be glad to do it; just you go to him."

The man's heart grew heavy, and he would not go. He said to himself, "It is not right," and yet he went. And when he came to the sea the water was quite purple and dark-blue, and grey and thick, and no longer so green and yellow, but it was still quiet. And he stood there and said,

> "Flounder, flounder in the sea,
> Come, I pray thee, here to me;
> For my wife, good Ilsabil,
> Wills not as I'd have her will."

"Well, what does she want, then?" said the Flounder. "Alas," said the man, half scared, "she wants to live in a great stone castle." "Go to it, then, she is standing before the door," said the Flounder.

Then the man went away, intending to go home, but when he got there, he found a great stone palace, and his wife was just standing on the steps going in, and she took him by the hand and said: "Come in." So he went in with her, and in the castle was a great hall paved with marble, and many servants, who flung wide the doors; and the walls were all bright with beautiful hangings, and in the rooms were chairs and tables of pure gold, and crystal chandeliers hung from the ceiling, and all the rooms and bedrooms had carpets, and food and wine of the very best were standing on all the tables, so that they nearly broke down beneath it. Behind the house, too, there was a great court-yard, with stables for horses and cows, and the very best of carriages; there was a magnificent large garden, too, with the most beautiful flowers and fruit-trees, and a park quite half a mile long, in which were stags, deer, and hares, and everything that could be desired. "Come," said the woman, "isn't that beautiful?" "Yes, indeed," said the man, "now let it be; and we will live in this beautiful castle and be content." "We will consider about that," said the woman, "and sleep upon it"; thereupon they went to bed.

Next morning the wife awoke first, and it was just daybreak, and from her bed she saw the beautiful country lying before her. Her husband was still stretching himself, so she poked him in the side with her elbow, and said, "Get up, husband, and just peep out of the window. Look you, couldn't we be the King over all that land? Go to the Flounder, we will be the King." "Ah, wife," said the man, "why should we be King? I do not want to be King." "Well," said the wife, "if you won't be King, I will; go to the Flounder, for I will be King." "Ah, wife," said the man, "why do you want to be King? I do not like to say that to him." "Why not?" said the woman; "go to him this instant; I must be King!" So the man went, and was quite unhappy because his wife wished to be King. "It is not right; it is not right," thought he. He did not wish to go, but yet he went.

And when he came to the sea, it was quite dark-grey, and the water heaved up from below, and smelt putrid. Then he went and stood by it, and said,

"Flounder, flounder in the sea,
Come, I pray thee, here to me;

For my wife, good Ilsabil,
Wills not as I'd have her will."

"Well, what does she want, then?" said the Flounder. "Alas," said the man, "she wants to be King." "Go to her; she is King already."

So the man went, and when he came to the palace, the castle had become much larger, and had a great tower and magnificent ornaments, and the sentinel was standing before the door, and there were numbers of soldiers with kettle-drums and trumpets. And when he went inside the house, everything was of real marble and gold, with velvet covers and great golden tassels. Then the doors of the hall were opened, and there was the court in all its splendour, and his wife was sitting on a high throne of gold and diamonds, with a great crown of gold on her head, and a sceptre of pure gold and jewels in her hand, and on both sides of her stood her maids-in-waiting in a row, each of them always one head shorter than the last.

Then he went and stood before her, and said: "Ah, wife, and now you are King." "Yes," said the woman, "now I am King." So he stood and looked at her, and when he had looked at her thus for some time, he said, "And now that you are King, let all else be, now we will wish for nothing more." "No, husband," said the woman, quite anxiously, "I find time passes very heavily, I can bear it no longer, go to the Flounder—I am King, but I must be Emperor, too." "Oh, wife, why do you wish to be Emperor?" "Husband," said she, "go to the Flounder. I will be Emperor." "Alas, wife," said the man, "he cannot make you Emperor; I may not say that to the fish. There is only one Emperor in the land. An Emperor the Flounder cannot make you! I assure you he cannot."

"What!" said the woman, "I am the King, and you are nothing but my husband; will you go this moment? go at once! If he can make a king he can make an emperor. I will be Emperor; go instantly." So he was forced to go. As the man went, however, he was troubled in mind, and thought to himself: "It will not end well; it will not end well! Emperor is too shameless! The Flounder will at last be tired out."

With that he reached the sea, and the sea was quite black and thick, and began to boil up from below, so that it threw up bubbles, and such a sharp wind blew over it that it curdled, and the man was afraid. Then he went and stood by it, and said,

> "Flounder, flounder in the sea,
> Come, I pray thee, here to me;
> For my wife, good Ilsabil,
> Wills not as I'd have her will."

"Well, what does she want, then?" said the Flounder. "Alas, Flounder," said he, "my wife wants to be Emperor." "Go to her," said the Flounder; "she is Emperor already."

So the man went, and when he got there the whole palace was made of polished marble with alabaster figures and golden ornaments, and soldiers were marching before the door blowing trumpets, and beating cymbals and drums; and in the house, barons, and counts, and dukes were going about as servants. Then they opened the doors to him, which were of pure gold. And when he entered, there sat his wife on a throne, which was made of one piece of gold, and was quite two miles high; and she wore a great golden crown that was three yards high, and set with diamonds and carbuncles, and in one hand she had the sceptre, and in the other the imperial orb; and on both sides of her stood the yeomen of the guard in two rows, each being smaller than the one before him, from the biggest giant, who was two miles high, to the very smallest dwarf, just as big as my little finger. And before it stood a number of princes and dukes.

Then the man went and stood among them, and said, "Wife, are you Emperor now?" "Yes," said she, "now I am Emperor." Then he stood and looked at her well, and when he had looked at her thus for some time, he said, "Ah, wife, be content, now that you are Emperor." "Husband," said she, "why are you standing there? Now, I am Emperor, but I will be Pope too; go to the Flounder." "Oh, wife," said the man, "what will you not wish for? You cannot be Pope; there is but one in Christendom; he cannot make you Pope." "Husband," said she, "I will be Pope, go immediately, I must be Pope this very day." "No, wife," said the man, "I do not like to say that to him; that would not do, it is too much; the Flounder can't make you Pope." "Husband," said she, "what nonsense! if

he can make an emperor he can make a pope. Go to him directly. I am Emperor, and you are nothing but my husband; will you go at once?"

Then he was afraid and went; but he was quite faint, and shivered and shook, and his knees and legs trembled. And a high wind blew over the land, and the clouds flew, and towards evening all grew dark, and the leaves fell from the trees, and the water rose and roared as if it were boiling, and splashed upon the shore; and in the distance he saw ships which were firing guns in their sore need, pitching and tossing on the waves. And yet in the midst of the sky there was still a small bit of blue, though on every side it was as red as in a heavy storm. So, full of despair, he went and stood in much fear and said,

> "Flounder, flounder in the sea,
> Come, I pray thee, here to me;
> For my wife, good Ilsabil,
> Wills not as I'd have her will."

"Well, what does she want, now?" said the Flounder. "Alas," said the man, "she wants to be Pope." "Go to her then," said the Flounder; "she is Pope already."

So he went, and when he got there, he saw what seemed to be a large church surrounded by palaces. He pushed his way through the crowd. Inside, however, everything was lighted up with thousands and thousands of candles, and his wife was clad in gold, and she was sitting on a much higher throne, and had three great golden crowns on, and round about her there was much ecclesiastical splendour; and on both sides of her was a row of candles the largest of which was as tall as the very tallest tower, down to the very smallest kitchen candle, and all the emperors and kings were on their knees before her, kissing her shoe. "Wife," said the man, and looked attentively at her, "are you now Pope?" "Yes," said she, "I am Pope." So he stood and looked at her, and it was just as if he was looking at the bright sun. When he had stood looking at her thus for a short time, he said: "Ah, wife, if you are Pope, do let well alone!" But she looked as stiff as a post, and did not move or show any signs of life. Then said he, "Wife, now that you are Pope, be satisfied, you cannot become anything greater now." "I will consider about that," said the woman. Thereupon they both went to bed, but she was not satisfied, and greediness let her have no sleep, for she was continually thinking what there was left for her to be.

The man slept well and soundly, for he had run about a great deal during the day; but the woman could not fall asleep at all, and flung herself from one side to the other the whole night through, thinking always what more was left for her to be, but unable to call to mind anything else. At length the sun began to rise, and when the woman saw the red of dawn, she sat up in bed and looked at it. And when, through the window, she saw the sun thus rising, she said, "Cannot I, too, order the sun and moon to rise?" "Husband," she said, poking him in the ribs with her elbows, "wake up! go to the Flounder, for I wish to be even as God is." The man was still half asleep, but he was so horrified that he fell out of bed. He thought he must have heard amiss, and rubbed his eyes, and said, "Alas, wife, what are you saying?" "Husband," said she, "if I can't order the sun and moon to rise, and have to look on and see the sun and moon rising, I can't bear it. I shall not know what it is to have another happy hour, unless I can make them rise myself." Then she looked at him so terribly that a shudder ran over him, and said, "Go at once; I wish to be like unto God." "Alas, wife," said the man, falling on his knees before her, "the Flounder cannot do that; he can make an emperor and a pope; I beseech you, go on as you are, and be Pope." Then she fell into a rage, and her hair flew wildly about her head, and she cried, "I will not endure this, I'll not bear it any longer; will you go this instant?" Then he put on his trousers and ran away like a madman. But outside a great storm was raging, and blowing so hard that he could scarcely keep his feet; houses and trees toppled over, the mountains trembled, rocks rolled into the sea, the sky was pitch black, and it thundered and lightened, and the sea came in with black waves as high as church-towers and mountains, and all with crests of white foam at the top. Then he cried, but could not hear his own words,

> "Flounder, flounder in the sea,
> Come, I pray thee, here to me;
> For my wife, good Ilsabil,
> Wills not as I'd have her will."

"Well, what does she want, then?" said the Flounder. "Alas," said he, "she wants to be like unto God." "Go to her, and you will find her back again in the dirty hovel." And there they are still living to this day.

RUMPELSTILTSKIN

This makes a splendid story for dramatization with puppets, either string puppets or hand. The children can cast the story into acts, line up their characters, and as they make the puppets, try out the dialogue with them. With children under ten-years-old hand puppets are easier to make and the dialogue is usually kept fluid. Children over ten may want to write parts of their dialogue or all of it.

There was once a miller who was poor, but he had one beautiful daughter. It happened one day that he came to speak with the king, and to give himself consequence, he told him that he had a daughter who could spin gold out of straw. The king said to the miller,

"That is an art that pleases me well; if your daughter is as clever as you say, bring her to my castle tomorrow, that I may put her to the proof."

When the girl was brought to him, he led her into a room that was quite full of straw, and gave her a wheel and spindle, and said,

"Now set to work, and if by the early morning you have not spun this straw to gold you shall die." And he shut the door himself, and left her there alone.

And so the poor miller's daughter was left there sitting, and could not think what to do for her life; she had no notion how to set to work to spin gold from straw, and her distress grew so great that she began to weep. Then all at once the door opened, and in came a little man, who said,

"Good evening, miller's daughter; why are you crying?"

"Oh!" answered the girl, "I have got to spin

"Rumpelstiltskin." From *Household Stories from the Brothers Grimm*, translated by Lucy Crane. By permission of The Macmillan Company, publishers

gold out of straw, and I don't understand the business."

Then the little man said,

"What will you give me if I spin it for you?"

"My necklace," said the girl.

The little man took the necklace, seated himself before the wheel, and whirr, whirr, whirr! three times round and the bobbin was full; then he took up another, and whirr, whirr, whirr! three times round, and that was full; and so he went on till the morning, when all the straw had been spun, and all the bobbins were full of gold. At sunrise came the king, and when he saw the gold he was astonished and very much rejoiced, for he was very avaricious. He had the miller's daughter taken into another room filled with straw, much bigger than the last, and told her that as she valued her life she must spin it all in one night. The girl did not know what to do, so she began to cry, and then the door opened, and the little man appeared and said,

"What will you give me if I spin all this straw into gold?"

"The ring from my finger," answered the girl.

So the little man took the ring, and began again to send the wheel whirring round, and by the next morning all the straw was spun into glistening gold. The king was rejoiced beyond measure at the sight, but as he could never have enough of gold, he had the miller's daughter taken into a still larger room full of straw, and said,

"This, too, must be spun in one night, and if you accomplish it you shall be my wife." For he thought, "Although she is but a miller's daugh-

ter, I am not likely to find any one richer in the whole world."

As soon as the girl was left alone, the little man appeared for the third time and said,

"What will you give me if I spin the straw for you this time?"

"I have nothing left to give," answered the girl.

"Then you must promise me the first child you have after you are queen," said the little man.

"But who knows whether that will happen?" thought the girl; but as she did not know what else to do in her necessity, she promised the little man what he desired, upon which he began to spin, until all the straw was gold. And when in the morning the king came and found all done according to his wish, he caused the wedding to be held at once, and the miller's pretty daughter became a queen.

In a year's time she brought a fine child into the world, and thought no more of the little man; but one day he came suddenly into her room, and said,

"Now give me what you promised me."

The queen was terrified greatly, and offered the little man all the riches of the kingdom if he would only leave the child; but the little man said, "No, I would rather have something living than all the treasures of the world."

Then the queen began to lament and to weep, so that the little man had pity upon her.

"I will give you three days," said he, "and if at the end of that time you cannot tell my name, you must give up the child to me."

Then the queen spent the whole night in thinking over all the names that she had ever heard, and sent a messenger through the land to ask far and wide for all the names that could be found. And when the little man came next day, (beginning with Caspar, Melchior, Balthazar) she repeated all she knew, and went through the whole list, but after each the little man said,

"That is not my name."

The second day the queen sent to inquire of all the neighbours what the servants were called, and told the little man all the most unusual and singular names, saying,

"Perhaps you are called Roast-ribs, or Sheepshanks, or Spindleshanks?" But he answered nothing but

"That is not my name."

The third day the messenger came back again, and said,

"I have not been able to find one single new name; but as I passed through the woods I came to a high hill, and near it was a little house, and before the house burned a fire, and round the fire danced a comical little man, and he hopped on one leg and cried,

"To-day do I bake, to-morrow I brew,
  The day after that the queen's child comes in;
  And oh! I am glad that nobody knew
  That the name I am called is Rumpelstiltskin!"

You cannot think how pleased the queen was to hear that name, and soon afterwards, when the little man walked in and said,

"Now, Mrs. Queen, what is my name?" she said at first,

"Are you called Jack?"

"No," he answered.

"Are you called Harry?" she asked again.

"No," answered he. And then she said,

"Then perhaps your name is Rumpelstiltskin!"

"The devil told you that! the devil told you that!" cried the little man, and in his anger he stamped with his right foot so hard that it went into the ground above his knee; then he seized his left foot with both his hands in such a fury that he split in two, and there was an end of him.

ONE-EYE, TWO-EYES, AND THREE-EYES

The little rhymes of this story suggest ancient charms or incantations.

There was once a woman who had three daughters, the eldest of whom was called One-Eye, because she had only one eye in the middle of her forehead, and the second, Two-Eyes, because she had two eyes like other folks, and the youngest, Three-Eyes, because she had three eyes; and her third eye was also in the centre of her forehead. However, as Two-Eyes saw just as other human beings did, her sisters and her mother could not endure her. They said to her, "You, with your two eyes, are no better than the common people; you do not belong to us!" They pushed her about, and threw old clothes to her, and gave her nothing to eat but what they left, and did everything that they could to make her unhappy. It came to pass that Two-Eyes had to go out into the fields and tend the goat, but she was still quite hungry, because her sisters had given her so little to eat. So she sat down on a ridge and began to weep, and so bitterly that two streams ran down from her eyes. And once when she looked up in her grief, a woman was standing beside her, who said, "Why are you weeping, little Two-Eyes?" Two-Eyes answered, "Have I not reason to weep, when I have two eyes like other people, and my sisters and mother hate me for it, and push me from one corner to another, throw old clothes at me, and give me nothing to eat but the scraps they leave? To-day they have given me so little that I am still quite hungry." Then the wise woman said, "Wipe away your tears, Two-Eyes, and I will tell you something to stop you ever suffering from hunger again; just say to your goat,

'Bleat, my little goat, bleat,
  Cover the table with something to eat,'

and then a clean well-spread little table will stand before you, with the most delicious food

"One-Eye, Two-Eyes, and Three-Eyes." From *Grimm's Household Tales,* translated by Margaret Hunt

upon it of which you may eat as much as you are inclined for; and when you have had enough, and have no more need of the little table, just say,

'Bleat, bleat, my little goat, I pray,
And take the table quite away,'

and then it will vanish again from your sight." Hereupon the wise woman departed. But Two-Eyes thought, "I must instantly make a trial, and see if what she said is true, for I am far too hungry," and she said,

"Bleat, my little goat, bleat,
Cover the table with something to eat,"

and scarcely had she spoken the words than a little table, covered with a white cloth, was standing there, and on it was a plate with a knife and fork, and a silver spoon; and the most delicious food was there also, warm and smoking as if it had just come out of the kitchen. Then Two-Eyes said the shortest prayer she knew, "Lord God, be with us always, Amen," and helped herself to some food, and enjoyed it. And when she was satisfied, she said, as the wise woman had taught her,

"Bleat, bleat, my little goat, I pray,
And take the table quite away,"

and immediately the little table and everything on it was gone again. "That is a delightful way of keeping house!" thought Two-Eyes, and was quite glad and happy.

In the evening, when she went home with her goat, she found a small earthenware dish with some food, which her sisters had set ready for her, but she did not touch it. Next day she again went out with her goat, and left the few bits of broken bread which had been handed to her, lying untouched. The first and second time that she did this, her sisters did not remark it at all, but as it happened every time, they did observe it, and said, "There is something wrong about Two-Eyes; she always leaves her food untasted, and she used to eat up everything that was given her; she must have discovered other ways of getting food." In order that they might learn the truth, they resolved to send One-Eye with Two-Eyes when she went to drive her goat to the pasture, to observe what Two-Eyes did when she was there, and whether any one brought her anything to eat and drink. So when Two-Eyes set out the next time, One-Eye went to her and said, "I will go with you to the pasture, and see that the goat is well taken care of, and driven where there is food." But Two-Eyes knew what was in One-Eye's mind, and drove the goat into high grass and said, "Come, One-Eye, we will sit down, and I will sing something to you." One-Eye sat down and was tired with the unaccustomed walk and the heat of the sun, and Two-Eyes sang constantly,

"One eye, wakest thou?
One eye, sleepest thou?"

until One-Eye shut her one eye, and fell asleep, and as soon as Two-Eyes saw that One-Eye was fast asleep, and could discover nothing, she said,

"Bleat, my little goat, bleat,
Cover the table with something to eat,"

and seated herself at her table and ate and drank until she was satisfied, and then she again cried,

"Bleat, bleat, my little goat, I pray,
And take the table quite away,"

and in an instant all was gone. Two-Eyes now awakened One-Eye, and said, "One-Eye, you want to take care of the goat, and go to sleep while you are doing it, and in the meantime the goat might run all over the world. Come, let us go home again." So they went home, and again Two-Eyes let her little dish stand untouched, and One-Eye could not tell her mother why she would not eat it, and to excuse herself said, "I fell asleep when I was out."

Next day the mother said to Three-Eyes, "This time you shall go and observe if Two-Eyes eats anything when she is out, and if any one fetches her food and drink, for she must eat and drink in secret." So Three-Eyes went to Two-Eyes, and said, "I will go with you and see if the goat is taken proper care of, and driven where there is food." But Two-Eyes knew what was in Three-

Eyes' mind, and drove the goat into high grass and said, "We will sit down, and I will sing something to you, Three-Eyes." Three-Eyes sat down and was tired with the walk and with the heat of the sun, and Two-Eyes began the same song as before, and sang,

> "Three eyes, are you waking?"

but then, instead of singing,

> "Three eyes, are you sleeping?"

as she ought to have done, she thoughtlessly sang,

> "Two eyes, are you sleeping?"

and sang all the time,

> "Three eyes, are you waking?
> Two eyes, are you sleeping?"

Then two of the eyes which Three-Eyes had, shut and fell asleep, but the third, as it had not been named in the song, did not sleep. It is true that Three-Eyes shut it, but only in her cunning, to pretend it was asleep too, but it blinked, and could see everything very well. And when Two-Eyes thought that Three-Eyes was fast asleep, she used her little charm,

> "Bleat, my little goat, bleat,
> Cover the table with something to eat,"

and ate and drank as much as her heart desired, and then ordered the table to go away again,

> "Bleat, bleat, my little goat, I pray,
> And take the table quite away,"

and Three-Eyes had seen everything. Then Two-Eyes came to her, waked her and said, "Have you been asleep, Three-Eyes? You are a good care-taker! Come, we will go home."

And when they got home, Two-Eyes again did not eat, and Three-Eyes said to the mother, "Now, I know why that high-minded thing there does not eat. When she is out, she says to the goat,

> 'Bleat, my little goat, bleat,
> Cover the table with something to eat,'

and then a little table appears before her covered with the best of food, much better than any we have here, and when she has eaten all she wants, she says,

> 'Bleat, bleat, my little goat, I pray,
> And take the table quite away,'

and all disappears. I watched everything closely. She put two of my eyes to sleep by using a certain form of words, but luckily the one in my forehead kept awake." Then the envious mother cried, "Dost thou want to fare better than we do? The desire shall pass away," and she fetched a butcher's knife, and thrust it into the heart of the goat, which fell down dead.

When Two-Eyes saw that, she went out full of trouble, seated herself on the ridge of grass at the edge of the field, and wept bitter tears. Suddenly the wise woman once more stood by her side, and said, "Two-Eyes, why are you weeping?" "Have I not reason to weep?" she answered. "The goat which covered the table for me every day when I spoke your charm has been killed by my mother, and now I shall again have to bear hunger and want." The wise woman said, "Two-Eyes, I will give you a piece of good advice; ask your sisters to give you the entrails of the slaughtered goat, and bury them in the ground in front of the house, and your fortune will be made." Then she vanished, and Two-Eyes went home and said to her sisters, "Dear sisters, do give me some part of my goat; I don't wish for what is good, but give me the entrails." Then they laughed and said, "If that's all you want, you can have it." So Two-Eyes took the entrails and buried them quietly in the evening, in front of the house-door, as the wise woman had counseled her to do.

Next morning, when they all awoke, and went to the house-door, there stood a strangely magnificent tree with leaves of silver, and fruit of gold hanging among them, so that in all the wide world there was nothing more beautiful or precious. They did not know how the tree could have come there during the night, but Two-Eyes saw that it had grown up out of the entrails of the goat, for it was standing on the exact spot where she had buried them. Then the mother said to One-Eye, "Climb up, my child, and gather some of the fruit of the tree for us." One-Eye climbed up, but when she was about to get hold of one of the golden apples, the branch escaped from her hands, and that happened each time, so that she could not pluck a single apple, let her do what she might. Then said the mother, "Three-Eyes, do you climb up; you with your three eyes can look about you better than One-Eye." One-Eye slipped down, and Three-Eyes climbed up. Three-Eyes was not more skilful, and might search as she liked, but the golden apples always escaped her. At length the mother grew impatient, and climbed up herself, but could get hold of the fruit no better than One-Eye and Three-Eyes, for she always clutched empty air.

Then said Two-Eyes, "I will just go up, perhaps I may succeed better." The sisters cried, "You indeed, with your two eyes, what can you do?" But Two-Eyes climbed up, and the golden apples did not get out of her way, but came into her hand of their own accord, so that she could pluck them one after the other, and brought a whole apronful down with her. The mother took them away from her, and instead of treating poor Two-Eyes any better for this, she and One-Eye and Three-Eyes were only envious, because Two-Eyes alone had been able to get the fruit, and they treated her still more cruelly.

It so befell that once when they were all standing together by the tree, a young knight came up. "Quick, Two-Eyes," cried the two sisters, "creep under this, and don't disgrace us!" and with all speed they turned an empty barrel which was standing close by the tree over poor Two-Eyes, and they pushed the golden apples, which she had been gathering, under it too. When the knight came nearer he was a handsome lord, who stopped and admired the magnificent gold and silver tree, and said to the two sisters, "To whom does this fine tree belong? Any one who would bestow one branch of it on me might in return for it ask whatsoever he desired." Then One-Eye and Three-Eyes replied that the tree belonged to them, and that they would give him a branch. They both took great trouble, but they were not able to do it, for the branches and fruit both moved away from them every time. Then

said the knight. "It is very strange that the tree should belong to you, and that you should still not be able to break a piece off." They again asserted that the tree was their property.

Whilst they were saying so, Two-Eyes rolled out a couple of golden apples from under the barrel to the feet of the knight, for she was vexed with One-Eye and Three-Eyes for not speaking the truth. When the knight saw the apples, he was astonished, and asked where they came from. One-Eye and Three-Eyes answered that they had another sister, who was not allowed to show herself, for she had only two eyes like any common person. The knight, however, desired to see her, and cried, "Two-Eyes, come forth." Then Two-Eyes, quite comforted, came from beneath the barrel, and the knight was surprised at her great beauty, and said, "Thou, Two-Eyes, canst certainly break off a branch from the tree for me." "Yes," replied Two-Eyes, "that I certainly shall be able to do, for the tree belongs to me." And she climbed up, and with the greatest ease, broke off a branch with beautiful silver leaves and golden fruit, and gave it to the knight. Then said the knight, "Two-Eyes, what shall I give thee for it?" "Alas!" answered Two-Eyes, "I suffer from hunger and thirst, grief and want, from early morning till late night; if you would take me with you, and deliver me from these things, I should be happy."

So the knight lifted Two-Eyes on to his horse and took her home with him to his father's castle, and there he gave her beautiful clothes, and meat and drink to her heart's content; and as he loved her so much he married her, and the wedding was solemnized with great rejoicing. When Two-Eyes was thus carried away by the handsome knight, her two sisters grudged her good fortune in downright earnest. "The wonderful tree, however, still remains with us," thought they, "and even if we can gather no fruit from it, still every one will stand still and look at it, and come to us and admire it. Who knows what good things may be in store for us?" But next morning, the tree had vanished, and all their hopes were at an end. When Two-Eyes looked out of the window of her own little room, to her great delight it was standing in front of it, and so it had followed her.

Two-Eyes lived a long time in happiness. Once

two poor women came to her in her castle, and begged for alms. She looked in their faces, and recognized her sisters, One-Eye and Three-Eyes, who had fallen into such poverty that they had to wander about and beg their bread from door to door. Two-Eyes, however, made them welcome, and was kind to them, and took care of them, so that they both with all their hearts repented the evil that they had done their sister in their youth.

THE GOOSE-GIRL

This is a somber romance in spite of the happy ending. The little rhyme the goose-girl says over Conrad's hat is certainly a powerful charm!

There was once upon a time an old Queen whose husband had been dead for many years, and she had a beautiful daughter. When the princess grew up she was betrothed to a prince who lived at a great distance. When the time came for her to be married, and she had to journey forth into the distant kingdom, the aged Queen packed up for her many costly vessels of silver and gold, and trinkets also of gold and silver; and cups and jewels, in short, everything which appertained to a royal dowry, for she loved her child with all her heart. She likewise sent her maid in waiting, who was to ride with her, and hand her over to the bridegroom, and each had a horse for the journey, but the horse of the King's daughter was called Falada, and could speak. So when the hour of parting had come, the aged mother went into her bedroom, took a small knife and cut her finger with it until it bled. Then she held a white handkerchief to it into which she let three drops of blood fall, gave it to her daughter and said, "Dear child, preserve this carefully, it will be of service to you on your way."

So they took a sorrowful leave of each other; the princess put the piece of cloth in her bosom, mounted her horse, and then went away to her bridegroom. After she had ridden for a while she felt a burning thirst, and said to her waiting-maid, "Dismount, and take my cup which you

"The Goose-Girl." From *Grimm's Household Tales,* translated by Margaret Hunt

have brought with you for me, and get me some water from the stream, for I should like to drink." "If you are thirsty," said the waiting-maid, "get off your horse yourself, and lie down and drink out of the water, I don't choose to be your servant." So in her great thirst the princess alighted, bent down over the water in the stream and drank, and was not allowed to drink out of the golden cup. Then she said: "Ah, Heaven!" and the three drops of blood answered: "If this your mother knew, her heart would break in two." But the King's daughter was humble, said nothing, and mounted her horse again. She rode some miles further, but the day was warm, the sun scorched her, and she was thirsty once more, and when they came to a stream of water, she again cried to her waiting-maid, "Dismount, and give me some water in my golden cup," for she had long ago forgotten the girl's ill words. But the waiting-maid said still more haughtily: "If you wish to drink, drink as you can, I don't choose to be your maid." Then in her great thirst the King's daughter alighted, bent over the flowing stream, wept and said, "Ah, Heaven!" and the drops of blood again replied, "If this your mother knew, her heart would break in two."

And as she was thus drinking and leaning right over the stream, the handkerchief with the three drops of blood fell out of her bosom, and floated away with the water without her observing it, so great was her trouble. The waiting-maid however, had seen it, and she rejoiced to think that she had now power over the bride, for since the princess had lost the drops of blood, she had become weak and powerless. So now when she wanted to mount her horse again, the one that was called Falada, the waiting-maid said, "Falada is more suitable for me, and my nag will do for you," and the princess had to be content with that. Then the waiting-maid, with many hard words, bade the princess exchange her royal apparel for her own shabby clothes; and at length she was compelled to swear by the clear sky above her, that she would not say one word of this to anyone at the royal court, and if she had not taken this oath she would have been killed on the spot. But Falada saw all this, and observed it well.

The waiting-maid now mounted Falada, and the true bride the bad horse, and thus they traveled onwards, until at length they entered the royal palace. There were great rejoicings over her arrival, and the prince sprang forward to meet her, lifted the waiting-maid from her horse, and thought she was his consort. She was conducted upstairs, but the real princess was left standing below.

Then the old King looked out of the window and saw her standing in the courtyard, and noticed how dainty and delicate and beautiful she was, and instantly went to the royal apartment, and asked the bride about the girl she had with her who was standing down below in the courtyard, and who she was. "I picked her up on my way for a companion; give the girl something to work at, that she may not stand idle." But the old King had no work for her, and knew of none, so he said, "I have a little boy who tends the geese, she may help him." The boy was called Conrad, and the true bride had to help him to tend the geese.

Soon afterwards the false bride said to the young King, "Dearest husband, I beg you to do me a favour." He answered, "I will do so most willingly." "Then send for the knacker, and have the head of the horse on which I rode here cut off, for it vexed me on the way." In reality, she was afraid that the horse might tell how she had behaved to the King's daughter. Then she succeeded in making the King promise that it should be done, and the faithful Falada was to die; this came to the ears of the real princess, and she secretly promised to pay the knacker a piece of gold if he would perform a small service for her. There was a great dark-looking gateway in the town, through which morning and evening she had to pass with the geese: would he be so good as to nail up Falada's head on it, so that she might see him again, more than once. The knacker's man promised to do that, and cut off the head, and nailed it fast beneath the dark gateway.

Early in the morning, when she and Conrad drove out their flock beneath this gateway, she said in passing,

"Alas, Falada, hanging there!"

Then the head answered,

"Alas, young Queen, how ill you fare!

If this your tender mother knew,
Her heart would surely break in two."

Then they went still further out of the town, and drove their geese into the country. And when they had come to the meadow, she sat down and unbound her hair which was like pure gold, and Conrad saw it and delighted in its brightness, and wanted to pluck out a few hairs. Then she said,

"Blow, blow, thou gentle wind, I say,
Blow Conrad's little hat away,
And make him chase it here and there,
Until I have braided all my hair,
And bound it up again."

And there came such a violent wind that it blew Conrad's hat far away across country, and he was forced to run after it. When he came back she had finished combing her hair and was putting it up again, and he could not get any of it. Then Conrad was angry, and would not speak to her, and thus they watched the geese until the evening, and then they went home.

Next day when they were driving the geese out through the dark gateway, the maiden said,

"Alas, Falada, hanging there!"

Falada answered,

"Alas, young Queen, how ill you fare!
If this your tender mother knew,
Her heart would surely break in two."

And she sat down again in the field and began to comb out her hair, and Conrad ran and tried to clutch it, so she said in haste,

"Blow, blow, thou gentle wind, I say,
Blow Conrad's little hat away,
And make him chase it here and there,
Until I have braided all my hair,
And bound it up again."

Then the wind blew, and blew his little hat off his head and far away, and Conrad was forced to run after it, and when he came back, her hair had been put up a long time, and he could get none of it, and so they looked after the geese till evening came.

But in the evening after they had got home,

Conrad went to the old King, and said, "I won't tend the geese with that girl any longer!" "Why not?" inquired the aged King. "Oh, because she vexes me the whole day long." Then the aged King commanded him to relate what it was that she did to him. And Conrad said, "In the morning when we pass beneath the dark gateway with the flock, there is a sorry horse's head on the wall, and she says to it,

'Alas, Falada, hanging there!'

And the head replies,

'Alas, young Queen, how ill you fare!
If this your tender mother knew,
Her heart would surely break in two.' "

And Conrad went on to relate what happened on the goose pasture and how when there he had to chase his hat.

The aged King commanded him to drive his flock out again next day, and as soon as morning came, he placed himself behind the dark gateway, and heard how the maiden spoke to the head of Falada, and then he too went into the country, and hid himself in the thicket in the meadow. There he soon saw with his own eyes the goose-girl and the goose-boy bringing their flock, and how after a while she sat down and unplaited her hair, which shone with radiance. And soon she said,

"Blow, blow, thou gentle wind, I say,
Blow Conrad's little hat away,
And make him chase it here and there,
Until I have braided all my hair,
And bound it up again."

Then came a blast of wind and carried off Conrad's hat, so that he had to run far away, while the maiden quietly went on combing and plaiting her hair, all of which the King observed. Then, quite unseen, he went away, and when the goose-girl came home in the evening, he called her aside, and asked why she did all these things. "I may not tell that, and I dare not lament my sorrows to any human being, for I have sworn not to do so by the heaven which is above me; if I had not done that, I should have lost my life." He urged her and left her no peace, but he could draw nothing from her. Then said he, "If you will not tell me anything, tell your sorrows to the iron-stove there," and he went away. Then she crept into the iron-stove, and began to weep and lament, and emptied her whole heart, and said, "Here am I deserted by the whole world, and yet I am a King's daughter, and a false waiting-maid has by force brought me to such a pass that I have been compelled to put off my royal apparel, and she has taken my place with my bridegroom, and I have to perform menial service as a goose-girl. If my mother did but know that, her heart would break."

The aged King, however, was standing outside by the pipe of the stove, and was listening to what she said, and heard it. Then he came back again, and bade her come out of the stove. And royal garments were placed on her, and it was marvellous how beautiful she was! The aged King summoned his son, and revealed to him that he had got the false bride who was only a waiting-maid, but that the true one was standing there, as the sometime goose-girl. The young King rejoiced with all his heart when he saw her beauty and youth, and a great feast was made ready to which all the people and all good friends were invited. At the head of the table sat the bridegroom with the King's daughter at one side of him, and the waiting-maid on the other, but the waiting-maid was blinded, and did not recognize the princess in her dazzling array. When they had eaten and drunk, and were merry, the aged King asked the waiting-maid as a riddle, what punishment a person deserved who had behaved in such and such a way to her master, and at the same time related the whole story, and asked what sentence such a person merited. Then the false bride said, "She deserves no better fate than to be stripped entirely naked, and put in a barrel which is studded inside with pointed nails, and two white horses should be harnessed to it, which will drag her along through one street after another, till she is dead." "It is you," said the aged King, "and you have pronounced your own sentence, and thus shall it be done unto you." And when the sentence had been carried out, the young King married his true bride, and both of them reigned over their kingdom in peace and happiness.

THE WATER OF LIFE

The last three stories in this German group are for children of eleven or twelve. They are all complex and somber. In "The Water of Life" we see a clear example of the folk tales as carriers of the moral code. The youngest son must be courteous and brave to prove himself worthy of finding the water of life.

There was once a King who had an illness, and no one believed that he would come out of it with his life. He had three sons who were much distressed about it, and went down into the palace-garden and wept. There they met an old man who inquired as to the cause of their grief. They told him that their father was so ill that he would most certainly die, for nothing seemed to cure him. Then the old man said, "I know of one more remedy, and that is the water of life; if he drinks of it, he will become well again; but it is hard to find." The eldest said, "I will manage to find it," and went to the sick King, and begged to be allowed to go forth in search of the water of life, for that alone could save him. "No," said the King, "the danger of it is too great. I would rather die." But he begged so long that the King consented. The prince thought in his heart, "If I bring the water, then I shall be best beloved of my father, and shall inherit the kingdom."

So he set out, and when he had ridden forth a little distance, a dwarf stood there in the road who called to him and said, "Whither away so fast?" "Silly shrimp," said the prince, very haughtily, "it is nothing to you," and rode on. But the little dwarf had grown angry, and had wished an evil wish. Soon after this the prince entered a ravine, and the further he rode the closer the mountains drew together, and at last the road became so narrow that he could not advance a step further; it was impossible either to turn his horse or to dismount from the saddle, and he was shut in there as if in prison. The sick King waited long for him, but he came not.

Then the second son said, "Father, let me go forth to seek the water," and thought to himself,

"The Water of Life." From *Grimm's Household Tales*, translated by Margaret Hunt

"If my brother is dead, then the kingdom will fall to me." At first the King would not allow him to go either, but at last he yielded, so the prince set out on the same road that his brother had taken, and he too met the dwarf, who stopped him to ask whither he was going in such haste. "Little shrimp," said the prince, "that is nothing to you," and rode on without giving him another look. But the dwarf bewitched him, and he, like the other, rode into a ravine and could neither go forwards nor backwards. So fare haughty people.

As the second son also remained away, the youngest begged to be allowed to go forth to fetch the water, and at last the King was obliged to let him go. When he met the dwarf and the latter asked him whither he was going in such haste, he stopped, gave him an explanation, and said, "I am seeking the water of life, for my father is sick unto death." "Do you know, then, where that is to be found?" "No," said the prince. "As you have borne yourself as is seemly, and not haughtily like your false brothers, I will give you the information and tell you how you may obtain the water of life. It springs from a fountain in the courtyard of an enchanted castle, but you will not be able to make your way to it, if I do not give you an iron wand and two small loaves of bread. Strike thrice with the wand on the iron door of the castle, and it will spring open; inside lie two lions with gaping jaws, but if you throw a loaf to each of them, they will be quieted. Then hasten to fetch some of the water of life before the clock strikes twelve, else the door will shut again, and you will be imprisoned."

The prince thanked him, took the wand and the bread, and set out on his way. When he arrived, everything was as the dwarf had said. The door sprang open at the third stroke of the wand, and when he had appeased the lions with the bread, he entered the castle, and came to a large and splendid hall, wherein sat some enchanted princes whose rings he drew off their fingers. A sword and a loaf of bread were lying there, which he carried away. After this, he entered a chamber, in which was a beautiful maiden who rejoiced when she saw him, kissed him, and told him that he had set her free, and should have the whole of her kingdom, and that

if he would return in a year their wedding should be celebrated; likewise she told him where the spring of the water of life was, and that he was to hasten and draw some of it before the clock struck twelve.

Then he went onwards, and at last entered a room where there was a beautiful newly-made bed, and as he was very weary, he felt inclined to rest a little. So he lay down and fell asleep. When he awoke, it was striking a quarter to twelve. He sprang up in a fright, ran to the spring, drew some water in a cup which stood near, and hastened away. But just as he was passing through the iron door, the clock struck twelve, and the door fell to with such violence that it carried away a piece of his heel. He, however, rejoicing at having obtained the water of life, went homewards, and again passed the dwarf. When the latter saw the sword and the loaf, he said, "With these you have won great wealth; with the sword you can slay whole armies, and the bread will never come to an end."

But the prince would not go home to his father without his brothers, and said, "Dear dwarf, can you not tell me where my two brothers are? They went out before I did in search of the water of life, and have not returned." "They are imprisoned between two mountains," said the dwarf. "I have condemned them to stay there, because they were so haughty." Then the prince begged until the dwarf released them; he warned him, however, and said, "Beware of them, for they have

bad hearts." When his brothers came, he rejoiced, and told them how things had gone with him, that he had found the water of life, and had brought a cupful away with him, and had rescued a beautiful princess, who was willing to wait a year for him, and then their wedding was to be celebrated, and he would obtain a great kingdom.

After that they rode on together, and chanced upon a land where war and famine reigned, and the King already thought he must perish, for the scarcity was so great. Then the prince went to him and gave him the loaf, wherewith he fed and satisfied the whole of his kingdom, and then the prince gave him the sword also, wherewith he slew the hosts of his enemies, and could now live in rest and peace. The prince then took back his loaf and his sword, and the three brothers rode on. But after this they entered two more countries where war and famine reigned, and each time the prince gave his loaf and his sword to the Kings, and had now delivered three kingdoms, and after that they went on board a ship and sailed over the sea. During the passage, the two eldest conversed apart and said, "The youngest has found the water of life and not we, for that our father will give him the kingdom,—the kingdom which belongs to us, and he will rob us of all our fortune." They then began to seek revenge, and plotted with each other to destroy him. They waited until once when they found him fast asleep, then they poured the water of life out of the cup, and took it for themselves, but into the cup they poured salt sea-water. Now therefore, when they arrived home, the youngest took his cup to the sick King in order that he might drink out of it, and be cured. But scarcely had he drunk a very little of the salt sea-water than he became still worse than before. And as he was lamenting over this, the two eldest brothers came, and accused the youngest of having intended to poison him, and said that they had brought him the true water of life, and handed it to him. He had scarcely tasted it, when he felt his sickness departing, and became strong and healthy as in the days of his youth. After that they both went to the youngest, mocked him, and said, "You certainly found the water of life, but you have had the pain, and we the gain; you should have been sharper, and should have kept your eyes open. We took it from you whilst you were asleep at sea, and when a year is over, one of us will go and fetch the beautiful princess. But beware that you do not disclose aught of this to our father; indeed he does not trust you, and if you say a single word, you shall lose your life into the bargain, but if you keep silent, you shall have it as a gift."

The old King was angry with his youngest son, and thought he had plotted against his life. So he summoned the court together, and had sentence pronounced upon his son, that he should be secretly shot. And once when the prince was riding forth to the chase, suspecting no evil, the King's huntsman was told to go with him, and when they were quite alone in the forest, the huntsman looked so sorrowful that the prince said to him, "Dear huntsman, what ails you?" The huntsman said, "I cannot tell you, and yet I ought." Then the prince said, "Say openly what it is, I will pardon you." "Alas!" said the huntsman, "I am to shoot you dead, the King has ordered me to do it." Then the prince was shocked, and said, "Dear huntsman, let me live; there, I give you my royal garments; give me your common ones in their stead." The huntsman said, "I will willingly do that, indeed I would not have been able to shoot you." Then they exchanged clothes, and the huntsman returned home; the prince, however, went further into the forest. After a time

three waggons of gold and precious stones came to the King for his youngest son, which were sent by the three Kings who had slain their enemies with the prince's sword, and maintained their people with his bread, and who wished to show their gratitude for it. The old King then thought, "Can my son have been innocent?" and said to his people, "Would that he were still alive, how it grieves me that I have suffered him to be killed!" "He still lives," said the huntsman, "I could not find it in my heart to carry out your command," and told the King how it had happened. Then a stone fell from the King's heart, and he had it proclaimed in every country that his son might return and be taken into favour again.

The princess, however, had a road made up to her palace which was quite bright and golden, and told her people that whosoever came riding straight along it to her, would be the right one and was to be admitted, and whoever rode by the side of it, was not the right one, and was not to be admitted. As the time was now close at hand, the eldest thought he would hasten to go to the King's daughter, and give himself out as her deliverer, and thus win her for his bride, and the kingdom to boot. Therefore he rode forth, and when he arrived in front of the palace, and saw the splendid golden road, he thought it would be a sin and a shame if he were to ride over that and turned aside, and rode on the right side of it. But when he came to the door, the servants told him he was not the right one, and was to go away again.

Soon after this the second prince set out, and when he came to the golden road, and his horse had put one foot on it, he thought it would be a sin and a shame to tread a piece of it off, and he turned aside and rode on the left side of it, and when he reached the door, the attendants told him he was not the right one, and he was to go away again. When at last the year had entirely expired, the third son likewise wished to ride out of the forest to his beloved, and with her forget his sorrows. So he set out and thought of her so incessantly, and wished to be with her so much, that he never noticed the golden road at all. So his horse rode onwards up the middle of it, and when he came to the door, it was opened and the princess received him with joy, and said he was her deliverer, and lord of the kingdom, and their wedding was celebrated with great rejoicing. When it was over she told him that his father invited him to come to him, and had forgiven him. So he rode thither, and told him everything; how his brothers had betrayed him, and how he had nevertheless kept silence. The old King wished to punish them, but they had put to sea, and never came back as long as they lived.

Scandinavian folk tales

Although the temper of the Scandinavian folk tales is, in the main, serious, they have also a drollery that equals the English tales. Peter Christian Asbjörnsen and Jörgen Moe, like the Grimm brothers, collected their stories from the lips of old storytellers and the stories have a dramatic and forthright quality that invariably characterizes such spontaneous narration. These tales were also fortunate in their translator, Sir George Webbe Dasent, who put them into such clear, vigorous English that their folk flavor and even the feeling of spontaneity are preserved. These qualities make them easy to tell and they should not be read if it is possible to learn them for telling. Since Dasent's day, Gudrun Thorne-Thomsen and Ingri d'Aulaire, both Norwegians, have retold these stories in even simpler style. Their books are fine sources for telling.

THE THREE BILLY GOATS GRUFF

This is a matchless little tale to tell, admirable in plot and economy of words. You will probably want to substitute for the Big Billy Goat Gruff's gruesome verse, the simpler, "Well, come along. I've two big spears to fight you with," and explain to the children, "By spears, of course, he meant his horns." This is fun for the five-year-olds to dramatize informally without any special costuming.

Once on a time there were three Billy Goats who were to go up to the hill-side to make themselves fat, and the name of all three was "Gruff."

On the way up was a bridge over a stream they had to cross; and under the bridge lived a great ugly Troll, with eyes as big as saucers and a nose as long as a poker.

So first of all came the youngest Billy Goat Gruff to cross the bridge.

"TRIP, TRAP! TRIP, TRAP!" went the bridge.

"WHO'S THAT tripping over my bridge?" roared the Troll.

"Oh! it is only I, the tiniest Billy Goat Gruff; and I'm going up to the hill-side to make myself fat," said the Billy Goat, with such a small voice.

"Now, I'm coming to gobble you up," said the Troll.

"Oh, no! pray don't take me. I'm too little, that I am," said the Billy Goat. "Wait a bit till the second Billy Goat Gruff comes; he's much bigger."

"Well! be off with you," said the Troll.

A little while after, came the second Billy Goat Gruff to cross the bridge.

"TRIP, TRAP! TRIP, TRAP! TRIP, TRAP!" went the bridge.

"WHO'S THAT tripping over my bridge?" roared the Troll.

"Oh! it's the second Billy Goat Gruff, and I'm going up to the hill-side to make myself fat," said the Billy Goat, who hadn't such a small voice.

"Now, I'm coming to gobble you up," said the Troll.

"Oh, no! don't take me. Wait a little till the big Billy Goat Gruff comes; he's much bigger."

"Very well! be off with you," said the Troll.

"The Three Billy Goats Gruff." From *Popular Tales from the Norse* by Peter Christian Asbjörnsen and Jörgen Moe, translated by Sir George Webbe Dasent. G. P. Putnam's Sons

But just then up came the big Billy Goat Gruff.

"TRIP, TRAP! TRIP, TRAP! TRIP, TRAP! TRIP, TRAP!" went the bridge, for the Billy Goat was so heavy that the bridge creaked and groaned under him.

"WHO'S THAT tramping over my bridge?" roared the Troll.

"IT'S I! THE BIG BILLY GOAT GRUFF," said the Billy Goat, who had an ugly hoarse voice of his own.

"Now, I'm coming to gobble you up," roared the Troll.

"Well, come along! I've got two spears,
And I'll poke your eyeballs out at your ears;
I've got besides two curling-stones,
And I'll crush you to bits, body and bones."

That was what the big Billy Goat said; and so he flew at the Troll, and poked him and knocked him, and crushed him to bits, body and bones, and tossed him out into the burn, and after that he went up to the hill-side. There the Billy Goats got so fat that they were scarce able to walk home again; and if the fat hasn't fallen off them, why they're still fat; and so—

"Snip, snap, snout,
This tale's told out."

THE PANCAKE

A simpler beginning is, "Once there was a mother who had seven hungry children." If you paraphrase "the goody, the good wife" two or three times, the children will have it.

Once on a time there was a goody who had seven hungry bairns, and she was frying a pancake for them. It was a sweet-milk pancake, and there it lay in the pan bubbling and frizzling so thick and good, it was a sight for sore eyes to look at. And the bairns stood round about, and the goodman sat by and looked on.

"Oh, give me a bit of pancake, mother, dear; I am so hungry," said one bairn.

"Oh, darling mother," said the second.

"Oh, darling, good mother," said the third.

"Oh, darling, good, nice mother," said the fourth.

"Oh, darling, pretty, good, nice mother," said the fifth.

"Oh, darling, pretty, good, nice, clever mother," said the sixth.

"Oh, darling, pretty, good, nice, clever, sweet mother," said the seventh.

So they begged for the pancake all round, the one more prettily than the other; for they were so hungry and so good.

"Yes, yes, bairns, only bide a bit till it turns itself,"—she ought to have said, "till I can get it turned,"—"and then you shall all have some—a lovely sweet-milk pancake; only look how fat and happy it lies there."

When the pancake heard that it got afraid, and in a trice it turned itself all of itself, and tried to jump out of the pan; but it fell back into it again t'other side up, and so when it had been fried a little on the other side too, till it got firmer in its flesh, it sprang out on the floor, and rolled off like a wheel through the door and down the hill.

"Holloa! Stop, pancake!" and away went the goody after it, with the frying-pan in one hand and the ladle in the other, as fast as she could, and her bairns behind her, while the goodman limped after them last of all.

"The Pancake." From *Tales from the Fjeld* by Peter Christian Asbjörnsen and Jörgen Moe, translated by Sir George Webbe Dasent. G. P. Putnam's Sons

"Hi! won't you stop? Seize it. Stop, pancake," they all screamed out, one after the other, and tried to catch it on the run and hold it; but the pancake rolled on and on, and in the twinkling of an eye it was so far ahead that they couldn't see it, for the pancake was faster on its feet than any of them.

So when it had rolled awhile it met a man.

"Good day, pancake," said the man.

"God bless you, Manny Panny!" said the pancake.

"Dear pancake," said the man, "don't roll so fast; stop a little and let me eat you."

"When I have given the slip to Goody Poody, and the goodman, and seven squalling children, I may well slip through your fingers, Manny Panny," said the pancake, and rolled on and on till it met a hen.

"Good day, pancake," said the hen.

"The same to you, Henny Penny," said the pancake.

"Pancake, dear, don't roll so fast; bide a bit and let me eat you up," said the hen.

"When I have given the slip to Goody Poody, and the goodman, and seven squalling children, and Manny Panny, I may well slip through your claws, Henny Penny," said the pancake, and so it rolled on like a wheel down the road.

Just then it met a cock.

"Good day, pancake," said the cock.

"The same to you, Cocky Locky," said the pancake.

"Pancake, dear, don't roll so fast, but bide a bit and let me eat you up."

"When I have given the slip to Goody Poody, and the goodman, and seven squalling children, and to Manny Panny, and Henny Penny, I may well slip through your claws, Cocky Locky," said the pancake, and off it set rolling away as fast as it could; and when it had rolled a long way it met a duck.

"Good day, pancake," said the duck.

"The same to you, Ducky Lucky."

"Pancake, dear, don't roll away so fast; bide a bit and let me eat you up."

"When I have given the slip to Goody Poody, and the goodman, and seven squalling children, and Manny Panny, and Henny Penny, and Cocky Locky, I may well slip through your fingers, Ducky Lucky," said the pancake, and with that it took to rolling and rolling faster than ever; and when it had rolled a long, long while, it met a goose.

"Good day, pancake," said the goose.

"The same to you, Goosey Poosey."

"Pancake, dear, don't roll so fast; bide a bit and let me eat you up."

"When I have given the slip to Goody Poody, and the goodman, and seven squalling children, and Manny Panny, and Henny Penny, and Cocky Locky, and Ducky Lucky, I can well slip through your feet, Goosey Poosey," said the pancake, and off it rolled.

So when it had rolled a long, long way farther, it met a gander.

"Good day, pancake," said the gander.

"The same to you, Gander Pander," said the pancake.

"Pancake, dear, don't roll so fast; bide a bit and let me eat you up."

"When I have given the slip to Goody Poody, and the goodman, and seven squalling children, and Manny Panny, and Henny Penny, and Cocky Locky, and Ducky Lucky, and Goosey Poosey, I may well slip through your feet, Gander Pander," said the pancake, which rolled off as fast as ever.

So when it had rolled a long, long time, it met a pig.

"Good day, pancake," said the pig.

"The same to you, Piggy Wiggy," said the pancake, which, without a word more, began to roll and roll like mad.

"Nay, nay," said the pig, "you needn't be in such a hurry; we two can then go side by side and see one another over the wood; they say it is not too safe in there."

The pancake thought there might be something in that, and so they kept company. But when they had gone awhile, they came to a brook. As for Piggy, he was so fat he swam safe across, it was nothing to him; but the poor pancake couldn't get over.

"Seat yourself on my snout," said the pig, "and I'll carry you over."

So the pancake did that.

"Ouf, ouf," said the pig, and swallowed the pancake at one gulp; and then, as the poor pancake could go no farther, why—this story can go no farther either.

WHY THE BEAR IS
STUMPY-TAILED

It has been said that all over the world, wherever there are bears, this story occurs. The folk tales are always warning the unwary against the folly of credulity.

One day the Bear met the Fox, who came slinking along with a string of fish he had stolen.

"Whence did you get those from?" asked the Bear.

"Oh! my Lord Bruin, I've been out fishing and caught them," said the Fox.

So the Bear had a mind to learn to fish too, and bade the Fox tell him how he was to set about it.

"Oh! it's an easy craft for you," answered the Fox, "and soon learnt. You've only got to go upon the ice, and cut a hole and stick your tail down into it; and so you must go on holding it there as long as you can. You're not to mind if

"Why the Bear Is Stumpy-Tailed." From *Popular Tales from the Norse*

your tail smarts a little; that's when the fish bite. The longer you hold it there the more fish you'll get; and then all at once out with it, with a cross pull sideways, and with a strong pull too."

Yes; the Bear did as the Fox had said, and held his tail a long, long time down in the hole, till it was fast frozen in. Then he pulled it out with a cross pull, and it snapped short off. That's why Bruin goes about with a stumpy tail this very day.

THE LAD WHO WENT
TO THE NORTH WIND

Here is a story that becomes more dramatic if you visualize the scenes and the characters. Children love the humor and the justice of the landlord's punishment.

Once on a time there was an old widow who had one son, and as she was poorly and weak, her son had to go up into the storehouse to fetch meal for cooking; but when he got outside the storehouse, and was just going down the steps, there came the North Wind, puffing and blowing, caught up the meal, and so away with it through the air. Then the Lad went back into the storehouse for more; but when he came out again on the steps, if the North Wind didn't come again and carry off the meal with a puff; and, more than that, he did so the third time. At this the Lad got very angry; and as he thought it hard that the North Wind should behave so, he decided he'd just look him up, and ask him to give back his meal.

So off he went, but the way was long, and he walked and walked; but at last he came to the North Wind's house.

"Good day!" said the Lad, "and thank you for coming to see us yesterday."

"GOOD DAY!" answered the North Wind, for his voice was loud and gruff, "AND THANKS FOR COMING TO SEE ME. WHAT DO YOU WANT?"

"Oh!" answered the Lad, "I only wished to

"The Lad Who Went to the North Wind." From *Popular Tales from the Norse*

ask you to be so good as to let me have back that meal you took from me on the storehouse steps, for we haven't much to live on; and if you're to go on snapping up the morsel we have, there'll be nothing for it but to starve."

"I haven't got your meal," said the North Wind; "but if you are in such need, I'll give you a cloth which will get you everything you want, if you only say, 'Cloth, spread yourself, and serve up all kinds of good dishes!' "

With this the Lad was well content. But, as the way was so long, he couldn't get home in one day, so he turned into an inn on the way; and when they were going to sit down to supper, he laid the cloth on a table which stood in the corner, and said,

"Cloth, spread yourself, and serve up all kinds of good dishes."

He had scarce said so before the cloth did as it was bid; and all who stood by thought it a fine thing, but most of all the landlord. So, when all were fast asleep, at dead of night, he took the Lad's cloth, and put another in its stead, just like the one he had got from the North Wind, but which couldn't so much as serve up a bit of dry bread.

So, when the Lad woke, he took his cloth and went off with it, and that day he got home to his mother.

"Now," said he, "I've been to the North Wind's house, and a good fellow he is, for he gave me this cloth, and when I only say to it, 'Cloth, spread yourself, and serve up all kind of good dishes,' I get any sort of food I please."

"All very true, I daresay," said his mother; "but seeing is believing, and I shan't believe it till I see it."

So the Lad made haste, drew out a table, laid the cloth on it, and said,

"Cloth, spread yourself, and serve up all kind of good dishes!"

But never a bit of dry bread did the cloth serve up.

"Well," said the Lad, "there's no help for it but to go to the North Wind again;" and away he went.

So he came to where the North Wind lived late in the afternoon.

"Good evening!" said the Lad.

"Good evening!" said the North Wind.

"I want my rights for that meal of ours which you took," said the Lad. "As for that cloth I got, it isn't worth a penny."

"I've got no meal," said the North Wind; "but yonder you have a ram which coins nothing but golden dollars as soon as you say to it, 'Ram, ram, make money!'"

So the lad thought this a fine thing; but as it was too far to get home that day, he turned in for the night at the same inn where he had slept before.

Before he called for anything, he tried the truth of what the North Wind had said of the ram, and found it all right; but, when the landlord saw that, he thought it was a famous ram, and, when the Lad had fallen asleep, he took another which couldn't coin gold dollars, and changed the two.

Next morning off went the Lad; and when he got home to his mother, he said,

"After all, the North Wind is a jolly fellow; for now he has given me a ram which can coin golden dollars if I only say, 'Ram, ram, make money!'"

"All very true, I daresay," said his mother; "but I shan't believe any such stuff until I see the dollars made."

"Ram, ram, make money!" said the Lad; but if the ram made anything it wasn't money.

So the Lad went back again to the North Wind, and blew him up and said the ram was worth nothing, and he must have his rights for the meal.

"Well!" said the North Wind; "I've nothing else to give you but that old stick in the corner yonder; but it's a stick of that kind that if you say,

'Stick, stick! lay on!' it lays on till you say,

'Stick, stick! now stop!'"

So as the way was long, the Lad turned in this night too to the landlord; but as he could pretty well guess how things stood as to the cloth and the ram, he lay down at once on the bench and began to snore, as if he were asleep.

Now the landlord, who easily saw that the stick must be worth something, hunted up one which was like it, and when he heard the Lad snore, was going to change the two; but just as the landlord was about to take it, the Lad bawled out:

"Stick, stick! lay on!"

So the stick began to beat the landlord, till he jumped over chairs, and tables, and benches, and yelled and roared,

"Oh my! oh my! bid the stick be still, else it will beat me to death, and you shall have back both your cloth and your ram."

When the Lad thought the landlord had got enough, he said,

"Stick, stick! now stop!"

Then he took the cloth and put it into his pocket, and went home with his stick in his hand, leading the ram by a cord round its horns; and so he got his rights for the meal he had lost.

BOOTS AND HIS BROTHERS

The name "Boots" came into the Norwegian tales by way of the distinguished British translator, Sir George Webbe Dasent. "Boots" is the English name for a boy who blacks the boots and does odds and ends of work. Perhaps it is enough to say to the children the first time you tell the story, "There was a poor man who had three sons, Peter, Paul, and John. And because John was the youngest son and had to black the boots, the shoes, of the others, he was called Boots." The d'Aulaires translate the name Espen Cinderlad, so take your choice. The children accept either one as a nickname.

Once on a time there was a man who had three sons, Peter, Paul, and John. John was Boots, of course, because he was the youngest. I can't say the man had anything more than these three sons, for he hadn't one penny to rub against another; and so he told his sons over and over again that they must go out into the world and try to earn their bread, for there at home there was nothing to be looked for but starving to death.

Now, a bit off from the man's cottage was the King's palace, and you must know, just against the King's windows a great oak had sprung up which was so stout and big that it took away all the light from the King's palace. The King had

"Boots and His Brothers." From *Popular Tales from the Norse* (slightly adapted)

said that he would give many, many dollars to the man who could fell the oak, but no one was man enough for that, for as soon as ever one chip of the oak's trunk flew off, two grew in its stead.

A well, too, the King wanted dug, that would hold water for the whole year; for all his neighbors had such wells, but he had none, and that he thought a shame. So the King said he would give any man who could dig him such a well as would hold water for the whole year round, both money and goods; but no one could do it, for the King's palace lay high, high up on a hill, and they hadn't dug a few inches before they came upon the living rock.

But as the King had set his heart on having these two things done, he had it given out far and wide, in all the churches of his kingdom, that he who could fell the big oak in the King's courtyard, and get him a well that would hold water the whole year round, should have the Princess and half the kingdom.

Well, you may easily know there was many a man who came to try his luck; but for all their hacking and hewing, and all their digging and delving, it was no good. The oak got bigger and stouter at every stroke, and the rock didn't get softer either. So one day those three brothers thought they'd set off and try too, and their father hadn't a word against it; for even if they didn't get the Princess and half the kingdom, it might happen they would get a place somewhere with a good master; and that was all he wanted. So when the brothers said they thought of going to the palace, their father said "yes" at once. So Peter, Paul, and Boots went off from their home.

Well, they hadn't gone far before they came to a firwood, and up along one side of it rose a steep hill-side, and as they went, they heard something hewing and hacking away up on the hill among the trees.

"I wonder now what it is that is hewing away up yonder," said Boots.

"You're always so clever with your wonderings," said Peter and Paul both at once. "What wonder is it, pray, that a woodcutter should stand and hack up on a hill-side?"

"Still, I'd like to see what it is, after all," said Boots, and up he went.

"Oh, if you're such a child, 'twill do you good to go and take a lesson," bawled out his brothers after him.

But Boots didn't care for what they said; he climbed the steep hill-side towards where the noise came, and when he reached the place, what do you think he saw? Why, an axe that stood there hacking and hewing, all of itself, at the trunk of a fir.

"Good day!" said Boots. "So you stand here all alone and hew, do you?"

"Yes; here I've stood and hewed and hacked a long, long time, waiting for you," said the Axe.

"Well, here I am at last," said Boots, as he took the axe, pulled it off its haft, and stuffed both head and haft into his wallet.

So when he got down again to his brothers, they began to jeer and laugh at him.

"And now, what funny thing was it you saw up yonder upon the hill-side?" they said.

"Oh, it was only an axe we heard," said Boots.

So when they had gone a bit farther, they came under a steep spur of rock, and up there they heard something digging and shovelling.

"I wonder now," said Boots, "what it is digging and shovelling up yonder at the top of the rock."

"Ah, you're always so clever with your wonderings," said Peter and Paul again, "as if you'd never heard a woodpecker hacking and pecking at a hollow tree."

"Well, well," said Boots, "I think it would be a piece of fun just to see what it really is."

And so off he set to climb the rock, while the others laughed and made game of him. But he didn't care a bit for that; up he climbed, and when he got near the top, what do you think he saw? Why, a spade that stood there digging and delving.

"Good day!" said Boots. "So you stand here all alone, and dig and delve!"

"Yes, that's what I do," said the Spade, "and that's what I've done this many a long day, waiting for you."

"Well, here I am," said Boots again, as he took the spade and knocked it off its handle, and put it into his wallet, and then went down again to his brothers.

"Well, what was it, so rare and strange," said

Peter and Paul, "that you saw up there at the top of the rock?"

"Oh," said Boots, "nothing more than a spade; that was what we heard."

So they went on again a good bit, till they came to a brook. They were thirsty, all three, after their long walk, and so they lay down beside the brook to have a drink.

"I wonder now," said Boots, "where all this water comes from."

"I wonder if you're right in your head," said Peter and Paul in one breath. "If you're not mad already, you'll go mad very soon, with your wonderings. Where the brook comes from, indeed! Have you never heard how water rises from a spring in the earth?"

"Yes; but still I've a great fancy to see where this brook comes from," said Boots.

So up alongside the brook he went, in spite of all that his brothers bawled after him. Nothing could stop him. On he went. So, as he went up and up, the brook got smaller and smaller, and at last, a little way farther on, what do you think he saw? Why, a great walnut, and out of that the water trickled.

"Good day!" said Boots again. "So you lie here, and trickle and run down all alone?"

"Yes, I do," said the Walnut; "and here have I trickled and run this many a long day, waiting for you."

"Well, here I am," said Boots, as he took up a lump of moss, and plugged up the hole, that the water mightn't run out. Then he put the walnut into his wallet and ran down to his brothers.

"Well, now," said Peter and Paul, "have you found out where the water comes from? A rare sight it must have been!"

"Oh, after all it was only a hole it ran out of," said Boots; and so the others laughed and made game of him again; but Boots didn't mind that a bit.

"After all, I had the fun of seeing it," said he.

So when they had gone a bit farther, they came to the King's palace; but as every one in the kingdom had heard how they might win the Princess and half the realm, if they could only fell the big oak and dig the King's well, so many had come to try their luck that the oak was now twice as stout and big as it had been at first, for

two chips grew for every one they hewed out with their axes, as I daresay you all bear in mind. So the King had now laid it down as a punishment, that if any one tried and couldn't fell the oak, he should be put on a barren island. But the two brothers didn't let themselves be scared by that; they were quite sure they could fell the oak, and Peter, as he was the eldest, was to try his hand first; but it went with him as with all the rest who had hewn at the oak; for every chip he cut out, two grew in its place. So the King's men seized him, and put him out on the island.

Now Paul, he was to try his luck, but he fared just the same; when he had hewn two or three strokes, they began to see the oak grow, and so the King's men seized him too, and put him out on the island.

So now Boots was to try.

"If your brothers could not cut down the tree, it is not likely that you can, Boots. You had better give up," said the King.

"Well, I'd like just to try," said Boots, and so he got leave. Then he took his axe out of his wallet and fitted it to its haft.

"Hew away!" said he to his axe; and away it hewed, making the chips fly again, so that it wasn't long before down came the oak.

When that was done Boots pulled out his spade, and fitted it to its handle.

"Dig away!" said he to the spade; and so the spade began to dig and delve till the earth and rock flew out in splinters, and so he had the well soon dug.

And when he had got it as big and deep as he chose, Boots took out his walnut and laid it in one corner of the well, and pulled the plug of moss out.

"Trickle and run," said Boots; and so the nut trickled and ran, till the water gushed out of the hole in a stream, and in a short time the well was brimfull.

Thus Boots had felled the oak which shaded the King's palace, and dug a well in the palace-yard, and so he got the Princess and half the kingdom, as the King had said; but it was lucky for Peter and Paul that they were off on the island, else they would have heard each hour and day how every one said, "Well, something came of Boots' wondering after all."

THE PRINCESS ON
THE GLASS HILL

If this story seems overly long, let Boots find only the Golden Horse and ride up the hill only once.

Once on a time there was a man who had a meadow which lay high up on the hill-side, and in the meadow was a barn, which he had built to keep his hay in. Now, I must tell you, there hadn't been much in the barn for the last year or two, for every St. John's night, when the grass stood greenest and deepest, the meadow was eaten down to the very ground the next morning, just as if a whole drove of sheep had been there feeding on it overnight. This happened once, and it happened twice; so at last the man grew weary of losing his crop of hay, and said to his sons—for he had three of them, and the youngest was nicknamed Boots, of course—that now one of them must just go and sleep in the barn in the outlying field when St. John's night came, for it was too good a joke that his grass should be eaten, root and blade, this year, as it had been the last two years. So whichever of them went must keep a sharp look-out; that was what their father said.

Well, the eldest son was ready to go and watch the meadow; trust him for looking after the grass! It shouldn't be his fault if man or beast, or the fiend himself got a blade of grass. So, when evening came, he set off to the barn, and lay down to sleep; but a little on in the night came such a clatter, and such an earthquake that walls and roof shook, and groaned, and creaked; then up jumped the lad, and took to his heels as fast as ever he could; nor dared he once look round till he reached home; and as for the hay, why it was eaten up this year just as it had been twice before.

The next St. John's night, the man said again it would never do to lose all the grass in the outlying field year after year in this way, so one of his sons must just trudge off to watch it, and watch it well too. Well, the next oldest son was ready to try his luck, so he set off, and lay down to sleep in the barn as his brother had done be-

"The Princess on the Glass Hill." From *Popular Tales from the Norse*

fore him; but as the night wore on, there came on a rumbling and quaking of the earth, worse even than on the last St. John's night, and when the lad heard it, he got frightened, and took to his heels as though he were running a race.

Next year the turn came to Boots; but when he made ready to go, the other two began to laugh, and to make game of him, saying,

"You're just the man to watch the hay, that you are; you, who have done nothing all your life but sit in the ashes and toast yourself by the fire."

But Boots did not care a pin for their chattering, and stumped away as evening drew on, up the hill-side to the outlying field. There he went inside the barn and lay down; but in about an hour's time the barn began to groan and creak, so that it was dreadful to hear.

"Well," said Boots to himself, "if it isn't worse than this, I can stand it well enough."

A little while after there came another creak and an earthquake, so that the litter in the barn flew about the lad's ears.

"Oh," said Boots to himself, "if it isn't worse than this, I daresay I can stand it out."

But just then came a third rumbling, and a third earthquake, so that the lad thought walls and roof were coming down on his head; but it passed off, and all was still as death about him.

"It'll come again, I'll be bound," thought Boots; but no, it did not come again; still it was and still it stayed; but after he had lain a little while he heard a noise as if a horse were standing just outside the barn-door, and cropping the grass. He stole to the door, and peeped through a chink, and there stood a horse feeding away. So big and fat and grand a horse, Boots had never set eyes on; by his side on the grass lay a saddle and bridle, and a full set of armour for a knight, all of brass, so bright that the light gleamed from it.

"Ho, ho!" thought the lad; "it's you, is it, that eats up our hay? I'll soon put a spoke in your wheel; just see if I don't."

So he lost no time, but took the steel out of his tinder-box, and threw it over the horse; then it had no power to stir from the spot, and became so tame that the lad could do what he liked with it. So he got on its back and rode off with it to a place which no one knew of, and there he put up the horse. When he got home his brothers laughed, and asked how he fared.

"You didn't lie long in the barn, even if you had the heart to go as far as the field."

"Well," said Boots, "all I can say is, I lay in the barn till the sun rose, and neither saw nor heard anything; I can't think what there was in the barn to make you both so afraid."

"A pretty story!" said his brothers; "but we'll soon see how you have watched the meadow." So they set off, but when they reached it, there stood the grass as deep and thick as it had been the night before.

Well, the next St. John's eve it was the same story over again; neither of the elder brothers dared to go out to the outlying field to watch the crop; but Boots, he had the heart to go, and everything happened just as it had happened the year before. First a clatter and an earthquake, then a greater clatter and another earthquake, and so on a third time; only this year the earthquakes were far worse than the year before. Then all at once everything was as still as death, and the lad heard how something was cropping the grass outside the barn-door, so he stole to the door, and peeped through a chink; and what do you think he saw? Why, another horse standing right up against the wall, and chewing and champing with might and main. It was far finer and fatter than the one which came the year before, and it had a saddle on its back and a bridle on its neck and a full suit of mail for a knight lay by its side, all of silver, and as grand as you would wish to see.

"Ho, ho!" said Boots to himself; "it's you that gobbles up our hay, is it? I'll soon put a spoke in your wheel"; and with that he took the steel out of his tinder-box, and threw it over the horse's crest, which stood as still as a lamb. Well, the lad rode this horse, too, to the hiding-place where he kept the other one, and after that he went home.

"I suppose you'll tell us," said one of his brothers, "there's a fine crop this year too, up in the hayfield."

"Well, so there is," said Boots; and off ran the others to see, and there stood the grass thick and deep, as it was the year before; but they didn't give Boots softer words for all that.

Now, when the third St. John's eve came, the two elder still hadn't the heart to lie out in the barn and watch the grass, for they had got so scared at heart the night they lay there before, that they couldn't get over the fright; but Boots, he dared to go; and, to make a long story short, the very same thing happened this time as had happened twice before. Three earthquakes came, one after the other, each worse than the one which went before; and when the last came, the lad danced about with the shock from one barn wall to the other; and after that, all at once, it was as still as death. Now when he had lain a little while he heard something tugging away at the grass outside the barn; so he stole again to the door-chink, and peeped out, and there stood a horse close outside—far, far bigger and fatter than the two he had taken before.

"Ho, ho!" said the lad to himself, "it's you, is it, that comes here eating up our hay? I'll soon stop that—I'll soon put a spoke in your wheel." So he caught up his steel and threw it over the horse's neck, and in a trice it stood as if it were nailed to the ground, and Boots could do as he pleased with it. Then he rode off with it to the hiding-place where he kept the other two, and then went home. When he got home his two brothers made game of him as they had done before, saying they could see he had watched the grass well, for he looked for all the world as if he were walking in his sleep, and many other spiteful things they said; but Boots gave no heed to them, only asking them to go and see for themselves; and when they went, there stood the grass as fine and deep this time as it had been twice before.

Now, you must know that the king of the country where Boots lived had a daughter, whom he would give only to the man who could ride up over the hill of glass, for there was a high, high hill, all of glass, as smooth and slippery as ice, close by the king's palace. Upon the tip-top of the hill the king's daughter was to sit, with three golden apples in her lap, and the man who could ride up and carry off the three golden apples was to have half the kingdom and the Princess to wife. This the king had stuck up on all the church-doors in his realm, and had given it out in many other kingdoms besides. Now, this Princess was so lovely that all who set eyes on her fell over head and ears in love with her whether they would or no. So I needn't tell you how all the princes and knights who heard of her were eager to win her to wife, and half the kingdom beside; and how they came riding from all parts of the world on high prancing horses, and clad in the grandest clothes, for there wasn't one of them who hadn't made up his mind that he, and he alone, was to win the Princess.

So when the day of trial came, which the king had fixed, there was such a crowd of princes and knights under the glass hill, that it made one's head to whirl to look at them; and everyone in the country who could even crawl along was off to the hill, for they were all eager to see the man who was to win the Princess.

So the two elder brothers set off with the rest; but as for Boots, they said outright he shouldn't go with them, for if they were seen with such a dirty changeling, all begrimed with smut from cleaning their shoes and sifting cinders in the dusthole, they said folk would make game of them.

"Very well," said Boots, "it's all one to me. I can go alone, and stand or fall by myself."

Now when the two brothers came to the hill of glass, the knights and princes were all hard at it, riding their horses till they were all in a foam; but it was no good, by my troth; for as soon as ever the horses set foot on the hill, down they slipped, and there wasn't one who could get a yard or two up; and no wonder, for the hill was as smooth as a sheet of glass and as steep as a house-wall. But all were eager to have the Princess and half the kingdom. So they rode and slipped, and slipped and rode, and still it was the same story over again. At last all their horses were so weary that they could scarce lift a leg, and in such a sweat that the lather dripped from them, and so the knights had to give up trying any more. So the king was just thinking that he would proclaim a new trial for the next day, to see if they would have better luck, when all at once a knight came riding up on so brave a steed that no one had ever seen the like of it in his born days, and the knight had mail of brass, and the horse, a brass bit in his mouth, so bright that the sunbeams shone from it. Then all the others called out to him he might just as well spare himself the trouble of riding at the hill, for it would lead to no good; but he gave no heed to

them, and put his horse at the hill, and went up it like nothing for a good way, about a third of the height; and when he had got so far, he turned his horse and rode down again. So lovely a knight the Princess thought she had never yet seen; and while he was riding, she sat and thought to herself—"Would to heaven he might only come up, and down the other side."

And when she saw him turning back, she threw down one of the golden apples after him, and it rolled down into his shoe. But when he got to the bottom of the hill he rode off so fast that no one could tell what had become of him. That evening all the knights and princes were to go before the king, that he who had ridden so far up the hill might show the apple the princess had thrown; but there was no one who had anything to show. One after the other they all came, but not a man of them could show the apple.

At even, the brothers of Boots came home too, and had such a long story to tell about the riding up the hill.

"First of all," they said, "there was not one of the whole lot who could get so much as a stride up; but at last came one who had a suit of brass mail, and a brass bridle and saddle, all so bright that the sun shone from them a mile off. He was a chap to ride, just! He rode a third of the way up the hill of glass and he could easily have ridden the whole way up, if he chose; but he turned round and rode down thinking, maybe, that was enough for once."

"Oh! I should so like to have seen him, that I should," said Boots, who sat by the fireside, and stuck his feet into the cinders as was his wont.

"Oh!" said his brothers, "you would, would you? You look fit to keep company with such high lords, nasty beast that you are, sitting there amongst the ashes."

Next day the brothers were all for setting off again; and Boots begged them this time, too, to let him go with them and see the riding; but no, they wouldn't have him at any price, he was too ugly and nasty, they said.

"Well, well," said Boots; "if I go at all, I must go by myself. I'm not afraid."

So when the brothers got to the hill of glass, all the princes and knights began to ride again, and you may fancy they had taken care to shoe their horses sharp; but it was no good—they rode and slipped, and slipped and rode, just as they had done the day before, and there was not one who could get so far as a yard up the hill. And when they had worn out their horses, so that they could not stir a leg, they were all forced to give it up as a bad job. So the king thought he might as well proclaim that the riding should take place the day after for the last time, just to give them one chance more; but all at once it came across his mind that he might as well wait a little longer to see if the knight in brass mail would come this day too. Well, they saw nothing of him; but all at once came one riding on a steed far, far braver and finer than that on which the knight of brass had ridden, and he had silver mail, and a silver saddle and bridle, all so bright that the sunbeams gleamed and glanced from them far away. Then the others shouted out to him again, saying he might as well hold hard and not try to ride up the hill, for all his trouble would be thrown away; but the knight paid no heed to them, and rode straight at the hill and right up it, till he had gone two-thirds of the way, and then he wheeled his horse round and rode down again. To tell the truth, the Princess liked him still better than the knight in brass, and she sat and wished he might only be able to come right up to the top, and down the other side; but when she saw him turning back, she threw the second apple after him, and it rolled down and fell into his shoe. But as soon as ever he had come down from the hill of glass, he rode off so fast that no one could see what became of him.

At even, when all were to go in before the king and the Princess, that he who had the golden apple might show it, in they went, one after the other; but there was no one who had any apple to show. The two brothers, as they had done on the former day, went home and told how things had gone, and how all had ridden at the hill and none got up.

"But, last of all," they said, "came one in a silver suit, and his horse had a silver saddle and a silver bridle. He was just a chap to ride; and he got two-thirds up the hill, and then turned back. He was a fine fellow and no mistake; and the Princess threw the second gold apple to him."

"Oh!" said Boots, "I should so like to have seen him too, that I should."

"A pretty story," they said. "Perhaps you think his coat of mail was as bright as the ashes you are always poking about and sifting, you nasty, dirty beast."

The third day everything happened as it had happened the two days before. Boots begged to go and see the sight, but the two wouldn't hear of his going with them. When they got to the hill there was no one who could get so much as a yard up it; and now all waited for the knight in silver mail, but they neither saw nor heard of him. At last came one riding on a steed, so brave that no one had ever seen his match; and the knight had a suit of golden mail, and a golden saddle and bridle, so wondrous bright that the sunbeams gleamed from them a mile off. The other knights and princes could not find time to call out to him not to try his luck, for they were amazed to see how grand he was. So he rode right at the hill, and tore up it like nothing, so that the Princess hadn't even time to wish that he might get up the whole way. As soon as ever he reached the top, he took the third golden apple from the Princess' lap, and then turned his horse and rode down again. As soon as he got down, he rode off at full speed, and out of sight in no time.

Now, when the brothers got home at even, you may fancy what long stories they told, how the riding had gone off that day; and amongst other things, they had a deal to say about the knight in golden mail.

"He was just a chap to ride!" they said; "so grand a knight isn't to be found in the wide world."

"Oh!" said Boots, "I should so like to have seen him, that I should."

"Ah!" said his brothers, "his mail shone a deal brighter than the glowing coals which you are always poking and digging at; nasty, dirty beast that you are."

Next day all the knights and princes were to pass before the king and the Princess—it was too late to do so the night before, I suppose—that he who had the gold apple might bring it forth; but one came after another, first the princes, and then the knights, and still no one could show the gold apple.

"Well," said the king, "someone must have it, for it was something that we all saw with our own eyes, how a man came and rode up and bore it off."

So he commanded that everyone who was in the kingdom should come up to the palace and see if he could show the apple. Well, they all came, one after another, but no one had the golden apple, and after a long time the two brothers of Boots came. They were the last of all, so the king asked them if there was no one else in the kingdom who hadn't come.

"Oh, yes," said they; "we have a brother, but he never carried off the golden apple. He hasn't stirred out of the dusthole on any of the three days."

"Never mind that," said the king; "he may as well come up to the palace like the rest."

So Boots had to go up to the palace.

"How, now," said the king; "have you got the golden apple? Speak out!"

"Yes, I have," said Boots; "here is the first, and here is the second, and here is the third too"; and with that he pulled all three golden apples out of his pocket, and at the same time threw off his sooty rags, and stood before them in his gleaming golden mail.

"Yes!" said the king; "you shall have my daughter and half my kingdom, for you well deserve both her and it."

So they got ready for the wedding, and Boots got the Princess to wife, and there was great merry-making at the bridal-feast, you may fancy, for they could all be merry though they couldn't ride up the hill of glass; and all I can say is, that if they haven't left off their merry-making yet, why, they're still at it.

GUDBRAND ON THE HILL-SIDE

The sly humor and tenderness of "Gudbrand on the Hill-side" are beautifully interpreted by Mrs. Gudrun Thorne-Thomsen in her record of this name, which she made for the American Library Association.

Once on a time there was a man whose name was Gudbrand; he had a farm which lay far, far away, upon a hill-side, and so they called him Gudbrand on the Hill-side.

Now, you must know this man and his good-wife lived so happily together, and understood one another so well, that all the husband did the wife thought so well done, there was nothing like it in the world, and she was always glad whatever he turned his hand to. The farm was their own land, and they had a hundred dollars lying at the bottom of their chest, and two cows tethered up in a stall in their farmyard.

So one day his wife said to Gudbrand,

"Do you know, dear, I think we ought to take one of our cows into town and sell it; that's what I think; for then we shall have some money in hand, and such well-to-do people as we ought to have ready money like the rest of the world. As for the hundred dollars at the bottom of the chest yonder, we can't make a hole in them, and I'm sure I don't know what we want with more than one cow. Besides, we shall gain a little in another way, for then I shall get off with only looking after one cow, instead of having, as now, to feed and litter and water two."

Well, Gudbrand thought his wife talked right good sense, so he set off at once with the cow on

"Gudbrand on the Hill-side." From *Popular Tales from the Norse*

his way to town to sell her; but when he got to the town, there was no one who would buy his cow.

"Well! well! never mind," said Gudbrand, "at the worst, I can only go back home again with my cow. I've both stable and tether for her, I should think, and the road is no farther out than in"; and with that he began to toddle home with his cow.

But when he had gone a bit of the way, a man met him who had a horse to sell, so Gudbrand thought 'twas better to have a horse than a cow, so he swopped with the man. A little farther on, he met a man walking along, and driving a fat pig before him, and he thought it better to have a fat pig than a horse, so he swopped with the man. After that he went a little farther, and a man met him with a goat; so he thought it better to have a goat than a pig, and he swopped with the man that owned the goat. Then he went on a good bit till he met a man who had a sheep, and he swopped with him too, for he thought it always better to have a sheep than a goat. After a while he met a man with a goose, and he swopped away the sheep for the goose; and when he had walked a long, long time, he met a man with a cock, and he swopped with him, for he thought in this wise, " 'Tis surely better to have a cock than a goose." Then he went on till the day was far spent, and he began to get very hungry, so he sold the cock for a shilling, and bought food with the money, for, thought Gudbrand on the Hill-side, " 'Tis always better to save one's life than to have a cock."

After that he went on home till he reached his nearest neighbour's house, where he turned in.

"Well," said the owner of the house, "how did things go with you in town?"

"Rather so so," said Gudbrand. "I can't praise my luck, nor do I blame it either"; and with that he told the whole story from first to last.

"Ah!" said his friend, "you'll get nicely hauled over the coals, that one can see, when you get home to your wife. Heaven help you, I wouldn't stand in your shoes for something."

"Well!" said Gudbrand on the Hill-side, "I think things might have gone worse with me; but now, whether I have done wrong or not, I have so kind a goodwife, she never has a word to say against anything that I do."

"Oh!" answered his neighbour, "I hear what you say, but I don't believe it for all that."

"Shall we lay a bet upon it?" asked Gudbrand on the Hill-side. "I have a hundred dollars at the bottom of my chest at home; will you lay as many against them?"

Yes, the friend was ready to bet; so Gudbrand stayed there till evening, when it began to get dark, and then they went together to his house, and the neighbour was to stand outside the door and listen, while the man went in to see his wife.

"Good evening!" said Gudbrand.

"Good evening!" said the goodwife. "Oh! is that you? Now, God be praised!"

Yes, it was he. So the wife asked how things had gone with him in town.

"Oh! only so so," answered Gudbrand; "not much to brag of. When I got to the town there was no one who would buy the cow, so you must know I swopped it away for a horse."

"For a horse!" said his wife; "well, that is good of you; thanks with all my heart. We are so well-to-do that we may drive to church, just as well as other people; and if we choose to keep a horse we have a right to get one, I should think. So run out, child, and put up the horse."

"Ah!" said Gudbrand, "but you see I've not got the horse after all; for when I got a bit farther on the road, I swopped it away for a pig."

"Think of that, now!" said the wife; "you did just as I should have done myself; a thousand thanks! Now I can have a bit of bacon in the house to set before people when they come to see me, that I can. What do we want with a horse? People would only say we had got so proud that we couldn't walk to church. Go out, child, and put up the pig in the stye."

"But I've not got the pig either," said Gudbrand; "for when I got a little farther on, I swopped it away for a milch goat."

"Bless us!" cried his wife, "how well you manage everything! Now I think it over, what should I do with a pig? People would only point at us and say, 'Yonder they eat up all they have got.' No! now I have got a goat, and I shall have milk and cheese, and keep the goat too. Run out, child, and put up the goat."

"Nay, but I haven't got the goat either," said Gudbrand, "for a little farther on I swopped it away, and got a fine sheep instead."

"You don't say so!" cried his wife; "why you do everything to please me, just as if I had been with you; what do we want with a goat? If I had it I should lose half my time in climbing up the hills to get it down. No! if I have a sheep, I shall have both wool and clothing, and fresh meat in the house. Run out, child, and put up the sheep."

"But I haven't got the sheep any more than the rest," said Gudbrand, "for when I had gone a bit farther, I swopped it away for a goose."

"Thank you! thank you! with all my heart!" cried his wife; "what should I do with a sheep? I have no spinning-wheel, nor carding-comb, nor should I care to worry myself with cutting, and shaping, and sewing clothes. We can buy clothes now, as we have always done; and now I shall have roast goose, which I have longed for so often; and, besides, down to stuff my little pillow with. Run out, child, and put up the goose."

"Ah!" said Gudbrand, "but I haven't the goose either; for when I had gone a bit farther I swopped it away for a cock."

"Dear me!" cried his wife, "how you think of everything! just as I should have done myself! A cock! think of that! why, it's as good as an eight-day clock, for every morning the cock crows at four o'clock, and we shall be able to stir our stumps in good time. What should we do with a goose? I don't know how to cook it; and as for my pillow, I can stuff it with cotton-grass. Run out, child, and put up the cock."

"But, after all, I haven't got the cock," said Gudbrand; "for when I had gone a bit farther, I got as hungry as a hunter, so I was forced to sell the cock for a shilling, for fear I should starve."

"Now, God be praised that you did so!" cried his wife; "whatever you do, you do it always just after my own heart. What should we do with a cock? We are our own masters, I should think, and can lie a-bed in the morning as long as we like. Heaven be thanked that I have got you safe back again! you do everything so well that I want neither cock nor goose; neither pigs nor kine."

Then Gudbrand opened the door and said,

"Well, what do you say now? Have I won the hundred dollars?" and his neighbour was forced to allow that he had.

THE HUSBAND WHO WAS TO MIND THE HOUSE

Wanda Gág made a delightful little book of this story and called it Gone Is Gone.

Once upon a time there was a man so surly and cross, he never thought his wife did anything right in the house. So, one evening in hay-making time, he came home, scolding and swearing, and showing his teeth and making a dust.

"Dear love, don't be so angry; there's a good man," said his goody; "to-morrow let's change our work. I'll go out with the mowers and mow, and you shall mind the house at home."

Yes, the husband thought that would do very well. He was quite willing, he said.

So, early next morning his goody took a scythe over her neck, and went out into the hay-field with the mowers and began to mow; but the man was to mind the house, and do the work at home.

First of all he wanted to churn the butter; but when he had churned a while, he got thirsty, and went down to the cellar to tap a barrel of ale. So, just when he had knocked in the bung, and was putting the tap into the cask, he heard overhead the pig come into the kitchen. Then off he ran up the cellar steps, with the tap in his hand, as fast as he could, to look after the pig, lest it should upset the churn; but when he got up, and saw that the pig had already knocked the churn over, and stood there, routing and grunting amongst the cream which was running all over the floor, he got so wild with rage that he quite forgot the ale-barrel, and ran at the pig as hard as he could. He caught it, too, just as it ran out of doors, and gave it such a kick that piggy lay for dead on the spot. Then all at once he remembered he had the tap in his hand; but when he got down to the cellar, every drop of ale had run out of the cask.

Then he went into the dairy and found enough cream left to fill the churn again, and so he began to churn, for butter they must have at dinner. When he had churned a bit, he remembered that their milking cow was still shut up in the byre, and hadn't had a bit to eat or a

"The Husband Who Was to Mind the House." From *Popular Tales from the Norse*

drop to drink all the morning, though the sun was high. Then all at once he thought 'twas too far to take her down to the meadow, so he'd just get her up on the housetop—for the house, you must know, was thatched with sods, and a fine crop of grass was growing there. Now their house lay close up against a steep down, and he thought if he laid a plank across to the thatch at the back he'd easily get the cow up.

But still he couldn't leave the churn, for there was his little babe crawling about on the floor, and "if I leave it," he thought, "the child is sure to upset it." So he took the churn on his back, and went out with it; but then he thought he'd better first water the cow before he turned her out on the thatch; so he took up a bucket to draw water out of the well; but, as he stooped down at the well's brink, all the cream ran out of the churn over his shoulders, and so down into the well.

Now it was near dinner-time, and he hadn't even got the butter yet; so he thought he'd best boil the porridge, and filled the pot with water, and hung it over the fire. When he had done that, he thought the cow might perhaps fall off the thatch and break her legs or her neck. So he got up on the house to tie her up. One end of the rope he made fast to the cow's neck, and the other he slipped down the chimney and tied round his own thigh; and he had to make haste, for the water now began to boil in the pot, and he had still to grind the oatmeal.

So he began to grind away; but while he was hard at it, down fell the cow off the housetop after all, and as she fell, she dragged the man up the chimney by the rope. There he stuck fast; and as for the cow, she hung halfway down the wall, swinging between heaven and earth, for she could neither get down nor up.

And now the goody had waited seven lengths and seven breadths for her husband to come and call them home to dinner; but never a call they had. At last she thought she'd waited long enough, and went home. But when she got there and saw the cow hanging in such an ugly place, she ran up and cut the rope in two with her scythe. But as she did this, down came her husband out of the chimney; and so when his old dame came inside the kitchen, there she found him standing on his head in the porridge-pot.

LITTLE FREDDY
WITH HIS FIDDLE

The Scandinavian tales are full of magic objects which assist those resourceful persons who learn how to use them. Freddy's fiddle is one of the gayest of these.

Once on a time there was a cottager who had an only son, and this lad was weakly, and hadn't much health to speak of; so he couldn't go out to work in the field.

His name was Freddy, and undersized he was too; and so they called him Little Freddy. At home there was little either to bite or sup, and so his father went about the country trying to bind him over as a cow-herd or an errand-boy; but there was no one who would take his son till he came to the sheriff, and he was ready to take him, for he had just packed off his errand-boy, and there was no one who would fill his place, for the story went that he was a skinflint.

But the cottager thought it was better there than nowhere; he would get his food, for all the pay he was to get was his board—there was nothing said about wages or clothes. So when the lad had served three years he wanted to leave, and then the sheriff gave him all his wages at one time. He was to have a penny a year. "It couldn't well be less," said the sheriff. And so he got threepence in all.

As for little Freddy, he thought it was a great sum, for he had never owned so much; but for all that, he asked if he wasn't to have something more.

"You have already had more than you ought to have," said the sheriff.

"Shan't I have anything, then, for clothes?" asked little Freddy; "for those I had on when I came here are worn to rags, and I have had no new ones."

And, to tell the truth, he was so ragged that the tatters hung and flapped about him.

"When you have got what we agreed on," said the sheriff, "and three whole pennies beside, I have nothing more to do with you. Be off!"

But for all that, he got leave just to go into the
"Little Freddy with His Fiddle." From *Tales from the Fjeld*

kitchen and get a little food to put in his script; and after that he set off on the road to buy himself more clothes. He was both merry and glad, for he had never seen a penny before; and every now and then he felt in his pockets as he went along to see if he had them all three. So when he had gone far and farther than far, he got into a narrow dale, with high fells on all sides, so that he couldn't tell if there were any way to pass out; and he began to wonder what there could be on the other side of those fells, and how he ever should get over them.

But up and up he had to go, and on he strode; he was not strong on his legs, and had to rest every now and then—and then he counted and counted how many pennies he had got. So when he had got quite up to the very top, there was nothing but a great plain overgrown with moss. There he sat him down, and began to see if his money was all right; and before he was aware of him a beggar-man came up to him, and he was so tall and big that the lad began to scream and screech when he got a good look of him, and saw his height and length.

"Don't you be afraid," said the beggar-man; "I'll do you no harm. I only beg for a penny, in God's name."

"Heaven help me!" said the lad. "I have only three pennies, and with them I was going to the town to buy clothes."

"It is worse for me than for you," said the beggar-man. "I have got no penny, and I am still more ragged than you."

"Well, then, you shall have it," said the lad.

So when he had walked on awhile he got weary, and sat down to rest again. But when he looked up there he saw another beggar-man, and he was still taller and uglier than the first; and so when the lad saw how very tall and ugly and long he was, he fell a-screeching.

"Now, don't you be afraid of me," said the beggar; "I'll not do you any harm. I only beg for a penny, in God's name."

"Now, may Heaven help me!" said the lad. "I've only got two pence, and with them I was going to the town to buy clothes. If I had only met you sooner, then—"

"It's worse for me than for you," said the beggar-man. "I have no penny, and a bigger body and less clothing."

"Well, you may have it," said the lad.

So he went awhile farther, till he got weary, and then he sat down to rest; but he had scarce sat down than a third beggar-man came to him. He was so tall and ugly and long, that the lad had to look up and up, right up to the sky. And when he took him all in with his eyes, and saw how very, very tall and ugly and ragged he was, he fell a-screeching and screaming again.

"Now, don't you be afraid of me, my lad," said the beggar-man; "I'll do you no harm; for I am only a beggar-man, who begs for a penny in God's name."

"May Heaven help me!" said the lad. "I have only one penny left, and with it I was going to the town to buy clothes. If I had only met you sooner, then—"

"As for that," said the beggar-man, "I have no penny at all, that I haven't, and a bigger body and less clothes, so it is worse for me than for you."

"Yes," said little Freddy, he must have the penny then—there was no help for it; for so each would have what belonged to him, and he would have nothing.

"Well," said the beggar-man, "since you have such a good heart that you gave away all that you had in the world, I will give you a wish for each penny." For you must know it was the same beggar-man who had got them all three; he had only changed his shape each time, that the lad might not know him again.

"I have always had such a longing to hear a fiddle go, and see folk so glad and merry that they couldn't help dancing," said the lad; "and so, if I may wish what I choose, I will wish myself such a fiddle, that everything that has life must dance to its tune."

"That he might have," said the beggar-man; but it was a sorry wish. "You must wish something better for the other two pennies."

"I have always had such a love for hunting and shooting," said little Freddy; "so if I may wish what I choose, I will wish myself such a gun that I shall hit everything I aim at, were it ever so far off."

"That he might have," said the beggar-man; but it was a sorry wish. "You must wish better for the last penny."

"I have always had a longing to be in company

with folk who were kind and good," said little Freddy; "and so, if I could get what I wish, I would wish it to be so that no one can say 'Nay' to the first thing I ask."

"That wish was not so sorry," said the beggar-man; and off he strode between the hills, and he saw him no more. And so the lad lay down to sleep, and the next day he came down from the fell with his fiddle and his gun.

First he went to the storekeeper and asked for clothes, and at one farm he asked for a horse, and at another for a sledge; and at this place he asked for a fur coat, and no one said him "Nay" —even the stingiest folk, they were all forced to give him what he asked for. At last he went through the country as a fine gentleman, and had his horse and his sledge; and so when he had gone a bit he met the sheriff with whom he had served.

"Good day, master," said little Freddy, as he pulled up and took off his hat.

"Good day," said the sheriff. And then he went on, "When was I ever your master?"

"Oh, yes," said little Freddy. "Don't you remember how I served you three years for three pence?"

"Heaven help us!" said the sheriff. "How you have got on all of a hurry! And pray, how was it that you got to be such a fine gentleman?"

"Oh, that's telling," said little Freddy.

"And are you full of fun, that you carry a fiddle about with you?" asked the sheriff.

"Yes, yes," said Freddy. "I have always had such a longing to get folk to dance; but the funniest thing of all is this gun, for it brings down almost anything that I aim at, however far it may be off. Do you see that magpie yonder, sitting in the spruce fir? What'll you bet I don't bag it as we stand here?"

On that the sheriff was ready to stake horse and groom, and a hundred dollars beside, that he couldn't do it; but as it was, he would bet all the money he had about him; and he would go to fetch it when it fell—for he never thought it possible for any gun to carry so far.

But as the gun went off down fell the magpie, and into a great bramble thicket; and away went the sheriff up into the brambles after it, and he picked it up and showed it to the lad. But in a trice little Freddy began to scrape his fiddle, and

the sheriff began to dance, and the thorns to tear him; but still the lad played on, and the sheriff danced, and cried, and begged till his clothes flew to tatters, and he scarce had a thread to his back.

"Yes," said little Freddy, "now I think you're about as ragged as I was when I left your service; so now you may get off with what you have got."

But first of all, the sheriff had to pay him what he had wagered that he could not hit the magpie.

So when the lad came to the town he turned aside into an inn, and he began to play, and all who came danced, and he lived merrily and well. He had no care, for no one would say him "Nay" to anything he asked.

But just as they were all in the midst of their fun, up came the watchmen to drag the lad off to the townhall; for the sheriff had laid a charge against him, and said he had waylaid him and robbed him, and nearly taken his life. And now he was to be hanged—they would not hear of anything else. But little Freddy had a cure for all trouble, and that was his fiddle. He began to play on it, and the watchmen fell a-dancing, till they lay down and gasped for breath.

So they sent soldiers and the guard on their way; but it was no better with them than with the watchmen. As soon as ever little Freddy scraped his fiddle, they were all bound to dance, so long as he could lift a finger to play a tune; but they were half dead long before he was tired. At last they stole a march on him, and took him while he lay asleep by night; and when they had caught him, he was doomed to be hanged on the spot, and away they hurried him to the gallows-tree.

There a great crowd of people flocked together to see this wonder, and the sheriff, he too was there; and he was so glad at last at getting amends for the money and the skin he had lost, and that he might see him hanged with his own eyes. But they did not get him to the gallows very fast, for little Freddy was always weak on his legs, and now he made himself weaker still. His fiddle and his gun he had with him also—it was hard to part him from them; and so, when he came to the gallows, and had to mount the steps, he halted on each step; and when he got to the top he sat down, and asked if they could deny him a wish, and if he might have leave to do one thing? He had such a longing, he said, to scrape a tune and play a bar on his fiddle before they hanged him.

"No, no," they said; "it were sin and shame to deny him that." For, you know, no one could gainsay what he asked.

But the sheriff he begged them, for God's sake, not to let him have leave to touch a string, else, it was all over with them altogether; and if the lad got leave, he begged them to bind him to the birch that stood there.

So little Freddy was not slow in getting his fiddle to speak, and all that were there fell a-dancing at once, those who went on two legs, and those who went on four; both the dean and the parson, and the lawyer, and the bailiff, and the sheriff, masters and men, dogs and swine—they all danced and laughed and screeched at one another. Some danced till they lay for dead; some danced till they fell into a swoon. It went badly with all of them, but worst of all with the sheriff; for there he stood bound to the birch, and he danced and scraped great bits off his back against the trunk. There was not one of them who thought of doing anything to little Freddy, and away he went with his fiddle and his gun, just as he chose; and he lived merrily and happily all his days, for there was no one who could say him "Nay" to the first thing he asked for.

EAST O' THE SUN
AND WEST O' THE MOON

This story might well be a fragment of an ancient myth, with the polar bear an obvious symbol of winter in a northern country. The tale is also pure romance and fulfills all the usual desires for food, warmth, luxury, security, and love. Omit three of the winds, if you wish.

Once on a time there was a poor husbandman who had so many children that he hadn't much of either food or clothing to give them. Pretty children they all were, but the prettiest was the youngest daughter, who was so lovely there was no end to her loveliness.

"East o' the Sun and West o' the Moon." From *Popular Tales from the Norse* (slightly adapted)

So one day, 'twas on a Thursday evening late at the fall of the year, the weather was so wild and rough outside, and it was so cruelly dark, and rain fell and wind blew, till the walls of the cottage shook again and again. There they all sat round the fire, busy with this thing and that. But just then, all at once, something gave three taps on the window-pane. Then the father went out to see what was the matter; and, when he got out of doors, what should he see but a great big White Bear.

"Good evening to you," said the White Bear.

"The same to you," said the man.

"Will you give me your youngest daughter? If you will, I'll make you as rich as you are now poor," said the Bear.

Well, the man would not be at all sorry to be so rich; but still he thought he must have a bit of a talk with his daughter first; so he went in and told them how there was a great White Bear waiting outside, who had given his word to make them so rich if he could only have the youngest daughter.

The lassie said "No!" outright. Nothing could get her to say anything else; so the man went out and settled it with the White Bear, that he should come again the next Thursday evening and get an answer. Meantime he talked his daughter over, and kept on telling her of all the riches they would get, and how well off she would be herself; and so at last she thought better of it, and washed and mended her rags, made herself as smart as she could, and was ready to start. I can't say her packing gave her much trouble.

Next Thursday evening came the White Bear to fetch her, and she got upon his back with her bundle, and off they went. So, when they had gone a bit of the way, the White Bear said,

"Are you afraid?"

No, she wasn't.

"Well, mind and hold tight by my shaggy coat, and then there's nothing to fear," said the Bear.

So she rode a long, long way, till they came to a great steep hill. There, on the face of it, the White Bear gave a knock, and a door opened, and they came into a castle, where there were many rooms all lit up; rooms gleaming with silver and gold; and there too was a table ready laid, and it was all as grand as grand could be.

Then the White Bear gave her a silver bell; and when she wanted anything, she was only to ring it, and she would get it at once.

Well, after she had eaten and drunk, and evening wore on, she got sleepy after her journey, and thought she would like to go to bed, so she rang the bell; and she had scarce taken hold of it before she came into a chamber, where there was a bed made, as fair and white as anyone would wish to sleep in, with silken pillows and curtains, and gold fringe. All that was in the room was gold or silver; but when she had gone to bed, and put out the light, she heard someone come into the next room. That was the White Bear, who threw off his beast shape at night; but she never saw him, for he always came after she put out the light, and before the day dawned he was up and off again. So things went on happily for a while; but at last she began to get silent and sorrowful; for there she went about all day alone, and she longed to go home to see her father and mother, and brothers and sisters, and that was why she was so sad and sorrowful, because she couldn't get to them.

"Well, well!" said the Bear, "perhaps there's a cure for all this; but you must promise me one thing, not to talk alone with your mother, but only when the rest are by to hear; for she'll take you by the hand and try to lead you into a room alone to talk; but you must mind and not do that, else you'll bring bad luck on both of us."

So one Sunday, the White Bear came and said now they could set off to see her father and mother. Well, off they started, she sitting on his back; and they went far and long. At last they came to a grand house, and there her brothers and sisters were running about out of doors at play, and everything was so pretty, 'twas a joy to see.

"This is where your father and mother live now," said the White Bear; "but don't forget what I told you, else you'll make us both unlucky."

No, bless you, she'd not forget, and when she had reached the house, the White Bear turned right about and left her.

Then she went in to see her father and mother, and there was such joy, there was no end to it. None of them thought they could thank her enough for all she had done for them. Now, they had everything they wished, as good as good could be, and they all wanted to know how she got on where she lived.

Well, she said, it was very good to live where she did; she had all she wished. What she said beside I don't know; but I don't think any of them had the right end of the stick, or that they got much out of her. But so in the afternoon, after they had done dinner, all happened as the White Bear had said. Her mother wanted to talk with her alone in her bed-room; but she minded what the White Bear had said, and wouldn't go up stairs.

"Oh, what we have to talk about will keep," she said, and put her mother off. But somehow or other, her mother got around her at last, and she had to tell her the whole story. So she said, how every night, when she had gone to a bed, someone came into the next room as soon as she had put out the light, and how she never saw him, because he was always up and away before the morning dawned; and how she went about woeful and sorrowing, for she thought she should so like to see him, and how all day long she walked about there alone, and how dull, and dreary, and lonesome it was.

"My!" said her mother; "perhaps it is a Troll. But now I'll teach you a lesson how to set eyes on him. I'll give you a bit of candle, which you can carry in your bosom. Just light that while he is asleep; but take care not to drop the tallow on him."

Yes, she took the candle, and hid it in her bosom, and as night drew on, the White Bear came and fetched her away.

But when they had gone a bit of the way, the White Bear asked if all hadn't happened as he had said.

Well, she couldn't say it hadn't.

"Now mind," said he, "if you have listened to your mother's advice, you have brought bad luck on us both, and then, all that has passed between us will be as nothing."

"No," she said, "I haven't listened to my mother's advice."

So when she reached home, and had gone to bed, it was the old story over again. There came someone into the next room. So at dead of night, she got up and struck a light, lit the candle, and went into the other room to see for herself who it was. She let the light shine on him, and so she saw that he was the loveliest Prince she had ever set eyes on, and she fell so deep in love with him on the spot, that she thought she couldn't live if she didn't give him a kiss there and then. And so she did; but as she kissed him, she dropped three hot drops of tallow on his shirt, and he woke up.

"What have you done?" he cried; "now you have made us both unlucky, for had you held out only this one year, I had been freed. For I have a stepmother who has bewitched me, so that I am a White Bear by day, and a Man by night. But now all ties are snapt between us; now I must set off from you to her. She lives in a castle which stands EAST O' THE SUN AND WEST O' THE MOON, and there, too, is a Princess, with a nose three ells long, and she's the wife I must have now."

She wept and took it ill, but there was no help for it; go he must.

Then she asked him if she mightn't go with him.

No, she mightn't.

"Tell me the way, then," she said, "and I'll search you out; that surely I may get leave to do."

"Yes," she might do that, he said; but there was no way to that place. It lay EAST O' THE SUN AND WEST O' THE MOON, and thither she'd never find her way.

Next morning when she woke up, both Prince and castle were gone, and there she lay on a little green patch, in the midst of the gloomy thick wood, and by her side lay the same bundle of rags she had brought with her from her old home.

So when she had rubbed the sleep out of her eyes, and wept till she was tired, she set out on her way, and walked many, many days, till she came to a lofty crag. Under it sat an old hag, and played with a gold apple which she tossed about. Her the lassie asked if she knew the way to the Prince, who lived with his stepmother in the castle that lay EAST O' THE SUN AND WEST O' THE MOON, and who was to marry the Princess with a nose three ells long.

"How did you come to know about him?" asked the old hag; "but maybe you are the lassie who ought to have had him?"

Yes, she was.

"So, so; it's you, is it?" said the old hag. "Well, all I know about him is that he lives in the castle that lies EAST O' THE SUN AND WEST O' THE MOON, and thither you'll come late or never; but still you may have the loan of my horse, and on him you may ride to my next neighbour. Maybe she'll be able to tell you; and when you get there, just give the horse a switch under the left ear, and beg him to be off home; and, stay, this gold apple you may take with you."

So she got upon the horse and rode a long, long time, till she came to another crag, under which sat another old hag, with a gold carding-comb. Her the lassie asked if she knew the way to the castle that lay EAST O' THE SUN AND WEST O' THE MOON, and she answered, like the first old hag, that she knew nothing about it, except it was east o' the sun and west o' the moon.

"And thither you'll come, late or never; but you shall have the loan of my horse to my next neighbour; maybe she'll tell you all about it; and when you get there, just switch the horse under the left ear and beg him to be off home."

And this old hag gave her the golden carding-comb; it might be she'd find some use for it, she said. So the lassie got up on the horse, and rode a far, far way, and a weary time; and so at last she came to another great crag, under which sat another hag, spinning with a golden spinning-wheel. Her, too, the lassie asked if she knew the way to the Prince, and where the castle was that lay EAST O' THE SUN AND WEST O' THE MOON. So it was the same thing over again.

"Maybe it's you who ought to have had the Prince?" said the old hag.

Yes, it was.

But she, too, didn't know the way a bit better than the other two. "East o' the sun and west o' the moon it was," she knew—that was all.

"And thither you'll come, late or never; but I'll lend you my horse, and then I think you'd best ride to the East Wind and ask him; maybe he knows those parts, and can blow you thither. But when you get to him, you need only give the horse a switch under the left ear, and he'll trot home of himself."

And so, too, she gave her the gold spinning-wheel. "Maybe you'll find use for it," said the old hag.

Then on she rode many, many days, a weary time, before she got to the East Wind's house; but at last she did reach it, and then she asked the East Wind if he could tell her the way to the Prince who dwelt east o' the sun and west o' the moon. Yes, the East Wind had often heard tell of it, the Prince and the castle, but he couldn't tell the way, for he had never blown so far.

"But, if you will, I'll go to my brother, the West Wind; maybe he knows, for he's much stronger. So, if you will just get on my back, I'll carry you thither."

Yes, she got on his back, and I should just think they went briskly along.

So when they got there, they went into the West Wind's house; and the East Wind said the lassie he had brought was the one who ought to have had the Prince who lived in the castle EAST O' THE SUN AND WEST O' THE MOON; and so she had set out to seek him, and how he had come with her, and would be glad to know if the West Wind knew how to get to the castle.

"Nay," said the West Wind, "so far I've never blown; but if you will, I'll go with you to our brother the South Wind, for he's much stronger than either of us, and he has flapped his wings far and wide. Maybe he'll tell you. You can get on my back, and I'll carry you to him."

Yes, she got on his back, and so they travelled to the South Wind, and were not so very long on the way, I should think.

When they got there, the West Wind asked him if he could tell the lassie the way to the castle that lay EAST O' THE SUN AND WEST O' THE MOON, for it was she who ought to have had the Prince who lived there.

"You don't say so! That's she, is it?" said the South Wind.

"Well, I have blustered about in most places in my time, but so far have I never blown; but if you will, I'll take you to my brother the North Wind; he is the oldest and strongest of the whole lot of us, and if he doesn't know where it is, you'll never find any one in the world to tell you. You can get on my back, and I'll carry you thither."

Yes! she got on his back and away he went from his house at a fine rate. And this time, too, she wasn't long on her way.

When they got to the North Wind's house, he was so wild and cross, cold puffs came from him a long way off.

"BLAST YOU BOTH, WHAT DO YOU WANT?" he roared out to them ever so far off, so that it struck them with an icy shiver.

"Well," said the South Wind, "you needn't be so foul-mouthed, for here I am, your brother, the South Wind, and here is the lassie who ought to have had the Prince who dwells in the castle that lies EAST O' THE SUN AND WEST O' THE MOON; and now she wants to ask you if you ever were there, and can tell her the way, for she would be so glad to find him again."

"YES, I KNOW WELL ENOUGH WHERE IT IS," said the North Wind; "once in my life I blew an aspen-leaf thither, but I was so tired I couldn't blow a puff for ever so many days after. But if you really wish to go thither, and aren't afraid to come along with me, I'll take you on my back and see if I can blow you thither."

Yes! with all her heart; she must and would get thither if it were possible in any way; and as for fear, however madly he went, she wouldn't be at all afraid.

"Very well, then," said the North Wind, "but you must sleep here to-night, for we must have the whole day before us, if we're to get thither at all."

Early the next morning the North Wind woke her, and puffed himself up, and blew himself out, and made himself so stout and big, 'twas gruesome to look at him; and so off they went high up through the air as if they would never stop till they got to the world's end.

Down below there was such a storm; it threw down long tracts of wood and many houses, and when it swept over the great sea, ships foundered by hundreds.

So they tore on and on—no one can believe how far they went—and all the while they still went over the sea, and the North Wind got more and more weary, and so out of breath he could scarce bring out a puff; and his wings drooped and drooped, till at last he sank so low that the crests of the waves dashed over his heels.

"Are you afraid?" said the North Wind.

No, she wasn't.

But they weren't very far from land; and the North Wind had still enough strength left in him that he managed to throw her up on the

between whiles she wept sore; but all she could do wouldn't wake him up. Next morning as soon as day broke, came the Princess with the long nose, and drove her out again.

So in the day-time she sat down under the castle windows and began to card with her golden carding-comb, and the same thing happened. The Princess asked what she wanted for it; and she said it wasn't for sale for gold or money, but if she might get leave to go to the Prince and be with him that night, the Princess should have it. But when she went up, she found him asleep again, and all she called, and all she shook, and wept, and prayed, she couldn't get life into him; and as soon as the first gray peep of day came, then came the Princess with the long nose, and chased her out again.

So in the day-time, the lassie sat down outside under the castle window, and began to spin with her golden spinning-wheel, and that, too, the Princess with the long nose wanted to have. So she threw up the window and asked what she wanted for it. The lassie said, as she had said twice before, it wasn't for sale for gold or money; but if she might go up to the Prince who was there, and be with him alone that night, she might have it.

Yes! she might do that and welcome. But now you must know there were some Christian folk who had been carried off thither, and as they sat in their room, which was next the Prince, they had heard how a girl had been in there, and wept and prayed, and called to him two nights running, and they told that to the Prince.

That evening when the Princess came with her sleeping potion, the Prince made as if he drank, but threw it over his shoulder for he could guess it was a sleeping potion. So, when the lassie came in, she found the Prince wide awake; and then she told him the whole story of how she had come thither.

"Ah," said the Prince, "you've just come in the very nick of time, for to-morrow is to be our wedding-day; and now I won't have the Long-nose, for you are the only lassie in the world who can set me free. I'll say I want to see what my wife is fit for, and beg her to wash the shirt which has the three spots of tallow on it; she'll say yes, for she doesn't know 'tis you who put them there; but that's a work only for Christian

shore under the windows of the castle which lay EAST O' THE SUN AND WEST O' THE MOON; but then he was so weak and worn out, he had to stay there and rest many days before he could get home again.

Next morning the lassie sat down under the castle window and began to play with the gold apple; and the first person she saw was the Long-nose who was to have the Prince.

"What do you want for your gold apple, you lassie?" said the Long-nose, and threw up the window.

"It's not for sale, for gold or money," said the lassie.

"If it's not for sale for gold or money, what is it that you will sell it for? You may name your own price," said the Princess.

"Well! if I may get to the Prince who lives here and be with him to-night, you shall have it," said the lassie whom the North Wind had brought.

Yes! she might; that could be done. So the Princess got the gold apple; but when the lassie came up to the Prince's bed-room at night he was fast asleep; she called him and shook him, and

folk, and not for a pack of Trolls; and so I'll say that I won't have any other for my bride than the woman who can wash them out, and ask you to do it."

The next day, when the wedding was to be, the Prince said,

"First of all, I'd like to see what my bride is fit for."

"Yes," said the step-mother with all her heart.

"Well," said the Prince, "I've got a fine shirt which I'd like for my wedding shirt; but somehow or other it has got three spots of tallow on it, which I must have washed out; and I have sworn never to take any other bride than the woman who's able to do that. If she can't, she's not worth having."

Well, that was no great thing, they said; so they agreed, and she with the long nose began to wash away as hard as she could, but the more she rubbed and scrubbed, the bigger the spots grew.

"Ah!" said the old hag, her mother, "you can't wash; let me try."

But she hadn't long taken the shirt in hand before it got far worse than ever, and with all her rubbing, and wringing, and scrubbing, the spots grew bigger and blacker, and the darker and uglier was the shirt.

Then all the Trolls began to wash, but the longer they washed, the blacker and uglier the shirt grew, till at last it was as black all over as if it had been up the chimney.

"Ah!" said the Prince, "you're none of you worth a straw; you can't wash. Why there, outside, sits a beggar lassie; I'll be bound she knows how to wash better than the whole lot of you. COME IN, LASSIE!" he shouted.

Well, in she came.

"Can you wash this shirt, lassie, you?" said he.

"I don't know," she said, "but I think I can."

And almost before she had taken it and dipped it in the water, it was as white as driven snow, and whiter still.

"Yes; you are the lassie for me," said the Prince.

At that the old hag flew into such a rage, she burst on the spot, and the Princess with the long nose after her, and the whole pack of Trolls after her—at least I have never heard a word about them since.

As for the Prince and the lassie, they took with them all the silver and gold, and flitted away as far as they could from the castle that lay EAST O' THE SUN and WEST O' THE MOON.

THE MOST OBEDIENT WIFE

The other stories in this group have all been Norwegian. This one is Danish and certainly a most amusing variant of "The Taming of the Shrew" theme. For the sake of the girls, be sure to follow it with the Czech "Clever Manka."

Long ago there was a rich farmer who had three daughters, all grown up and marriageable, and all three very pretty. The eldest of them was the prettiest, and she was also the cleverest, but she was so quarrelsome and obstinate, that there was never any peace in the house. She constantly contradicted her father, who was a kind, peace-loving man, and she quarrelled with her sisters, although they were very good-natured girls.

Many wooers came to the farm, and one of them wished to marry the eldest daughter. The farmer said that he had no objection to him as a son-in-law, but at the same time he thought it his duty to tell the suitor the truth. Accordingly he warned him that his eldest daughter was so violent and strong-minded that no one could live in peace with her. As some compensation for these faults, she would receive three hundred pounds more in her dowry than would her two sisters. That was, of course, very attractive, but the young man thought over the matter and, after he had been visiting the house for some time, he altered his mind and asked for the hand of the second daughter. The daughter accepted him, and, as her father was willing, the two became man and wife and lived very happily together.

Then came another wooer, from another part of the country, and he also wanted to marry the eldest daughter. The father warned him, as he had cautioned the first wooer; telling him that she would receive three hundred pounds more than her youngest sister, but that he must be careful, for she was so stubborn and quarrelsome that nobody could live in peace with her. So the

"The Most Obedient Wife." From *Danish Fairy Tales* by Svend Grundtvig. Thomas Y. Crowell Company, New York. Reprinted by permission of the publisher

second wooer changed his mind and asked for the hand of the youngest daughter. They married shortly after and lived happily and peacefully together.

The eldest sister was now alone with her father, but she did not treat him any better than before, and grew even more ill-humoured because her two sisters had found favour in the eyes of the first two wooers. She was obstinate and quarrelsome, violent and bad-tempered, and she grew more so from day to day.

At last another wooer came, and he was neither from their own district nor even from their country, but from a distant land. He went to the farmer and asked for the hand of his eldest daughter. "I do not want her to marry at all," said the father, "it would be a shame to allow her to do so; she is so ill-tempered and violent that no human being could live in peace with her and I do not want to be the cause of such unhappiness." But the wooer remained firm; he wanted her, he said, whatever her faults might be. At length the father yielded, provided that his daughter were willing to marry the young man, for, after all, he would be glad to get rid of her, and as he had told the suitor the whole truth about her, his conscience was clear. Accordingly, the young man wooed the girl, and she did not hesitate long, but accepted the offer, for she was tired of sitting at home a despised and spurned spinster.

The wooer said that he had no time to remain with them just then, as he must return home at once, and, as soon as the wedding day was fixed, he rode away. He also told them not to wait for him at the farm on the day of the wedding, he would appear in good time at the church. When the day came the farmer drove with his daughter to the church, where a great company of wedding guests had assembled; the bride's sisters and brothers-in-law were there, and all the village people arrived in their Sunday clothes. The bridegroom was there also, but in ordinary travelling garments; and so the couple walked up to the altar and were married.

As soon as the ceremony was over, the bridegroom took his young wife by the hand and led her out of the church. He sent a message to his father-in-law asking him to excuse their absence from the marriage feast, as they had no time to waste. He had not driven in a coach, as is the custom at weddings, but travelled on horseback, on a fine big grey horse, with an ordinary saddle, and a couple of pistols in the saddlebags. He had brought no friends or relations with him, only a big dog, that lay beside the horse during the ceremony. The bridegroom lifted his bride on to the pommel, as if she had been a feather, jumped into the saddle, put the spurs to his horse and rode off with the dog trotting behind. The marriage party standing at the church door looked after them, and shook their heads in amazement. Then they got into their carriages, drove back to the house, and partook of the marriage feast without bride or bridegroom.

The bride did not like this at all, but as she did not want to quarrel with her bridegroom so soon, she held her tongue for a time; but as he did not speak either, she at last broke the ice and said that it was a very fine horse they were riding. "Yes," he replied; "I have seven other horses at home in my stables, but this is my favourite; it is the most valuable of all, and I like it best." Then she remarked that she liked the beautiful dog also. "It is indeed a jewel of a dog," he said, "and has cost me a lot of money."

After a while they came to a forest, where the bridegroom sprang from his horse and cut a thin switch from a willow-tree. This he wound three times round his finger, then tied it with a thread and gave it to his bride, saying: "This is my wedding gift to you. Take good care of it, and carry it about with you always! You will not repent it." She thought it a strange wedding gift, but put it in her pocket, and they rode on again. Presently the bride dropped her glove, and the bridegroom said to the dog: "Pick it up, Fido!" But the dog took no notice, and left the glove on the ground. Then his master drew his pistol from the holster, shot the dog, and rode on, leaving it lying dead. "How could you be so cruel?" said his bride. "I never say a thing twice," was the reply, and they journeyed on in silence.

After some time they came to a running stream that they had to cross. There being only a ford, and no bridge, the man said to his horse: "Take good care! Not a drop must soil my bride's dress!" When they had crossed, however, the dress was badly soiled, and the husband lifted his bride from the horse, drew out the other pistol and shot the horse, so that it fell dead to the ground. "Oh, the poor horse!" cried the bride. "Yes, but I never say a thing twice," answered her husband. Then he took saddle, bridle, and cover from the horse; bridle and cover he carried himself, but the saddle he gave to his young wife, and said: "You can carry that; we shall soon be home." He walked on in silence, and the bride quickly put the saddle on her back and followed him; she had no desire to make him say it twice.

Soon they arrived at his dwelling place, a very fine farm. The menservants and maidservants rushed to the door and received them, and the husband said to them: "See, this is my wife and your mistress. Whatever she tells you, you are to do, just as if I had ordered it." Then he led her indoors and showed her everything—living-rooms and bedrooms, kitchen and cellar, brew-house and dairy—and said to her: "You will look after everything indoors, I attend to everything out-of-doors," and then they sat down to supper, and soon after went to bed.

Days, weeks and months passed; the young wife attended to all household matters while her husband looked after the farm, and not a single angry word passed between them. The servants had been accustomed to obey their master implicitly, and now they obeyed their mistress likewise, and so six months passed without there having arisen any necessity for the husband to say the same thing twice to his wife. He was always kind and polite to her, and she was always gentle and obedient.

One day he said to her: "Would you not like to visit your relations?" "Yes, dear husband, I should like to do so very much, if it is convenient," she replied. "It is quite convenient," he said, "but you have never mentioned it. It shall be done at once; get ready, while I have the horses put to the carriage." He went to the stable and saw to everything, while his wife ran upstairs to dress as quickly as possible for the journey. The husband drove up, cracked his whip and asked: "Are you ready?" "Yes, dear," came the reply, and she came running out and entered the carriage. She had not quite finished dressing and carried some of her things in her hand, and these she put on in the carriage.

Then they started. When they had driven nearly half the distance, they saw a great flock of ravens flying across the road. "What beautiful white birds!" said the husband. "No, they are black, dear!" said his wife. "I think it is going to rain," he said, turned the horses, and drove home again. She understood perfectly why he had done so; it was the first time that she had contradicted him, but she showed no resentment, and the two conversed in quite a friendly fashion all the way home. The horses were put into the stable—and it did not rain.

When a month had passed, the husband said one morning: "I believe it is going to be fine to-day. Would you not like to visit your relations?" She wished to do so very much indeed, and she hastened a little more than the last time, so that when her husband drove up and cracked his whip, she was quite ready and mounted the carriage beside him. They had driven considerably more than half the distance, when they met a large flock of sheep and lambs. "What a fine pack of wolves!" said the husband. "You mean sheep, dear!" said the wife. "I think it will rain before evening," said the husband, looking up at the sky. "It will be better for us to drive home again." With these words he turned the horses and drove back home. They conversed in a friendly manner until they reached home; but it did not rain.

When another month had passed, the husband said one morning to his wife: "We really must see whether we cannot manage to visit your relations. What do you say to our driving across to-day? It looks as though the day would be fine." His wife thought so too; she was ready very soon and they set out. They had not travelled far when they saw a great flock of swans flying along over their heads. "That was a fine flock of storks," said the husband. "Yes, so it was, dear," said his wife, and they drove on; there was no change in the weather that day, so that they reached her father's farm in due course. He received them joyfully and sent at once for his two other daughters and their husbands, and a very merry family meeting it was.

The three married sisters went into the kitchen together, because they could talk more freely there, and they had a great deal to tell each other; the two younger ones in particular had many questions to ask their elder sister, because they had not seen her for a very long time. Then they helped to prepare the dinner; it goes without saying that nothing was too good for this festive occasion.

The three brothers-in-law sat meanwhile with their father-in-law in the sitting-room and they, too, had much to tell and ask each other. Then said the old farmer: "This is the first time that you have all three been gathered together under my roof, and I should like to ask you frankly how you are pleased with your wives." The husbands who had married the two younger, good-tempered sisters said at once that they were perfectly satisfied and lived very happily. "But how do you get on with yours?" the father-in-law asked the husband of the eldest sister. "Nobody ever married a better wife than I did," was the reply. "Well, I should like to see which of you has the most obedient wife," said the father-in-law, and then he fetched a heavy silver jug and filled it to the top with gold and silver coins. This he placed in the middle of the table before the three men, and said that he would give it to him who had the most obedient wife.

They put the matter to the test at once. The husband who had married the youngest sister went to the kitchen door and called: "Will you come here a moment, Gerda, please; as quickly as possible!" "All right, I am coming," she answered, but it was some time before she came, because as she explained, she had first to talk about something with one of her sisters. "What do you want with me?" she asked. The husband made some excuse, and she went out again.

Now it was the turn of the man who had married the middle sister. "Please come here a moment, Margaret!" he called. She also answered: "Yes, I am coming at once," but it was a good while before she came; she had had something in her hands and was compelled to put it down first. The husband invented some excuse, and she went out again.

Then the third husband went to the kitchen door, opened it slightly and just said: "Christine!"—"Yes!" she answered, as she stood there with a large dish of food in her hands. "Take this from me!" she said quickly to her sisters, but they looked at her in amazement and did not take the dish. Bang! she dropped it right on the middle of the kitchen floor, rushed into the room and asked: "What do you wish, dear?" —"Oh, I only wanted to see you," he said, "but since you are here, you may as well take that jug standing on the table; it is yours, with all that is in it.—You might also show us what you got from me as a marriage gift on your wedding day."—"Yes, dear, here it is," she said, and drew the willow ring from her bosom, where she had kept it ever since. The husband handed it to his father-in-law and asked: "Can you put that ring straight?"—No, that was impossible without breaking it. "Well, you see now," said the husband, "if I had not bent the twig when it was green, I could not have made it into this shape."

After that they sat down to a merry meal, then the husband of the oldest sister returned home with her, and they lived for many years very happily together.

French folk tales

"Sleeping Beauty," "Cinderella," and "The Master Cat" are taken from Perrault's versions of eight French folk tales. "Beauty and the Beast" and "The White Cat" are by two well-known French women and mark the beginning of the modern fanciful tale, although both suggest folk origin. Mme. de Beaumont wisely kept her "Beauty and the Beast" close to the simplicity of the traditional tale. "The White Cat" by Mme. d'Aulony is more elaborate and sophisticated but still retains much of the magic formula of folk tale construction. "The Mouse-Princess" and "The Grey Palfrey" are taken from Barbara Picard's recent collection of traditional French legends and stories. These two stories and "The White Cat" are for the oldest children, twelve to fourteen, while the others belong to the usual fairy tale age—eight to ten.

THE SLEEPING BEAUTY
IN THE WOOD

This version omits the second episode in which the ogress (Night) eats up Beauty's children (Dawn and Day) and threatens Beauty (the Sun), since that section is not suitable for telling to children. However, students of folklore will be interested in the omitted section, which is a clear evidence of myth origin.

There were formerly a king and a queen, who were sorry they had no children; so sorry that it cannot be expressed. They went to all the waters in the world; vows, pilgrimages, all ways were tried, and all to no purpose.

At last, however, the queen had a daughter. There was a very fine christening; and the princess had for her godmothers all the fairies they could find in the whole kingdom—they found seven. By this means the princess had all the perfections imaginable.

After the christening, all the company returned to the king's palace, where was prepared a great feast for the fairies. There was placed before every one of them a magnificent cover with a case of massive gold, wherein were a spoon, knife and fork, all of pure gold set with diamonds and rubies. But as they were sitting down at table they saw come into the hall a very old fairy, who had not been invited. It was above fifty years since she had been seen, and she was believed to be either dead or enchanted.

The king ordered her a cover, but could not furnish her with a case of gold because seven only had been made for the seven fairies. The old fairy fancied she was slighted and muttered some threats between her teeth. One of the young fairies, who sat by her, overheard how she grumbled. Judging that she might give the little princess some unlucky gift the young fairy went, as soon as they rose from the table, and hid herself behind the hangings, that she might speak last and repair, as much as she could, any evil which the old fairy intended.

"The Sleeping Beauty in the Wood." From *The Blue Fairy Book* edited by Andrew Lang. Used by permission of Longmans, Green and Company, Inc.

Meanwhile all the fairies began to give their gifts to the princess. The youngest for her gift said that the princess should be the most beautiful person in the world; the next, that she should have the wit of an angel; the third, that she should have wonderful grace in everything she did; the fourth, that she should dance perfectly; the fifth, that she should sing like a nightingale; and the sixth, that she should play all kinds of music to perfection.

The old fairy's turn coming next, with her head shaking more with spite than age, she said that the princess should have her hand pierced with a spindle and die of the wound. This terrible gift made the whole company tremble, and everybody fell a-crying.

At this very instant the young fairy came out from behind the hangings, and spoke these words aloud:

"Assure yourselves, O King and Queen, that your daughter shall not die. It is true, I have no power to undo entirely what my elder has done. The princess shall indeed pierce her hand with a spindle. But instead of dying, she shall only fall into a profound sleep, which shall last a hundred years. After a hundred years a king's son shall come and wake her."

The king, to avoid misfortune, immediately forbade spinning with a distaff and spindle, or to have so much as a spindle in the house. About fifteen or sixteen years after, the king and queen being gone to one of their pleasure houses, the young princess was diverting herself by running up and down the palace. She came into a little room at the top of the tower, where a good old woman was spinning with her spindle. This good woman had never heard of the king's proclamation against spindles.

"What are you doing there, goody?" said the princess.

"I am spinning, my pretty child," said the old woman.

"Ha," said the princess, "this is very pretty. How do you do it? Give it to me so I may see."

She had no sooner taken the spindle than it ran into her hand, and she fell down in a swoon.

The good old woman cried out for help. People came and threw water upon the princess' face, unlaced her, struck her on the palms of her hands, and rubbed her temples with Hungary water. But nothing would bring her to herself.

And now the king, who came up at the noise, bethought himself of the prediction of the fairies and, judging very well that this must necessarily come to pass since the fairies had said it, caused the princess to be carried into the finest apartment in his palace and laid upon a bed all embroidered with gold and silver.

One would have taken her for a little angel, she was so very beautiful, for her swooning had not dimmed her complexion: her cheeks were carnation and her lips were coral. Indeed her eyes were shut, but she was heard to breathe softly, which satisfied those about her she was not dead. The king commanded them not to disturb her, but let her sleep quietly till her hour of awakening was come.

The good fairy, who had saved the life of the princess by condemning her to sleep a hundred years, was in the kingdom of Matakin, twelve thousand leagues off, when this accident befell the princess. But she was instantly informed of it by a little dwarf, who had boots with which he could go seven leagues in one stride. The fairy came immediately, in a fiery chariot drawn by dragons.

The king handed her out of the chariot, and she approved everything he had done. But she touched with her wand everything in the palace —except the king and queen—governesses, maids of honor, ladies of the bed-chamber, gentlemen, officers, stewards, cooks, undercooks, scullions, guards with their beefeaters, pages, footmen. She likewise touched all the horses in the stables, the great dogs in the outward court and pretty little Mopsey too, the princess' little spaniel, which lay by her on the bed.

Immediately upon her touching them they all fell asleep that they might not awake before their mistress and might be ready to wait upon her when she wanted them. The very spits at the fire, as full as they could hold of partridges and pheasants, fell asleep also. All this was done in a moment. Fairies are not long in doing their magic.

And now the king and the queen, having kissed their dear child without waking her, went out of the palace, and in a quarter of an hour's time there grew up all round about the park such a vast number of trees, great and small, bushes and brambles, twining one with another, that neither man nor beast could pass through. Nothing could be seen but the very tops of the towers, and those only from a great distance.

When a hundred years were gone and passed the son of the king then reigning, who was of another family, being gone a-hunting, asked what those towers were which he saw in the middle of a great thick wood?

All answered according to the story they had heard. Some said it was a ruinous old castle, haunted by spirits; others, that all the sorcerers and witches of the country kept their night meetings there. The common opinion was that an ogre lived there, who carried thither all the little children he could catch.

The prince was at a loss, not knowing what to believe, when a very aged countryman spoke to him:

"May it please Your Royal Highness, it is now about fifty years since I heard from my father, who heard my grandfather say, there was in this castle a princess, who must sleep there a hundred years, and should be awakened by a king's son."

The young prince was all on fire at these words. Believing in this rare adventure, and pushed on by love and honor, he resolved that moment to look into it. Scarce had he advanced toward the wood when all the great trees, the bushes and brambles gave way of themselves to let him pass. He walked up a long avenue to the castle. What surprised him a little was that he saw none of his people could follow him. The trees closed behind him again as soon as he had passed through. However, he did not cease from continuing his way; a young prince is always valiant.

He came into a spacious outward court, where everything he saw might have frozen the most fearless person with horror. There was a frightful silence, and there was nothing to be seen but stretched-out bodies of men and animals, all seeming to be dead. He knew, however, by the ruby faces of the beefeaters, that they were only asleep; and their goblets, wherein still remained some drops of wine, showed plainly that they fell asleep in their cups.

The prince then crossed a court paved with marble, went up the stairs, and came into the guard chamber, where guards were standing in their ranks, with their muskets upon their shoulders, and snoring as loud as they could. After that he went through several rooms full of gentlemen and ladies, all asleep, some standing, others sitting. At last he came into a chamber all gilded with gold, where he saw upon a bed, the curtains of which were open, the finest sight a young prince ever beheld—a princess, who appeared to be about fifteen or sixteen years of age, and whose bright and resplendent beauty had somewhat in it divine. He approached with trembling and admiration and fell down before her upon his knees.

And now, as the enchantment was at an end, the princess awoke, and looking on him with eyes more tender than the first view might seem to admit, "Is it you, my Prince?" said she. "I have waited a long while."

The prince, charmed with these words, and much more with the manner in which they were spoken, knew not how to show his joy and gratitude. He assured her he loved her better than he did himself. Their discourse was not well connected, they did weep more than talk—little eloquence, a great deal of love. He was more at a loss than she, and we need not wonder at it: she had time to think on what to say to him; for it is very probable—though history mentions nothing of it—that the good fairy, during so long a sleep, had given her very agreeable dreams. In short, they talked four hours together, and yet they said not half what they had to say.

Meanwhile all the palace awoke; everyone thought upon their particular business, and as all of them were not in love they were ready to die for hunger. The chief lady of honor, being as sharp set as other folks, grew very impatient and told the princess loudly that supper was served. The prince helped the princess to rise. She was dressed magnificently, but his royal highness took care not to tell her she was dressed like his great-grandmother and had a point band peeping over a high collar. She looked not a bit the less charming and beautiful for all that.

They went into the great hall of looking glasses, where they supped, and were served by the princess' officers. The violins and hautboys played old tunes, very excellent, even though it

was now above a hundred years since they had been played. After they had feasted, the whole court assembled in the chapel of the castle where the lord almoner married Beauty to the prince. In due time, the prince carried his bride away to his own kingdom where they lived in great happiness ever after.

CINDERELLA or
THE LITTLE GLASS SLIPPER

Here is the favorite theme of fiction writers of every age—the misunderstood, lowly maiden who finally comes into her own. No wonder folk tales record 345 variants of this story. Popular magazines, soap operas, and moving pictures are still overworking this theme. This French version is probably the first one recorded in European countries and remains the favorite.

Once there was a gentleman who married, for his second wife, the proudest and most haughty woman that was ever seen. She had, by a former husband, two daughters of her own humor, who were, indeed, exactly like her in all things. He had likewise a young daughter but of unparalleled goodness and sweetness of temper, which she took from her mother, who was the best creature in the world.

No sooner were the ceremonies of the wedding over but the mother began to show herself in her true colors. She could not bear the good qualities of this pretty girl, and all the less because they made her own daughters appear the more odious. She employed her in the meanest work of the house: scouring the dishes and tables and scrubbing madam's room, also those of her daughters. The girl slept in a sorry garret, upon a wretched straw bed, while her sisters lay in fine rooms, with floors all inlaid, upon beds of the very newest fashion, and where they had looking glasses so large they might see themselves at full length from head to foot.

The poor girl bore all patiently and dared not

"Cinderella or The Little Glass Slipper." From *The Blue Fairy Book* edited by Andrew Lang. Used by permission of Longmans, Green and Company, Inc.

tell her father who would have rattled her off, for his wife governed him entirely. When she had done her work, she used to go into the chimney corner and sit down among cinders and ashes, which caused her to be called Cinderwench. But the younger, who was not so rude and uncivil as the elder, called her Cinderella. However, Cinderella, notwithstanding her mean apparel, was a hundred times handsomer than her sisters, though they were always dressed very richly.

It happened that the king's son gave a ball and invited all persons of fashion to it. The two sisters were also invited, for they cut a very grand figure among the quality. They were delighted at this invitation and wonderfully busy in choosing such gowns, petticoats and headdresses as might become them. This was a new trouble to Cinderella, for it was she who ironed her sisters' linen and plaited their ruffles, while they talked all day long of nothing but how they should be dressed.

"For my part," said the elder, "I will wear my red-velvet suit with French trimming."

"And I," said the younger, "shall have my usual petticoat. But then, to make amends for that, I will put on my gold-flowered manteau, and my diamond stomacher, which is far from being the most ordinary one in the world."

They sent for the best tirewoman they could get to make up their headdresses and adjust their double pinners, and they had their red brushes and patches from Mademoiselle de la Poche.

Cinderella was likewise consulted in all these matters, for she had excellent notions, and advised them always for the best and offered her services to dress their hair, which they were very willing she should do. As she was doing this, they said to her:

"Cinderella, would you not like to go to the ball?"

"Alas," she said, "you only jeer at me. It is not for such as I to go thither."

"You are in the right of it," replied they. "It would certainly make people laugh to see a cinderwench at a palace ball."

Anyone but Cinderella would have dressed their heads awry, but she was very good and dressed them perfectly. They were almost two days without eating, so much were they transported with joy. They broke above a dozen of laces in trying to be laced up close, that they might have a fine slender shape, and they were continually at their looking glass. At last the happy day came. They went to court, and Cinderella followed them with her eyes as long as she could, and when she had lost sight of them, she fell a-crying.

Her godmother, who saw her all in tears, asked her what was the matter.

"I wish I could—I wish I could—" She was not able to speak the rest, being interrupted by her tears and sobbing.

This godmother of hers, who was a fairy, said to her, "You wish to go to the ball. Is it not so?"

"Yes," cried Cinderella, with a great sigh.

"Well," said her godmother, "be a good girl, and I will contrive that you shall go." Then she said to her, "Run into the garden and bring me a pumpkin."

Cinderella went immediately to gather the finest one and brought it to her godmother, not being able to imagine how this pumpkin could make her go to the ball. Her godmother scooped out all the inside of it, leaving nothing but the rind; which done, she struck it with her wand, and the pumpkin was instantly turned into a fine coach, gilded all over with gold.

She then went to look into her mousetrap, where she found six mice, all alive. She told Cinderella to lift up the little trap door, when, giving each mouse, as it went out, a little tap with her wand, the mouse was at that moment turned into a fine horse. Altogether they made a very fine set of six horses of a beautiful mouse-colored gray.

Being at a loss for a coachman, Cinderella said, "I will go and see if there is a rat in the rat-trap—we may make a coachman of him."

"You are in the right," replied her godmother. "Go and look."

Cinderella brought the trap to her, and in it there were three huge rats. The fairy made choice of the one which had the largest beard, and having touched him with her wand, he was turned into a fat, jolly coachman, who had the smartest whiskers eyes ever beheld. After that, she said to her:

"Go again into the garden, and you will find six lizards behind the watering pot; bring them to me."

Cinderella had no sooner done so than her godmother turned them into six footmen, who skipped up immediately behind the coach, with their liveries all covered with gold and silver. They clung as close behind each other as if they had done nothing else their whole lives. The fairy then said to Cinderella:

"Well, you see here an equipage fit to take you to the ball. Are you not pleased with it?"

"Oh, yes," cried Cinderella, "but must I go thither as I am, in these old rags?"

Her godmother just touched her with her wand, and at the same instant her clothes were turned into cloth of gold and silver, all beset with jewels. This done, she gave her a pair of glass slippers, the prettiest in the whole world. Being thus decked out, Cinderella climbed into her coach, but her godmother, above all things, commanded her not to stay till after midnight, telling her, at the same time, that if she stayed one moment longer, the coach would be a pumpkin again, her horses mice, her coachman a rat, her footmen lizards, and her clothes would become just as they were before.

Cinderella promised her godmother she would not fail to leave the ball before midnight. And then away she drove, scarce able to contain herself for joy. The king's son, who was told that a great princess, whom nobody knew, had come, ran out to receive her. He gave her his hand as she alighted from the coach and led her into the hall, among all the company. There was immediately a profound silence. They left off dancing, and the violins ceased to play, so attentive was everyone to contemplate the singular beauties of the unknown newcomer. Nothing was then heard but the confused noise of:

"Ha! How handsome she is! Ha! How handsome she is!"

The king himself, old as he was, could not help watching her and telling the queen softly that it was a long time since he had seen so beautiful and lovely a creature. All the ladies were busied in considering her clothes and headdress, that they might have some made next day after the same pattern, provided they could meet with such fine materials and find able hands to make them.

The king's son conducted her to the most honorable seat, and afterward took her out to dance with him, and she danced so gracefully that all more and more admired her. A fine collation was served, whereof the young prince ate not a morsel, so intently was he busied in gazing on Cinderella.

She sat down by her sisters, showing them a thousand civilities, giving them part of the oranges and citrons with which the prince had presented her, which very much surprised them, for they did not know her. While Cinderella was thus amusing her sisters, she heard the clock strike eleven and three-quarters, whereupon she immediately made a curtsy to the company and hastened away as fast as she could.

Reaching home, she ran to seek out her godmother and, after having thanked her, said she could not but heartily wish she might go the next day to the ball, because the king's son had asked her. As she was eagerly telling her godmother whatever had passed at the ball, her two sisters knocked at the door, which Cinderella ran and opened.

"How long you have stayed!" cried she, rubbing her eyes and stretching herself as if she had been just waked out of her sleep. She had not, however, had any inclination to sleep since they went from home.

"If you had been at the ball," said one of her sisters, "you would not have been tired with it. There came thither the finest princess, the most beautiful ever seen with mortal eyes; she showed us a thousand civilities and gave us oranges and citrons."

Cinderella seemed very indifferent in the matter but asked them the name of that princess. They told her they did not know it and that the king's son would give all the world to know who she was. At this Cinderella, smiling, replied:

"She must, then, be very beautiful indeed. How happy you have been! Could not I see her? Ah, dear Miss Charlotte, do lend me your yellow clothes which you wear every day."

"Ay, to be sure," cried Miss Charlotte, "lend my clothes to a dirty cinderwench! I should be a fool."

Cinderella, indeed, expected such an answer and was very glad of the refusal, for she would have been sadly put to it if her sister had done what she asked for jestingly.

The next day the two sisters were at the ball,

and so was Cinderella, but dressed more magnificently than before. The king's son was always by her and never ceased his compliments and kind speeches to her. All this was so far from being tiresome that she quite forgot what her godmother had commanded her. At last, she counted the clock striking twelve when she took it to be no more than eleven. She then rose up and fled, as nimble as a deer. The prince followed but could not overtake her. She left behind one of her glass slippers which the prince took up most carefully. Cinderella reached home, quite out of breath, and in her old clothes, having nothing left of all her finery but one of the little slippers, fellow to the one she had dropped.

The guards at the palace gate were asked if they had not seen a princess go out. They seen nobody but a young girl, very meanly dressed, and who had more the air of a poor country wench than a gentlewoman.

When the two sisters returned from the ball Cinderella asked them if they had been well diverted, and if the fine lady had been there. They told her, yes, but that she hurried away immediately when it struck twelve and with so much haste that she dropped one of her little glass slippers, the prettiest in the world. The king's son had taken it up. He had done nothing but look at her all the time at the ball, and most certainly he was very much in love with the beautiful girl who owned the glass slipper.

What they said was very true, for a few days afterward the king's son caused it to be proclaimed, by sound of trumpet, that he would marry her whose foot this slipper fit. They whom he employed began to try it upon the princesses, then the duchesses, and all the court, but in vain. It was brought to the two sisters, who each did all she possibly could to thrust her foot into the slipper. But they could not effect it. Cinderella, who saw all this, and knew her slipper, said to them, laughing:

"Let me see if it will not fit me."

Her sisters burst out laughing and began to banter her. The gentleman who was sent to try the slipper looked earnestly at Cinderella and, finding her very handsome, said it was but just she should try, and that he had orders to let everyone make trial.

He obliged Cinderella to sit down, and putting the slipper to her foot, he found it went on easily and fitted her as if it had been made of wax. The astonishment of her two sisters was great, but still greater when Cinderella pulled out of her pocket the other slipper and put it on her foot. Thereupon, in came her godmother who, having touched Cinderella's clothes with her wand, made them richer and more magnificent than any she had worn before.

And now her two sisters found her to be that fine, beautiful lady they had seen at the ball. They threw themselves at her feet to beg pardon for all the ill-treatment they had made her undergo. Cinderella raised them up and, as she embraced them, cried that she forgave them with all her heart and desired them always to love her.

She was conducted to the young prince. He thought her more charming than ever and, a few days after, married her. Cinderella, who was no less good than beautiful, gave her two sisters lodgings in the palace, and that very same day matched them with two great lords of the court.

THE MASTER CAT

Of all the wise and resourceful fairy animals of the folk tales, Puss in Boots is the cleverest. It will be interesting to compare Gustave Doré's romantic illustration of Puss with a modern artist's interpretation of the Master Cat as a saucy, impudent rascal, shown on page 105.

There was a miller who left no more estate to the three sons he had than his mill, his donkey and his cat. The division was soon made. Neither scrivener nor attorney was sent for; they would soon have eaten up all the poor patrimony. The eldest had the mill, the second the donkey, and the youngest nothing but the cat. The poor young fellow was quite comfortless at having so poor a lot.

"My brothers," said he, "may get their living handsomely enough by joining their stocks together. But for my part, when I have eaten my cat, and made me a muff of his skin, I must die of hunger."

"The Master Cat." From *The Blue Fairy Book* edited by Andrew Lang. Used by permission of Longmans, Green and Company, Inc.

The cat, who heard all this, said to him with a grave and serious air, "Do not thus afflict yourself, my good master. You need only give me a bag, and have a pair of boots made for me that I may scamper through the brambles. You shall see you have not so bad a portion with me as you imagine."

The cat's master had often seen him play a great many cunning tricks to catch rats and mice; he used to hide himself in the meal, and make as if he were dead; so he did not altogether despair. When the cat had what he asked for, he booted himself very gallantly, and putting his bag about his neck he held the strings of it in his two forepaws and went into a warren where was a great abundance of rabbits. He put bran and lettuce into his bag and, stretching out at length as if he were dead, he waited for some young rabbits, not yet acquainted with the deceits of the world, to come and rummage for what he had put into his bag.

Scarce had he lain down but he had what he wanted: a rash and foolish young rabbit jumped into his bag. Monsieur Puss, immediately drawing close the strings, killed him without pity. Proud of his prey, he went with it to the palace, and asked to speak with his majesty. He was shown into the king's apartment and making a low reverence, said to him:

"I have brought you, sir, a rabbit from the warren, which my noble lord, the Master of Carabas"—for that was the title Puss was pleased to give his master—"has commanded me to present to Your Majesty from him."

"Tell your master," said the king, "that I thank him, and that he gives me a great deal of pleasure."

Another time the cat hid himself among some standing corn, holding his bag open. When a brace of partridges ran into it, he drew the strings and so caught them both. He made a present of these to the king as he had the rabbit. The king, in like manner, received the partridges with great pleasure, and ordered some money to be given to him.

The cat continued thus for two or three months to carry to his majesty, from time to time, game of his master's taking. One day in particular, when he knew for certain that the king was to take the air along the riverside with his daughter, the most beautiful princess in the world, he said to his master:

"If you will follow my advice your fortune is made. You have nothing to do but wash yourself in the river, where I shall show you, and leave the rest to me."

The Marquis of Carabas did what the cat advised him to do, without knowing why or wherefore. While he was washing, the king passed by, and the cat began to cry out:

"Help! Help! My Lord Marquis of Carabas is going to be drowned."

At this the king put his head out of the coach window, and finding it was the cat who had so often brought him such good game, he commanded his guards to run immediately to the assistance of his lordship the Marquis of Carabas. While they were drawing him out of the river, the cat came up to the coach and told the king that, while his master was washing, there came by some rogues, who went off with his clothes, though he had cried out, 'Thieves! Thieves!' several times, as loud as he could.

This cunning cat had hidden them under a great stone. The king immediately commanded the officers of his wardrobe to run and fetch one of his best suits for the Marquis of Carabas.

The fine clothes set off his good mien, for he was well made and very handsome in his person.

The king's daughter took a secret inclination to him, and the Marquis of Carabas had no sooner cast two or three respectful and tender glances upon her than she fell in love with him to distraction. The king would needs have him come into the coach and take the air with them. The cat, quite overjoyed to see his project begin to succeed, marched on before, and meeting with some countrymen, who were mowing a meadow, he said to them:

"Good people, you who are mowing, if you do not tell the king that the meadow you mow belongs to my Lord Marquis of Carabas, you shall be chopped as small as herbs for the pot."

The king did not fail to ask the mowers to whom the meadow belonged.

"To my Lord Marquis of Carabas," they answered altogether, for the cat's threat had made them terribly afraid.

"You see, sir," said the marquis, "this is a meadow which never fails to yield a plentiful harvest every year."

The Master Cat, who still went on before, met with some reapers, and said to them, "Good people, you who are reaping, if you do not tell the king that all this corn belongs to the Marquis of Carabas you shall be chopped as small as herbs for the pot."

The king, who passed by a moment after, wished to know to whom all that corn belonged.

"To my Lord Marquis of Carabas," replied the reapers, and the king was very well pleased with it, as well as with the marquis, whom he congratulated thereupon. The Master Cat, who went always before, said the same words to all he met, and the king was astonished at the vast estates of the Marquis of Carabas.

Monsieur Puss came at last to a stately castle, the master of which was an ogre, the richest ever known. All the lands which the king had then gone over belonged to this ogre. The cat, who had taken care to inform himself who this ogre was and what he could do, asked to speak with him, saying he could not pass so near his castle without paying his respects to him.

The ogre received him as civilly as an ogre could and made him sit down.

"I have been assured," said the cat, "that you have the gift of being able to change yourself into any sort of creature. You can, for example,

transform yourself into a lion or elephant and the like."

"That is true," answered the ogre briskly, "and to convince you, you shall see me now become a lion."

Puss was so badly terrified at the sight of a lion so near him that he immediately got into the rain gutter, not without abundance of trouble and danger, because of his boots. They were of no use walking upon the tiles. A little while after, when Puss saw that the ogre had resumed his natural form, he came down and owned he had been very much frightened.

"I have been moreover informed," said the cat, "but I know not how to believe it, that you have also the power to take on the shape of the smallest animal; for example, to change yourself into a rat or a mouse; but I must own to you I take this to be impossible."

"Impossible!" cried the ogre. "You shall see that presently."

At the same time he changed himself into a mouse and began to run about the floor. Puss no sooner perceived this than he fell upon him and ate him up.

Meanwhile the king, who saw, as he passed, this fine castle of the ogre's, had a mind to go into it. Puss, who heard the noise of his majesty's coach running over the drawbridge, ran out, and said to the king:

"Your Majesty is welcome to this castle of my Lord Marquis of Carabas."

"What, my Lord Marquis!" cried the king. "And does this castle also belong to you? There can be nothing finer than this court and all the stately buildings which surround it. Let us go in, if you please."

The marquis gave his hand to the princess and followed the king, who went first. They passed into a spacious hall, where they found a magnificent collation, which the ogre had prepared for his friends, who were that very day to visit him, but dared not enter, knowing the king was there. His majesty was charmed with the good qualities of the Lord Marquis of Carabas, as was his daughter, and seeing the vast estate he possessed, said to him:

"It will be owing to yourself only, my Lord Marquis, if you are not my son-in-law."

The marquis, making several low bows, accepted the honor which his majesty conferred upon him, and forthwith, that very same day, married the princess.

Puss became a great lord, and never ran after mice any more.

BEAUTY AND THE BEAST

This story, like the Norse "East o' the Sun" and the Greek "Cupid and Psyche," has a unique charm of its own. Perhaps its appeal lies in Beauty's compassion for her poor Beast and her ability to see beyond his ugly exterior to his goodness and his pitiableness.

Once upon a time, in a far-off country, there lived a merchant who was enormously rich. As he had six sons and six daughters, however, who were accustomed to having everything they fancied, he did not find he had a penny too much. But misfortunes befell them. One day their house caught fire and speedily burned to the ground, with all the splendid furniture, books, pictures, gold, silver and precious goods it contained. The father suddenly lost every ship he had upon the sea, either by dint of pirates, shipwreck or fire. Then he heard that his clerks in distant countries, whom he had trusted entirely, had proved unfaithful. And at last from great wealth he fell into the direst poverty.

All that he had left was a little house in a desolate place at least a hundred leagues from the town. The daughters at first hoped their friends, who had been so numerous while they were rich, would insist on their staying in their houses, but they soon found they were left alone. Their former friends even attributed their misfortunes to their own extravagance and showed no intention of offering them any help.

So nothing was left for them but to take their departure to the cottage, which stood in the midst of a dark forest. As they were too poor to have any servants, the girls had to work hard, and the sons, for their part, cultivated the fields to earn their living. Roughly clothed, and living in the simplest way, the girls regretted unceasingly the luxuries and amusements of their for-

"Beauty and the Beast." From *The Blue Fairy Book* edited by Andrew Lang. Used by permission of Longmans, Green and Company, Inc.

mer life. Only the youngest daughter tried to be brave and cheerful.

She had been as sad as anyone when misfortune first overtook her father, but soon recovering her natural gaiety, she set to work to make the best of things, to amuse her father and brothers as well as she could, and to persuade her sisters to join her in dancing and singing. But they would do nothing of the sort, and because she was not as doleful as themselves, they declared this miserable life was all she was fit for. But she was really far prettier and cleverer than they were. Indeed, she was so lovely she was always called Beauty.

After two years, their father received news that one of his ships, which he had believed lost, had come safely into port with a rich cargo. All the sons and daughters at once thought that their poverty was at an end and wanted to set out directly for the town; but their father, who was more prudent, begged them to wait a little, and though it was harvest time, and he could ill be spared, determined to go himself to make inquiries.

Only the youngest daughter had any doubt but that they would soon again be as rich as they were before. They all loaded their father with commissions for jewels and dresses which it would have taken a fortune to buy; only Beauty did not ask for anything. Her father, noticing her silence, said:

"And what shall I bring for you, Beauty?"

"The only thing I wish for is to see you come home safely," she answered.

But this reply vexed her sisters, who fancied she was blaming them for having asked for such costly things. Her father, however, was pleased, but as he thought she certainly ought to like pretty presents, he told her to choose something.

"Well, dear Father," she said, "as you insist upon it, I beg that you will bring me a rose. I have not seen one since we came here, and I love them so much."

The merchant set out, only to find that his former companions, believing him to be dead, had divided his cargo between them. After six months of trouble and expense he found himself as poor as when he started on his journey. To make matters worse, he was obliged to return in the most terrible weather. By the time he was within a few leagues of his home he was almost exhausted with cold and fatigue. Though he knew it would take some hours to get through the forest, he resolved to go on. But night overtook him, and the deep snow and bitter frost made it impossible for his horse to carry him any farther. The only shelter he could get was the hollow trunk of a great tree, and there he crouched all the night, which seemed to him the longest he had ever known. The howling of the wolves kept him awake, and when at last day broke the falling snow had covered up every path, and he did not know which way to turn.

At length he made out some sort of path, but it was so rough and slippery that he fell down more than once. Presently it led him into an avenue of trees which ended in a splendid castle. It seemed to the merchant very strange that no snow had fallen in the avenue of orange trees, covered with flowers and fruit. When he reached the first court of the castle he saw before him a flight of agate steps. He went up them and passed through several splendidly furnished rooms.

The pleasant warmth of the air revived him, and he felt very hungry; but there seemed to be nobody in all this vast and splendid palace. Deep silence reigned everywhere, and at last, tired of roaming through empty rooms and galleries, he stopped in a room smaller than the rest, where a clear fire was burning and a couch was drawn up cosily before it. Thinking this must be prepared for someone who was expected, he sat down to wait till he should come and very soon fell into a sweet sleep.

When his extreme hunger wakened him after several hours, he was still alone; but a little table, with a good dinner on it, had been drawn up close to him. He lost no time in beginning his meal, hoping he might soon thank his considerate host, whoever it might be. But no one appeared, and even after another long sleep, from which he awoke completely refreshed, there was no sign of anybody, though a fresh meal of dainty cakes and fruit was prepared upon the little table at his elbow.

Being naturally timid, the silence began to terrify him, and he resolved to search once more through all the rooms; but it was of no use, there was no sign of life in the palace! Then he

went down into the garden, and though it was winter everywhere else, here the sun shone, the birds sang, the flowers bloomed, and the air was soft and sweet. The merchant, in ecstasies with all he saw and heard, said to himself:

"All this must be meant for me. I will go this minute and bring my children to share all these delights."

In spite of being so cold and weary when he reached the castle, he had taken his horse to the stable and fed it. Now he thought he would saddle it for his homeward journey, and he turned down the path which led to the stable. This path had a hedge of roses on each side of it, and the merchant thought he had never seen such exquisite flowers. They reminded him of his promise to Beauty, and he stopped and had just gathered one to take to her when he was startled by a strange noise behind him. Turning round, he saw a frightful Beast, which seemed to be very angry and said in a terrible voice:

"Who told you you might gather my roses? Was it not enough that I sheltered you in my palace and was kind to you? This is the way you show your gratitude, by stealing my flowers! But your insolence shall not go unpunished."

The merchant, terrified by these furious words, dropped the fatal rose, and, throwing himself on his knees, cried, "Pardon me, noble sir. I am truly grateful for your hospitality, which was so magnificent I could not imagine you would be offended by my taking such a little thing as a rose."

But the Beast's anger was not lessened by his speech.

"You are very ready with excuses and flattery," he cried. "But that will not save you from the death you deserve."

Alas, thought the merchant, if my daughter Beauty could only know into what danger her rose has brought me! And in despair he began to tell the Beast all his misfortunes and the reason of his journey, not forgetting to mention Beauty's request.

"A king's ransom would hardly have procured all that my other daughters asked for," he said. "But I thought I might at least take Beauty her rose. I beg you to forgive me, for you see I meant no harm."

The Beast said, in a less furious tone, "I will

forgive you on one condition—that you will give me one of your daughters."

"Ah," cried the merchant, "If I were cruel enough to buy my own life at the expense of one of my children's, what excuse could I invent to bring her here?"

"None," answered the Beast. "If she comes at all she must come willingly. On no other condition will I have her. See if any one of them is courageous enough, and loves you enough, to come and save your life. You seem to be an honest man so I will trust you to go home. I give you a month to see if any of your daughters will come back with you and stay here, to let you go free. If none of them is willing, you must come alone, after bidding them good-bye forever, for then you will belong to me. And do not imagine that you can hide from me, for if you fail to keep your word I will come and fetch you!" added the Beast grimly.

The merchant accepted this proposal. He promised to return at the time appointed, and then, anxious to escape from the presence of the Beast, he asked permission to set off at once. But the Beast answered that he could not go until the next day.

"Then you will find a horse ready for you," he said. "Now go and eat your supper and await my orders."

The poor merchant, more dead than alive, went back to his room, where the most delicious supper was already served on the little table drawn up before a blazing fire. But he was too terrified to eat and only tasted a few of the dishes, for fear the Beast should be angry if he did not obey his orders. When he had finished, the Beast warned him to remember their agreement and to prepare his daughter exactly for what she had to expect.

"Do not get up tomorrow," he added, "until you see the sun and hear a golden bell ring. Then you will find your breakfast waiting for you, and the horse you are to ride will be ready in the courtyard. He will also bring you back again when you come with your daughter a month hence. Farewell. Take a rose to Beauty, and remember your promise!"

The merchant lay down until the sun rose. Then, after breakfast, he went to gather Beauty's rose and mounted his horse, which carried him off so swiftly that in an instant he had lost sight of the palace. He was still wrapped in gloomy thoughts when it stopped before the door of his cottage.

His sons and daughters, who had been uneasy at his long absence, rushed to meet him, eager to know the result of his journey which, seeing him mounted upon a splendid horse and wrapped in a rich mantle, they supposed to be favorable. But he hid the truth from them at first, only saying sadly to Beauty as he gave her the rose:

"Here is what you asked me to bring you. Little you know what it has cost."

Presently he told them his adventures from beginning to end, and then they were all very unhappy. The girls lamented loudly over their lost hopes, and the sons declared their father should not return to the terrible castle. But he reminded them he had promised to go back. Then the girls were very angry with Beauty and said it was all her fault. If she had asked for something sensible this would never have happened.

Poor Beauty, much distressed, said to them, "I have indeed caused this misfortune, but who could have guessed that to ask for a rose in the middle of summer would cause so much misery? But as I did the mischief it is only just that I should suffer for it. I will therefore go back with my father to keep his promise."

At first nobody would hear of it. Her father and brothers, who loved her dearly, declared nothing should make them let her go. But Beauty was firm. As the time drew near she divided her little possessions between her sisters, and said good-bye to everything she loved. When the fatal day came she encouraged and cheered her father as they mounted together the horse which had brought him back. It seemed to fly rather than gallop but so smoothly that Beauty was not frightened. Indeed, she would have enjoyed the journey if she had not feared what might happen at the end of it. Her father still tried to persuade her to go back, but in vain.

While they were talking the night fell. Then, to their great surprise, wonderful colored lights began to shine in all directions, and splendid fireworks blazed out before them; all the forest was illuminated. They even felt pleasantly warm,

though it had been bitterly cold before. They reached the avenue of orange trees and saw that the palace was brilliantly lighted from roof to ground, and music sounded softly from the courtyard.

"The Beast must be very hungry," said Beauty, trying to laugh, "if he makes all this rejoicing over the arrival of his prey." But, in spite of her anxiety, she admired all the wonderful things she saw.

When they had dismounted, her father led her to the little room. Here they found a splendid fire burning, and the table daintily spread with a delicious supper.

Beauty, who was less frightened now that she had passed through so many rooms and seen nothing of the Beast, was quite willing to begin, for her long ride had made her very hungry. But they had hardly finished their meal when the noise of the Beast's footsteps was heard approaching, and Beauty clung to her father in terror, which became all the greater when she saw how frightened he was. But when the Beast really appeared, though she trembled at the sight of him, she made a great effort to hide her horror, and saluted him respectfully.

This evidently pleased the Beast. After looking at her he said, in a tone that might have struck terror into the boldest heart, though he did not seem to be angry:

"Good evening, old man. Good evening, Beauty."

The merchant was too terrified to reply, but Beauty answered sweetly, "Good evening, Beast."

"Have you come willingly?" asked the Beast. "Will you be content to stay here when your father goes away?"

Beauty answered bravely that she was quite prepared to stay.

"I am pleased with you," said the Beast. "As you have come of your own accord, you may remain. As for you, old man," he added, turning to the merchant, "at sunrise tomorrow take your departure. When the bell rings, get up quickly and eat your breakfast, and you will find the same horse waiting to take you home."

Then turning to Beauty, he said, "Take your father into the next room, and help him choose gifts for your brothers and sisters. You will find two traveling trunks there; fill them as full as you can. It is only just that you should send them something very precious as a remembrance."

Then he went away, after saying, "Good-bye, Beauty; good-bye, old man." Beauty was beginning to think with great dismay of her father's departure, but they went into the next room, which had shelves and cupboards all around it. They were greatly surprised at the riches it contained. There were splendid dresses fit for a queen, with all the ornaments to be worn with them, and when Beauty opened the cupboards she was dazzled by the gorgeous jewels lying in heaps upon every shelf. After choosing a vast quantity, which she divided between her sisters —for she had made a heap of the wonderful dresses for each of them—she opened the last chest, which was full of gold.

"I think, Father," she said, "that, as the gold will be more useful to you, we had better take out the other things again, and fill the trunks with it."

So they did this, but the more they put in, the more room there seemed to be, and at last they put back all the jewels and dresses they had taken out, and Beauty even added as many more of the jewels as she could carry at once. Even then the trunks were not too full, but they were so heavy an elephant could not have carried them!

"The Beast was mocking us!" cried the merchant. "He pretended to give us all these things, knowing that I could not carry them away."

"Let us wait and see," answered Beauty. "I cannot believe he meant to deceive us. All we can do is to fasten them up and have them ready."

So they did this and returned to the little room where they found breakfast ready. The merchant ate his with a good appetite, as the Beast's generosity made him believe he might perhaps venture to come back soon and see Beauty. But she felt sure her father was leaving her forever, so she was very sad when the bell rang sharply.

They went down into the courtyard, where two horses were waiting, one loaded with the two trunks, the other for him to ride. They were pawing the ground in their impatience to start, and the merchant bade Beauty a hasty farewell. As soon as he was mounted he went off at such

a pace she lost sight of him in an instant. Then Beauty began to cry and wandered sadly back to her own room. But she soon found she was very sleepy, and as she had nothing better to do she lay down and instantly fell asleep. And then she dreamed she was walking by a brook bordered with trees, and lamenting her sad fate, when a young prince, handsomer than anyone she had ever seen, and with a voice that went straight to her heart, came and said to her:

"Ah, Beauty, you are not so unfortunate as you suppose. Here you will be rewarded for all you have suffered elsewhere. Your every wish shall be gratified. Only try to find me out, no matter how I may be disguised, for I love you dearly, and in making me happy you will find your own happiness. Be as true-hearted as you are beautiful, and we shall have nothing left to wish for."

"What can I do, Prince, to make you happy?" said Beauty.

"Only be grateful," he answered, "and do not trust too much to your eyes. Above all, do not desert me until you have saved me from my cruel misery."

After this she thought she found herself in a room with a stately and beautiful lady, who said to her, "Dear Beauty, try not to regret all you have left behind you; you are destined for a better fate. Only do not let yourself be deceived by appearances."

Beauty found her dreams so interesting that she was in no hurry to awake, but presently the clock roused her by calling her name softly twelve times. Then she arose and found her dressing-table set out with everything she could possibly want, and when her toilet was finished, she found dinner waiting in the room next to hers. But dinner does not take very long when one is alone, and very soon she sat down cosily in the corner of a sofa, and began to think about the charming prince she had seen in her dream.

"He said I could make him happy," said Beauty to herself. "It seems, then, that this horrible Beast keeps him a prisoner. How can I set him free? I wonder why they both told me not to trust to appearances? But, after all, it was only a dream, so why should I trouble myself about it? I had better find something to do to amuse myself."

So she began to explore some of the many rooms of the palace. The first she entered was lined with mirrors. Beauty saw herself reflected on every side and thought she had never seen such a charming room. Then a bracelet which was hanging from a chandelier caught her eye, and on taking it down she was greatly surprised to find that it held a portrait of her unknown admirer, just as she had seen him in her dream. With great delight she slipped the bracelet on her arm and went on into a gallery of pictures, where she soon found a portrait of the same handsome prince, as large as life, and so well painted that as she studied it he seemed to smile kindly at her.

Tearing herself away from the portrait at last, she passed into a room which contained every musical instrument under the sun, and here she amused herself for a long while in trying them and singing. The next room was a library, and she saw everything she had ever wanted to read as well as everything she had read. By this time it was growing dusk, and wax candles in diamond and ruby candlesticks lit themselves in every room.

Beauty found her supper served just at the time she preferred to have it, but she did not see anyone or hear a sound, and though her father had warned her she would be alone, she began to find it rather dull.

Presently she heard the Beast coming and wondered tremblingly if he meant to eat her now. However, he did not seem at all ferocious, and only said gruffly:

"Good evening, Beauty."

She answered cheerfully and managed to conceal her terror. The Beast asked how she had been amusing herself, and she told him all the rooms she had seen. Then he asked if she thought she could be happy in his palace; and Beauty answered that everything was so beautiful she would be very hard to please if she could not be happy. After about an hour's talk Beauty began to think the Beast was not nearly so terrible as she had supposed at first. Then he rose to leave her, and said in his gruff voice:

"Do you love me, Beauty? Will you marry me?"

"Oh, what shall I say?" cried Beauty, for she was afraid to make the Beast angry by refusing.

"Say yes or no without fear," he replied.

"Oh, no, Beast," said Beauty hastily.

"Since you will not, good night, Beauty," he said.

And she answered, "Good night, Beast," very glad to find her refusal had not provoked him. After he was gone she was very soon in bed and dreaming of her unknown prince.

She thought he came and said, "Ah, Beauty! Why are you so unkind to me? I fear I am fated to be unhappy for many a long day still."

Then her dreams changed, but the charming prince figured in them all. When morning came her first thought was to look at the portrait and see if it was really like him, and she found it certainly was.

She decided to amuse herself in the garden, for the sun shone, and all the fountains were playing. She was astonished to find that every place was familiar to her, and presently she came to the very brook and the myrtle trees where she had first met the prince in her dream. That made her think more than ever he must be kept a prisoner by the Beast.

When she was tired she went back to the palace and found a new room full of materials for every kind of work—ribbons to make into bows and silks to work into flowers. There was an aviary full of rare birds, which were so tame they flew to Beauty as soon as they saw her and perched upon her shoulders and her head.

"Pretty little creatures," she said, "how I wish your cage was nearer my room that I might often hear you sing!" So saying she opened a door and found to her delight that it led into her own room, though she had thought it was on the other side of the palace.

There were more birds in a room farther on, parrots and cockatoos that could talk, and they greeted Beauty by name. Indeed, she found them so entertaining that she took one or two back to her room, and they talked to her while she was at supper. The Beast paid her his usual visit and asked the same questions as before, and then with a gruff good night he took his departure, and Beauty went to bed to dream of her mysterious prince.

The days passed swiftly in different amusements, and after a while Beauty found another strange thing in the palace, which often pleased her when she was tired of being alone. There was one room which she had not noticed particularly; it was empty, except that under each of the windows stood a very comfortable chair. The first time she had looked out of the window it seemed a black curtain prevented her from seeing anything outside. But the second time she went into the room, happening to be tired, she sat down in one of the chairs, when instantly the curtain was rolled aside, and a most amusing pantomime was acted before her. There were dances and colored lights, music and pretty dresses, and it was all so gay that Beauty was in ecstasies. After that she tried the other seven windows in turn, and there was some new and surprising entertainment to be seen from each of them so Beauty never could feel lonely any more. Every evening after supper the Beast came to see her, and always before saying good night asked her in his terrible voice:

"Beauty, will you marry me?"

And it seemed to Beauty, now she understood him better, that when she said, "No, Beast," he went away quite sad. Her happy dreams of the handsome young prince soon made her forget the poor Beast, and the only thing that disturbed her was being told to distrust appearances, to let her heart guide her, and not her eyes. Consider as she would, she could not understand.

So everything went on for a long time, until at last, happy as she was, Beauty began to long for the sight of her father and her brothers and sisters. One night, seeing her look very sad, the Beast asked her what was the matter. Beauty had quite ceased to be afraid of him. Now she knew he was really gentle in spite of his ferocious looks and his dreadful voice. So she answered that she wished to see her home once more. Upon hearing this the Beast seemed sadly distressed, and cried miserably:

"Ah, Beauty, have you the heart to desert an unhappy Beast like this? What more do you want to make you happy? Is it because you hate me that you want to escape?"

"No, dear Beast," answered Beauty softly, "I do not hate you, and I should be very sorry never to see you any more, but I long to see my father again. Only let me go for two months, and I promise to come back to you and stay for the rest of my life."

The Beast, who had been sighing dolefully while she spoke, now replied, "I cannot refuse you anything you ask, even though it should cost me my life. Take the four boxes you will find in the room next to your own and fill them with everything you wish to take with you. But remember your promise and come back when the two months are over, for if you do not come in good time you will find your faithful Beast dead. You will not need any chariot to bring you back. Only say good-bye to all your brothers and sisters the night before you come away and, when you have gone to bed, turn this ring round upon your finger, and say firmly, 'I wish to go back to my palace and see my Beast again.' Good night, Beauty. Fear nothing, sleep peacefully, and before long you shall see your father once more."

As soon as Beauty was alone she hastened to fill the boxes with all the rare and precious things she saw about her, and only when she was tired of heaping things into them did they seem to be full. Then she went to bed, but could hardly sleep, for joy. When at last she began to dream of her beloved prince she was grieved to see him stretched upon a grassy bank, sad and weary, and hardly like himself.

"What is the matter?" she cried.

But he looked at her reproachfully, and said, "How can you ask me, cruel one? Are you not leaving me to my death perhaps?"

"Ah, don't be so sorrowful!" cried Beauty. "I am only going to assure my father that I am safe and happy. I have promised the Beast faithfully I will come back, and he would die of grief if I did not keep my word!"

"What would that matter to you?" asked the prince. "Surely you would not care?"

"Indeed I should be ungrateful if I did not care for such a kind Beast," cried Beauty indignantly. "I would die to save him from pain. I assure you it is not his fault he is so ugly."

Just then a strange sound woke her—someone was speaking not very far away; and opening her eyes she found herself in a room she had never seen before, which was certainly not as splendid as those she had seen in the Beast's palace. Where could she be? She rose and dressed hastily and then saw that the boxes she had packed the night before were all in the room. Suddenly she heard her father's voice and rushed out to greet him joyfully. Her brothers and sisters were astonished at her appearance, for they had never expected to see her again. Beauty asked her father what he thought her strange dreams meant and why the prince constantly begged her not to trust to appearances. After much consideration he answered:

"You tell me yourself that the Beast, frightful as he is, loves you dearly and deserves your love and gratitude for his gentleness and kindness. I think the prince must mean you to understand you ought to reward him by doing as he wishes, in spite of his ugliness."

Beauty could not help seeing that this seemed probable; still when she thought of her dear prince who was so handsome, she did not feel at all inclined to marry the Beast. At any rate, for two months she need not decide but could enjoy herself with her sisters. Though they were rich now, and lived in a town again and had plenty of acquaintances, Beauty found that nothing amused her very much. She often thought of the palace, where she was so happy, especially as at home she never once dreamed of her dear prince, and she felt quite sad without him.

Then her sisters seemed quite used to being without her, and even found her rather in the way, so she would not have been sorry when the two months were over but for her father and brothers. She had not the courage to say good-bye to them. Every day when she rose she meant to say it at night, and when night came she put it off again, until at last she had a dismal dream which helped her to make up her mind.

She thought she was wandering in a lonely path in the palace gardens, when she heard groans. Running quickly to see what could be the matter, she found the Beast stretched out upon his side, apparently dying. He reproached her faintly with being the cause of his distress, and at the same moment a stately lady appeared, and said very gravely:

"Ah, Beauty, see what happens when people do not keep their promises! If you had delayed one day more, you would have found him dead."

Beauty was so terrified by this dream that the very next evening she said good-bye to her father and her brothers and sisters, and as soon as she was in bed she turned her ring round upon her finger, and said firmly:

"I wish to go back to my palace and see my Beast again."

Then she fell asleep instantly, and only woke up to hear the clock saying, "Beauty, Beauty," twelve times in its musical voice, which told her she was really in the palace once more. Everything was just as before, and her birds were so glad to see her, but Beauty thought she had never known such a long day. She was so anxious to see the Beast again that she felt as if suppertime would never come.

But when it came no Beast appeared. After listening and waiting for a long time, she ran down into the garden to search for him. Up and down the paths and avenues ran poor Beauty, calling him. No one answered, and not a trace of him could she find. At last, she saw that she was standing opposite the shady path she had seen in her dream. She rushed down it, and sure enough, there was the cave, and in it lay the Beast—asleep, so Beauty thought. Quite glad to have found him, she ran up and stroked his head, but to her horror he did not move or open his eyes.

"Oh, he is dead, and it is all my fault!" cried Beauty, crying bitterly.

But then, looking at him again, she fancied he still breathed. Hastily fetching some water from the nearest fountain, she sprinkled it over his face, and to her great delight he began to revive.

"Oh, Beast, how you frightened me!" she cried. "I never knew how much I loved you until just now, when I feared I was too late to save your life."

"Can you really love such an ugly creature as I am?" asked the Beast faintly. "Ah, Beauty, you came only just in time. I was dying because I thought you had forgotten your promise. But go back now and rest, I shall see you again by-and-by."

Beauty, who had half expected he would be angry with her, was reassured by his gentle voice and went back to the palace, where supper was awaiting her.

And afterward the Beast came in as usual and talked about the time she had spent with her father, asking if she had enjoyed herself and if they had all been glad to see her.

Beauty quite enjoyed telling him all that had happened to her. When at last the time came for him to go, he asked, as he had so often asked before:

"Beauty, will you marry me?"

She answered softly, "Yes, dear Beast."

As she spoke a blaze of light sprang up before the windows of the palace; fireworks crackled and guns banged, and across the avenue of orange trees, in letters all made of fireflies, was written: *Long live the prince and his bride.*

Turning to ask the Beast what it could all mean, Beauty found he had disappeared, and in its place stood her long-loved prince! At the same moment the wheels of a chariot were heard upon the terrace, and two ladies entered the room. One of them Beauty recognized as the stately lady she had seen in her dreams; the other was so queenly that Beauty hardly knew which to greet first. But the one she already knew said to her companion:

"Well, Queen, this is Beauty, who has had the courage to rescue your son from the terrible enchantment. They love each other, and only your consent to their marriage is wanting to make them perfectly happy."

"I consent with all my heart," cried the queen. "How can I ever thank you enough, charming girl, for having restored my dear son to his natural form?" And then she tenderly embraced Beauty and the prince, who had meanwhile been greeting the fairy and receiving her congratulations.

"Now," said the fairy to Beauty, "I suppose you would like me to send for all your brothers and sisters to dance at your wedding?"

And so she did, and the marriage was celebrated the very next day with the utmost splendor, and Beauty and the prince lived happily ever after.

THE WHITE CAT

Once upon a time there was a King who had three sons. The day came when they were grown so big and strong that he began to fear they would be planning to rule in his place. This would cause trouble among themselves and his

"The White Cat." From *The White Cat and Other French Fairy Tales* by Comtesse d'Aulnoy, arranged by Rachel Field. Copyright, 1928, by The Macmillan Company and used with their permission

subjects. Now the King was not so young as he once had been but nevertheless he had no notion of giving up his kingdom then and there. So after much thought he hit upon a scheme which should keep them too busily occupied to interfere in the affairs of state. Accordingly he called the three into his private apartments where he spoke to them with great kindliness and concern of his plans for the future.

"I am planning to retire from the affairs of state. But I do not wish my subjects to suffer from this change. Therefore, while I am still alive, I shall transfer my crown to one of you. I shall not follow the usual custom of leaving the crown to my eldest son, but whichever one of you shall bring me the handsomest and most intelligent little dog shall become my heir."

The Princes were greatly surprised by this strange request, but they could not very well refuse to humor their father's whim; and since there was luck in it for the two younger sons and the elder of the three was a timid, rather spiritless fellow, they agreed readily enough. The King then bade them farewell after first distributing jewels and money among them and adding that a year from that day at the same place and hour they should return to him with their little dogs.

Within sight of the city gates stood a castle where the three often spent many days in company with their young companions. Here they agreed to part and to meet again in a year before proceeding with their trophies to the King; and so having pledged their good faith, and changing their names that they might not be known, each set off upon a different road.

It would take far too long to recount the adventures of all three Princes so I shall tell only of those that befell the youngest, for a more gay and well-mannered Prince never lived, nor one so handsome and accomplished.

Scarcely a day passed that he did not buy a dog or two, greyhounds, mastiffs, bloodhounds, pointers, spaniels, water dogs, lapdogs; but the instant he found a handsomer one he let the first go and kept the new purchase, since it would have been impossible for him to carry them all on his journeyings. He went without fixed plan or purpose and so he continued for many days until at last darkness and a terrible storm overtook him at nightfall in a lonely forest. Thunder and lightning rumbled and flashed; rain fell in torrents; the trees seemed to close more densely about him until at last he could no longer find his way. When he had wandered thus for some time he suddenly saw a glint of light between the tree trunks. Feeling certain that this must mean a shelter of some sort he pressed on till he found himself approaching the most magnificent castle he had ever seen. The gate was of gold and covered with jewels of such brilliance that it was their light which had guided him to the spot. In spite of the rain and storm he caught glimpses of walls of finest porcelain decorated with pictures of the most famous fairies from the beginning of the world up to that very day: Cinderella, Graciosa, Sleeping Beauty, and a hundred others. As he admired all this magnificence he noticed a rabbit's foot fastened to the golden gates by a chain of diamonds. Marveling greatly at such a lavish display of precious gems, the young Prince pulled at the rabbit's foot and straightway an unseen bell of wonderful sweetness rang; the gate was opened by hundreds of tiny hands and others pushed him forward while he hesitated amazed upon the threshold. He moved on wonderingly, his hand on the hilt of his sword until he was reassured by two voices singing a welcome. Again he felt himself being pushed, this time toward a gate of coral opening upon an apartment of mother-of-pearl from which he passed into others still more richly decorated and alight with wax candles and great chandeliers sparkling with a thousand rainbows.

He had passed through perhaps sixty such rooms when the hands that guided him made a sign for him to stop. He saw a large armchair moving by itself toward a fireplace at the same moment that the fire began to blaze and the hands, which he now observed to be very small and white, carefully drew off his wet clothes and handed him others so fine and richly embroidered they seemed fit for a wedding day. The hands continued to dress him, until at last, powdered and attired more handsomely than he had ever been in his life before, the Prince was led into a banquet hall. Here the four walls were decorated solely with paintings representing famous cats, Puss-in-Boots and others whom he

was quick to recognize. Even more astonishing than this was the table set for two with its gold service and crystal cups.

There was an orchestra composed entirely of cats. One held a music book with the strangest notes imaginable; another beat time with a little baton; and all the rest strummed tiny guitars.

While the Prince stared in amazement, each cat suddenly began to mew in a different key and to claw at the guitar strings. It was the strangest music ever heard! The Prince would have thought himself in bedlam had not the palace itself been so marvelously beautiful. So he stopped his ears and laughed heartily at the various poses and grimaces of these strange musicians. He was meditating upon the extraordinary sights he had already seen in the castle, when he beheld a little figure entering the hall. It was scarcely more than two feet in height and wrapped in a long gold crêpe veil. Before it walked two cats dressed in deep mourning and wearing cloaks and swords, while still others followed, some carrying rat-traps full of rats and mice in cages.

By this time the Prince was too astonished to think. But presently the tiny pink figure approached him and lifted its veil. He now beheld the most beautiful little white cat that ever was or ever will be. She had such a very youthful and melancholy air and a mewing so soft and sweet that it went straight to the young Prince's heart.

"Son of a King," she said to him, "thou art welcome; my mewing Majesty beholds thee with pleasure."

"Madam," responded the Prince, bowing as low as possible before her, "it is very gracious of you to receive me with so much attention, but you do not appear to me to be an ordinary little cat. The gift of speech which you have and this superb castle you inhabit are certainly evidence to the contrary."

"Son of a King," rejoined the White Cat, "I pray that you will cease to pay me compliments. I am plain in my speech and manners, but I have a kind heart. Come," she added, to her attendants, "let them serve supper and bid the concert cease, for the Prince does not understand what they are singing."

"And are they singing words, madam?" he asked incredulously.

"Certainly," she answered, "we have very gifted poets here, as you will see if you remain long enough."

Supper was then served to them by the same hands that had guided him there, and a very strange meal it was. There were two dishes of each course—one soup, for instance, being of savory pigeons while the other had been made of nicely fattened mice. The sight of this rather took away the Prince's appetite until his hostess, who seemed to guess what was passing in his mind, assured him that his own dishes had been specially prepared and contained no rats and mice of any kind. Her charming manners convinced the Prince that the little Cat had no wish to deceive him, so he began to eat and drink with great enjoyment. During their meal he happened to observe that on one paw she wore a tiny miniature set in a bracelet. This surprised him so that he begged her to let him examine it more closely. He had supposed it would be the picture of Master Puss, but what was his astonishment to find it the portrait of a handsome young man who bore a strange resemblance to himself! As he stared at it, the White Cat was heard to sigh so deeply and with such profound sadness that the Prince became even more curious; but he dared not question one so affected. Instead he entertained her with tales of court life, with which, to his surprise, he found her well acquainted.

After supper the White Cat led her guest into another Hall, where upon a little stage twelve cats and twelve monkeys danced in the most fantastic costumes. So the evening ended in great merriment; and after the Cat had bade the Prince a gracious good night the same strange hands conducted him to his own apartment, where in spite of the softness of his bed he spent half the night trying to solve the mystery of the castle and his extraordinary little hostess.

But when morning came he was no nearer to an answer to his questionings, so he allowed the pair of hands to help him dress and lead him into the palace courtyard. Here a vast company of cats in hunting costume were gathering to the sound of the horn. A fête day indeed! The White Cat was going to hunt and wished the Prince to accompany her. Now the mysterious hands presented him with a wooden horse. He made some objection to mounting it, but it proved to be an excellent charger, and a tireless galloper. The White Cat rode beside him on a monkey, the handsomest and proudest that ever was seen. She had thrown off her long veil and wore a military cap which made her look so bold that she frightened all the mice in the neighborhood. Never was there a more successful hunt. The cats outran all the rabbits and hares and a thousand skillful feats were performed to the gratification of the entire company. Tiring of the hunt at last the White Cat took up a horn no bigger than the Prince's little finger and blew upon it with so loud and clear a tone it could be heard ten leagues away. Scarcely had she sounded two or three flourishes when all the cats in the countryside seemed to appear. By land and sea and through the air they all came flocking to her call, dressed in every conceivable costume. So, followed by this extraordinary train, the Prince rode back with his hostess to the castle.

That night the White Cat put on her gold veil again and they dined together as before. Being very hungry the Prince ate and drank heartily, and this time the food had a strange effect upon him. All recollection of his father and the little dog he was to find for him slipped from his mind. He no longer thought of anything but of gossiping with the White Cat and enjoying her kind and gracious companionship. So the days passed in pleasant sport and amusement and the night in feasting and conversation. There was scarcely one in which he did not discover some new charm of the little White Cat. Now he had forgotten even the land of his birth. The hands continued to wait upon him and supply every want till he began to regret that he could not become a cat himself to live forever in such pleasant company.

"Alas," he confessed to the White Cat at last, "how wretched it makes me even to think of leaving you! I have come to love you so dearly. Could you not become a woman or else make me a cat?"

But though she smiled at his wish, the look she turned upon him was very strange.

A year passes away quickly when one has neither pain nor care, when one is merry and in good health. The Prince took no thought of time, but the White Cat was not so forgetful.

"There are only three days left to look for the little dog you were to bring to the King, your father," she reminded him. "Your two brothers have already found several very beautiful ones."

At her words the Prince's memory returned to him and he marveled at his strange forgetfulness.

"What spell would have made me forget what was most important to me in the whole world?" he cried in despair. "My honor and my fortune are lost unless I can find a dog that will win a kingdom for me and a horse swift enough to carry me home again in this short time!"

So, believing this to be impossible, he grew very sorrowful. Then the White Cat spoke to him with great reassurance.

"Son of a King," she said, "do not distress yourself so. I am your friend. Remain here another day, and though it is five hundred leagues from here to your country the good wooden horse will carry you there in less than twelve hours' time."

"But it is not enough for me to return to my father, dear Cat," said the Prince. "I must take him a little dog as well."

"And so you shall," replied she. "Here is a walnut which contains one more beautiful than the Dog Star."

"Your Majesty jests with me," he protested.

"Put the walnut to your ear then," insisted the Cat, "and you will hear it bark."

He obeyed her, and as he held the walnut to his ear a faint "Bow-wow" came from within, more tiny and shrill than a cricket on a winter night. The Prince could scarcely believe his ears or contain his curiosity to see so diminutive a creature. But he was wise enough to follow the White Cat's advice not to open the walnut till he should reach his father's presence.

It was a sad leave-taking between the Prince and the White Cat. A thousand times he thanked her, but though he urged her to return to court with him, she only shook her head and sighed deeply as upon the night of his arrival. So he galloped away at last on the wooden horse, which bore him more swiftly than the wind to the appointed place.

He reached the castle even before his two brothers and enjoyed the sight of their surprise at seeing a wooden horse champing at the bit in the courtyard. The two brothers were so busy telling of their various adventures that they took little note of their younger brother's silence concerning his, but when the time came to show one another their dogs the two were vastly amused at sight of an ugly cur which the young Prince had brought along, pretending to consider it a marvel of beauty. Needless to say the elder Princes smiled with secret satisfaction to think how far superior were their own dogs, for though they wished their brother no ill luck, they had no wish to see him ruling over the kingdom.

Next morning the three set out together in the same coach. The two eldest brothers carried baskets filled with little dogs too delicate and beautiful to be touched, while the youngest carried the poor cur as if it also was precious. By no outward sign did he betray the presence of the walnut with its precious occupant which was safely hidden in his pocket. No sooner did the three set foot in the palace than all the court crowded around to welcome the returned travelers and see the results of their journeyings. The King received them with great joy, professing delight over the little dogs his two elder sons brought out for his inspection. But the more he studied their merits, the more puzzled he became, so nearly were they alike in beauty and grace. The two brothers were already beginning to dispute with one another as to which deserved the crown when the younger brother stepped forward, holding upon the palm of his hand the walnut so lately presented to him by the White Cat. Opening it without more ado, he revealed a tiny dog lying upon cotton. So perfectly formed was it and so small that it could pass through a little finger ring without touching any part of it. It was more delicate than thistledown and its coat shone with colors of the rainbow. Nor was this all; immediately it was released from its kennel, the little creature arose on its hind legs and began to go through the steps of a tarantella, with tiny castanets and all the airs and graces of a Spanish dancer!

The King was dumbfounded and even the two brothers were forced to acknowledge that such a beautiful and gifted dog had never been seen before. But their father was in no mood to give up his kingdom, so he announced that he had decided upon another test of their skill. This time he would give them a year to travel over land and sea in search of a piece of cloth so fine it would pass through the eye of the finest Venetian-point lace needle.

So the Prince remounted his wooden horse and set off at full speed, for now he knew exactly where he wanted to go. So great was his eagerness to see the beautiful White Cat once more that he could scarcely contain himself until her castle came into view. This time every window was alight to welcome him and the faithful pair of hands which had waited on him so well before were ready to take the bridle of the wooden horse and lead it back to the stable while the Prince hurried to the White Cat's private apartments.

He found her lying on a little couch of blue satin with many pillows. Her expression was sad until she caught sight of him. Then she sprang up and began to caper about him delightedly.

"Oh, dear Prince," cried she, "I had scarcely dared to hope for your return. I am generally so unfortunate in matters that concern me."

A thousand times must the grateful Prince caress her and recount his adventures, which perhaps she knew more about than he guessed. And now he told her of his father's latest whim—how he had set his heart upon having a piece of cloth that could pass through the eye of the finest needle. For his own part he did not believe it was possible to find such a thing, but he believed that if any one could help him in this quest it would be his dear White Cat. She listened attentively to all he told her and finally explained with a thoughtful air that this was a matter demanding careful consideration. There were, it seemed, some cats in her castle who could spin with extraordinary skill, and she added that she would also put a paw to the work herself so that he need not trouble himself to search farther.

The Prince was only too delighted to accept this offer and he and his charming hostess sat down to supper together, after which a magnificent display of fireworks was set off in his honor. And once more the days passed in enchanted succession. The ingenious White Cat knew a thousand different ways of entertaining her guest, so that he never once thought of missing human society. Indeed, he was probably the first

person in the world to spend a whole year of complete contentment with only cats for company.

The second year slipped away as pleasantly as the first. The Prince could scarcely think of anything that the tireless hands did not instantly supply, whether books, jewels, pictures, old things or new. In short, he had but to say, "I want a certain gem that is in the cabinet of the Great Mogul, or the King of Persia, or such and such a statue in Corinth or any part of Greece," and he saw it instantly before him, without knowing how it came or who brought it. It is not unpleasant at all to find oneself able to possess any treasure in the world. No wonder our Prince was happy!

But the White Cat who was ever watchful of his welfare, warned him that the hour of departure was approaching and that he might make himself easy in his mind about the piece of cloth, for she had a most wonderful one for him. She added that it was her intention this time to furnish him with an equipage worthy of his high birth, and without waiting for his reply, beckoned him to the window overlooking the castle courtyard. Here he saw an open coach of gold and flame-color with a thousand gallant devices to please the mind and eye. It was drawn by twelve horses as white as snow, four-and-four abreast, with harnesses of flaming velvet embroidered with diamonds and gold. A hundred other coaches, each with eight horses and filled with superbly attired noblemen followed, escorted by a thousand bodyguards whose uniforms were so richly embroidered you could not see the material beneath. But the most remarkable part of this cavalcade was that a portrait of the White Cat was to be seen everywhere, in coach device, uniform, or worn as a decoration on the doublets of those who rode in the train, as if it were some newly created order that had been conferred upon them.

"Go now," said the White Cat to the Prince. "Appear at the court of the King, your father, in such magnificence that he cannot fail to be impressed and to bestow upon you the crown which you deserve. Here is another walnut. Crack it in his presence and you will find the piece of cloth you asked of me."

"Oh, dear White Cat," he answered tenderly,

"I am so overcome by your goodness that I would gladly give up my hopes of power and future grandeur to stay here with you the rest of life."

"Son of a King," she answered, "I am convinced of your kindness of heart. A kind heart is a rare thing among princes who would be loved by all, yet not love any one themselves. But you are the proof that there is an exception to this rule. I give you credit for the affection you have shown to a little white cat that after all is good for nothing but to catch mice."

So the Prince kissed her paw and departed.

This time the two brothers arrived at their father's palace before him, congratulating themselves that their young brother must be dead or gone for good. They lost no time in displaying the cloths they had brought, which were indeed so fine that they could pass through the eye of a large needle but not through the small eye of the needle the King had already selected. At this there arose a great murmuring at court. The friends of the two Princes took sides among themselves as to which had fulfilled the bargain better. But this was interrupted by a flourish of trumpets announcing the arrival of their younger brother.

The magnificence of his train fairly took away the breath of the King and his court, but their astonishment grew even greater when, after saluting his father, the young Prince brought out the walnut. This he cracked with great ceremony only to find, instead of the promised piece of cloth, a cherry stone. At sight of this the King and the court exchanged sly smiles. Nothing daunted, the Prince cracked the cherry stone, only to find a kernel inside. Jeers and murmurs ran through the great apartment. The Prince must be a fool indeed! He made no answer to them, but even he began to doubt the White Cat's words as he found next a grain of wheat and within that the smallest millet seed. "Oh, White Cat, White Cat! Have you betrayed me?" he muttered between his teeth. Even as he spoke he felt a little scratch upon his hand, so sharp that it drew blood. Taking this to be some sort of sign, the Prince proceeded to open the millet seed. Before the incredulous eyes of the whole court he drew out of it a piece of cloth four hundred yards long and marvelously embroidered with colored birds and beasts, with trees and fruits and flowers, with shells and jewels and even with suns and moons and countless stars. There were also portraits of Kings and Queens of the past upon it and of their children and children's children, not forgetting the smallest child, and each dressed perfectly in the habit of his century.

The sight of this was almost too much for the King. He could scarcely find the needle. Through its eye the wonderful piece of cloth was able to pass not only once, but six times, before the jealous gaze of the two older Princes. But the King was still far from ready to give up his kingdom. Once more he turned to his children.

"I am going to put your obedience to a new and final test," he told them. "Go and travel for another year and whichever one of you brings back with him the most beautiful Princess shall marry her and be crowned King on his wedding day. I pledge my honor that after this I shall ask no further favors of you."

So off the three went again, the youngest Prince still in a good humor although he had the least cause to be since he had twice been the acknowledged winner of the wager. But he was not one to dispute his father's will, so soon he and all his train were taking the road back to his dear White Cat. She knew the very day and hour of his arrival, and all along the way flowers had been strewn and perfume made the air sweet. Once more the castle gate was opened to him and the strange hands took him in charge while all the cats climbed into the trees to welcome their returning visitor.

"So, my Prince," said the White Cat when he reached her side at last, "once more you have returned without the crown. But no matter," she added as he opened his lips to explain. "I know that you are bound to take back the most beautiful Princess to court and I will find one for you, never fear. Meantime, let us amuse ourselves and be merry."

The third year passed for the young Prince as had the two others, and since nothing runs away faster than time passed without trouble or care, it is certain that he would have completely forgotten the day of his return to court had not the White Cat reminded him of it. This time, however, she told him that upon him alone depended his fate. He must promise to do whatever she asked of him. The Prince agreed readily enough until he heard her command him to cut off her head and tail and fling them into the fire.

"I!" cried the Prince, aghast, "I be so barbarous as to kill my dear White Cat? This is some trick to try my heart, but you should be sure of its gratitude."

"No, no, Son of a King," she answered, "I know your heart too well for that. But fate is stronger than either of us, and you must do as I bid you. It is the only way; and you must believe me, for I swear it on the honor of a Cat."

Tears came into the eyes of the Prince at the mere thought of cutting off the head of so amiable and pretty a creature. He tried to say all the most tender things he could think of, hoping to distract her. But she persisted that she wished to die by his hand because it was the only means of preventing his brothers from winning the crown. So piteously did she beg him that at last, all of a tremble, he drew his sword. With faltering hand he cut off the head and tail of his dear White Cat.

Next moment the most remarkable transformation took place before his very eyes. The body of the little White Cat suddenly changed into that of a young girl, the most graceful ever seen. But this was as nothing compared to the beauty and sweetness of her face, where only the shining brightness of the eyes gave any hint of the cat she had so recently been. The Prince was struck dumb with surprise and delight. He opened his eyes wider still to look at her, and what was his amazement to behold a troop of lords and ladies entering the apartment, each with a cat's skin flung over an arm. They advanced, and throwing themselves at the feet of their Queen, expressed their joy at seeing her once more restored to her natural form. She received them with great affection, but presently she desired them to leave her alone with the Prince.

"Behold, my dear Prince," she said as soon as they had done so, "I am released of a terrible enchantment, too long a tale to tell you now. Suffice it to say that this portrait which you saw upon my paw when I was a cat, was given to me by my guardian fairies during the time of my trial. I supposed it was of my first, unhappy love who was so cruelly taken from me and whose resemblance to you is so striking. Conceive my joy then, to find that it is of the Prince who has my entire heart and who was destined to rescue me from my enchantment."

And she bowed low before our Prince, who was so filled with joy and wonder that he would have remained there forever telling her of his love, had she not reminded him that the hour for his return to his father's court was almost upon them. Taking him by the hands, she led him into the courtyard to a chariot even more magnificent than the one she had provided before. The rest were equally gorgeous, the horses shod with emeralds held in place by diamond nails, with such gold and jeweled trappings as were never seen before or since. But the young Prince had eyes for nothing beyond the beauty of his companion.

Just before they reached the outskirts of the city, they sighted the Prince's two brothers with their trains driving toward them from opposite directions. At this the Princess hid herself in a small throne of rock crystal and precious gems while the Prince remained alone in the coach. His two brothers, each accompanied by a charming lady, greeted him warmly but expressed surprise and curiosity that he should be alone. To these questions he replied that he had been so unfortunate as not to have met with any lady of sufficient beauty to bring with him to court. He added, however, that he had instead a very rare and gifted White Cat. At this the brothers laughed loudly and exchanged pleased glances, for now they were convinced that he was indeed a simpleton and they need have no fears of his outwitting them a third time.

Through the streets of the city the two elder Princes rode with their ladies in open carriages, while the youngest Prince came last. Behind him was borne the great rock crystal, at which every one gazed in wonder.

The two Princes eagerly charged up the palace stairs with their Princesses, so anxious were they for their father's approval. The King received them graciously, but once more had difficulty in deciding which should have the prize. So he turned to his youngest son, who stood alone before him. "Have you returned empty-handed this time?" he asked.

"In this rock your Majesty will find a little White Cat," he answered, "one which mews so sweetly and has such velvet paws that you cannot but be delighted with it."

But before the surprised King could reach the crystal, the Princess touched an inner spring. It flew open revealing her in all her beauty, more dazzling than the sun itself. Her hair fell in golden ringlets; she was crowned with flowers and she moved with incomparable grace in her gown of white and rose-colored gauze. Even the King himself could not resist such loveliness, but hastened to acknowledge her undisputed right to wear the crown.

"But I have not come to deprive your Majesty of a throne which you fill so admirably," she said, bowing before him graciously. "I was born the heiress to six kingdoms of my own, so permit me to offer one to you and to each of your elder sons. I ask no other favors of you than your friendship and that your youngest son shall be my husband. Three kingdoms will be quite enough for us."

And so in truth they found them.

THE GREY PALFREY

Kind beasts often come to the aid of the struggling heroes or heroines of folk tales, but never more romantically than in this tale.

In the county of Champagne there once lived a knight. He was young and handsome and brave, and indeed he was all things that a good knight should be; but he was poor, owning little land and only one small manor set in a forest, among the trees and away from the road.

This young knight went much to the tourneying, often going many miles from his home to where tournaments were being held, not only for the sake of the honour he would gain by his courage and skill, but for the prizes and for the ransoms he might ask from those he overthrew, for it was by these ransoms that he lived and bought all that was needed for himself and for

"The Grey Palfrey." From *French Legends, Tales and Fairy Stories* by Barbara Leonie Picard. Reprinted by permission of Henry A. Walck, Inc.

his servants and his few followers. Though his garments were always neat and his helmet and his hauberk polished bright, his clothes were plain and his armour none of the best, and the food he ate, though there was enough of it, was no rich fare.

But one thing this knight owned that would not have shamed the wealthiest lord, and that was a grey palfrey, the favourite among his few horses, with sleek and glossy hide and a mane and a tail like flowing silver, so that no one, seeing it, did not stop to admire. Very fleet was this palfrey, and it had not its match in all Champagne. It was the envy of the countryside, and many were the rich lords who sought to buy it from the knight. Yet poor as he was, not for all the wealth in the world would he have parted with his palfrey, for he counted it his friend; and so indeed it proved to be.

Some two miles from this knight's manor, beside the road which ran through the forest, stood the castle of a duke. Old he was, and rich, and very miserly, forever seeking to add wealth to wealth. He had one daughter, the only young and gracious thing in all his castle, and it was this maiden whom the poor knight loved, and she loved him in return. But because he was poor, though of good repute, her father would never have considered him as a suitor; and since the maiden was never permitted to leave the castle, they might only speak together secretly, through a crack in the castle wall.

Every day at the same hour, when he was not at the tourneying, the knight would ride on the grey palfrey from his manor to the castle of the Duke, by a secret path through the forest which he alone used. And every day when she might, the maiden would await his coming at the castle wall, and they would talk of their love for a few happy moments. But not every day could she leave her father's side, or steal away unobserved, so on many days the knight would wait in vain to see her before riding sadly home along the secret path. Yet this made the times when they met all the sweeter.

One day the knight could bear it no longer, and since he knew the maiden cared nothing for riches, and would have been content as his wife had he been a peasant and lived in a hovel, he went to the castle and asked to speak with her father. The old Duke welcomed him courteously, since fair words cost nothing, and the young knight said, "Lord, there is a favour I would ask of you."

"And what might it be?" said the Duke.

"I am poor," said the knight, "but I am nobly born, and my honour is unquestioned, and no man has ever been able to speak ill of me. I love your daughter and I know that she loves me. I am here to ask for her hand in marriage."

The old Duke went as pale as his white beard in his anger. "There is not a lord in all France, nor a prince in all Christendom, whom I could not buy for my daughter, if I wished her to marry. She is not for a poor knight such as you. Now begone from my castle and never speak to me of such matters again."

Heavy at heart, the knight rode home, but since the maiden loved him he did not lose all hope, and a day or two later he rode to a distant town where a great tournament was to be held, thinking that there he might win a small measure of those riches, which, if carefully saved, might cause the old Duke to relent.

At that time a lord, wealthy and old as the Duke himself, came to visit him, and after they had talked long together of the things they had done when young and the memories they had in common, the lord said, "We are both rich, but were our riches combined, they would be even greater. Were you to give me your daughter as a wife, I would ask no dowry with her, but you and I, thus linked by a marriage, might share our wealth for the rest of our days. What say you to this, my old friend?"

The Duke was glad and rubbed his hands together and nodded many times. "You have spoken well, it shall be as you say. In all France there will be none richer than we two."

The Duke set about preparations for the marriage and cared nothing for his daughter's tears, inviting some score or more guests for the wedding, old friends of his and the bridegroom's, greybeards all. And because of his avarice, he sent to his neighbours in the countryside, asking the loan of a horse or two from each, that there might be mounts enough to carry the guests and their squires along the road through the forest to the church. And so little shame he had, that he sent to the young knight to borrow his grey palfrey, that his daughter might ride to her wedding on the finest horse in all Champagne.

The young knight had returned from the tourneying, well pleased enough with life, for he had easily been the best of all the knights gathered there, and every prize he had carried home to his little manor in the forest; so that it seemed to him he was perhaps a step nearer that which he had set his heart upon. When he heard the Duke's message, he asked, "Why does your master wish to borrow my horse?"

And the Duke's servant answered, "So that my master's daughter may ride upon it tomorrow to her wedding at the church."

When the young knight learnt how the maiden he loved was to marry the old lord, he thought that his heart would break, and at first he would have refused with indignation the Duke's request. But then he thought, "Not for the sake of her father, but to do honour to the lady I love, will I lend my palfrey. It is I whom she loves, she will have no joy of this marriage, and perhaps it will comfort her a little if I send her the palfrey which is my friend." So he saddled and bridled the palfrey and gave it to the serving-man, and then he went to his own room and would neither eat nor drink, but flung himself down upon his bed and wept.

In the Duke's castle, on the eve of the wedding, his guests made merry, feasting and drinking deep, and since they were, like himself, all old, when the time came for them to go to rest, they were in truth most weary. But very early in the morning, before dawn indeed, while the moon still shown brightly, the watchman roused them that they might be at the church betimes. Grumbling and half asleep, the guests clothed themselves and gathered in the courtyard where their horses waited. Yawning, they climbed into the saddles and set out upon their way, with the Duke and the old lord at their head. And after all the others came the maiden on the grey palfrey, with her father's old seneschal to watch over her. She was clad in a fair gown, and over it a scarlet mantle trimmed with costly fur, but her face was pale and she wept, and she had not slept all night for sorrow.

In the moonlight they left the castle and took the forest road which led to the church; yet since the way was narrow and branches overhung the track, they might not ride two abreast, but followed each other one by one through the forest, with the old seneschal at the very end, after the weeping bride.

A little way along the road, from habit, the palfrey turned aside, taking the secret path that its master had so often used; and because the old seneschal was nodding and dozing as he rode, he never missed the maiden. Deep into the forest, along the secret way went the palfrey, and in terror the maiden looked about her. But though she was fearful, she did not cry out, for she thought, "I had rather be lost in the forest and devoured by the wild beasts, than live without the knight I love." And she let the palfrey carry her where it would.

After two miles, in the dim light of early dawn, the palfrey stopped before a small manor set among the trees and waited for the gate to be opened. The watchman peeped out through a grille and called, "Who is there?" And, trembling, the maiden answered, "I am alone and lost in the forest. Have pity on me and give me shelter till sunrise."

But the watchman, looking closely, knew his master's palfrey, and made all haste to where he was. "Lord," he said, "at the gate stands your palfrey, and on its back is a lady so lovely that I think she can be no mortal maid. Is it your will that I should let her in?"

The young knight leapt off his bed and ran to the gate and flung it wide and caught the maiden in his arms. When they had done with kissing and weeping for joy, he asked her, "How did you come here?" And she answered, "It was your grey palfrey that brought me, for I should not have known the way."

"Since you are here," said the knight, "here shall you stay, if you will it."

"It is all I ask, to be with you for ever," she said.

So the knight called for his chaplain, and with no delay he and the maiden were married, and in all the manor there was great rejoicing.

When the Duke and the old lord and their friends reached the church they found that the maiden was not with them, and they set themselves to search for her, all about the forest. But by the time the Duke came upon the little manor set among the trees, his daughter was a

wife, and there was nothing he could do about it, save give the marriage his blessing, which he did with an ill grace. But little the young knight and his lady cared for that.

THE MOUSE-PRINCESS

There is something sad about the Mouse-Princess, and the youngest Prince is so humble and so loyal that their story achieves a tenderness unusual in folk tales.

In the days that are passed there lived a king who had three sons. He had ruled well and wisely for more years than he liked to remember, and one day he thought to himself how he was growing old and might well hand the cares of state and governing to a younger man, so that for the time that remained to him he might enjoy a well-earned rest, while one of his sons took his place as king. But the problem that faced him was to which of his three sons he should give his crown and the responsibility that went with it.

The two elder princes were gay, gallant young men, at home in any company and well liked by everyone; but the youngest was a quiet, shy youth, well meaning and kindly enough, but given too much to thinking and reading to meet with his brothers' approval, and, let it be said, over fond of his own company to be altogether pleasing to others. The King saw the merits of each of his sons, but he saw also their disabilities. The two elder were perhaps a little too casual and easy going, a degree too fond of letting things look after themselves; while the youngest was, it is undeniable, rather too serious-minded, and given, besides, to making mountains out of mole-hills.

As the King was pondering his problem, he remembered the young men's mother, his good queen who was dead, and he thought, "Whatever a man is, it is his wife who helps him to be what he will become. Whichever of my sons suc-

"The Mouse-Princess." From *French Legends, Tales and Fairy Stories* by Barbara Leonie Picard. Reprinted by permission of Henry Z. Walck, Inc.

ceeds me, if he has a good queen, he will be half-way to being a good king." He considered then the qualities which go to make a good queen, having always in his mind the picture of his own beloved wife. "She must be patient," he thought, "she must be neat and deft, and she must not despise the simple, necessary things of life. Yet she must have beauty and dignity and noble bearing, and above all, she must be gracious and truly royal."

The King sent for his three sons, and to each of them he handed a hank of flax, saying, "I would know what manner of maiden she is who may one day be queen in your dear mother's place. Go, each of you, and give this flax to the lady of your choice, bid her spin it into thread, and when seven days are passed, bring me the thread she has spun."

The two elder brothers each loved a noble maiden of the court, the one a countess and the other the daughter of a duke, and at once they took the flax and went to their ladies, repeating their father's words and saying that they doubted not that on the results of their spinning would rest the choice of a successor. The Countess and the Duke's daughter were both proud and beautiful; indeed, there was little to choose between them for looks and arrogance. They were skilled in all the accomplishments of noblewomen: they could sing prettily enough and play upon the lute, and they could dance a measure trippingly; but they had never learnt to spin. However, when she saw a crown within her grasp, each of them eagerly set to work upon the flax, bidding her lover have no fear of the result.

But the youngest brother had no lady whom he loved. He was shy and confused in the company of maidens, feeling that they despised him for his lack of gallantry and his inability to talk sweet nonsense which he did not mean. He took his hank of flax, put it in his pocket, and rode out alone from the palace into the forest, depressed and despondent, worrying and teasing himself as to what his father would say to him, in seven days' time, when he gave him back the unspun flax. But he knew that he could not, not even to gain a crown, ask any maiden to spin the flax for him, and risk her scorn and her refusal.

Now, in a neighbouring kingdom, a few years

before, the daughter of the King and Queen had had the misfortune to displease a witch, who had immediately turned her into a mouse. "A mouse shall you stay," the witch had said, "until you have made me laugh." As that witch had never been known to laugh, and was, besides, very ill-tempered, there seemed no likelihood of the Princess ever regaining her own shape. The King and the Queen would have been ready to care for their daughter in the form of a mouse for the rest of their lives, and give her every comfort: the best cheese for every meal and a room with ample holes in the wainscotting; but there were too many cats in that palace, and the mouse-princess took fright and ran away, right out of the palace and right out of the kingdom, and into the land ruled over by the old King who had three sons. There in a forest she came upon a ruined tower, all overgrown with ivy and yellow toadflax, and in this tower she made her home.

On the day when the King had given his sons the flax, the mouse was sitting on top of her ruined wall at the time when the youngest Prince rode by. She saw him come, and kept very still. It was a part of the forest where the Prince had never been before, and when he noticed the ruined tower, he felt that it was well fitted to his mood, and he dismounted and sat down upon a fallen block of stone. Seeing him so dejected, the mouse ran down the wall and went to him. Sitting up on her hind legs a yard or so from his feet, she asked him what ailed him. Had he been a less thoughtful person, he might have been surprised to hear a mouse speak, but as it was, he saw no reason why a mouse should not speak as well as a man. Since a courteous question deserves a courteous reply, the Prince told the mouse his troubles, and when he had finished, she said, "If you will permit it, I can help you."

"How can a mouse help me?" asked the Prince.

"Give me the flax and return here in seven days, and you shall see what you shall see."

Since the Prince had no one else to whom he dared give the flax, he saw no harm in giving it to the mouse. He pulled it out of his pocket, laid it down beside her, thanked her politely and rode away.

Seven days later he returned to the ruined tower, and there he found the mouse waiting for him, a little box beside her. "Take this box to the King," she said, "and let him open it."

Being himself kindly and good natured, the Prince did not doubt that the mouse would have done her best for him, and seeing that there was no one else to do as much, he thanked her gratefully and rode back to the palace. When he arrived, he found that his brothers were there before him, bringing the thread spun by their ladies. They laughed at their brother when they saw how he carried no thread but only a little box, and with confidence they gave their spools of thread to the King. He looked at them, turned them this way and that, unwound a length of thread from each, and then he sighed and laid them by. For the Countess's thread was as thick as hempen rope, while the thread spun by the Duke's daughter was so thin and uneven that a child could easily have snapped it. The King smiled encouragingly at his youngest son, who had held back, abashed by his brothers' taunts. "Where is your thread, my son?" The youngest Prince came forward and held out the little box. "It is here, father."

The King took the box and opened it. Inside was a ball of thread as fine as hair and as bright, but so strong that however hard he tugged at it, it would not break.

The two elder brothers looked at one another, eyebrows raised, and the King looked at his youngest son, wondering. But he said nothing, and only laid the ball of thread aside, as he had done with the spools. Then he smiled at his three sons. "The thread is only the beginning," he said, "it is the finished cloth which completes the task." And he gave to each of the young men a reel of linen thread spun by the chief spinning maid of the palace. It was neither so thick as the Countess's thread, nor yet so fine as the thread which the mouse had given the youngest Prince, and unlike the thread of the Duke's daughter, it was strong enough. "Go," he said, "and give this thread to the ladies of your choice, and bid them weave a length of cloth from it. When seven days are passed, bring the cloth to me."

The two elder brothers hurried to their ladies,

who had, naturally, never learnt to weave. But nothing daunted, thinking of the crown that was so close, they set to work as best they might.

The youngest brother put the reel of thread in his pocket and rode from the palace alone. This time he went straight to the ruined tower in the forest. "Little mouse, little mouse," he called, and there she was, her bright eyes gleaming, looking down at him from the top of the wall. "Did you give the box to the king?" she asked.

"I did, little mouse."

"And what did he say?"

"Why, he said nothing."

"That is well," she replied, and ran down the wall to his feet. "But why are you still sad?" He told her. "If you wish it, I will help you," she said.

He smiled, a little cheered. "If you would help me again, I should always be grateful."

"Give me the thread." He took it out of his pocket and laid it before her. "Come back in seven days," she said, "and you shall see what you shall see." And he thanked her and rode away.

Seven days later he returned to the ruined tower, and there was the mouse waiting for him, a little box by her side. "Take this box to the King," she said, "and let him open it."

He spent an hour or two with her, sitting on a block of fallen stone, talking of this and that; and she seemed to him an intelligent and likeable companion indeed. Then he took the little box, thanked her, and rode back to the palace. When he arrived he found his two brothers there before him, bringing the cloth woven by their ladies, and when they saw that he carried nothing but a wooden box which seemed too small to hold a length of cloth, they smiled their relief at each other. With confidence they gave their cloth to the King, who took each length in his hands and sighed and laid it by. The cloth woven by the Countess was so coarse and stiff that it could almost have stood up by itself, while the cloth woven by the Duke's daughter would have made a passable fisherman's net. The King looked at his youngest son. "Where is your cloth?" he asked.

The youngest Prince held out the little box. "It is here, father."

The King opened the box and pulled out, yard by yard, a length of cloth so soft and fine that the small box could easily contain it. Yet it was strong, with the warp and the woof even and smooth.

The two elder brothers looked at one another, frowning and angry, and the King looked at his youngest son, wondering. But he said nothing and only laid the length of cloth aside, next to the others. Then he smiled at his sons. "I have seen," he said, "what your ladies can do, and how skilled they are. But surely the final test of fitness to be a queen is in the bearing of the lady herself, and not in the skill of her hands. At midday tomorrow, let each of you come here with his bride, and I will tell you which of you shall be king in my place."

The two elder brothers hurried off to the Countess and the Duke's daughter, and the two ladies were thrown into a great flutter. The rest of that day they spent trying on their best gowns, choosing out their finest jewels, and strutting and preening themselves before their mirrors.

But the youngest Prince rode out of the palace, and because it was a habit with him by now, he went to the ruined tower. "Little mouse, little mouse, are you there?" And there she was, peeping out through a spray of honeysuckle which hung over a window-sill. "Did you give the box to the King?"

"I did, little mouse."

"And what did he say?"

"Why, nothing."

"That is well," she said. And she ran down the stem of the honeysuckle, out of the window and across to his feet.

"No," said the Prince, "it is not well. I shall never be a king." He sat down upon the grass and the mouse stood beside his hand. "What has your father asked of you now?" she said.

"That at midday tomorrow I shall bring him the lady who is to be my bride, the lady who spun the thread and wove the cloth. But alas, little mouse, there is no lady."

The mouse was silent; and the Prince, too, said nothing for many minutes, then he looked at the mouse and saw a large tear trickling down her nose. He tried hard to smile and to sound as though he did not care. "This time you cannot help me, little mouse, but you have done enough already, and you must not think that I am ungrateful because I am sad." He took a ring off his finger. "See, here is a gift for you to remember me by." He laid it gently beside her on the grass and stood up. "Good-bye, little mouse, and thank you." He mounted his horse and rode away, and she cried out after him, "I will help you. I will find a way." But he only turned and shook his head and smiled at her.

All that night the mouse-princess thought and thought, but she could think of no way to help the Prince, and in the morning she still had no plan. But as it approached midday, she could not bear not to be with him to comfort him when his brothers came with their brides and he had none. So she picked up his ring in her mouth and she ran and she ran through the forest until she reached the highway. And there she stopped, for she could run no farther. At that moment a man came by with a crate of chickens for the market. The mouse stepped out into his path, dropped the ring, sat up and spoke to him. "Good friend," she said, "give me your black cock, and make me a bridle and saddle, that I may ride on him."

The man was so surprised to hear a mouse speak and so amused by her request, that he thought, "It will be worth the loss of the price of my black cock, just to have such a story to tell." He made a bridle out of plaited grasses and a saddle out of a dock leaf, and saddled and bridled the cock. The mouse thanked him, took up the ring in her mouth and mounted upon the back of the cock, and away they went, towards the palace of the King.

Now, it happened that the way to the palace lay past the castle where the witch lived who had put the spell on the Princess, and her servant was at the window when the mouse rode by on the cock. The servant burst out laughing. "Idle wench," scolded the witch, "what are you laughing at?"

"Why, mistress, I have never seen such a sight in my life!" But the girl could say no more for laughing.

"You foolish creature," said the witch, and she came angrily to the window. But when she looked out and saw the mouse riding on the cock, she, who had never been known even to smile, found herself laughing until the tears ran down her cheeks. And in that moment the mouse became a princess, in silk and velvet and pearls, with a crown upon her head, riding on a black horse with green and golden trappings.

Promptly at midday, the two elder Princes, with their brides beside them, came before the King; and the youngest Prince followed after them, alone.

Nothing could have been more splendid than the sight offered by the Countess and the Duke's daughter. Their gowns were so stiff with jewels that it was a marvel the ladies could move at all, and they flashed so brightly that the King's eyes were almost dazzled. And as for their regal dignity, why, if the Countess had tilted her head much higher, she would surely have tripped and fallen; while as for the disdain of the Duke's daughter, it seemed to include even the King himself.

The two elder brothers presented their brides, and the two ladies curtsied to the King. He spoke to them kindly, and kissed each of them upon the cheek. "You have my blessing, daughters," he said. He turned to the two Princes. "My sons, you have chosen suitably." The Princes bowed to their father and kissed his hand, self-satisfaction glowing in their hearts, for they had not seen the twinkle in his eyes. But the Countess and the Duke's daughter glared haughtily at one another over their bridegroom's heads, all their past friendship forgotten in their present rivalry.

The King beckoned to his youngest son. "Where is your bride?" he asked.

The youngest Prince knelt before his father. "Father, I have none," he said, and hung his head in shame, whilst his brothers grinned at one another.

At that moment the chamberlain hurried in and whispered to the King. The King smiled a little. "Bring her in," he said.

A minute or so later, the Princess was curtseying to the King, and a few seconds after that, she was standing by the youngest Prince; and there was not a lady in all that court who would not have seemed like a serving-wench beside her.

"Look up, my son," said the King, "and see your bride."

The Prince looked up and saw the loveliest maiden he had ever dreamt of, with a crown upon her head; unconscious of the richness of her garments, graceful and gracious and perfectly at ease, she smiled at him, and he felt neither awkward nor shy. He rose and asked in wonder, "Who are you?"

"I am your bride," she said.

He looked at her and loved her in that instant; then he looked at his brothers and saw their anger, he looked at the Countess and at the Duke's daughter and saw their jealousy and of how little worth they were, and he looked at the King and saw the smile on his lips, and he knew that he had but to say a single word and the crown would be his. Yet he could not say that word. He turned away from the Princess and said, "This is not my bride. If any should be my bride, it should be the little mouse who spun the yarn and wove the cloth for me."

"But I was the mouse," said the Princess. "See, here is your ring." And she held it out to him. He took it and put it on her finger and kissed her; and that is the end of the tale.

Italian folk tales

The following two stories are from Old Italian Tales, *retold by Domenico Vittorini. The book is a treasure for the storyteller. Some of the stories are adapted from oral sources, and one is taken from Boccaccio, that master of the storytelling art. The whole collection of twenty tales has unusual variety, an earthy sort of humor, and a vigorous sense of justice. Told with simplicity and respect for sources, these lively tales prove again how little human nature differs from country to country.*

MARCH AND THE SHEPHERD

This duel of wits between two tricksters, with the shepherd always the winner, makes the wry humor of the conclusion quite acceptable.

One morning, in the very beginning of spring, a shepherd led his sheep to graze, and on the way he met March.

"Good morning," said March. "Where are you going to take your sheep to graze today?"

"Well, March, today I am going to the mountains."

"Fine, Shepherd. That's a good idea. Good luck." But to himself March said, "Here's where I have some fun, for today I'm going to fix you."

And that day in the mountains the rain came down in buckets; it was a veritable deluge. The shepherd, however, had watched March's face very carefully and noticed a mischievous look on it. So, instead of going to the mountains, he had remained in the plains. In the evening, upon returning home, he met March again.

"Well, Shepherd, how did it go today?"

"It couldn't have been better. I changed my mind and went to the plains. A very beautiful day. Such a lovely warm sun."

"Really? I'm glad to hear it," said March, but he bit his lip in vexation. "Where are you going tomorrow?"

"Tomorrow I'm going to the plains, too. With this fine weather, I would be crazy if I went to the mountains."

"Oh, really? Fine! Farewell."

And they parted.

But the shepherd didn't go to the plains again; he went to the mountains. And on the plains March brought rain and wind and hail— a punishment indeed from heaven. In the evening he met the shepherd homeward bound.

"Good evening, Shepherd. How did it go today?"

"Very well indeed. Do you know? I changed my mind again and went to the mountains after all. It was heavenly there. What a day! What a sky! What a sun!"

"I'm really happy to hear it, Shepherd. And where are you going tomorrow?"

"Well, tomorrow I'm going to the plains. I see dark clouds over the mountains. I wouldn't want to find myself too far from home."

To make a long story short, whenever the shepherd met March, he always told him the opposite of what he planned to do the next day, so March was never able to catch him. The end of the month came and on the last day, the thirtieth, March said to the shepherd, "Well, Shepherd, how is everything?"

"Things couldn't be any better. This is the end of the month and I'm out of danger. There's nothing to fear now; I can begin to sleep peacefully."

"That's true," said March. "And where are you going tomorrow?"

The shepherd, certain that he had nothing to fear, told March the truth. "Tomorrow," he said, "I shall go to the plains. The distance is shorter and the work less hard."

"Fine. Farewell."

March hastened to the home of his cousin April and told her the whole story. "I want you to lend me at least one day," he said. "I am determined to catch this shepherd." Gentle April was unwilling, but March coaxed so hard that finally she consented.

The following morning the shepherd set off for the plains. No sooner had his flock scattered when there arose a storm that chilled his very heart. The sharp wind howled and growled; snow fell in thick icy flakes; hail pelted down. It was all the shepherd could do to get his sheep back into the fold.

That evening as the shepherd huddled in a corner of his hearth, silent and melancholy, March paid him a visit.

"Good evening, Shepherd," he said.

"Good evening, March."

"How did it go today?"

"I'd rather not talk about it," said the shepherd. "I can't understand what happened. Not even in the middle of January have I ever seen a storm like the one on the plains today. It seemed as if all the devils had broken loose from hell. Today I had enough rough weather to last me the whole year. And, oh, my poor sheep!"

Then at last was March satisfied.

And from that time on March has had thirty-one days because, as it is said in Tuscany, the rascal never returned to April the day he borrowed from her.

THE MOST PRECIOUS

POSSESSION

This tale starts off as if it were to be a variant of "Dick Whittington" without the rags-to-riches theme, but the conclusion is different.

There was a time when Italian traders and explorers, finding the way to the East blocked by the Turks, turned west in their search for new lands to trade with—a search that led to the discovery of the New World.

In those days there lived in Florence a merchant by the name of Ansaldo. He belonged to the Ormanini family, known not only for its wealth but for the daring and cunning of its young men. It happened that on one of his trips in search of adventure and trade, Ansaldo ventured beyond the Strait of Gibraltar and, after battling a furious storm, landed on one of the Canary Islands.

The king of the island welcomed him cordially, for the Florentines were well known to him. He ordered a magnificent banquet prepared and arranged to have it served in the sumptuous hall, resplendent with mirrors and gold, in which he had received Ansaldo.

When it was time to serve the meal, Ansaldo noticed with surprise that a small army of youths, carrying long stout sticks, entered and lined up against the walls of the banquet hall. As each guest sat down, one of the youths took up a place directly behind him, the stick held in readiness to strike.

Ansaldo wondered what all this meant and wracked his brain for some clue to these odd goings-on. He didn't have long to wait. Suddenly, a horde of huge ferocious rats poured into the hall and threw themselves upon the food that was being served. Pandemonium broke loose as

"The Most Precious Possession." Reprinted by permission of David McKay Company, Inc., New York, from *Old Italian Tales,* copyright © 1958 by Domenico Vittorini

the boys darted here and there, wielding the sticks.

For many years the Florentines had enjoyed the reputation of being the cleverest people on earth, able to cope with any situation. Ansaldo saw a chance to uphold the tradition. He asked the king's permission to go back to his ship, and returned shortly with two big Persian cats. These animals were much admired and loved by the Florentines and Venetians who had first seen them in the East and who had brought many of them back to Italy. Ever since, one or two cats always completed the crew of a ship when it set out on a long journey.

Ansaldo let the cats go and before long the entire hall was cleared of the revolting and destructive rats.

The astonished and delighted king thought he was witnessing a miracle. He could not find words enough to thank Ansaldo whom he hailed as the saviour of the island, and when Ansaldo made him a present of the cats, his gratitude knew no bounds.

After a pleasant visit, Ansaldo made ready to sail for home. The king accompanied him to his ship and there he showered him with rich and rare gifts, much gold and silver, and many precious stones of all kinds and colors—rubies, topazes, and diamonds.

Ansaldo was overwhelmed not only by these costly gifts but by the king's gratitude and the praises he heaped upon him and on the cats. As for the latter, they were regarded with awe by all the islanders and as their greatest treasure by the king and the entire royal household.

When Ansaldo returned home he regaled his friends with the account of his strange adventure. There was among them a certain Giocondo de' Fifanti who was as rich in envy as he was poor in intelligence. He thought: "If the island king gave Ansaldo all these magnificent gifts for two mangy cats, what will he not give me if I present him with the most beautiful and precious things that our city of Florence has to offer?" No sooner said than done. He purchased lovely belts, necklaces, bracelets studded with diamonds, exquisite pictures, luxurious garments and many other expensive gifts and took ship for the now famous Canary Islands.

After an uneventful crossing he arrived in

port and hastened to the royal palace. He was received with more pomp than was Ansaldo. The king was greatly touched by the splendor of Giocondo's gifts and wanted to be equally generous. He held a long consultation with his people and then informed Giocondo happily that they had decided to let him share with his visitor their most precious possession. Giocondo could hardly contain his curiosity. However, the day of departure finally arrived and found Giocondo on his ship, impatiently awaiting the visit of the king. Before long, the king, accompanied by the entire royal household and half the islanders, approached the ship. The king himself carried the precious gift on a silken cushion. With great pride he put the cushion into Giocondo's outstretched greedy hands. Giocondo was speechless. On the cushion, curled up in sleepy, furry balls, were two of the kittens that had been born to the Persian cats Ansaldo had left on the island.

The old story does not go on to say whether Giocondo, on his return to Florence, ever regaled his friends with the tale of *his* adventure!

Spanish folk tales

So lively and varied are the Spanish folk tales that a good storyteller will wish to look up more of them than this collection has room for. They range from nursery tales to elaborate stories of mature content. See bibliography.

THE HALF-CHICK

Before telling this story, explain to the children about weathervanes, and show them the picture of the weathercock on p. 132.

There was once upon a time a handsome, black Spanish hen, who had a large brood of chickens. They were all fine, plump little birds, except the youngest who was quite unlike his brothers and sisters. This one looked just as if he had been cut in two. He had only one leg, and one wing, and one eye and he had half a head and half a beak. His mother shook her head sadly as she looked at him and said:

"My youngest born is only a half-chick. He can never grow up a tall handsome cock like his brothers. They will go out into the world and rule over poultry yards of their own. But this poor little fellow will always have to stay at home with his mother." And she called him Medio Pollito, which is Spanish for half-chick.

Now though Medio Pollito was such an odd, helpless-looking little thing, his mother soon found he was not at all willing to remain under her wing and protection. Indeed, in character he was as unlike his brothers and sisters as he was in appearance. They were good, obedient chickens, and when the old hen called them, they chirped and ran back to her side. But Medio Pollito had a roving spirit in spite of his one leg, and when his mother called him to return to the coop, he pretended he could not hear because he had only one ear.

When she took the whole family out for a walk in the fields, Medio Pollito would hop away by himself and hide among the Indian corn. Many an anxious moment his brothers and sisters had looking for him, while his mother ran to and fro cackling in fear and dismay.

As he grew older he became more self-willed and disobedient. His manner to his mother was often rude and his temper to the other chickens disagreeable.

One day he had been out for a longer expedition than usual in the fields. On his return he strutted up to his mother with a peculiar little hop and kick which was his way of walking and, cocking his one eye at her in a very bold way, he said:

"Mother, I am tired of this life in a dull farmyard, with nothing but a dreary maize field to look at. I'm off to Madrid to see the king."

"To Madrid, Medio Pollito!" exclaimed his mother. "Why, you silly chick, it would be a long journey for a grown-up cock; a poor little thing like you would be tired out before you had gone half the distance. No, no, stay at home with your mother and some day, when you are bigger, we will go on a little journey together."

But Medio Pollito had made up his mind. He would not listen to his mother's advice, nor to the prayers and entreaties of his brothers and sisters.

"What is the use of our crowding each other in this poky little place?" he said. "When I have a fine courtyard of my own at the king's palace, I shall perhaps ask some of you to come and pay me a short visit." And scarcely waiting to say good-bye to his family, away he stumped down the high road that led to Madrid.

"Be sure you are kind and civil to everyone you meet," called his mother, running after him. But he was in such a hurry to be off he did not wait to answer her or even to look back.

A little later in the day, as he was taking a short cut through a field, he passed a stream. Now the stream was choked and overgrown with weeds and water plants so its waters could not flow freely.

"Oh, Medio Pollito!" it cried, as the half-chick hopped along its banks. "Do come and help me by clearing away these weeds."

"Help you, indeed!" exclaimed Medio Pollito, tossing his head and shaking the few feathers in his tail. "Do you think I have nothing to do but waste my time on such trifles? Help yourself, and don't trouble busy travelers. I am off to Madrid to see the king." And hoppity-kick, hoppity-kick, away stumped Medio Pollito.

A little later he came to a fire that had been left by some gypsies in a wood. It was burning very low and would soon be out.

"Oh, Medio Pollito," cried the fire, in a weak wavering voice as the half-chick approached, "in a few minutes I shall go quite out unless you put some sticks and dry leaves upon me. Do help me or I shall die!"

"Help you, indeed!" answered Medio Pollito. "I have other things to do. Gather sticks for yourself and don't trouble me. I am off to Ma-

drid to see the king." And hoppity-kick, hoppity-kick, away stumped Medio Pollito.

The next morning, as he was nearing Madrid, he passed a large chestnut tree in whose branches the wind was caught and entangled.

"Oh, Medio Pollito," called the wind, "do hop up here and help me get free of these branches. I cannot come away and it is so uncomfortable."

"It is your own fault for going there," answered Medio Pollito. "I can't waste all my morning stopping here to help you. Just shake yourself off and don't hinder me, for I am off to Madrid to see the king." And hoppity-kick, hoppity-kick, away stumped Medio Pollito in great glee, for the towers and roofs of Madrid were now in sight.

When he entered the town he saw before him

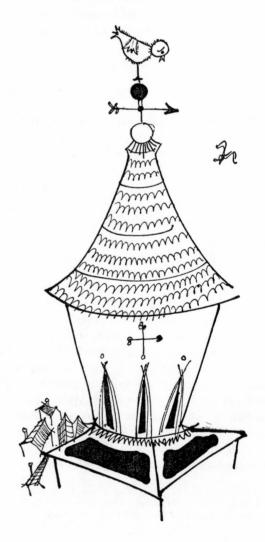

a great splendid house, with soldiers standing before the gates. This he knew must be the royal palace, and he determined to hop up to the front gate and wait there until the king came out. But as he was hopping past one of the back windows, the king's cook saw him.

"Here is the very thing I want," he exclaimed, "for the king has just sent a message that he must have chicken broth for his dinner!" And opening the window he stretched out his arm, caught Medio Pollito, and popped him into the broth pot standing near the fire. Oh, how wet and clammy the water felt as it went over Medio Pollito's head, making his feathers cling to his side.

"Water, water," he cried in his despair, "do have pity upon me and do not wet me like this."

"Ah, Medio Pollito," replied the water, "you would not help me when I was a little stream away in the fields and now you must be punished."

Then the fire began to burn and scald Medio Pollito. He hopped from one side of the pot to the other, trying to get away from the heat, and crying out in pain:

"Fire, fire! Do not scorch me like this. You cannot think how it hurts."

"Ah, Medio Pollito," answered the fire, "you would not help me when I was dying away in the wood. You are being punished."

At last, just when the pain was so great Medio Pollito thought he must die, the cook lifted up the lid of the pot to see if the broth was ready for the king's dinner.

"Look here," he cried in horror, "this chicken is quite useless! It is burned to a cinder. I can't send it up to the royal table." And opening the window he threw Medio Pollito out into the street. But the wind caught him up and whirled him through the air so quickly Medio Pollito could scarcely breathe, and his heart beat against his side till he thought it would break.

"Oh, wind," he gasped out, "if you hurry me along like this you will kill me. Do let me rest a moment, or—" But he was so breathless he could not finish his sentence.

"Ah, Medio Pollito," replied the wind, "when I was caught in the branches of the chestnut tree you would not help me. Now you are punished." And he swirled Medio Pollito over the roofs of the houses till they reached the highest church in the town, and there he left him fastened to the top of the steeple.

And there stands Medio Pollito to this day. If you go to Madrid and walk through the streets till you come to the highest church, you will see Medio Pollito perched on his one leg on the steeple, with his one wing drooping at his side, and gazing sadly out of his one eye over the town.

THE JOKES OF SINGLE-TOE

Padre Porko is a unique character in Spanish folklore. He is the gentlemanly pig, wise, witty, and urbane. He solves his own and his neighbors' problems with nonchalance. Look up the other stories in the book that bears his name. They are all good to tell.

"Chestnuts are ripening and falling on the other side of the canal," said the black-headed sparrow, teetering on the edge of the table.

"Oh, but it's too early for chestnuts," observed the Padre. "It takes two or three frosty nights to open the prickles."

"Well, if you can't believe me," said the sparrow, ruffling his collar, "ask the squirrel. He keeps track of the nuts."

So the Padre asked Single-Toe (so named because he had only one on his left front foot). The squirrel put his paw beside his nose as though he were trying to think up an answer to a riddle. "I'll try to let you know in three days," he mumbled, "but don't do anything about chestnuts until you see me again." And he went off in such a rush that even the good Padre grew suspicious.

An hour later he laid down his pipe and beckoned to Mrs. Wren. "Do you mind having a little fly around the wood to see what the squirrel family is up to this morning?"

She came back twittering all over. "The squirrels, for miles around, are all in the grove across the canal, throwing down the chestnuts for dear life. Single-Toe is making them work all the

"The Jokes of Single-Toe." From *Padre Porko* by Robert Davis, Holiday House. Copyright, 1939, by Robert Davis.

harder, and giggling at something he seems to think very funny."

"Oh, the rascal," chuckled the Padre. "The sly little one-toed sinner! He will give me an answer in three days, will he? Yes, indeed, after he has gathered all the best nuts." He called to his housekeeper. "Mrs. Hedge-Hog, bring me three of the oatmeal sacks from the cupboard and some strong string." And folding the bags inside his belt, he trotted off, pushing his wheelbarrow.

Up among the leaves, busy pulling the polished nuts out of the burrs, Single-Toe and his relatives did not hear the Padre arrive. Patter, plop, plop, plop, patter—the brown nuts were falling on the grass.

"What a lark," beamed the Padre, stuffing four or five into his mouth at once. "And this year they are sweeter and juicier than they have been for a long time." He made little piles of the biggest ones, and began filling his sacks. Finally he had all the wheelbarrow would carry. Bouncing the last bag up and down so he could tie the string around the top, he called out in his silkiest voice, "Many thanks, Single-Toe. You will see that I have taken only the big ones. I do hope that the prickers haven't made your paws sore."

There was a sudden calm in the chestnut grove. The squirrels came leaping down to a low bough, from where they could send sour looks after the Padre, trundling his barrow along toward the bridge. He was singing,

With chestnuts roasting in a row,
    I love to hear them sizzle.
I care not how the winds may blow,
    Nor how the rain-drops drizzle.
I welcome every Jack and Jill
    Who knocks upon my door.
We toast our toes and eat our fill,
    For there are plenty more.

One day three or four weeks later the Padre was doing a little carpentering under the umbrella pine, when something behind him sniffed. He jumped, and dropped two nails out of his mouth. There, under the table, tears running down their noses, were Mrs. Single-Toe and the four children.

"Bless my blue-eyed buttons," exclaimed the Padre, spitting out the rest of the nails. "What can be as wrong as all that?"

"It's Papa," said the oldest boy. "He's been in a hole by the old oak for four days, and is almost starved."

"But why doesn't he come home?" said the Padre. "The oak isn't far away."

"The fox won't let him," sobbed Madame Single-Toe.

"And why not?"

"He's mad because of Papa's jokes," the youngest child explained.

The Padre's mouth opened in a wide grin. "More of the jokes that other people don't find funny, eh? Well, I'll take a stroll by the twisted oak and have a talk with the fox." As he started off, he called over his shoulder, "Mrs. Hedge-Hog, you might give these youngsters a couple of the pickled chestnuts we keep for company." He winked solemnly at Mrs. Single-Toe, who blushed.

The fox was lying with his muzzle just an inch from the hole. He did not budge, nor lift his eye when the Padre wished him good morning. "I've got him this time," he snarled. "Four days I've been watching this hole. My mother brings my meals and keeps guard while I eat. He'll not get away *this* time!"

"He is a nuisance with his jokes, I admit," said the Padre peaceably, "but he doesn't do any real harm. Don't you think a good scare would be enough for him?"

"No, I don't," snapped the fox. "And don't you mix in this business, Padre, with your talk about kindness. What I've suffered from that little pest you'd never believe. First he dropped a tomato on my nose—a tomato that was too ripe. And then he dribbled pitch all over my head and neck while I was asleep. So don't waste your time." The fox advanced his red tongue hungrily to the very edge of the hole.

The Padre walked away, deep in thought. His generous heart was very unhappy. What should he say to the near-orphans in his kitchen? There must be some way to save him. Suddenly he saw some crows gossiping in a dead pine. "Will one of you black boys do me a favor, in a great hurry?" he called.

"Certainly, Don Porko," they all cawed.

"Fly low through the woods, and tell every

rabbit you see that I want their road commissioner to come to my house for dinner. Say that I'm going to have celery root and cabbage, chopped in parsley."

The Padre's guest was promptness itself. He used a turnip leaf as a napkin, and when he had wiped his whiskers, ate the napkin. "It makes less for Ma'am Hedge-Hog to clear up," he explained.

"Now for serious business," said the Padre, leading the way to the garden, when they had finished their second glass of dandelion wine. "I have invited you here as an expert. We will draw a map." He made a cross in the soft earth with a stick. "Here is the oak that the lightning split. And here in front of it, so, is a rabbit hole that was begun, but never finished. Do you follow me?"

The road commissioner nodded. "I know it perfectly. The workman was caught by an owl when he came up with some dirt."

"Now," continued the Padre, "how far is the bottom of this unfinished hole from one of your regular tunnels, and how long would it take to dig up to it?"

"About half a jump," replied the road commissioner. "The 'Alley to the Ivy Rock' runs very close to that unfinished hole. A good digger can do a medium-sized jump of tunnel in half a day. I should say it would take two hours to dig upwards from 'Ivy Rock Alley' and join the hole."

The Padre beckoned the road commissioner to follow him to the cellar. Scraping away the sand, he laid bare ten carrots, each as smooth and straight as an orange-colored candle. "These are yours, Mr. Commissioner, if you will do this little job of digging for me."

The bargain was soon struck. "One thing more," said the Padre, as the commissioner was lolloping away. "You will find a friend of mine in the unfinished hole. Don't let him make a noise, but bring him here the moment you can get him free. I'll be waiting."

Daylight was fading when the rabbit returned, covered with damp earth to his armpits. He was supporting a hoarse, hungry, and grimy red squirrel. The Padre welcomed them, pointing to the cupboard. "Sh-h-h-sh, go and see what's inside, Single-Toe."

One might have thought a hundred squirrels were behind the cupboard door, such was the hugging and chattering, the rubbing of noses, and the scratching of ears. Single-Toe was invited to stay for a light lunch, even after the road commissioner had left for his burrow, the biggest carrot in his mouth.

Safe, fed, and warmed, the red squirrel became his own gay self again. He began to chuckle, then to shake with merriment. "Ha, ha, ha! That silly old fox is still there, watching an empty hole! Won't it be a priceless joke, if I climb the oak and drop a rotten egg on his nose?"

At the word "joke," Mrs. Single-Toe, the four little squirrels, and the good Padre, all stiffened.

"Don't you ever say that word again," said his wife. "Do you hear, no more jokes, never, never."

Single-Toe wilted. "Yes," he confessed, not daring to meet the Padre's eye, "jokes aren't always so terribly funny, are they? Not even for the joker."

Irish folk tales

How is it possible to characterize the hero tales, the sorrowful romances, the drolls, the strange half-world of faery with its enchantments and spells, which mark the Celtic fairy tales? Great variety of plots and beauty of style have come from the lips of Irish storytellers, and far less humor than most people seem to expect. Indeed, so few and far between are the drolls and so numerous the somber tales of heroism and romance which come to tragic ends that the Irish tales as a whole have never been popular with children. The two examples given here are as different in plot and style as possible. "Connla and the Fairy Maiden" is more typical than the amusing "King O'Toole."

KING O'TOOLE AND HIS GOOSE

Stories of the saints walking the earth and taking part in men's affairs were fairly common in the Middle Ages. Usually, they were serious stories but here is a hilarious exception.

Och, I thought all the world, far and near, had heerd of King O'Toole—well, well, but the darkness of mankind is untollable! Well, sir, you must know, as you didn't hear it afore, that there was a king, called King O'Toole, who was a fine old king in the old ancient times, long ago; and it was he that owned the churches in the early days. The king, you see, was the right sort; he was the real boy, and loved sport as he loved his life, and hunting in particular; and from the rising o' the sun, up he got and away he went over the mountains after the deer; and fine times they were.

Well, it was all mighty good, as long as the king had his health; but, you see, in the course of time the king grew old, by raison he was stiff in his limbs, and when he got stricken in years, his heart failed him, and he was lost entirely for want o' diversion, because he couldn't go a-hunting no longer; and, by dad, the poor king was obliged at last to get a goose to divert him. Oh, you may laugh, if you like, but it's truth I'm telling you; and the way the goose diverted him was this-a-way: You see, the goose used to swim across the lake, and go diving for trout and catch fish on a Friday for the king, and flew every other day round about the lake, diverting the poor king. All went on mighty well until, by dad, the goose got stricken in years like her master, and couldn't divert him no longer; and then it was that the poor king was lost entirely. The king was walkin' one mornin' by the edge of the lake, lamentin' his cruel fate, and thinking of drowning himself, that could get no diversion in life, when all of a sudden, turning round the corner, whom should he meet but a mighty decent young man coming up to him.

"God save you," says the king to the young man.

"God save you kindly, King O'Toole," says the young man.

"King O'Toole and His Goose." From *Celtic Fairy Tales*, edited by Joseph Jacobs. By permission of G. P. Putnam's Sons and Frederick Muller Ltd., London

"True for you," says the king. "I am King O'Toole," says he, "prince and plennypenny-tinchery of these parts," says he; "but how came ye to know that?" says he.

"Oh, never mind," says Saint Kavin.

You see it was Saint Kavin, sure enough—the saint himself in disguise and nobody else. "Oh, never mind," says he, "I know more than that. May I make bold to ask how is your goose, King O'Toole?" says he.

"Blur-an-agers, how came ye to know about my goose?" says the king.

"Oh, no matter; I was given to understand it," says Saint Kavin.

After some more talk the king says, "What are you?"

"I'm an honest man," says Saint Kavin.

"Well, honest man," says the king, "and how is it you make your money so aisy?"

"By makin' old things as good as new," says Saint Kavin.

"Is it a tinker you are?" says the king.

"No," says the saint; "I'm no tinker by trade, King O'Toole; I've a better trade than a tinker," says he—"What would you say," says he, "if I made your old goose as good as new?"

My dear, at the word of making his goose as good as new, you'd think the poor old king's eyes were ready to jump out of his head. With that the king whistled, and down came the poor goose, just like a hound, waddling up to the poor cripple, her master, and as like him as two peas. The minute the saint clapt his eyes on the goose, "I'll do the job for you," says he, "King O'Toole."

"By Jaminee!" says King O'Toole, "if you do, I'll say you're the cleverest fellow in the seven parishes."

"Oh, by dad," says Saint Kavin, "you must say more nor that—my horn's not so soft all out," says he, "as to repair your old goose for nothing; what'll you gi' me if I do the job for you?—that's the chat," says Saint Kavin.

"I'll give you whatever you ask," says the king; "isn't that fair?"

"Divil a fairer," says the saint, "that's the way to do business. Now," says he, "this is the bargain I'll make with you, King O'Toole: will you gi' me all the ground the goose flies over, the first offer, after I make her as good as new?"

Well, my dear, it was a beautiful sight to see the king standing with his mouth open, looking at his poor old goose flying as light as a lark, and better than ever she was; and when she lit at his feet, patted her on the head, and "Ma vourneen," says he, "but you are the darlint o' the world."

"And what do you say to me," says Saint Kavin, "for making her the like?"

"By Jabers," says the king, "I say nothing beats the art o' man, barring the bees."

"And do you say no more nor that?" says Saint Kavin.

"And that I'm beholden to you," says the king.

"But will you gi'e me all the ground the goose flew over?" says Saint Kavin.

"I will," says King O'Toole, "and you're welcome to it," says he, "though it's the last acre I have to give."

"But you'll keep your word true," says the saint.

"As true as the sun," says the king.

"It's well for you, King O'Toole, that you said that word," says he; "for if you didn't say that word, the divil the bit o' your goose would ever fly agin."

When the king was as good as his word, Saint Kavin was pleased with him; and then it was that he made himself known to the king. "And," says he, "King O'Toole, you're a decent man, for I only came here to try you. You don't know me," says he, "because I'm disguised."

"Musha! then," says the king, "who are you?"

"I'm Saint Kavin," said the saint, blessing himself.

"Oh, queen of heaven!" says the king, making the sign of the cross between his eyes, and falling down on his knees before the saint; "is it the great Saint Kavin," says he, "that I've been discoursing all this time without knowing it," says he, "all as one as if he was a lump of a gossoon? —and so you're a saint?" says the king.

"I am," says Saint Kavin.

"By Jabers, I thought I was only talking to a dacent boy," says the king.

"Well, you know the difference now," says the saint. "I'm Saint Kavin," says he, "the greatest of all the saints."

And so the king had his goose as good as new to divert him as long as he lived; and the saint

"I will," says the king.

"You won't go back o' your word?" says Saint Kavin.

"Honour bright!" says King O'Toole, holding out his fist.

"Honour bright!" says Saint Kavin, back again, "it's a bargain. Come here!" says he to the poor old goose—"come here, you unfortunate ould cripple, and it's I that'll make you the sporting bird." With that, my dear, he took up the goose by the two wings—"Criss o' my cross an you," says he, markin' her to grace with the blessed sign at the same minute—and throwing her up in the air, "whew," says he, jist givin' her a blast to help her; and with that, my jewel, she took to her heels, flyin' like one o' the eagles themselves, and cutting as many capers as a swallow before a shower of rain.

supported him after he came into his property, as I told you, until the day of his death—and that was soon after; for the poor goose thought he was catching a trout one Friday; but, my jewel, it was a mistake he made—and instead of a trout, it was a thieving horse-eel; and instead of the goose killing a trout for the king's supper —by dad, the eel killed the king's goose—and small blame to him; but he didn't ate her, because he darn't ate what Saint Kavin had laid his blessed hands on.

CONNLA AND
THE FAIRY MAIDEN

This is an ancient story that goes back to the pre-Christian times of the Druids. Some think it is one of the most ancient of recorded stories. It is a good example of romance between a fairy maiden and a mortal. Notice the description of fairyland, which the poet William Butler Yeats translated as the "Land of Heart's Desire."

Connla of the Fiery Hair was son of Conn of the Hundred Fights. One day as he stood by the side of his father on the height of Usna, he saw a maiden clad in strange attire towards him coming.

"Whence comest thou, maiden?" said Connla.

"I come from the Plains of the Ever Living," she said, "there where is neither death nor sin. There we keep holiday alway, nor need we help from any in our joy. And in all our pleasure we have no strife. And because we have our homes in the round green hills, men call us the Hill Folk."

The king and all with him wondered much to hear a voice when they saw no one. For save Connla alone, none saw the Fairy Maiden.

"To whom art thou talking, my son?" said Conn the king.

Then the maiden answered, "Connla speaks to a young, fair maid, whom neither death nor old age awaits. I love Connla, and now I call him away to the Plain of Pleasure, Moy Mell,

"Connla and the Fairy Maiden." From *Celtic Fairy Tales*, edited by Joseph Jacobs. By permission of G. P. Putnam's Sons and Frederick Muller Ltd., London

where Boadag is king for aye, nor has there been sorrow or complaint in that land since he held the kingship. Oh, come with me, Connla of the Fiery Hair, ruddy as the dawn, with thy tawny skin. A fairy crown awaits thee to grace thy comely face and royal form. Come, and never shall thy comeliness fade, nor thy youth, till the last awful day of judgment."

The king in fear at what the maiden said, which he heard though he could not see her, called aloud to his Druid, Coran by name.

"O Coran of the many spells," he said, "and of the cunning magic, I call upon thy aid. A task is upon me too great for all my skill and wit, greater than any laid upon me since I seized the kingship. A maiden unseen has met us, and by her power would take from me my dear, my comely son. If thou help not, he will be taken from thy king by woman's wiles and witchery."

Then Coran the Druid stood forth and chanted his spells towards the spot where the maiden's voice had been heard. And none heard her voice again, nor could Connla see her longer. Only as she vanished before the Druid's mighty spell, she threw an apple to Connla.

For a whole month from that day Connla would take nothing, either to eat or to drink, save only from that apple. But as he ate, it grew again and always kept whole. And all the while there grew within him a mighty yearning and longing after the maiden he had seen.

But when the last day of the month of waiting came, Connla stood by the side of the king his father on the Plain of Arcomin, and again he saw the maiden come towards him, and again she spoke to him.

" 'Tis a glorious place, forsooth, that Connla holds among shortlived mortals awaiting the day of death. But now the folk of life, the ever-living ones, beg and bid thee come to Moy Mell, the Plain of Pleasure, for they have learnt to know thee, seeing thee in thy home among thy dear ones."

When Conn the king heard the maiden's voice, he called to his men aloud and said:

"Summon swift my Druid Coran, for I see she has again this day the power of speech."

Then the maiden said: "O mighty Conn, Fighter of a Hundred Fights, the Druid's power is little loved; it has little honour in the mighty land, peopled with so many of the upright. When the Law comes, it will do away with the Druid's magic spells that issue from the lips of the false black demon."

Then Conn the king observed that since the coming of the maiden Connla his son spoke to none that spake to him. So Conn of the Hundred Fights said to him, "Is it to thy mind what the woman says, my son?"

"'Tis hard upon me," said Connla; "I love my own folk above all things; but yet a longing seizes me for the maiden."

When the maiden heard this, she answered and said: "The ocean is not so strong as the waves of thy longing. Come with me in my curragh, the gleaming, straight-gliding crystal ca-noe. Soon can we reach Boadag's realm. I see the bright sun sink, yet far as it is, we can reach it before dark. There is, too, another land worthy of thy journey, a land joyous to all that seek it. Only wives and maidens dwell there. If thou wilt, we can seek it and live there alone together in joy."

When the maiden ceased to speak, Connla of the Fiery Hair rushed away from his kinsmen and sprang into the curragh, the gleaming, straight-gliding crystal canoe. And then they all, king and court, saw it glide away over the bright sea towards the setting sun, away and away, till eye could see it no longer. So Connla and the Fairy Maiden went forth on the sea, and were no more seen, nor did any know whither they came.

A Finnish folk tale

The Finns are said to have the largest collection of folk tales in manuscript form of any national group. They are not well known in this country, perhaps because of difficult names and long descriptions but those which have been translated are colorful and worth using.

HIDDEN LAIVA

OR THE GOLDEN SHIP

Men's dreams of flying are so graphically expressed in this story that parts of it sound like a report of an airplane flight. The romance has some amusing ups and downs but the princess seems to improve with age.

In olden days there lived a woodsman whose name was Toivo. Every day, with his bow and arrows slung across his shoulder, he used to wander through the wild forests of Finland. One day in his wanderings he came to a high jagged mountain where no man had ever set foot before. For this was the mountain where the Gnomes lived, and there in a dark hidden cavern lay Hiitola, the Gnomes' home.

"Hidden Laiva or the Golden Ship." From *Tales from a Finnish Tupa* by James Cloyd Bowman and Margery Bianco. Published by Albert Whitman & Company, Chicago

When the Gnomes saw Toivo, they all crowded round him and began shouting: "You come at just the right moment! If you will settle our quarrel and help us to divide our gold fairly between us, we will give you money and a golden ship."

It happened that the parents of these Gnomes had died just a few days before, and the Gnomes had fallen heir to all their wealth. They were very busy trying to divide it up. The whole mountain side was strewn with golden spoons and golden dishes and golden carriages. There was a lot of money, too, great shining gold pieces lying all about. The Gnomes were very greedy; each wanted to have more than his own share and so they couldn't come to any agreement about it all.

Toivo stared about him at all this wealth strewn around. More beautiful than the dishes or carriages was a ship of gold that stood on a high rock shining in the sun. The ship caught Toivo's eye at once.

"How do you make this ship go?" he asked the Gnomes.

The largest of the Gnomes stepped forward. He had a turned-up nose, a shaggy pointed red beard and short bandy legs. He hopped into the golden ship and said:

"Why, you just lift this upper what-you-may-call-it with your hand, and push the lower one with your foot, and the ship will race with the wind like a wild tern."

As soon as Toivo had learned the trick, he made a bargain with the Gnomes.

"If you will give me the golden ship and fill it with golden spoons and dishes, and fill my pockets with money, I'll show you how to settle your quarrel."

"Agreed!" shouted the Gnomes, and they began scrambling about in a great hurry to do as he asked.

Toivo set an arrow to his bow and said:

"I am going to shoot an arrow, and the first one to find it will be your King. He will settle your affairs."

"That's wonderful! Now we'll be happy again," shouted the Gnomes.

Toivo stretched his bow and sent the arrow whistling through the air. All the Gnomes went rushing after it. Then Toivo jumped into the golden ship, he pulled with his hand and he pushed with his foot, there was a loud whir-rr, and the ship leaped down the steep mountain and far out across the sea.

Soon after Toivo brought it to a perfect landing before the King's castle.

It happened that the King's daughter was on the castle steps at that very moment. She was sitting with her chin in her hands, dreaming of the day that some brave prince would come riding up to marry her, when all at once she saw the golden ship.

"This must surely be a prince from some wonderful country," she said to herself, "to come riding over land and sea in a ship like that!"

And she came dancing down the castle steps.

"Take me in your golden ship, dear Prince," she said, "and I will be your bride!"

But Toivo could only stammer, "Sweet Princess, you're making a big mistake, I'm merely Toivo, a common woodsman. I'm not good enough to touch the shoes on your feet. There are plenty of Kings' sons who would be glad and proud to be your husband!"

But the Princess was so excited about the golden ship and the golden spoons and the golden dishes that she didn't care whether Toivo was only a woodsman or what he was.

"It doesn't matter a bit," she said. "Take me in your ship, that's all, and I'll be your bride."

"You're making fun of me," Toivo answered her. "No one but a King's son would be good enough for the likes of you."

The Princess ran into the castle and back again, her arms heaped with costly clothes.

"Dress up in these," she laughed, "and you'll be a Prince too!" And back she ran to fetch food and drink.

Toivo was so humble he dared not even lay a finger on those fine clothes. He felt that he was not even good enough to be the Princess's servant. And he gazed at her in fear and trembling as she paced back and forth before the golden ship, begging him to marry her.

But at the end of seven days he saw that she was really unhappy because he refused her, so he said:

"Gentle Princess, if you really want to make a bargain with a humble woodsman, step into the ship."

As soon as she was seated, he fell on his knees and asked:

"Where would you like to sail, gentle Princess, in this golden ship?"

"To the very middle of the sea. I've heard tell there is an island there ten miles long where the berry bushes are loaded to the ground with red and purple fruit, and where the birds sing day and night."

Toivo pushed with his hand and pulled with his foot, and off flew the golden ship over land and sea. Soon it dived from the sky, right down to the center of an island, and stopped there. Toivo jumped out and ran to look for the purple and red berries.

The first berries that he found were yellow. Toivo tasted them, and before he knew what was happening he fell to the ground in a deep sleep. The Princess waited impatiently for him to come back. At first she thought he was lost. But after three days she decided that he had deserted her, and she grew very angry.

"Die here, you low-bred knave!" she cried. "I shall turn the golden ship round and sail right home again."

So she pulled with her hand and pushed with her foot, and flew back to the castle, while poor Toivo still lay sprawled out on the ground fast asleep.

At the end of another day, Toivo woke up. He searched everywhere, but he could not find the golden ship nor the Princess. His beautiful golden spoons and dishes were gone, too. All he had left was a pocketful of money.

As he hunted high and low, he grew faint with hunger. Before him was a bush laden with purple berries. Toivo filled his left pocket with the fruit, thrust a berry into his mouth and began crunching it between his teeth. All at once he felt horns growing out from his head, monstrous pronged horns like the antlers of a wild moose. They were heavy and they hurt terribly.

"It would be better if I'd stayed hungry," he thought. "These horns are driving me crazy! If a ship should come, the sailors will take me for a wild beast and shoot me."

As he looked for some safe place in which to hide, he saw a bush with red berries on it. He filled his right pocket this time, and crunched one of the red berries between his teeth. No sooner had he done so than the heavy horns fell by magic from his head and he became the most handsome man in the world.

Next day a ship appeared over the edge of

the sea. Toivo ran up and down the beach shouting to the sailors. "Take me with you, good friends, take me away before I die on this island. Bring me to the King's castle and I will pay you well."

The sailors gladly took Toivo and set him down before the King's castle. There he walked through the garden and came to a clear sparkling pool. He sat down on the edge of the pool and dipped his tired feet in the water.

It so happened that the King's Butler was coming to draw water. He said to Toivo:

"My good man, tired you may be, but if the King hears that you've been dipping your dusty feet into his drinking water, he'll have your head cut off!"

"My good sir," said Toivo, "the water will soon be clear again, but I'm sorry for my mistake. Let me show you a secret."

And he took a shining red berry from his right pocket and gave it to the Butler. The Butler crunched the berry between his teeth, and at once became the handsomest man in the kingdom, next of course to Toivo himself. He was so delighted that he hid Toivo in a corner of the pantry where the King would not find him.

At dinner time the Princess saw how wonderfully changed the Butler was in his looks, and it made her very curious.

"What has made you so handsome all of a sudden?" she asked him.

"I met a man in the garden who gave me a shining red berry," he whispered. "I ate it, and the charm worked. I became as you now see me."

"Find that man," the Princess said. "Tell him if he'll only make me beautiful too, I'll marry him."

"I'm afraid he's gone," the Butler said. "He wanted to hide, because he was afraid someone would cut his head off if they found him here."

"Tell him not to be frightened," the Princess said. "I will protect him. Bring him into the secret chamber and I'll give him food and drink."

The Butler went to fetch Toivo, and when they returned they found the Princess waiting with food and drink all set out. When the Princess saw Toivo, he was so handsome that she did not know him at all. While he was eating she said:

"If you can make me as beautiful as you are handsome, I'll be your bride."

Toivo became hot with anger, for he thought the Princess had grown tired of him on the island and had run away, stealing his golden ship and leaving him there to die. He did not know of the long time she had waited there.

"No, gentle Princess," he said. "I'm only a poor servant. There is many a King's son who would gladly marry you."

"Only believe me," she said. "I will dress you in a uniform of a General in the King's Army. I will fill your pockets with gold. I will give you a magic golden ship! Only please, please make me as beautiful as you are handsome, and let us be married."

"Very well," said Toivo at last. "Have it your way. Eat this berry."

He took a purple berry from his left pocket, and as the Princess crunched the berry between her teeth a pair of monstrous pronged horns grew out from her head, as heavy and huge as the horns of a wild elk!

As for Toivo, he got very frightened at what he had done, and ran off to hide.

The Princess set up a great hullabaloo, and everyone came running. When the King saw the horns he tried to cut them away, but they were hard as iron and firmly fixed to her head. So then he ordered his two strongest soldiers to follow behind the Princess everywhere she went and carry the weight of the horns while she walked.

No wonder the whole court was upset! The King and the Queen and all the ladies and gentlemen in waiting could talk of nothing but the poor Princess and her terrible plight. In despair the King at last sent soldiers into every part of his kingdom with this message:

"Whoever will cure the King's daughter by removing her monstrous horns shall receive the hand of the King's daughter in marriage and be raised to the highest command in the King's Army."

From every part of the kingdom came doctors and healers and magicians. They tried all their medicines and potions, all their spells and wonders. But it was wasted work, for the horns still remained.

At last, after many days, Toivo came forward from the crowd and knelt before the King, saying:

"O King, please let me try my cure."

"I doubt if you can do anything, my lad," the King said. "You can see for yourself how all these wise men have failed, one after another. They have eaten and drunk to their own luck, but my poor daughter remains the same."

"But, King, I am the only one who knows the right charm," Toivo begged. "If you'll let me try, I'm sure I can take away the horns."

"Try, then, and if the horns do fall from my daughter's head, I'll make you the highest general in my army."

"Send all these doctors and healers away," said Toivo, "and command your soldiers to make merry, for I will surely make your daughter the most beautiful woman in the kingdom!"

So the King commanded all the doctors and healers and magicians to go home, and the soldiers to make merry, while Toivo was left alone to work his cure.

Toivo said to the maidservant:

"Go, girl, and put dry sticks in the *sauna* (bath house) hearth. Make a hot fire to heat the stones in the Princess's bath house."

And to the page boy he said:

"Run quick to the deep wild forest, boy, and fetch me three long straight willow twigs. With these I will make the horns disappear."

The *sauna* was made ready with warm water and heated stones. The long straight willow twigs were brought and laid in the bath house, too. Then Toivo called for the Princess. He sent the maidservant outside and shut the door. He set the Princess on a bench. He tore the clothing from her shoulders and began to beat her soundly with the willow twigs.

"I'll teach you to run away with my golden ship and leave me to die in the middle of the sea!" he shouted between the strokes. "I'll teach you, you cruel woman, to steal my golden spoons and my golden dishes! I am Toivo, the man you promised to marry if I would take you to a far-off island! I'll teach you!"

The Princess's shoulders were soon red and welted from the blows of the willow twigs. She cried:

"Stop beating me, stop beating me, poor man, and I'll explain everything. Only stop, and I promise never to harm you again!"

"Very well then, explain," said Toivo gruffly.

"It was like this," the Princess began. "For three long days and nights I waited for you. I can't tell you how lonely it seemed, there on that island in the middle of the sea. Every moment I expected some horrible monster to come and swallow me alive. I felt sure you had deserted me, and you can't blame me for being so frightened that I flew back home in your golden ship. How can you doubt that I loved you from the very beginning, and still do!"

When Toivo heard this he threw away the willow twigs and fell on his knees before her. "Forgive me, forgive me for being angry with you, gentle Princess! I will never lift my hand against you again."

As he spoke, Toivo drew a shining red berry from his right pocket. The Princess crunched it between her teeth; at once the ugly horns fell from her head and her face became as fair as a new-blown rose.

Toivo called the maidservant. She dressed the Princess in fine linen; upon her head she set the tall bridal crown, covered with jewels, and upon her feet soft shoes woven of the finest white birch bark in all the King's land.

When the people saw the Princess in her white robe, her thick golden braids falling to her knees, her blue eyes shining and her skin like the fairest rose-petal, they knew she had become the most beautiful woman in the kingdom.

The King was so happy he declared a holiday throughout the whole land. Everywhere people ate, drank and danced all night long.

Toivo became the King's highest general. He married his Princess and they all lived happily ever after.

Czechoslovakian folk tales

The Czech stories have been fortunate in their translator. The clear, vigorous English preserves the peculiar folk flavor of the tales and their humor.

BUDULINEK

It is interesting to note the numbers of stories which warn children not to let anyone in the house when they are alone. This is an exceptionally exciting story for the seven- and eight-year-olds and readily lends itself to amusing illustration.

There was once a little boy named Budulinek. He lived with his old Granny in a cottage near a forest.

Granny went out to work every day. In the morning when she went away she always said:

"Budulinek." From *The Shoemaker's Apron*, copyright 1920 by Parker Fillmore; renewed 1948 by Louise Fillmore. Reprinted by permission of Harcourt, Brace and Company, Inc.

"There, Budulinek, there's your dinner on the table and mind, you mustn't open the door no matter who knocks!"

One morning Granny said:

"Now, Budulinek, today I'm leaving you some soup for your dinner. Eat it when dinner time comes. And remember what I always say: don't open the door no matter who knocks."

She went away and pretty soon Lishka, the sly

old mother fox, came and knocked on the door.

"Budulinek!" she called. "You know me! Open the door! Please!"

Budulinek called back:

"No, I mustn't open the door."

But Lishka, the sly old mother fox, kept on knocking.

"Listen, Budulinek," she said: "if you open the door, do you know what I'll do? I'll give you a ride on my tail!"

Now Budulinek thought to himself:

"Oh, that would be fun to ride on the tail of Lishka, the fox!"

So Budulinek forgot all about what Granny said to him every day and opened the door.

Lishka, the sly old thing, came into the room and what do you think she did? Do you think she gave Budulinek a ride on her tail? Well, she didn't. She just went over to the table and gobbled up the bowl of soup that Granny had put there for Budulinek's dinner and then she ran away.

When dinner time came Budulinek hadn't anything to eat.

In the evening when Granny came home, she said:

"Budulinek, did you open the door and let anyone in?"

Budulinek was crying because he was so hungry, and he said:

"Yes, I let in Lishka, the old mother fox, and she ate up all my dinner, too!"

Granny said:

"Now, Budulinek, you see what happens when you open the door and let some one in. Another time remember what Granny says and don't open the door."

The next morning Granny cooked some porridge for Budulinek's dinner and said:

"Now, Budulinek, here's some porridge for your dinner. Remember, while I'm gone you must not open the door no matter who knocks."

Granny was no sooner out of sight than Lishka came again and knocked on the door.

"Oh, Budulinek!" she called. "Open the door and let me in!"

But Budulinek said:

"No, I won't open the door!"

"Oh, now, Budulinek, please open the door!" Lishka begged. "You know me! Do you know what I'll do if you open the door? I'll give you a ride on my tail! Truly I will!"

Budulinek thought to himself:

"This time maybe she will give me a ride on her tail."

So he opened the door.

Lishka came into the room, gobbled up Budulinek's porridge, and ran away without giving him any ride at all.

When dinner time came Budulinek hadn't anything to eat.

In the evening when Granny came home she said:

"Budulinek, did you open the door and let anyone in?"

Budulinek was crying again because he was so hungry, and he said:

"Yes, I let in Lishka, the old mother fox, and she ate up all my porridge, too!"

"Budulinek, you're a bad boy!" Granny said. "If you open the door again, I'll have to spank you! Do you hear?"

The next morning before she went to work, Granny cooked some peas for Budulinek's dinner.

As soon as Granny was gone he began eating the peas, they were so good.

Presently Lishka, the fox, came and knocked on the door.

"Budulinek!" she called. "Open the door! I want to come in!"

But Budulinek wouldn't open the door. He took his bowl of peas and went to the window and ate them there where Lishka could see him.

"Oh, Budulinek!" Lishka begged. "You know me! Please open the door! This time I promise you I'll give you a ride on my tail! Truly I will!"

She just begged and begged until at last Budulinek opened the door. Then Lishka jumped into the room and do you know what she did? She put her nose right into the bowl of peas and gobbled them all up!

Then she said to Budulinek:

"Now get on my tail and I'll give you a ride!"

So Budulinek climbed on Lishka's tail and Lishka went running around the room faster and faster until Budulinek was dizzy and just had to hold on with all his might.

Then, before Budulinek knew what was happening, Lishka slipped out of the house and ran off swiftly into the forest, home to her hole, with Budulinek still on her tail! She hid Budulinek down in her hole with her own three children and she wouldn't let him out. He had to stay there with the three little foxes and they all teased him and bit him. And then wasn't he sorry he had disobeyed his Granny! And, oh, how he cried!

When Granny came home she found the door open and no little Budulinek anywhere. She looked high and low, but no, there was no little Budulinek. She asked everyone she met had they seen her little Budulinek, but nobody had. So poor Granny just cried and cried, she was so lonely and sad.

One day an organ-grinder with a wooden leg began playing in front of Granny's cottage. The music made her think of Budulinek.

"Organ-grinder," Granny said, "here's a penny for you. But, please, don't play any more. Your music makes me cry."

"Why does it make you cry?" the organ-grinder asked.

"Because it reminds me of Budulinek," Granny said, and she told the organ-grinder all about Budulinek and how somebody had stolen him away.

The organ-grinder said:

"Poor Granny! I tell you what I'll do: as I

go around and play my organ I'll keep my eyes open for Budulinek. If I find him I'll bring him back to you."

"Will you?" Granny cried. "If you bring me back my little Budulinek I'll give you a measure of rye and a measure of millet and a measure of poppy seed and a measure of everything in the house!"

So the organ-grinder went off and everywhere he played his organ he looked for Budulinek. But he couldn't find him.

At last one day while he was walking through the forest he thought he heard a little boy crying. He looked around everywhere until he found a fox's hole.

"Oho!" he said to himself. "I believe that wicked old Lishka must have stolen Budulinek! She's probably keeping him here with her own three children! I'll soon find out."

So he put down his organ and began to play. And as he played he sang softly:

"One old fox
And two, three, four,
And Budulinek
He makes one more!"

Old Lishka heard the music playing and she said to her oldest child:

"Here, son, give the old man a penny and tell him to go away because my head aches."

So the oldest little fox climbed out of the hole and gave the organ-grinder a penny and said:

"My mother says, please will you go away because her head aches."

As the organ-grinder reached over to take the penny, he caught the oldest little fox and stuffed him into a sack. Then he went on playing and singing:

"One old fox
And two and three
And Budulinek
Makes four for me!"

Presently Lishka sent out her second child with a penny and the organ-grinder caught the second little fox in the same way and stuffed it also into the sack. Then he went on grinding his organ and softly singing:

"One old fox
And another for me,
And Budulinek
He makes the three."

"I wonder why that old man still plays his organ," Lishka said and sent out her third child with a penny.

So the organ-grinder caught the third little fox and stuffed it also into the sack. Then he kept on playing and singing softly:

"One old fox—
I'll soon get you!—
And Budulinek
He makes just two."

At last Lishka herself came out. So he caught her, too, and stuffed her in with her children. Then he sang:

"Four naughty foxes
Caught alive!
And Budulinek
He makes the five!"

The organ-grinder went to the hole and called down:

"Budulinek! Budulinek! Come out!"

As there were no foxes left to hold him back, Budulinek was able to crawl out.

When he saw the organ-grinder he cried and said:

"Oh, please, Mr. Organ-Grinder, I want to go home to my Granny!"

"I'll take you home to your Granny," the organ-grinder said, "but first I must punish these naughty foxes."

The organ-grinder cut a strong switch and gave the four foxes in the sack a terrible beating until they begged him to stop and promised that they would never again do anything to Budulinek.

Then the organ-grinder let them go and he took Budulinek home to Granny.

Granny was delighted to see her little Budulinek and she gave the organ-grinder a measure of rye and a measure of millet and a measure of poppy seed and a measure of everything else in the house.

And Budulinek never again opened the door!

CLEVER MANKA

This is a good example of the humor in Czech stories. It especially delights girls after hearing "The Most Obedient Wife."

There was once a rich farmer who was as grasping and unscrupulous as he was rich. He was always driving a hard bargain and always getting the better of his poor neighbors. One of these neighbors was a humble shepherd who in return for service was to receive from the farmer a heifer. When the time of payment came the farmer refused to give the shepherd the heifer and the shepherd was forced to lay the matter before the burgomaster.

The burgomaster, who was a young man and as yet not very experienced, listened to both sides and when he had deliberated he said:

"Instead of deciding this case, I will put a riddle to you both and the man who makes the best answer shall have the heifer. Are you agreed?"

The farmer and the shepherd accepted this proposal and the burgomaster said:

"Well then, here is my riddle: What is the swiftest thing in the world? What is the sweetest thing? What is the richest? Think out your answers and bring them to me at this same hour tomorrow."

The farmer went home in a temper.

"What kind of a burgomaster is this young fellow!" he growled. "If he had let me keep the heifer I'd have sent him a bushel of pears. But now I'm in a fair way of losing the heifer for I can't think of any answer to his foolish riddle."

"What is the matter, husband?" his wife asked.

"It's that new burgomaster. The old one would have given me the heifer without any argument, but this young man thinks to decide the case by asking us riddles."

When he told his wife what the riddle was, she cheered him greatly by telling him that she knew the answers at once.

"Why, husband," said she, "our gray mare must be the swiftest thing in the world. You know yourself nothing ever passes us on the road. As for the sweetest, did you ever taste

"Clever Manka." From *The Shoemaker's Apron*, copyright 1920 by Parker Fillmore; renewed 1948 by Louise Fillmore. Reprinted by permission of Harcourt, Brace and Company, Inc.

honey any sweeter than ours? And I'm sure there's nothing richer than our chest of golden ducats that we've been laying by these forty years."

The farmer was delighted.

"You're right, wife, you're right! That heifer remains ours!"

The shepherd when he got home was downcast and sad. He had a daughter, a clever girl named Manka, who met him at the door of his cottage and asked:

"What is it, father? What did the burgomaster say?"

The shepherd sighed.

"I'm afraid I've lost the heifer. The burgomaster set us a riddle and I know I shall never guess it."

"Perhaps I can help you," Manka said. "What is it?"

So the shepherd gave her the riddle and the next day as he was setting out for the burgomaster's, Manka told him what answers to make.

When he reached the burgomaster's house, the farmer was already there rubbing his hands and beaming with self-importance.

The burgomaster again propounded the riddle and then asked the farmer his answers.

The farmer cleared his throat and with a pompous air began:

"The swiftest thing in the world? Why, my dear sir, that's my gray mare, of course, for no other horse ever passes us on the road. The sweetest? Honey from my beehives, to be sure. The richest? What can be richer than my chest of golden ducats!"

And the farmer squared his shoulders and smiled triumphantly.

"H'm," said the young burgomaster, dryly. Then he asked:

"What answers does the shepherd make?"

The shepherd bowed politely and said:

"The swiftest thing in the world is thought for thought can run any distance in the twinkling of an eye. The sweetest thing of all is sleep for when a man is tired and sad what can be sweeter? The richest thing is the earth for out of the earth come all the riches of the world."

"Good!" the burgomaster cried. "Good! The heifer goes to the shepherd!"

Later the burgomaster said to the shepherd:

"Tell me, now, who gave you those answers? I'm sure they never came out of your own head."

At first the shepherd tried not to tell, but when the burgomaster pressed him he confessed that they came from his daughter, Manka. The burgomaster, who thought that he would like to make another test of Manka's cleverness, sent for ten eggs. He gave them to the shepherd and said:

"Take these eggs to Manka and tell her to have them hatched out by tomorrow and to bring me the chicks."

When the shepherd reached home and gave Manka the burgomaster's message, Manka laughed and said: "Take a handful of millet and go right back to the burgomaster. Say to him: 'My daughter sends you this millet. She says that if you plant, grow it, and have it harvested by tomorrow, she'll bring you the ten chicks and you can feed them the ripe grain.'"

When the burgomaster heard this, he laughed heartily.

"That's a clever girl of yours," he told the shepherd. "If she's as comely as she is clever, I think I'd like to marry her. Tell her to come to see me, but she must come neither by day nor by night, neither riding nor walking, neither dressed nor undressed."

When Manka received this message she waited until the next dawn when night was gone and day not yet arrived. Then she wrapped herself in a fishnet and, throwing one leg over a goat's back and keeping one foot on the ground, she went to the burgomaster's house.

Now I ask you: did she go dressed? No, she wasn't dressed. A fishnet isn't clothing. Did she go undressed? Of course not, for wasn't she covered with a fishnet? Did she walk to the burgomaster's? No, she didn't walk for she went with one leg thrown over a goat. Then did she ride? Of course she didn't ride for wasn't she walking on one foot?

When she reached the burgomaster's house she called out:

"Here I am, Mr. Burgomaster, and I've come neither by day nor by night, neither riding nor walking, neither dressed nor undressed."

The young burgomaster was so delighted with Manka's cleverness and so pleased with her comely looks that he proposed to her at once and in a short time married her.

"But understand, my dear Manka," he said, "you are not to use that cleverness of yours at my expense. I won't have you interfering in any of my cases. In fact if ever you give advice to any one who comes to me for judgment, I'll turn you out of my house at once and send you home to your father."

All went well for a time. Manka busied herself in her house-keeping and was careful not to interfere in any of the burgomaster's cases.

Then one day two farmers came to the burgomaster to have a dispute settled. One of the farmers owned a mare which had foaled in the marketplace. The colt had run under the wagon of the other farmer and thereupon the owner of the wagon claimed the colt as his property.

The burgomaster, who was thinking of something else while the case was being presented, said carelessly:

"The man who found the colt under his wagon is, of course, the owner of the colt."

As the owner of the mare was leaving the burgomaster's house, he met Manka and stopped to tell her about the case. Manka was ashamed of her husband for making so foolish a decision and she said to the farmer:

"Come back this afternoon with a fishing net and stretch it across the dusty road. When the burgomaster sees you he will come out and ask you what you are doing. Say to him that you're catching fish. When he asks you how you can expect to catch fish in a dusty road, tell him it's just as easy for you to catch fish in a dusty road as it is for a wagon to foal. Then he'll see the injustice of his decision and have the colt returned to you. But remember one thing: you mustn't let him find out that it was I who told you to do this."

That afternoon when the burgomaster chanced to look out the window he saw a man stretching a fishnet across the dusty road. He went out to him and asked: "What are you doing?"

"Fishing."

"Fishing in a dusty road? Are you daft?"

"Well," the man said, "it's just as easy for me to catch fish in a dusty road as it is for a wagon to foal."

Then the burgomaster recognized the man as the owner of the mare and he had to confess that what he said was true.

"Of course the colt belongs to your mare and must be returned to you. But tell me," he said, "who put you up to this? You didn't think of it yourself."

The farmer tried not to tell but the burgomaster questioned him until he found out that Manka was at the bottom of it. This made him very angry. He went into the house and called his wife.

"Manka," he said, "do you forget what I told you would happen if you went interfering in any of my cases? Home you go this very day. I don't care to hear any excuses. The matter is settled. You may take with you the one thing you like best in my house for I won't have people saying that I treated you shabbily."

Manka made no outcry.

"Very well, my dear husband, I shall do as you say: I shall go to my father's cottage and take with me the one thing I like best in your house. But don't make me go until after supper. We have been very happy together and I should like to eat one last meal with you. Let us have no more words but be kind to each other as we've always been and then part as friends."

The burgomaster agreed to this and Manka prepared a fine supper of all the dishes of which her husband was particularly fond. The burgo-master opened his choicest wine and pledged Manka's health. Then he set to, and the supper was so good that he ate and ate and ate. And the more he ate, the more he drank until at last he grew drowsy and fell sound asleep in his chair. Then without awakening him Manka had him carried out to the wagon that was waiting to take her home to her father.

The next morning when the burgomaster opened his eyes, he found himself lying in the shepherd's cottage.

"What does this mean?" he roared out.

"Nothing, dear husband, nothing!" Manka said. "You know you told me I might take with me the one thing I liked best in your house, so of course I took you! That's all."

For a moment the burgomaster rubbed his eyes in amazement. Then he laughed loud and heartily to think how Manka had outwitted him.

"Manka," he said, "you're too clever for me. Come on, my dear, let's go home."

So they climbed back into the wagon and drove home.

The burgomaster never again scolded his wife but thereafter whenever a very difficult case came up he always said:

"I think we had better consult my wife. You know she's a very clever woman."

Russian folk tales

Russian folk tales are, on the whole, bloody and horrible but full of excitement and color. Arthur Ransome in his Old Peter's Russian Tales *has toned them down a bit, and most of the stories in that collection are good for storytelling. Folklore has inspired some well-known Russian music and, since these stories belong to the children eleven to fourteen, it is well to use the stories as introductions to the music. The stories lend themselves to dramatization and illustration.*

SADKO

This story, which has the strangeness of a dream, inspired an opera and may be dramatized by older children, either with puppet or human actors. At the conclusion of the story, the intro-duction of Maroosia and old Peter seems to shatter the spell of the tale. Why not omit them and end with the speculative, "And what happened after that? Well, some say Sadko took his dulcimer and swam out again. . . ."

"Sadko." From *Old Peter's Russian Tales,* edited by Arthur Ransome, Thomas Nelson and Sons Ltd.

In Novgorod in the old days there was a young man—just a boy he was—the son of a rich merchant who had lost all his money and died. So

Sadko was very poor. He had not a kopeck in the world, except what the people gave him when he played his dulcimer for their dancing. He had blue eyes and curling hair, and he was strong, and would have been merry; but it is dull work playing for other folk to dance, and Sadko dared not dance with any young girl, for he had no money to marry on, and he did not want to be chased away as a beggar. And the young women of Novgorod, they never looked at the handsome Sadko. No; they smiled with their bright eyes at the young men who danced with them, and if they ever spoke to Sadko, it was just to tell him sharply to keep the music going or to play faster.

So Sadko lived alone with his dulcimer, and made do with half a loaf when he could not get a whole, and with crust when he had no crumb. He did not mind so very much what came to him, so long as he could play his dulcimer and walk along the banks of the little river Volkhov[1] that flows by Novgorod, or on the shores of the lake, making music for himself, and seeing the pale mists rise over the water, and dawn or sunset across the shining river.

"There is no girl in all Novgorod as pretty as my little river," he used to say, and night after night he would sit by the banks of the river or on the shores of the lake, playing the dulcimer and singing to himself.

Sometimes he helped the fishermen on the lake, and they would give him a little fish for his supper in payment for his strong young arms.

And it happened that one evening the fishermen asked him to watch their nets for them on the shore, while they went off to take their fish to sell them in the square at Novgorod.

Sadko sat on the shore, on a rock, and played his dulcimer and sang. Very sweetly he sang of the fair lake and the lovely river—the little river that he thought prettier than all the girls of Novgorod. And while he was singing he saw a whirlpool in the lake, little waves flying from it across the water, and in the middle a hollow down into the water. And in the hollow he saw the head of a great man with blue hair and a gold crown. He knew that the huge man was the Tzar of the

[1] The Volkhov would be a big river if it were in England, and Sadko and old Peter called it little only because they loved it.

Sea. And the man came nearer, walking up out of the depths of the lake—a huge, great man, a very giant, with blue hair falling to his waist over his broad shoulders. The little waves ran from him in all directions as he came striding up out of the water.

Sadko did not know whether to run or stay; but the Tzar of the Sea called out to him in a great voice like wind and water in a storm,—

"Sadko of Novgorod, you have played and sung many days by the side of this lake and on the banks of the little river Volkhov. My daughters love your music, and it has pleased me too. Throw out a net into the water, and draw it in, and the waters will pay you for your singing. And if you are satisfied with the payment, you must come and play to us down in the green palace of the sea."

With that the Tzar of the Sea went down again into the waters of the lake. The waves closed over him with a roar, and presently the lake was as smooth and calm as it had ever been.

Sadko thought, and said to himself: "Well, there is no harm done in casting out a net." So he threw a net out into the lake.

He sat down again and played on his dulcimer and sang, and when he had finished his singing the dusk had fallen and the moon shone over the lake. He put down his dulcimer and took hold of the ropes of the net, and began to draw it up out of the silver water. Easily the ropes came, and the net, dripping and glittering in the moonlight.

"I was dreaming," said Sadko; "I was asleep when I saw the Tzar of the Sea, and there is nothing in the net at all."

And then, just as the last of the net was coming ashore, he saw something in it, square and dark. He dragged it out, and found it was a coffer. He opened the coffer, and it was full of precious stones—green, red, gold—gleaming in the light of the moon. Diamonds shone there like little bundles of sharp knives.

"There can be no harm in taking these stones," says Sadko, "whether I dreamed or not."

He took the coffer on his shoulder, and bent under the weight of it, strong though he was. He put it in a safe place. All night he sat and watched by the nets, and played and sang, and planned what he would do.

In the morning the fishermen came, laughing and merry after their night in Novgorod, and they gave him a little fish for watching their nets; and he made a fire on the shore, and cooked it and ate it as he used to do.

"And that is my last meal as a poor man," says Sadko. "Ah me! who knows if I shall be happier?"

Then he set the coffer on his shoulder and tramped away for Novgorod.

"Who is that?" they asked at the gates.

"Only Sadko, the dulcimer player," he replied.

"Turned porter?" said they.

"One trade is as good as another," said Sadko, and he walked into the city. He sold a few of the stones, two at a time, and with what he got for them he set up a booth in the market. Small things led to great, and he was soon one of the richest traders in Novgorod.

And now there was not a girl in the town who could look too sweetly at Sadko. "He has golden hair," says one. "Blue eyes like the sea," says another. "He could lift the world on his shoulders," says a third. A little money, you see, opens everybody's eyes.

But Sadko was not changed by his good fortune. Still he walked and played by the little river Volkhov. When work was done and the traders gone, Sadko would take his dulcimer and play and sing on the banks of the river. And still he said, "There is no girl in all Novgorod as pretty as my little river." Every time he came back from his long voyages—for he was trading far and near, like the greatest of merchants—he went at once to the banks of the river to see how his sweetheart fared. And always he brought some little present for her and threw it into the waves.

For twelve years he lived unmarried in Novgorod, and every year made voyages, buying and selling, and always growing richer and richer. Many were the mothers of Novgorod who would have liked to see him married to their daughters. Many were the pillows that were wet with the tears of the young girls, as they thought of the blue eyes of Sadko and his golden hair.

And then, in the twelfth year since he walked into Novgorod with the coffer on his shoulder, he was sailing a ship on the Caspian Sea, far, far away. For many days the ship sailed on, and

Sadko sat on deck and played his dulcimer and sang of Novgorod and of the little river Volkhov that flows under the walls of the town. Blue was the Caspian Sea, and the waves were like furrows in a field, long lines of white under the steady wind, while the sails swelled and the ship shot over the water.

And suddenly the ship stopped.

In the middle of the sea, far from land, the ship stopped and trembled in the waves, as if she were held by a big hand.

"We are aground!" cry the sailors; and the captain, the great one, tells them to take soundings. Seventy fathoms by the bow it was, and seventy fathoms by the stern.

"We are not aground," says the captain, "unless there is a rock sticking up like a needle in the middle of the Caspian Sea!"

"There is magic in this," say the sailors.

"Hoist more sail," says the captain; and up go the white sails, swelling out in the wind, while the masts bend and creak. But still the ship lay shivering, and did not move, out there in the middle of the sea.

"Hoist more sail yet," says the captain; and up go the white sails, swelling and tugging, while the masts creak and groan. But still the ship lay there shivering and did not move.

"There is an unlucky one aboard," says an old sailor. "We must draw lots and find him, and throw him overboard into the sea."

The other sailors agreed to this. And still Sadko sat, and played his dulcimer and sang.

The sailors cut pieces of string, all of a length, as many as there were souls in the ship, and one of those strings they cut in half. Then they made them into a bundle, and each man plucked one string. And Sadko stopped his playing for a moment to pluck a string, and his was the string that had been cut in half.

"Magician, sorcerer, unclean one!" shouted the sailors.

"Not so," said Sadko. "I remember now an old promise I made, and I keep it willingly."

He took his dulcimer in his hand, and leapt from the ship into the blue Caspian Sea. The waves had scarcely closed over his head before the ship shot forward again, and flew over the waves like a swan's feather, and came in the end safely to her harbour.

"And what happened to Sadko?" asked Maroosia.

"You shall hear, little pigeon," said old Peter, and he took a pinch of snuff. Then he went on.

Sadko dropped into the waves, and the waves closed over him. Down he sank, like a pebble thrown into a pool, down and down. First the water was blue, then green, and strange fish with goggle eyes and golden fins swam round him as he sank. He came at last to the bottom of the sea.

And there, on the bottom of the sea, was a palace built of green wood. Yes, all the timbers of all the ships that have been wrecked in all the seas of the world are in that palace, and they are all green, and cunningly fitted together, so that the palace is worth a ten days' journey only to see it. And in front of the palace Sadko saw two big kobbly sturgeons, each a hundred and fifty feet long, lashing their tails and guarding the gates. Now, sturgeons are the oldest of all fish, and these were the oldest of all sturgeons.

Sadko walked between the sturgeons and through the gates of the palace. Inside there was a great hall, and the Tzar of the Sea lay resting in the hall, with his gold crown on his head and his blue hair floating round him in the water, and his great body covered with scales lying along the hall. The Tzar of the Sea filled the hall—and there is room in that hall for a village. And there were fish swimming this way and that in and out of the windows.

"Ah, Sadko," says the Tzar of the Sea, "you took what the sea gave you, but you have been a long time in coming to sing in the palaces of the sea. Twelve years I have lain here waiting for you."

"Great Tzar, forgive," says Sadko.

"Sing now," says the Tzar of the Sea, and his voice was like the beating of waves.

And Sadko played on his dulcimer and sang.

He sang of Novgorod and of the little river Volkhov which he loved. It was in his song that none of the girls of Novgorod were as pretty as the little river. And there was the sound of wind over the lake in his song, the sound of ripples under the prow of a boat, the sound of ripples on the shore, the sound of the river flowing past the tall reeds, the whispering sound of the river at night. And all the time he played cunningly on the dulcimer. The girls of Novgorod had

never danced to so sweet a tune when in the old days Sadko played his dulcimer to earn kopecks and crusts of bread.

Never had the Tzar of the Sea heard such music.

"I would dance," said the Tzar of the Sea, and he stood up like a tall tree in the hall.

"Play on," said the Tzar of the Sea, and he strode through the gates. The sturgeons guarding the gates stirred the water with their tails.

And if the Tzar of the Sea was huge in the hall, he was huger still when he stood outside on the bottom of the sea. He grew taller and taller, towering like a mountain. His feet were like small hills. His blue hair hung down to his waist, and he was covered with green scales. And he began to dance on the bottom of the sea.

Great was that dancing. The sea boiled, and ships went down. The waves rolled as big as houses. The sea overflowed its shores, and whole towns were under water as the Tzar danced mightily on the bottom of the sea. Hither and thither rushed the waves, and the very earth shook at the dancing of that tremendous Tzar.

He danced till he was tired, and then he came back to the palace of green wood, and passed the sturgeons, and shrank into himself and came through the gates into the hall, where Sadko still played on his dulcimer and sang.

"You have played well and given me pleasure," says the Tzar of the Sea. "I have thirty daughters, and you shall choose one and marry her, and be a Prince of the Sea."

"Better than all maidens I love my little river," says Sadko; and the Tzar of the Sea laughed and threw his head back, with his blue hair floating all over the hall.

And then there came in the thirty daughters of the Tzar of the Sea. Beautiful they were, lovely, and graceful; but twenty-nine of them passed by, and Sadko fingered his dulcimer and thought of his little river.

There came in the thirtieth, and Sadko cried out aloud. "Here is the only maiden in the world as pretty as my little river!" says he. And she looked at him with eyes that shone like stars reflected in the river. Her hair was dark, like the river at night. She laughed, and her voice was like the flowing of the river.

"And what is the name of your little river?" says the Tzar.

"It is the little river Volkhov that flows by Novgorod," says Sadko; "but your daughter is as fair as the little river, and I would gladly marry her if she will have me."

"It is a strange thing," says the Tzar, "but Volkhov is the name of my youngest daughter."

He put Sadko's hand in the hand of his youngest daughter, and they kissed each other. And as they kissed, Sadko saw a necklace round her neck, and knew it for one he had thrown into the river as a present for his sweetheart.

She smiled, and "Come!" says she, and took him away to a palace of her own, and showed him a coffer; and in that coffer were bracelets and rings and earrings—all the gifts that he had thrown into the river.

And Sadko laughed for joy, and kissed the youngest daughter of the Tzar of the Sea, and she kissed him back.

"O my little river!" says he; "there is no girl in all the world but thou as pretty as my little river."

Well, they were married, and the Tzar of the Sea laughed at the wedding feast till the palace shook and the fish swam off in all directions.

And after the feast Sadko and his bride went off together to her palace. And before they slept she kissed him very tenderly, and she said,—

"O Sadko, you will not forget me? You will play to me sometimes, and sing?"

"I shall never lose sight of you, my pretty one," says he; "and as for music, I will sing and play all the day long."

"That's as may be," says she, and they fell asleep.

And in the middle of the night Sadko happened to turn in bed, and he touched the Princess with his left foot, and she was cold, cold, cold as ice in January. And with that touch of cold he woke, and he was lying under the walls of Novgorod, with his dulcimer in his hand, and one of his feet was in the little river Volkhov, and the moon was shining.

"O grandfather! And what happened to him after that?" asked Maroosia.

"There are many tales," said old Peter. "Some say he went into the town, and lived on alone until he died. But I think with those who say

that he took his dulcimer and swam out into the middle of the river, and sank under water again, looking for his little Princess. They say he found her, and lives still in the green palaces of the bottom of the sea; and when there is a big storm, you may know that Sadko is playing on his dulcimer and singing, and that the Tzar of the Sea is dancing his tremendous dance, down there, on the bottom, under the waves."

"Yes, I expect that's what happened," said Ivan. "He'd have found it very dull in Novgorod, even though it is a big town."

THE FIRE-BIRD,
THE HORSE OF POWER,
AND THE PRINCESS VASILISSA

This story has the color and the extravagant magic of an Oriental tale. It may well be used as an introduction to the Stravinsky "Firebird" music. The story also lends itself to dramatization, but because of the bird and the horse, puppets are a better medium than child actors.

Once upon a time a strong and powerful Tzar ruled in a country far away. And among the servants was a young archer, and this archer had a horse—a horse of power—such a horse as belonged to the wonderful men of long ago—a great horse with a broad chest, eyes like fire, and hoofs of iron. There are no such horses nowadays. They sleep with the strong men who rode them, the bogatirs, until the time comes when Russia has need of them. Then the great horses will thunder up from under the ground, and the valiant men leap from the graves in the armour they have worn so long. The strong men will sit those horses of power, and there will be swinging of clubs and thunder of hoofs, and the earth will be swept clean from the enemies of God and the Tzar. So my grandfather used to say, and he was as much older than I as I am older than you, little ones, and so he should know.

Well, one day long ago, in the green time of

"The Fire-bird, the Horse of Power, and the Princess Vasilissa." From *Old Peter's Russian Tales*, edited by Arthur Ransome, Thomas Nelson and Sons Ltd.

the year, the young archer rode through the forest on his horse of power. The trees were green; there were little blue flowers on the ground under the trees; the squirrels ran in the branches, and the hares in the undergrowth; but no birds sang. The young archer rode along the forest path and listened for the singing of the birds, but there was no singing. The forest was silent, and the only noises in it were the scratching of four-footed beasts, the dropping of fir cones, and the heavy stamping of the horse of power in the soft path.

"What has come to the birds?" said the young archer.

He had scarcely said this before he saw a big curving feather lying in the path before him. The feather was larger than a swan's, larger than an eagle's. It lay in the path, glittering like a flame; for the sun was on it, and it was a feather of pure gold. Then he knew why there was no singing in the forest. For he knew that the fire-bird had flown that way, and that the feather in the path before him was a feather from its burning breast.

The horse of power spoke and said,

"Leave the golden feather where it lies. If you take it you will be sorry for it, and know the meaning of fear."

But the brave young archer sat on the horse of power and looked at the golden feather, and wondered whether to take it or not. He had no wish to learn what it was to be afraid, but he thought, "If I take it and bring it to the Tzar my master, he will be pleased; and he will not send me away with empty hands, for no tzar in the world has a feather from the burning breast of the fire-bird." And the more he thought, the more he wanted to carry the feather to the Tzar. And in the end he did not listen to the words of the horse of power. He leapt from the saddle, picked up the golden feather of the fire-bird, mounted his horse again, and galloped back through the green forest till he came to the palace of the Tzar.

He went into the palace, and bowed before the Tzar and said,—

"O Tzar, I have brought you a feather of the fire-bird."

The Tzar looked gladly at the feather, and then at the young archer.

"Thank you," says he; "but if you have brought me a feather of the fire-bird, you will be able to bring me the bird itself. I should like to see it. A feather is not a fit gift to bring to the Tzar. Bring the bird itself, or, I swear by my sword, your head shall no longer sit between your shoulders!"

The young archer bowed his head and went out. Bitterly he wept, for he knew now what it was to be afraid. He went out into the courtyard, where the horse of power was waiting for him, tossing its head and stamping on the ground.

"Master," says the horse of power, "why do you weep?"

"The Tzar has told me to bring him the fire-bird, and no man on earth can do that," says the young archer, and he bowed his head on his breast.

"I told you," says the horse of power, "that if you took the feather you would learn the meaning of fear. Well, do not be frightened yet, and do not weep. The trouble is not now; the trouble lies before you. Go back to the Tzar and ask him to have a hundred sacks of maize scattered over the open field, and let this be done at midnight."

The young archer went back into the palace and begged the Tzar for this, and the Tzar ordered that at midnight a hundred sacks of maize should be scattered in the open field.

Next morning, at the first redness in the sky, the young archer rode out on the horse of power, and came to the open field. The ground was scattered all over with maize. In the middle of the field stood a great oak with spreading boughs. The young archer leapt to the ground, took off the saddle, and let the horse of power loose to wander as he pleased about the field. Then he climbed up into the oak and hid himself among the green boughs.

The sky grew red and gold, and the sun rose. Suddenly there was a noise in the forest round the field. The trees shook and swayed, and almost fell. There was a mighty wind. The sea piled itself into waves with crests of foam, and the fire-bird came flying from the other side of the world. Huge and golden and flaming in the sun, it flew, dropped down with open wings into the field, and began to eat the maize.

The horse of power wandered in the field. This way he went, and that, but always he came

a little nearer to the fire-bird. Nearer and nearer came the horse. He came close up to the fire-bird, and then suddenly stepped on one of its spreading fiery wings and pressed it heavily to the ground. The bird struggled, flapping mightily with its fiery wings, but it could not get away. The young archer slipped down from the tree, bound the fire-bird with three strong ropes, swung it on its back, saddled the horse, and rode to the palace of the Tzar.

The young archer stood before the Tzar, and his back was bent under the great weight of the fire-bird, and the broad wings of the bird hung on either side of him like fiery shields, and there was a trail of golden feathers on the floor. The young archer swung the magic bird to the foot of the throne before the Tzar; and the Tzar was glad, because since the beginning of the world no tzar had seen the fire-bird flung before him like a wild duck caught in a snare.

The Tzar looked at the fire-bird and laughed with pride. Then he lifted his eyes and looked at the young archer, and says he,

"As you have known how to take the fire-bird, you will know how to bring me my bride, for whom I have long been waiting. In the land of Never, on the very edge of the world, where the red sun rises in flame from behind the sea, lives the Princess Vasilissa. I will marry none but her. Bring her to me, and I will reward you with silver and gold. But if you do not bring her, then, by my sword, your head will no longer sit between your shoulders!"

The young archer wept bitter tears, and went out into the courtyard where the horse of power was stamping the ground with its hoofs of iron and tossing its thick mane.

"Master, why do you weep?" asked the horse of power.

"The Tzar has ordered me to go to the land of Never, and to bring back the Princess Vasilissa."

"Do not weep—do not grieve. The trouble is not yet; the trouble is to come. Go to the Tzar and ask him for a silver tent with a golden roof, and for all kinds of food and drink to take with us on the journey."

The young archer went in and asked the Tzar for this, and the Tzar gave him a silver tent with silver hangings and a gold-embroidered roof, and every kind of rich wine and the tastiest of foods.

Then the young archer mounted the horse of power and rode off to the land of Never. On and on he rode, many days and nights, and came at last to the edge of the world, where the red sun rises in flame from behind the deep blue sea.

On the shore of the sea the young archer reined in the horse of power, and the heavy hoofs of the horse sank in the sand. He shaded his eyes and looked out over the blue water, and there was the Princess Vasilissa in a little silver boat, rowing with golden oars.

The young archer rode back a little way to where the sand ended and the green world began. There he loosed the horse to wander where he pleased, and to feed on the green grass. Then on the edge of the shore, where the green grass ended and grew thin and the sand began, he set up the shining tent, with its silver hangings and its gold-embroidered roof. In the tent he set out the tasty dishes and the rich flagons of wine which the Tzar had given him, and he sat himself down in the tent and began to regale himself, while he waited for the Princess Vasilissa.

The Princess Vasilissa dipped her golden oars in the blue water, and the little silver boat moved lightly through the dancing waves. She sat in the little boat and looked over the blue sea to the edge of the world, and there, between the golden sand and the green earth, she saw the tent standing, silver and gold in the sun. She dipped her oars, and came nearer to see it the better. The nearer she came the fairer seemed the tent, and at last she rowed to the shore and grounded her little boat on the golden sand, and stepped out daintily and came up to the tent. She was a little frightened, and now and again she stopped and looked back to where the silver boat lay on the sand with the blue sea beyond it. The young archer said not a word, but went on regaling himself on the pleasant dishes he had set out there in the tent.

At last the Princess Vasilissa came up to the tent and looked in.

The young archer rose and bowed before her. Says he—

"Good-day to you, Princess! Be so kind as to come in and take bread and salt with me, and taste my foreign wines."

And the Princess Vasilissa came into the tent and sat down with the young archer, and ate sweetmeats with him, and drank his health in a golden goblet of the wine the Tzar had given him. Now this wine was heavy, and the last drop from the goblet had no sooner trickled down her little slender throat than her eyes closed against her will, once, twice, and again.

"Ah me!" says the Princess, "it is as if the night itself had perched on my eyelids, and yet it is but noon."

And the golden goblet dropped to the ground from her little fingers, and she leant back on a cushion and fell instantly asleep. If she had been beautiful before, she was lovelier still when she lay in that deep sleep in the shadow of the tent.

Quickly the young archer called to the horse of power. Lightly he lifted the Princess in his strong young arms. Swiftly he leapt with her into the saddle. Like a feather she lay in the hollow of his left arm, and slept while the iron hoofs of the great horse thundered over the ground.

They came to the Tzar's palace, and the young archer leapt from the horse of power and carried the Princess into the palace. Great was the joy of the Tzar; but it did not last for long.

"Go, sound the trumpets for our wedding," he said to his servants; "let all the bells be rung."

The bells rang out and the trumpets sounded, and at the noise of the horns and the ringing of the bells the Princess Vasilissa woke up and looked about her.

"What is this ringing of bells," says she, "and this noise of trumpets? And where, oh, where is the blue sea, and my little silver boat with its golden oars?" And the princess put her hand to her eyes.

"The blue sea is far away," says the Tzar, "and for your little silver boat I give you a golden throne. The trumpets sound for our wedding, and the bells are ringing for our joy."

But the Princess turned her face away from the Tzar; and there was no wonder in that, for he was old, and his eyes were not kind.

And she looked with love at the young archer; and there was no wonder in that either, for he was a young man fit to ride the horse of power.

The Tzar was angry with the Princess Vasilissa, but his anger was as useless as his joy.

"Why, Princess," says he, "will you not marry me, and forget your blue sea and your silver boat?"

"In the middle of the deep blue sea lies a great stone," says the Princess, "and under that stone is hidden my wedding dress. If I cannot wear that dress I will marry nobody at all."

Instantly the Tzar turned to the young archer, who was waiting before the throne.

"Ride swiftly back," says he, "to the land of Never, where the red sun rises in flame. There—do you hear what the Princess says?—a great stone lies in the middle of the sea. Under that stone is hidden her wedding dress. Ride swiftly. Bring back that dress, or, by my sword, your head shall no longer sit between your shoulders!"

The young archer wept bitter tears, and went out into the courtyard, where the horse of power was waiting for him, champing its golden bit.

"There is no way of escaping death this time," he said.

"Master, why do you weep?" asked the horse of power.

"The Tzar has ordered me to ride to the land of Never, to fetch the wedding dress of the Princess Vasilissa from the bottom of the deep blue sea. Besides, the dress is wanted for the Tzar's wedding, and I love the Princess myself."

"What did I tell you?" says the horse of power.

"I told you that there would be trouble if you picked up the golden feather from the fire-bird's burning breast. Well, do not be afraid. The trouble is not yet; the trouble is to come. Up! into the saddle with you, and away for the wedding dress of the Princess Vasilissa!"

The young archer leapt into the saddle, and the horse of power, with his thundering hoofs, carried him swiftly through the green forests and over the bare plains, till they came to the edge of the world, to the land of Never, where the red sun rises in flame from behind the deep blue sea. There they rested, at the very edge of the sea.

The young archer looked sadly over the wide waters, but the horse of power tossed its mane and did not look at the sea, but on the shore. This way and that it looked, and saw at last a huge lobster moving slowly, sideways, along the golden sand.

Nearer and nearer came the lobster, and it was a giant among lobsters, the tzar of all the lobsters; and it moved slowly along the shore, while the horse of power moved carefully and as if by accident, until it stood between the lobster and the sea. Then, when the lobster came close by, the horse of power lifted an iron hoof and set it firmly on the lobster's tail.

"You will be the death of me!" screamed the lobster—as well he might, with the heavy foot of the horse of power pressing his tail into the sand. "Let me live, and I will do whatever you ask of me."

"Very well," says the horse of power; "we will let you live," and he slowly lifted his foot. "But this is what you shall do for us. In the middle of the blue sea lies a great stone, and under that stone is hidden the wedding dress of the Princess Vasilissa. Bring it here."

The lobster groaned with the pain in his tail. Then he cried out in a voice that could be heard all over the deep blue sea. And the sea was disturbed, and from all sides lobsters in thousands made their way towards the bank. And the huge lobster that was the oldest of them all and the tzar of all the lobsters that live between the rising and the setting of the sun, gave them the order and sent them back into the sea. And the young archer sat on the horse of power and waited.

After a little time the sea was disturbed again, and the lobsters in their thousands came to the shore, and with them they brought a golden casket in which was the wedding dress of the Princess Vasilissa. They had taken it from under the great stone that lay in the middle of the sea.

The tzar of all the lobsters raised himself painfully on his bruised tail and gave the casket into the hands of the young archer, and instantly the horse of power turned himself about and galloped back to the palace of the Tzar, far, far away, at the other side of the green forests and beyond the treeless plains.

The young archer went into the palace and gave the casket into the hands of the Princess, and looked at her with sadness in his eyes, and she looked at him with love. Then she went away into an inner chamber, and came back in her wedding dress, fairer than the spring itself. Great was the joy of the Tzar. The wedding feast was made ready, and the bells rang, and flags waved about the palace.

The Tzar held out his hand to the Princess, and looked at her with his old eyes. But she would not take his hand.

"No," says she; "I will marry nobody until the man who brought me here has done penance in boiling water."

Instantly the Tzar turned to his servants and ordered them to make a great fire, and to fill a great cauldron with water and set it on the fire, and, when the water should be at its hottest, to take the young archer and throw him into it, to do penance for having taken the Princess Vasilissa away from the land of Never.

There was no gratitude in the mind of that Tzar.

Swiftly the servants brought wood and made a mighty fire, and on it they laid a huge cauldron of water, and built the fire around the walls of the cauldron. The fire burned hot and the water steamed. The fire burned hotter, and the water bubbled and seethed. They made ready to take the young archer, to throw him into the cauldron.

"Oh, misery!" thought the young archer. "Why did I ever take the golden feather that had fallen from the fire-bird's burning breast? Why did I not listen to the wise words of the horse of power?" And he remembered the horse of power, and he begged the Tzar,

"O lord Tzar, I do not complain. I shall presently die in the heat of the water on the fire. Suffer me, before I die, once more to see my horse."

"Let him see his horse," says the Princess.

"Very well," says the Tzar. "Say good-bye to your horse, for you will not ride him again. But let your farewells be short, for we are waiting."

The young archer crossed the courtyard and came to the horse of power, who was scraping the ground with his iron hoofs.

"Farewell, my horse of power," says the young archer. "I should have listened to your words of wisdom, for now the end is come, and we shall never more see the green trees pass above us and the ground disappear beneath us, as we race the wind between the earth and the sky."

"Why so?" says the horse of power.

"The Tzar has ordered that I am to be boiled to death—thrown into that cauldron that is seething on the great fire."

"Fear not," says the horse of power, "for the Princess Vasilissa has made him do this, and the end of these things is better than I thought. Go back, and when they are ready to throw you in the cauldron, do you run boldly and leap yourself into the boiling water."

The young archer went back across the courtyard, and the servants made ready to throw him into the cauldron.

"Are you sure that the water is boiling?" says the Princess Vasilissa.

"It bubbles and seethes," said the servants.

"Let me see for myself," says the Princess, and she went to the fire and waved her hand above the cauldron. And some say there was something in her hand, and some say there was not.

"It is boiling," says she, and the servants laid hands on the young archer; but he threw them from him, and ran and leapt boldly before them all into the very middle of the cauldron.

Twice he sank below the surface, borne around with the bubbles and foam of the boiling water. Then he leapt from the cauldron and stood before the Tzar and the Princess. He had become so beautiful a youth that all who saw cried aloud in wonder.

"This is a miracle," says the Tzar. And the Tzar looked at the beautiful young archer and thought of himself—of his age, of his bent back, and his gray beard, and his toothless gums. "I too will become beautiful," thinks he, and he rose from his throne and clambered into the cauldron, and was boiled to death in a moment.

And the end of the story? They buried the Tzar, and made the young archer Tzar in his place. He married the Princess Vasilissa, and lived many years with her in love and good fellowship. And he built a golden stable for the horse of power, and never forgot what he owed him.

A CLEVER JUDGE

Babette Deutsch, one of the authors of Tales of Faraway Folk *from which this story is taken, identifies "A Clever Judge" as a Kirghiz folk tale. In the introduction she says: "The people who tell this tale live on the vast steppes or prairies of southwestern Asia. They are herders of cattle, sheep, and goats. And they are clever fellows, too, as you shall see."*

There lived a man in the steppes who was famous for his justice and wisdom. At that time if a man was known for his fairness, people came to him from far and wide to ask him to settle their disputes. And so it was that one day two villagers appeared before this wise man and asked him to settle their quarrel.

"Tell me your story," the judge said to the plaintiff.

"I had to leave my village," said the plaintiff, "for I had business elsewhere. And all my wealth was a hundred gold coins. I did not come by them easily. I had to work hard for them, and I did not want them to be stolen while I was away. Nor did I care to carry so much money with me on my journey. So I entrusted these gold coins for safekeeping to this man here. When I got back from my journey, he denied that he had ever received the money from me."

"And who saw you give him these hundred gold coins?" asked the judge.

"No one saw it. We went together to the heart of the forest and there I handed him the coins."

"What have you to say to this?" the judge asked, turning to the defendant.

The defendant shrugged his shoulders.

"I don't know what he is talking about," said the man. "I never went to the forest with him. I never saw his gold coins."

"Do you remember the place where you handed over the money?" the judge asked the plaintiff.

"Of course I do. It was under a tall oak. I remember it very well. I can point it out with no trouble at all."

"So you do have a witness, after all," said the judge. "Here, take my signet ring, go to the tall tree under which you stood when you handed over the money, set the seal of my signet ring against the trunk, and bid the tree appear before me to bear out the truth of your story."

The plaintiff took the signet ring and went off to carry out the demand of the judge. The defendant remained behind and waited for his return.

After some time had passed, the judge turned to the defendant and asked, "Do you think he has reached the oak by this time?"

"No, not yet," was the answer.

After further time had passed, the judge again turned to the defendant and asked, "Do you think he has reached the tree by this time?"

"Yes," was the answer, "by now he must have reached it."

Not long after that the plaintiff returned.

"Well?" asked the judge.

"I did just as you said," replied the plaintiff. "I walked as far as the forest and then I went on until I came to the tall oak under which we stood when I handed over my gold coins. I set the seal of your signet ring against the trunk of the tree and I bade it appear before you as a witness. But the tree refused to budge."

"Never mind," said the judge. "The oak has appeared before me and it has borne witness in your favor."

At that the defendant exclaimed, "How can you say such a thing! I have been here all this while and no tree has stalked into the place."

"But," replied the judge, "you said that you had not been in the forest at all. And yet when I asked you whether the plaintiff had reached the oak, first you answered that he could not have reached it, and the second time you said that he must surely have reached it. Therefore, you *were* in the forest and you remembered where the oak was under which you stood when the plaintiff handed his gold coins to you for safekeeping. Now you must not only return him his hundred gold pieces, but you must also pay a fine for having tried to cheat him."

So the tree was a witness without budging, and justice was done.

A Polish folk tale

It has been a long time since the Polish folk tales were available. The tale reprinted here is taken from The Jolly Tailor, *an old and excellent collection of representative stories recently reissued. The ten stories in the collection are all good examples of the storyteller's art, vigorously and sincerely told.*

KING BARTEK

Young girls will like this romantic story of a royal disguise that serves to reveal both the haughty hypocrite and the true-hearted maiden.

"King Bartek." From *The Jolly Tailor and Other Fairy Tales Translated from the Polish* by Lucia Merecka Borski and Kate B. Miller. Copyright 1928, © 1956 by Longmans, Green and Company

On the outskirts of a village, in a hut fallen almost to ruins, there lived a very poor widow with her two daughters, Bialka and Spiewna. Both of them were so beautiful that their fame spread over seven mountains, over seven seas. Even at the king's palace the rumors were heard. Many of the knights wished to go at once and woo the girls.

The King disliked to lose his knights, as he

had planned a great war, and besides he did not have much faith in the rumors. Instead of granting permission to the knights to go, he sent some of his faithful messengers to see the maidens and bring back pictures of Bialka and Spiewna.

The rumors were true. The pictures brought back by the messengers exceeded everybody's expectations. Spiewna was a true sister to the lily; Bialka, to the red rose. The first had azure eyes, the other, eyes dark as the Black Sea; one was proud of her long, golden braids, the other of her raven black braids. The first one had the beauty of a sunny day in her face, the other, the charm of a May night. The knights became enamored of the maidens; no one could keep them from departing. Even the King himself, as he was young and thought of marriage, scratched himself behind the ear and looked at the pictures with great pleasure. The war was put off, the court was desolated, and only the King and his Jester, Pieś, who was old and ugly like the seven mortal sins, were left there.

For a long, long time the knights did not come back. They were enjoying themselves; or it might be the other way around, Bialka and Spiewna, sure of their beauty might be taking their time picking and choosing, like sparrows in poppy seeds. The knights in love unwound entangled thread, killed partridges in the air, and sang serenades. Be it as it may, their long absence annoyed the King and he grew impatient and ill-tempered.

"Pieś," he onced addressed the Jester, "do you know what I am thinking about?"

"I know, Your Lordship!"

"How?"

"Because our thoughts walk the same paths."

"I wonder!" laughed the King.

"Your Lordship wishes to go to the widow's daughters."

"You guessed!" cried the young King, rejoicing.

"Then we shall go together," said Pieś. "But we must change our places; I, a King; Your Lordship, a Jester."

"What an idea!" said the young ruler, shocked a bit.

"There won't be much of a difference," smiled the Jester.

"No, I shall not do it! You may, if you wish,

become a King, but I shall put on a peasant's garb and call myself Bartek."

"As you please!" answered Pieś. "Something unpleasant may come of it though."

"Why?" asked the King, now Bartek.

"A King, be he as ugly and humpbacked as I am, will always have preference over Bartek. And then who knows? Your Highness may fall in love with either Spiewna or Bialka."

The youthful lord became alarmed.

"So much the better!" he said after a while, and added in a whisper, "The heart that loves will not fool itself."

They went on their journey.

In the meantime the widow's hut was as noisy as a beehive. One brought musicians, another singers. The hut changed into a music box adorned with garlands and flowers, as if in celebration of a holiday. The knights reveled, the girls danced, song followed song, and jokes, one after another. The mother's white bonnet swung on her white hair from one ear to the other from happiness.

Bialka liked Przegoń (Pshegon) more than all the others. Spiewna chose none as yet. Neither her mother's persuasion nor her sister's scoffs did any good. The girl's heart had not awakened yet, and without love she did not wish to marry even the richest of knights.

The betrothal of Przegoń to Bialka was announced. She had her wedding dress made, goods for which were brought by Przegoń. The jewelry, one could not describe, it could be gathered in measures.

Bialka was overwhelmed with joy, was triumphant with her success. She looked down on her sister with haughtiness and consoled her mother with scornful words.

"Do not worry, Mother! Spiewna awaits a prince. She will become wiser when she has to grow rue, and then I, Przegoń's wife, will try to get her an organist. Also I shall find a suitable nook for you, Mother."

Her mother's heart grieved, but what could she answer?

Then one day a golden carriage drove up before the door. All three of them ran quickly to the window, and Bialka shouted:

"The King has come!"

Sudden confusion possessed the hut. The old

widow trotted to the kitchen to prepare some fowl for His Majesty, the King, while Bialka snatched a hand-mirror and a comb and turning to her sister called in a commanding voice:

"Don't you dare to call the King's attention to yourself!"

Spiewna stopped in astonishment.

"Do you hear me?" shouted Bialka.

"I hear, but I don't understand."

"You don't understand—you don't understand!"

"For—how—" began Spiewna.

"Don't dare to call the King's attention to yourself!"

"What do you care about the King when you have Przegoń?

"Have I or not, that is nothing to you!" grumbled Bialka. "And better take my advice, otherwise—you shall see!"

His Majesty, the King, was far from good looking. He was ugly, old, his right arm was higher than the left, and he was also limping. But all this was covered with the golden crown, was concealed by the purple cloak and was straightened by the long robe richly embroidered with pearls. Upon seeing the sisters, he at once laid his royal gifts at their feet, and loaded them with compliments. Spiewna refused all the gifts, she accepted only a white rose, which she pinned into her hair.

"How beautiful he is!" whispered Bialka.

"How ridiculous he is!" replied Spiewna.

Bialka looked at her with anger.

Among the King's numerous attendants, there was a young and handsome page, called Bartek. Spiewna's eyes met the youth's gaze. Bartek, dazzled with the girl's beauty, did not take his eyes off her, and when the King offered jewels to Bialka, he came near Spiewna and said:

"All my riches is this fife. It plays beautifully and the time will come when I shall present you with its song."

Spiewna, standing on the threshold, blushed like a rose, and Bialka seeing this, maliciously whispered in her ear:

"Just the kind of a husband for you. Keep away from the King!"

"And Przegoń?" questioned Spiewna.

"You may have him," threw out Bialka.

Przegoń did not see the King, but he learned of his arrival and of his gifts to Bialka. He wished to speak to Bialka, but she, busy with her guest, who exaggerated his compliments and promised golden mountains, did not care to see him. He stayed away from his unfaithful sweetheart and waited to see what time would bring forth.

One night, and 'twas a night with the full moon, a scented intoxicating night, under the window of the room where both sisters slept, there came sounds of a guitar accompanied by a song.

"The King!" murmured Bialka and she jumped to the window.

The King sang:

Out of the mist thou shalt have palaces,
For thy comfort and pleasures I will care
And pay with gold for thy every smile.
Attired, bejewelled like a peacock
Thou shalt be Queen in the royal gardens.

"Do you hear, do you hear?" said Bialka to Spiewna. "Thus sings the King!"

Then later under the window fluted the country fife. Bialka looked out of the window and

noticed Bartek. Seeing her sister moved by the sad and sweet tones of the fife, she roared with laughter.

The fife stopped playing and they heard this song:

> Do not come to me with pretense
> But with love in thy pure eyes
> That knows another's love.
> Be not touched with a royal gown
> That is worn by a fool's soul,
> A soul that knows not what is love.

"Thus sings Bartek!" called Spiewna.

"Ha-ha-ha!" rang out Bialka's venomous laughter. She leaned over the window and called aloud into the silent night:

"Drive away the fool, Your Majesty, who has the boldness to interrupt your song and insult your royal soul! Order him away, for he steals from us this beautiful night!"

"I will punish him more severely than you think," was the answer, "because to-morrow he will marry your sister."

"And when we?" asked Bialka.

"Even now. Come to me!"

Bialka jumped out of the window, and there she met face to face with Przegoń.

"What are you doing here?" she asked him haughtily.

"I came to wish you happiness with this— king's Jester," replied Przegoń pointing to Pieś.

"What? What?" cried Bialka, looking with frightened eyes at the splendid dress, like a king's.

And in the room, where Spiewna remained, Bartek's fife rang out followed by a song:

> 'Tis hard to find true love
> Under an alluring purple gown,
> Infirmity shall remain in heart
> With all the roses torn aside.
> Ugly looks and lameness and a hump
> May all be covered with a royal cloak.
> The King wished for a true heart;
> The fool desired fun and laughter;
> And both are satisfied.
> Therefore the fool dressed like a King
> The King put on the peasant's garb.
> Now, maiden, cry for thy alluring loss
> And understand these prophesying words:
> That people are not judged by looks
> But by their hearts and deeds.

The golden carriage came to the door, a thousand torches were lighted, a thousand knights with Przegoń at the head surrounded the royal carriage, into which Spiewna was led with her bridesmaids, and they all went to the King's palace to celebrate the wedding. The mother rejoiced at Spiewna's happiness, but she grieved over the neglected Bialka, who had to grow sixteen beds of rue before she married an old organist.

East Indian folk tales

The East Indian tales are numerically enormous, but only a small percentage of them is suitable for children. The ancestors of many European tales are to be found in the East Indian collections, and also from India comes a multitude of talking beast stories. These are from an ancient collection of Indian fables called the Jatakas, *which are birth stories of Gautama Buddha in his progressive reincarnations in the forms of different animals. When references to the Buddha are omitted, a good talking beast tale remains and for this reason the* Jatakas *are included with the folk tales instead of with the fables. They are generally moralistic in tone but somehow manage to preserve their story values, as these four examples demonstrate. Young children readily accept the animal that speaks, but children over nine or ten are sometimes skeptical.*

THE HARE THAT RAN AWAY

This ancient story is one of a series about the wise Buddha in his successive animal incarnations. The story may begin without the reference to Buddha, "Once there was a wise Lion who did much to help his fellow creatures and he found there was much to be done. For instance, there was a little nervous Hare. . . ."

And it came to pass that the Buddha (to be) was born again as a Lion. Just as he had helped his fellow-men, he now began to help his fellow-animals, and there was a great deal to be done. For instance, there was a little nervous Hare who was always afraid that something dreadful was going to happen to her. She was always saying: "Suppose the Earth were to fall in, what would happen to me?" And she said this so often that at last she thought it really was about to happen. One day, when she had been saying over and over again, "Suppose the Earth were to fall in, what would happen to me?" she heard a slight noise: it really was only a heavy fruit which had fallen upon a rustling leaf, but the little Hare was so nervous she was ready to believe anything, and she said in a frightened tone: "The Earth *is* falling in." She ran away as fast as she could go, and presently she met an old brother Hare, who said: "Where are you running to, Mistress Hare?"

And the little Hare said: "I have no time to stop and tell you anything. The Earth is falling in, and I am running away."

"The Earth is falling in, is it?" said the old brother Hare, in a tone of much astonishment; and he repeated this to *his* brother hare, and *he* to *his* brother hare, and *he* to *his* brother hare, until at last there were a hundred thousand brother hares, all shouting: "The Earth is falling in." Now presently the bigger animals began to take the cry up. First the deer, and then the sheep, and then the wild boar, and then the buffalo, and then the camel, and then the tiger, and then the elephant.

Now the wise Lion heard all this noise and wondered at it. "There are no signs," he said, "of the Earth falling in. They must have heard

"The Hare That Ran Away." From *Eastern Stories and Legends* by Marie Shedlock, published and copyright, 1920, E. P. Dutton & Co., Inc., New York, renewed, 1948. By permission also of George Routledge & Sons Ltd., London

something." And then he stopped them all short and said: "What is this you are saying?"

And the Elephant said: "I remarked that the Earth was falling in."

"How do you know this?" asked the Lion.

"Why, now I come to think of it, it was the Tiger that remarked it to me."

And the Tiger said: "*I* had it from the Camel," and the Camel said: "*I* had it from the Buffalo." And the buffalo from the wild boar, and the wild boar from the sheep, and the sheep from the deer, and the deer from the hares, and the Hares said: "Oh! *we* heard it from *that* little Hare."

And the Lion said: "Little Hare, *what* made you say that the Earth was falling in?"

And the little Hare said: "I *saw* it."

"You saw it?" said the Lion. "Where?"

"Yonder by the tree."

"Well," said the Lion, "come with me and I will show you how——"

"No, no," said the Hare, "I would not go near that tree for anything, I'm *so* nervous."

"But," said the Lion, "I am going to take you on my back." And he took her on his back, and begged the animals to stay where they were until they returned. Then he showed the little Hare how the fruit had fallen upon the leaf, making the noise that had frightened her, and she said: "Yes, I see—the Earth is *not* falling in." And the Lion said: "Shall we go back and tell the other animals?"

And they went back. The little Hare stood before the animals and said: "The Earth is *not* falling in." And all the animals began to repeat this to one another, and they dispersed gradually, and you heard the words more and more softly:

"The Earth is *not* falling in," etc., etc., etc., until the sound died away altogether.

GRANNY'S BLACKIE

Once upon a time a rich man gave a baby Elephant to a woman.

She took the best of care of this great baby and soon became very fond of him.

"Granny's Blackie." From *Jataka Tales* by Ellen C. Babbitt. Copyright, 1912, Century Company. Reprinted by permission of the publishers, Appleton-Century-Crofts, Inc.

The children in the village called her Granny, and they called the Elephant "Granny's Blackie."

The Elephant carried the children on his back all over the village. They shared their goodies with him and he played with them.

"Please, Blackie, give us a swing," they said to him almost every day.

"Come on! Who is first?" Blackie answered and picked them up with his trunk, swung them high in the air, and then put them down again, carefully.

But Blackie never did any work.

He ate and slept, played with the children, and visited with Granny.

One day Blackie wanted Granny to go off to the woods with him.

"I can't go, Blackie, dear. I have too much work to do."

Then Blackie looked at her and saw that she was growing old and feeble.

"I am young and strong," he thought. "I'll see if I cannot find some work to do. If I could bring some money home to her, she would not have to work so hard."

So next morning, bright and early, he started down to the river bank.

There he found a man who was in great trouble. There was a long line of wagons so heavily loaded that the oxen could not draw them through the shallow water.

When the man saw Blackie standing on the bank he asked, "Who owns this Elephant? I want to hire him to help my Oxen pull these wagons across the river."

A child standing near by said, "That is Granny's Blackie."

"Very well," said the man, "I'll pay two pieces of silver for each wagon this Elephant draws across the river."

Blackie was glad to hear this promise. He went into the river, and drew one wagon after another across to the other side.

Then he went up to the man for the money.

The man counted out one piece of silver for each wagon.

When Blackie saw that the man had counted out but one piece of silver for each wagon, instead of two, he would not touch the money at all. He stood in the road and would not let the wagons pass him.

The man tried to get Blackie out of the way, but not one step would he move.

Then the man went back and counted out another piece of silver for each of the wagons and put the silver in a bag tied around Blackie's neck.

Then Blackie started for home, proud to think that he had a present for Granny.

The children had missed Blackie and had asked Granny where he was, but she said she did not know where he had gone.

They all looked for him but it was nearly night before they heard him coming.

"Where have you been, Blackie? And what is that around your neck?" the children cried, running to meet their playmate.

But Blackie would not stop to talk with his playmates. He ran straight home to Granny.

"Oh, Blackie!" she said. "Where have you been? What is in that bag?" And she took the bag off his neck.

Blackie told her that he had earned some money for her.

"Oh, Blackie, Blackie," said Granny, "how hard you must have worked to earn these pieces of silver! What a good Blackie you are!"

And after that Blackie did all the hard work and Granny rested, and they were both very happy.

THE TIGER, THE BRAHMAN, AND THE JACKAL

There are a series of jackal stories in which the jackal is generally the trickster who is finally caught and punished, but in this story the tables are turned. Children will be satisfied with the explanation that a brahman is a wise, good man. Further details are unnecessary.

Once upon a time a tiger was caught in a trap. He tried in vain to get out through the bars, and rolled and bit with rage and grief when he failed.

By chance a poor Brahman came by. "Let me out of this cage, O pious one!" cried the tiger.

"The Tiger, the Brahman, and the Jackal." From *Tales of the Punjab* compiled by Flora Annie Steel, Macmillan and Co., Ltd. By permission of The Macmillan Company, New York and Macmillan & Co. Ltd., London

"Nay, my friend," replied the Brahman mildly, "you would probably eat me if I did."

"Not at all!" swore the tiger with many oaths; "on the contrary, I should be for ever grateful, and serve you as a slave!"

Now when the tiger sobbed and sighed and wept and swore, the pious Brahman's heart softened, and at last he consented to open the door of the cage. Out popped the tiger, and, seizing the poor man, cried, "What a fool you are! What is to prevent my eating you now, for after being cooped up so long I am just terribly hungry!"

In vain the Brahman pleaded for his life; the most he could gain was a promise to abide by the decision of the first three things he chose to question as to the justice of the tiger's action.

So the Brahman first asked a *pîpal* tree what it thought of the matter, but the *pîpal* tree replied coldly, "What have you to complain about? Don't I give shade and shelter to every one who passes by, and don't they in return tear down my branches to feed their cattle? Don't whimper—be a man!"

Then the Brahman, sad at heart, went farther afield till he saw a buffalo turning a well-wheel; but he fared no better from it, for it answered, "You are a fool to expect gratitude! Look at me! While I gave milk they fed me on cotton-seed and oil-cake, but now I am dry they yoke me here, and give me refuse as fodder!"

The Brahman, still more sad, asked the road to give him its opinion.

"My dear sir," said the road, "how foolish you are to expect anything else! Here am I, useful to everybody, yet all, rich and poor, great and small, trample on me as they go past, giving me nothing but the ashes of their pipes and the husks of their grain!"

On this the Brahman turned back sorrowfully, and on the way he met a jackal, who called out, "Why, what's the matter, Mr. Brahman? You look as miserable as a fish out of water!"

Then the Brahman told him all that had occurred. "How very confusing!" said the jackal, when the recital was ended; "would you mind telling me over again? for everything seems so mixed up!"

The Brahman told it all over again, but the jackal shook his head in a distracted sort of way, and still could not understand.

"It's very odd," said he sadly, "but it all seems to go in at one ear and out at the other! I will go to the place where it all happened, and then perhaps I shall be able to give a judgment."

So they returned to the cage, by which the tiger was waiting for the Brahman, and sharpening his teeth and claws.

"You've been away a long time!" growled the savage beast, "but now let us begin our dinner."

"*Our* dinner!" thought the wretched Brahman, as his knees knocked together with fright; "what a remarkably delicate way of putting it!"

"Give me five minutes, my lord!" he pleaded, "in order that I may explain matters to the jackal here, who is somewhat slow in his wits."

The tiger consented, and the Brahman began the whole story over again, not missing a single detail, and spinning as long a yarn as possible.

"Oh, my poor brain! oh, my poor brain!" cried the jackal, wringing his paws. "Let me see! how did it all begin? You were in the cage, and the tiger came walking by——"

"Pooh!" interrupted the tiger, "what a fool you are! *I* was in the cage."

"Of course!" cried the jackal, pretending to tremble with fright; "yes! I was in the cage—no, I wasn't—dear! dear! where are my wits? Let me see—the tiger was in the Brahman, and the cage came walking by—no, that's not it either! Well, don't mind me, but begin your dinner, for I shall never understand!"

"Yes, you shall!" returned the tiger, in a rage at the jackal's stupidity; "I'll *make* you understand! Look here—I am the tiger——"

"Yes, my lord!"

"And that is the Brahman——"

"Yes, my lord!"

"And that is the cage——"

"Yes, my lord!"

"And I was in the cage—do you understand?"

"Yes—no—Please, my lord——"

"Well?" cried the tiger, impatiently.

"Please, my lord!—how did you get in?"

"How!—why, in the usual way, of course!"

"Oh dear me!—my head is beginning to whirl again! Please don't be angry, my lord, but what is the usual way?"

At this the tiger lost patience, and, jumping into the cage, cried, "This way! Now do you understand how it was?"

"Perfectly!" grinned the jackal, as he dexterously shut the door; "and if you will permit me to say so, I think matters will remain as they were!"

THE BANYAN DEER

There was once a Deer the color of gold. His eyes were like round jewels, his horns were white as silver, his mouth was red like a flower, his hoofs were bright and hard. He had a large body and a fine tail.

He lived in a forest and was king of a herd of five hundred Banyan Deer. Near by lived another herd of Deer, called the Monkey Deer. They, too, had a king.

The king of that country was fond of hunting the Deer and eating deer meat. He did not like to go alone so he called the people of his town to go with him, day after day.

The townspeople did not like this for while they were gone no one did their work. So they decided to make a park and drive the Deer into it. Then the king could go into the park and hunt and they could go on with their daily work.

They made a park, planted grass in it and provided water for the Deer, built a fence all around it and drove the Deer into it.

Then they shut the gate and went to the king to tell him that in the park near by he could find all the Deer he wanted.

The king went at once to look at the Deer. First he saw there the two Deer kings, and granted them their lives. Then he looked at their great herds.

Some days the king would go to hunt the Deer, sometimes his cook would go. As soon as any of the Deer saw them they would shake with fear and run. But when they had been hit once or twice they would drop down dead.

The King of the Banyan Deer sent for the King of the Monkey Deer and said, "Friend, many of the Deer are being killed. Many are wounded besides those who are killed. After this suppose one from my herd goes up to be killed one day, and the next day let one from your herd go up. Fewer Deer will be lost this way."

The Monkey Deer agreed. Each day the Deer whose turn it was would go and lie down, placing its head on the block. The cook would come and carry off the one he found lying there.

One day the lot fell to a mother Deer who had

"The Banyan Deer." From *Jataka Tales* by Ellen C. Babbitt. Copyright, 1912, Century Company. Reprinted by permission of the publishers, Appleton-Century-Crofts. Inc.

a young baby. She went to her king and said, "O King of the Monkey Deer, let the turn pass me by until my baby is old enough to get along without me. Then I will go and put my head on the block."

But the king did not help her. He told her that if the lot had fallen to her she must die.

Then she went to the King of the Banyan Deer and asked him to save her.

"Go back to your herd. I will go in your place," said he.

The next day the cook found the King of the Banyan Deer lying with his head on the block.

The cook went to the king, who came himself to find out about this.

"King of the Banyan Deer! did I not grant you your life? Why are you lying here?"

"O great King!" said the King of the Banyan Deer, "a mother came with her young baby and told me that the lot had fallen to her. I could not ask any one else to take her place, so I came myself."

"King of the Banyan Deer! I never saw such kindness and mercy. Rise up. I grant your life and hers. Nor will I hunt any more the Deer in either park or forest."

A tale from the "Arabian Nights"

The source of the Arabian Nights is lost in antiquity. Some of the tales seem to stem from ancient India, others from North Africa, and others from Persia. In the Moslem world, where they were preserved, they were not considered polite literature but circulated in the market places or the coffee houses. The first translation of the stories into French, in 1704, was made by Antoine Galland from a manuscript that came from Syria but was written in Egypt. However confused their source, the "thousand and one tales" have been spellbinding young readers ever since. Today, perhaps because of rival media of entertainment, they are not so much read. Their interminable length is undoubtedly the chief obstacle to their popularity, for they contain stories within stories, episodes upon episodes, magic and more magic. Modern adapters of these tales have practiced an economy of incident that was lacking in the original, but even greatly cut versions have a color, dramatic plot construction, and a use of magic that are weird and enthralling. Perhaps this sample will send some of the children to a collection of the tales for further reading.

ALADDIN AND
THE WONDERFUL LAMP

There once lived a poor tailor, who had a son called Aladdin, a careless, idle boy who would do nothing but play all day long in the streets with little idle boys like himself. This so grieved the father that he died; yet, in spite of his mother's tears and prayers, Aladdin did

"Aladdin and the Wonderful Lamp." From *Arabian Nights*, copyright 1946, and *Arabian Nights Entertainments*, copyright 1898, edited by Andrew Lang. Used by permission of Longmans, Green and Company, Inc.

not mend his ways. One day, when he was playing in the streets as usual, a stranger asked him his age, and if he were not the son of Mustapha the tailor. "I am, sir," replied Aladdin; "but he died a long while ago."

On this the stranger, who was a famous African magician, fell on his neck and kissed him, saying: "I am your uncle, and knew you from your likeness to my brother. Go to your mother and tell her I am coming."

Aladdin ran home, and told his mother of his newly found uncle. "Indeed, child," she said, "your father had a brother, but I always thought he was dead." However, she prepared supper, and bade Aladdin seek his uncle, who came laden with wine and fruit. He presently fell down and kissed the place where Mustapha used to sit, bidding Aladdin's mother not to be surprised at not having seen him before, as he had been forty years out of the country. He then turned to Aladdin, and asked him his trade, at which the boy hung his head, while his mother burst into tears. On learning that Aladdin was idle and would learn no trade, he offered to take a shop for him and stock it with merchandise. Next day he bought Aladdin a fine suit of clothes and took him all over the city, showing him the sights, and brought him home at nightfall to his mother, who was overjoyed to see her son so fine.

Next day the magician led Aladdin into some beautiful gardens a long way outside the city gates. They sat down by a fountain and the magician pulled a cake from his girdle, which he divided between them. They then journeyed onwards till they almost reached the mountains. Aladdin was so tired that he begged to go back, but the magician beguiled him with pleasant stories, and led him on in spite of himself. At last they came to two mountains divided by a narrow valley. "We will go no farther," said the false uncle. "I will show you something wonderful; only do you gather up sticks while I kindle a fire."

When it was lit the magician threw on it a powder he had about him, at the same time saying some magical words. The earth trembled a little and opened in front of them, disclosing a square flat stone with a brass ring in the middle to raise it by. Aladdin tried to run away, but the magician caught him and gave him a blow that knocked him down. "What have I done, uncle?" he said piteously; whereupon the magician said more kindly: "Fear nothing, but obey me. Beneath this stone lies a treasure which is to be yours, and no one else may touch it; so you must do exactly as I tell you."

At the word treasure Aladdin forgot his fears, and grasped the ring as he was told, saying the names of his father and grandfather. The stone came up quite easily and some steps appeared. "Go down," said the magician; "at the foot of those steps you will find an open door leading into three large halls. Tuck up your gown and go through them without touching anything, or you

will die instantly. These halls lead into a garden of fine fruit trees. Walk on till you come to a niche in a terrace where stands a lighted lamp. Pour out the oil it contains, and bring it to me." He drew a ring from his finger and gave it to Aladdin, bidding him prosper.

Aladdin found everything as the magician had said, gathered some fruit off the trees, and, having got the lamp, arrived at the mouth of the cave. The magician cried out in a great hurry: "Make haste and give me the lamp." This Aladdin refused to do until he was out of the cave. The magician flew into a terrible passion, and throwing some more powder on the fire, he said something, and the stone rolled back into its place.

The magician left Persia forever, which plainly showed that he was no uncle of Aladdin's, but a cunning magician, who had read in his magic books of a wonderful lamp, which would make him the most powerful man in the world. Though he alone knew where to find it, he could only receive it from the hand of another. He had picked out the foolish Aladdin for this purpose, intending to get the lamp and kill him afterwards.

For two days Aladdin remained in the dark, crying and lamenting. At last he clasped his hands in prayer, and in so doing, rubbed the ring, which the magician had forgotten to take from him. Immediately an enormous and frightful genie rose out of the earth, saying: "What wouldst thou with me? I am the Slave of the Ring, and will obey thee in all things."

Aladdin fearlessly replied: "Deliver me from this place!" whereupon the earth opened, and he found himself outside. As soon as his eyes could bear the light he went home, but fainted on the threshold. When he came to himself, he told his mother what had passed, and showed her the lamp and the fruits he had gathered in the garden, which were in reality precious stones. He then asked for some food.

"Alas! child," she said, "I have nothing in the house, but I have spun a little cotton and will go and sell it."

Aladdin bade her keep her cotton, for he would sell the lamp instead. As it was very dirty, she began to rub it, that it might fetch a higher price. Instantly a hideous genie appeared and asked what she would have. She fainted away, but Aladdin, snatching the lamp, said boldly: "Fetch me something to eat!"

The genie returned with a silver bowl, twelve silver plates containing rich meats, two silver cups, and two bottles of wine. Aladdin's mother, when she came to herself, said: "Whence comes this splendid feast?"

"Ask not, but eat," replied Aladdin. So they sat at breakfast till it was dinner-time and Aladdin told his mother about the lamp. She begged him to sell it, and have nothing to do with devils. "No," said Aladdin, "since chance hath made us aware of its virtues, we will use it and the ring likewise, which I shall always wear on my finger." When they had eaten all the genie had brought, Aladdin sold one of the silver plates, and so on till none were left. He then had recourse to the genie, who gave him another set of plates, and thus they lived for many years.

One day Aladdin heard an order from the Sultan proclaiming that everyone was to stay at home and close his shutters while the Princess, his daughter, went to and from the bath. Aladdin was seized by a desire to see her face, which was very difficult, as she always went veiled. He hid himself behind the door of the bath and peeped through a chink. The Princess lifted her veil as she went in, and looked so beautiful that Aladdin fell in love with her at first sight. He went home so changed that his mother was frightened. He told her he loved the Princess so deeply that he could not live without her, and meant to ask her in marriage of her father. His mother, on hearing this, burst out laughing; but Aladdin at last prevailed upon her to go before the Sultan and carry his request. She fetched a napkin and laid in it the magic fruits from the enchanted garden, which sparkled and shone like the most beautiful jewels. She took these with her to please the Sultan, and set out, trusting in the lamp.

The Grand-Vizier and the lords of council had just gone in as she entered the hall and placed herself in front of the Sultan. He, however, took no notice of her. She went every day for a week, and stood in the same place. When the council broke up on the sixth day the Sultan said to his Vizier: "I see a certain woman in the audience-chamber every day carrying something in a napkin. Call her next time, that I may find out what

she wants." Next day, at a sign from the Vizier, she went up to the foot of the throne and remained kneeling till the Sultan said to her: "Rise, good woman, and tell me what you want." She hesitated, so the Sultan sent away all but the Vizier, and bade her speak freely, promising to forgive her beforehand for anything she might say. She then told him of her son's violent love for the Princess.

"I prayed him to forget her," she said, "but in vain; he threatened to do some desperate deed if I refused to go and ask your Majesty for the hand of the Princess. Now I pray you to forgive not me alone, but my son Aladdin."

The Sultan asked her kindly what she had in the napkin, whereupon she unfolded the jewels and presented them. He was thunderstruck, and turning to the Vizier said: "What sayest thou? Ought I not to bestow the Princess on one who values her at such a price?" The Vizier, who wanted her for his own son, begged the Sultan to withhold her for three months, in the course of which he hoped his son would contrive to make him a richer present. The Sultan granted this, and told Aladdin's mother that, though he consented to the marriage, she must not appear before him again for three months.

Aladdin waited patiently for nearly three months, but after two had elapsed, his mother, going into the city to buy oil, found everyone rejoicing, and asked what was going on. "Do you not know," was the answer, "that the son of the Grand-Vizier is to marry the Sultan's daughter tonight?"

Breathless, she ran and told Aladdin, who was overwhelmed at first, but presently bethought him of the lamp. He rubbed it, and the genie appeared, saying: "What is thy will?"

Aladdin replied: "The Sultan, as thou knowest, has broken his promise to me, and the Vizier's son is to have the Princess. My command is that tonight you bring hither the bride and bride-groom."

"Master, I obey," said the genie. Aladdin then went to his chamber, where, sure enough, at midnight the genie transported the bed containing the Vizier's son and the Princess.

"Take this new-married man," he said, "and put him outside in the cold, and return at daybreak." Whereupon the genie took the Vizier's son out of bed, leaving Aladdin with the Princess. "Fear nothing," Aladdin said to her; "you are my wife, promised to me by your unjust father, and no harm shall come to you." The Princess was too frightened to speak, and passed the most miserable night of her life, while Aladdin lay down beside her and slept soundly. At the appointed hour the genie fetched in the shivering bridegroom, laid him in his place, and transported the bed back to the palace.

Presently the Sultan came to wish his daughter good-morning. The unhappy Vizier's son jumped up and hid himself, while the Princess would not say a word, and was very sorrowful. The Sultan sent her mother to her, who said: "How comes it, child, that you will not speak to your father? What has happened?" The Princess sighed deeply, and at last told her mother how, during the night, the bed had been carried into some strange house, and what had passed there. Her mother did not believe her in the least, but bade her rise and consider it an idle dream.

The following night exactly the same thing happened, and next morning, on the Princess's refusing to speak, the Sultan threatened to cut off her head. She then confessed all, bidding him ask the Vizier's son if it were not so. The Sultan told the Vizier to ask his son, who owned the truth, adding that, dearly as he loved the Princess, he had rather die than go through another such fearful night, and wished to be separated from her. His wish was granted, and there was an end of feasting and rejoicing.

When the three months were over, Aladdin sent his mother to remind the Sultan of his promise. She stood in the same place as before, and the Sultan, who had forgotten Aladdin, at once remembered him, and sent for her. On seeing her poverty the Sultan felt less inclined than ever to keep his word, and asked the Vizier's advice, who counseled him to set so high a value on the Princess that no man living could come up to it. The Sultan then turned to Aladdin's mother, saying: "Good woman, a Sultan must remember his promises, and I will remember mine, but your son must first send me forty basins of gold brimful of jewels, carried by forty black slaves, led by as many white ones, splendidly dressed. Tell him that I await his answer."

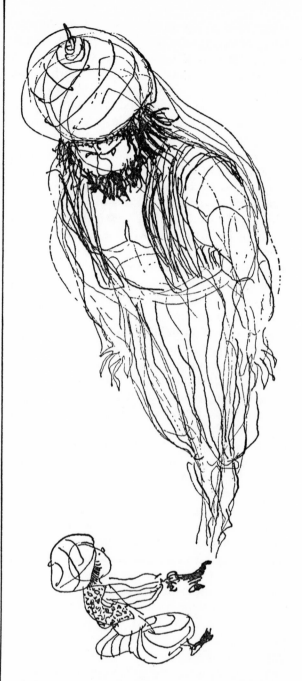

The mother of Aladdin bowed low and went home, thinking all was lost. She gave Aladdin the message, adding: "He may wait long enough for your answer!"

"Not so long, mother, as you think," her son replied. "I would do a great deal more than that for the Princess." He summoned the genie, and in a few moments the eighty slaves arrived, and filled up the small house and garden. Aladdin made them set out to the palace, two and two, followed by his mother. They were so richly dressed, with such splendid jewels in their girdles, that everyone crowded to see them and the basins of gold they carried on their heads.

They entered the palace and, after kneeling before the Sultan, stood in a half-circle round the throne with their arms crossed, while Aladdin's mother presented them to the Sultan. He hesitated no longer, but said: "Good woman, return and tell your son that I wait for him with open arms." She lost no time in telling Aladdin, bidding him make haste. But Aladdin first called the genie.

"I want a scented bath," he said, "a richly embroidered habit, a horse surpassing the Sultan's, and twenty slaves to attend me. Besides this, six slaves, beautifully dressed, to wait on my mother; and lastly, ten thousand pieces of gold in ten purses." No sooner said than done. Aladdin mounted his horse and passed through the streets, the slaves strewing gold as they went. Those who had played with him in his childhood knew him not, he had grown so handsome. When the Sultan saw him he came down from his throne, embraced him, and led him into a hall where a feast was spread, intending to marry him to the Princess that very day. But Aladdin refused, saying, "I must build a palace fit for her," and took his leave.

Once home, he said to the genie: "Build me a palace of the finest marble, set with jasper, agate, and other precious stones. In the middle you shall build me a large hall with a dome, its four walls of massy gold and silver, each side having six windows, whose lattices, all except one, which is to be left unfinished, must be set with diamonds and rubies. There must be stables and horses and grooms and slaves; go and see about it!"

The palace was finished by next day, and the genie carried him there and showed him all his orders faithfully carried out, even to the laying of a velvet carpet from Aladdin's palace to the Sultan's. Aladdin's mother then dressed herself carefully, and walked to the palace with her slaves, while he followed her on horseback. The Sultan sent musicians with trumpets and cymbals to meet them, so that the air resounded with music and cheers. She was taken to the Princess, who saluted her and treated her with great honor. At night the Princess said good-bye to her father, and set out on the carpet for Aladdin's palace, with his mother at her side, and followed by the hundred slaves. She was charmed at the sight of Aladdin, who ran to receive her. "Princess," he said, "blame your beauty for my boldness if I have displeased you." She told him that, having seen him, she willingly obeyed her father in this matter. After the wedding had taken place Aladdin led her into the hall, where a feast was spread, and she supped with him, after which they danced till midnight.

Next day Aladdin invited the Sultan to see the palace. On entering the hall with the four-and-twenty windows, with their rubies, diamonds, and emeralds, he cried: "It is a world's wonder! There is only one thing that surprises me. Was it by accident that one window was left unfinished?"

"No, sir, by design," returned Aladdin. "I wished your Majesty to have the glory of finishing this palace."

The Sultan was pleased, and sent for the best jewelers in the city. He showed them the unfinished window, and bade them fit it up like the others. "Sir," replied their spokesman, "we cannot find jewels enough."

The Sultan had his own fetched, which they soon used, but to no purpose, for in a month's time the work was not half done. Aladdin, knowing that their task was vain, bade them undo their work and carry the jewels back, and the genie finished the window at his command. The Sultan was surprised to receive his jewels again and visited Aladdin, who showed him the window finished. The Sultan embraced him, the envious Vizier meanwhile hinting that it was the work of enchantment. Aladdin had won the hearts of the people by his gentle bearing. He was made captain of the Sultan's armies, and won several battles for him, but remained modest and courteous as before and lived thus in peace and content for several years.

But far away in Africa the magician remembered Aladdin and by his magic arts discovered that Aladdin, instead of perishing miserably in the cave, had escaped and had married a Princess with whom he was living in great honor and wealth. He knew that the poor tailor's son could only have accomplished this by means of the lamp and traveled night and day till he reached the capital of China, bent on Aladdin's ruin. As he passed through the town he heard people talking everywhere about a marvelous palace. "Forgive my ignorance," he said. "What is this palace you speak of?"

"Have you not heard of Prince Aladdin's palace," was the reply, "the greatest wonder of the world? I will direct you if you have a mind to see it."

The magician thanked him who spoke, and having seen the palace knew that it had been raised by the genie of the lamp and became half mad with rage. He determined to get hold of the lamp and again plunge Aladdin into the deepest poverty. Unluckily, Aladdin had gone a-hunting for eight days, which gave the magician plenty of time. He bought a dozen copper lamps, put them into a basket, and went to the palace, crying, "New lamps for old!" followed by a jeering crowd.

The Princess, sitting in the hall of four-and-twenty windows, sent a slave to find out what the noise was about, who came back laughing, so that the Princess scolded her. "Madam," replied the slave, "who can help laughing to see an old fool offering to exchange fine new lamps for old ones?"

Another slave, hearing this, said: "There is an old one on the cornice there which he can have." Now this was the magic lamp, which Aladdin had left there, as he could not take it out hunting with him. The Princess, not knowing its value, laughingly bade the slave take it and make the exchange. She went and said to the magician: "Give me a new lamp for this."

He snatched it and bade the slave take her choice, amid the jeers of the crowd. Little he cared, but left off crying his lamps, and went out of the city gates to a lonely place, where he remained till nightfall, when he pulled out the lamp and rubbed it. The genie appeared and at the magician's command carried him, together with the palace and the Princess in it, to a lonely place in Africa.

Next morning the Sultan looked out of the window toward Aladdin's palace and rubbed his eyes, for it was gone. He sent for the Vizier and asked what had become of the palace. The Vizier looked out too, and was lost in astonishment. He again put it down to enchantment, and this time the Sultan believed him, and sent thirty men on horseback to fetch Aladdin in chains. They met him riding home, bound him, and forced him to go with them on foot. The people, however, who loved him, followed, armed, to see that he came to no harm. He was carried before the Sultan, who ordered the executioner to cut off his head. The executioner made Aladdin kneel down, bandaged his eyes, and raised his scimitar to strike. At that instant the Vizier, who saw that the crowd had forced their way into the courtyard and were scaling the walls to rescue Aladdin, called to the executioner to stay his hand. The people, indeed, looked so threatening that the Sultan gave way and ordered Aladdin to be unbound, and pardoned him in the sight of the crowd. Aladdin now begged to know what he had done.

"False wretch!" said the Sultan, "come hither," and showed him from the window the place where his palace had stood. Aladdin was so amazed that he could not say a word. "Where is the palace and my daughter?" demanded the Sultan. "For the first I am not so deeply concerned, but my daughter I must have, and you must find her or lose your head."

Aladdin begged for forty days in which to find her, promising if he failed, to return and suffer death at the Sultan's pleasure. His prayer was granted, and he went forth sadly from the Sultan's presence. For three days he wandered about like a madman, asking everyone what had become of his palace, but they only laughed and pitied him. He came to the banks of a river, and knelt down to say his prayers before throwing himself in. In so doing he rubbed the magic ring he still wore. The genie he had seen in the cave appeared, and asked his will. "Save my life, genie," said Aladdin, "and bring my palace back."

"That is not in my power," said the genie; "I am only the Slave of the Ring, you must ask the Slave of the Lamp."

"Even so," said Aladdin, "but thou canst take me to the palace, and set me down under my dear wife's window." He at once found himself in Africa, under the window of the Princess, and fell asleep out of sheer weariness.

He was awakened by the singing of the birds, and his heart was lighter. He saw plainly that all his misfortunes were owing to the loss of the lamp, and vainly wondered who had robbed him of it. That morning the Princess rose earlier than she had done since she had been carried into Africa by the magician, whose company she was forced to endure once a day. She, however, treated him so harshly that he dared not live there altogether. As she was dressing, one of her women looked out and saw Aladdin. The Princess ran and opened the window, and at the noise she made Aladdin looked up. She called to him to come to her, and great was the joy of these lovers at seeing each other again.

After he had kissed her Aladdin said: "I beg of you, Princess, in God's name, before we speak of anything else, for your own sake and mine, tell me what has become of an old lamp I left on the cornice in the hall of windows when I went hunting."

"Alas!" she said, "I am the innocent cause of our sorrows," and told him of the exchange of the lamp.

"Now I know," cried Aladdin, "that we have to thank the African magician for this! Where is the lamp?"

"He carries it about with him," said the Princess. "I know, for he pulled it out of his breast to show me. He wishes me to break my faith with you and marry him, saying that you were beheaded by my father's command. He is forever speaking ill of you, but I only reply by my tears. If I persist, I doubt not that he will use violence."

Aladdin comforted her and left her for a while. He changed clothes with the first person he met in the town, and having bought a certain powder, returned to the Princess, who let him in by a little side door. "Put on your most beautiful dress," he said to her, "and receive the magician with smiles, leading him to believe that you have forgotten me. Invite him to sup with you, and say you wish to taste the wine of his country. He will go for some, and while he is gone, I will tell you what to do."

She listened carefully to Aladdin, and when he left her, arrayed herself gaily for the first time since she left China. She put on a girdle and head-dress of diamonds, and seeing in a glass that she looked more beautiful than ever, received

the magician, saying, to his great amazement: "I have made up my mind that Aladdin is dead, and that all my tears will not bring him back to me, so I am resolved to mourn no more, and have therefore invited you to sup with me; but I am tired of the wines of China, and would fain taste those of Africa."

The magician flew to his cellar, and the Princess put the powder Aladdin had given her in her cup. When he returned she asked him to drink her health in the wine of Africa, handing him her cup in exchange for his as a sign she was reconciled to him. Before drinking, the magician made her a speech in praise of her beauty, but the Princess cut him short, saying: "Let me drink first, and you shall say what you will afterwards." She set her cup to her lips and kept it there, while the magician drained his to the dregs and fell back lifeless. The Princess then opened the door to Aladdin, and flung her arms round his neck, but Aladdin put her away, bidding her leave him, as he had more to do. He then went to the dead magician, took the lamp out of his vest, and bade the genie carry the palace and all in it back to China. This was done, and the Princess in her chamber only felt two little shocks, and little thought she was at home again.

The Sultan, who was sitting in his closet, mourning for his lost daughter, happened to look up, and rubbed his eyes, for there stood the palace as before! He hastened thither, and Aladdin received him in the hall of the four-and-twenty windows, with the Princess at his side. Aladdin told him what had happened, and showed him the dead body of the magician, that he might believe. A ten days' feast was proclaimed, and it seemed as if Aladdin might now live the rest of his life in peace; but it was not to be.

The African magician had a younger brother, who was, if possible, more wicked and more cunning than himself. He traveled to China to avenge his brother's death, and went to visit a pious woman called Fatima, thinking she might be of use to him. He entered her cell and clapped a dagger to her breast, telling her to rise and do his bidding on pain of death. He changed clothes with her, colored his face like hers, put on her veil, and murdered her, that she might tell no tales. Then he went towards the palace of Aladdin, and all the people, thinking he was the holy woman, gathered round him, kissing his hands and begging his blessing. When he got to the palace there was such a noise going on round him that the Princess bade her slave look out of the window and ask what was the matter. The slave said it was the holy woman, curing people by her touch of their ailments, whereupon the Princess, who had long desired to see Fatima, sent for her. On coming to the Princess, the magician offered up a prayer for her health and prosperity. When he had done, the Princess made him sit by her, and begged him to stay with her always. The false Fatima, who wished for nothing better, consented, but kept his veil down for fear of discovery. The Princess showed him the hall, and asked him what he thought of it. "It is truly beautiful," said the false Fatima. "In my mind it wants but one thing."

"And what is that?" said the Princess.

"If only a roc's egg," replied he, "were hung up from the middle of this dome, it would be the wonder of the world."

After this the Princess could think of nothing but a roc's egg, and when Aladdin returned from hunting he found her in a very ill humor. He begged to know what was amiss, and she told him that all her pleasure in the hall was spoilt for the want of a roc's egg hanging from the dome. "If that is all," replied Aladdin, "you shall soon be happy."

He left her and rubbed the lamp, and when the genie appeared commanded him to bring a roc's egg. The genie gave such a loud and terrible shriek that the hall shook. "Wretch!" he cried, "is it not enough that I have done everything for you, but you must command me to bring my master and hang him up in the midst of this dome? You and your wife and your palace deserve to be burnt to ashes; but this request does not come from you, but from the brother of the African magician whom you destroyed. He is now in your palace disguised as the holy woman —whom he murdered. He it was who put that wish into your wife's head. Take care of yourself, for he means to kill you." So saying the genie disappeared.

Aladdin went back to the Princess, saying his head ached, and requesting that the holy Fatima should be fetched to lay her hands on it. But when the magician came near, Aladdin, seizing his dagger, pierced him to the heart.

"What have you done?" cried the Princess. "You have killed the holy woman!"

"Not so," replied Aladdin, "but a wicked magician," and told her of how she had been deceived.

After this Aladdin and his wife lived in peace. He succeeded the Sultan when he died, and reigned for many years, leaving behind him a long line of kings.

Japanese folk tales

Since Japanese folk tales have been out of print for a time, it is good to see them reappearing in fresh editions and excellent translations. Libraries will have some of the earlier collections on their shelves and students of folklore will find them a colorful and rewarding group with strong moral overtones.

MOMOTARO: BOY-OF-THE-PEACH

After hearing this story, children will be delighted to discover the amusing little poem about Momotaro in Time for Poetry.

Once long, long ago, there lived a kind old man and a kind old woman in a small village in Japan.

"Momotaro: Boy-of-the-Peach." From *The Dancing Kettle and Other Japanese Folk Tales*, copyright, 1949, by Yoshiko Uchida. Reprinted by permission of Harcourt, Brace and Company, Inc.

One fine day, they set out from their little cottage together. The old man went toward the mountains to cut some firewood for their kitchen, and the old woman went toward the river to do her washing.

When the old woman reached the shore of the river, she knelt down beside her wooden tub and began to scrub her clothes on a round, flat stone. Suddenly she looked up and saw something very strange floating down the shallow river. It was a big, big peach; bigger than the round wooden tub that stood beside the old woman.

Rumbley-bump and a-bumpety-bump . . . Rumbley-bump and a-bumpety-bump. The big peach rolled closer and closer over the stones in the stream.

"My gracious me!" the old woman said to herself. "In all my long life I have never seen a peach of such great size and beauty. What a fine present it would make for the old man. I do think I will take it home with me."

Then the old woman stretched out her hand just as far as she could, but no matter how hard she stretched, she couldn't reach the big peach.

"If I could just find a long stick, I would be able to reach it," thought the old woman, looking around, but all she could see were pebbles and sand.

"Oh, dear, what shall I do?" she said to herself. Then suddenly she thought of a way to bring the beautiful big peach to her side. She began to sing out in a sweet, clear voice,

"The deep waters are salty!
The shallow waters are sweet!
Stay away from the salty water,
And come where the water is sweet."

She sang this over and over, clapping her hands in time to her song. Then, strangely enough, the big peach slowly began to bob along toward the shore where the water was shallow.

Rumbley-bump and a-bumpety-bump . . . Rumbley-bump and a-bumpety-bump. The big peach came closer and closer to the old woman and finally came to a stop at her feet.

The old woman was so happy, she picked the big peach up very carefully and quickly carried it home in her arms. Then she waited for the old man to return so she could show him her lovely present. Toward evening the old man came home with a big pack of wood on his back.

"Come quickly, come quickly," the old woman called to him from the house.

"What is it? What is the matter?" the old man asked as he hurried to the side of the old woman.

"Just look at the fine present I have for you," said the old woman happily as she showed him the big round peach.

"My goodness! What a great peach! Where in the world did you buy such a peach as this?" the old man asked.

The old woman smiled happily and told him how she had found the peach floating down the river.

"Well, well, this is a fine present indeed," said the old man, "for I have worked hard today and I am very hungry."

Then he got the biggest knife they had, so he could cut the big peach in half. Just as he was ready to thrust the sharp blade into the peach, he heard a tiny voice from inside.

"Wait, old man! Don't cut me!" it cried, and before the surprised old man and woman could say a word, the beautiful big peach broke in two, and a sweet little boy jumped out from inside. The old man and woman were so surprised, they could only raise their hands and cry out, "Oh, oh! My goodness!"

Now the old man and woman had always wanted a child of their own, so they were very, very happy to find such a fine little boy, and decided to call him "Momotaro," which means boy-of-the-peach. They took very good care of the little boy and grew to love him dearly, for he was a fine young lad. They spent many happy years together, and before long Momotaro was fifteen years old.

One day Momotaro came before the old man and said, "You have both been good and kind to me. I am very grateful for all you have done, and now I think I am old enough to do some good for others too. I have come to ask if I may leave you."

"You wish to leave us, my son? But why?" asked the old man in surprise.

"Oh, I shall be back in a very short time," said Momotaro. "I wish only to go to the Island of the Ogres, to rid the land of those harmful creatures. They have killed many good people, and have stolen and robbed throughout the country. I wish to kill the ogres so they can never harm our people again."

"That is a fine idea, my son, and I will not stop you from going," said the old man.

So that very day, Momotaro got ready to start out on his journey. The old woman prepared some millet cakes for him to take along on his trip, and soon Momotaro was ready to leave. The old man and woman were sad to see him go and called, "Be careful, Momotaro! Come back safely to us."

"Yes, yes, I shall be back soon," he answered. "Take care of yourselves while I am away," he added, and waved as he started down the path toward the forest.

He hurried along, for he was anxious to get to the Island of the Ogres. While he was walking through the cool forest where the grass grew long and high, he began to feel hungry. He sat down at the foot of a tall pine tree and carefully unwrapped the *furoshiki*[1] which held his little millet cakes. "My, they smell good," he thought. Suddenly he heard the tall grass rustle and saw something stalking through the grass toward him. Momotaro blinked hard when he saw what it was. It was a dog as big as a calf! But Momotaro was not frightened, for the dog just said, "Momotaro-san, Momotaro-san, what is it you are eating that smells so good?"

"I'm eating a delicious millet cake which my good mother made for me this morning," he answered.

The dog licked his chops and looked at the cake with hungry eyes. "Please, Momotaro-san," he said, "just give me one of your millet cakes, and I will come along with you to the Island of the Ogres. I know why you are going there, and I can be of help to you."

"Very well, my friend," said Momotaro. "I will take you along with me," and he gave the dog one of his millet cakes to eat.

As they walked on, something suddenly leaped from the branches above and jumped in front of Momotaro. He stopped in surprise and found that it was a monkey who had jumped down from the trees.

"Greetings, Momotaro-san!" called the monkey

[1] Pronounced foo-ro-shee-kee, a square cloth used to wrap and carry articles.

happily. "I have heard that you are going to the Island of the Ogres to rid the land of these plundering creatures. Take me with you, for I wish to help you in your fight."

When the dog heard this he growled angrily. "Grruff," he said to the monkey. "*I* am going to help Momotaro-san. We do not need the help of a monkey such as you! Out of our way! Grruff, grruff," he barked angrily.

"How dare you speak to me like that?" shrieked the monkey, and he leaped at the dog, scratching with his sharp claws. The dog and the monkey began to fight each other, biting, clawing, and growling. When Momotaro saw this he pushed them apart and cried, "Here, here, stop it, you two! There is no reason why you both cannot go with me to the Island of the Ogres. I shall have two helpers instead of one!" Then he took another millet cake from his *furoshiki* and gave it to the monkey.

Now there were three of them going down the path to the edge of the woods. The dog in front, Momotaro in the middle, and the monkey walking in the rear. Soon they came to a big field and just as they were about to cross it, a large pheasant hopped out in front of them. The dog jumped at it with a growl, but the pheasant fought back with such spirit that Momotaro ran over to stop the dog. "We could use a brave bird such as you to help us fight the ogres. We are on our way to their island this very day. How would you like to come along with us?"

"Oh, I would like that indeed, for I would like to help you rid the land of these evil and dangerous ogres," said the pheasant happily.

"Then here is a millet cake for you, too," said Momotaro, giving the pheasant a cake, just as he had to the monkey and the dog.

Now there were four of them going to the Island of the Ogres, and as they walked down the path together, they became very good friends.

Before long they came to the water's edge and Momotaro found a boat big enough for all of them. They climbed in and headed for the Island of the Ogres. Soon they saw the island in the distance wrapped in gray, foggy clouds. Dark stone walls rose up above towering cliffs and large iron gates stood ready to keep out any who tried to enter.

Momotaro thought for a moment, then turned

to the pheasant and said, "You alone can wing your way over their high walls and gates. Fly into their stronghold now, and do what you can to frighten them. We will follow as soon as we can."

So the pheasant flew far above the iron gates and stone walls and down onto the roof of the ogres' castle. Then he called to the ogres, "Momotaro-san has come to rid the land of you and your many evil deeds. Give up your stolen treasures now, and perhaps he will spare your lives!"

When the ogres heard this, they laughed and shouted. "HO, HO, HO! We are not afraid of a little bird like you! We are not afraid of little Momotaro!"

The pheasant became very angry at this, and flew down, pecking at the heads of the ogres with his sharp, pointed beak. While the pheasant was fighting so bravely, the dog and monkey helped Momotaro to tear down the gates, and they soon came to the aid of the pheasant.

"Get away! Get away!" shouted the ogres, but the monkey clawed and scratched, the big dog growled and bit the ogres, and the pheasant flew about, pecking at their heads and faces. So fierce were they that soon the ogres began to run away. Half of them tumbled over the cliffs as they ran and the others fell pell-mell into the sea. Soon only the Chief of the Ogres remained. He threw up his hands, and then bowed low to Momotaro. "Please spare me my life, and all our stolen treasures are yours. I promise never to rob or kill anyone again," he said.

Momotaro tied up the evil ogre, while the monkey, the dog and the pheasant carried many boxes filled with jewels and treasures down to their little boat. Soon it was laden with all the treasures it could hold, and they were ready to sail toward home.

When Momotaro returned, he went from one family to another, returning the many treasures which the ogres had stolen from the people of the land.

"You will never again be troubled by the Ogres of Ogre Island!" he said to them happily.

And they all answered, "You are a kind and brave lad, and we thank you for making our land safe once again."

Then Momotaro went back to the home of the old man and woman with his arms full of jewels and treasures from Ogre Island. My, but the old man and woman were glad to see him once again, and the three of them lived happily together for many, many years.

URASHIMA TARO AND
THE PRINCESS OF THE SEA

This story is a bit like "Sadko" and Washington Irving's "Rip Van Winkle."

Long, long ago, in a small village of Japan, there lived a fine young man named Urashima Taro. He lived with his mother and father in a thatched-roof house which overlooked the sea. Each morning he was up before the sun, and went out to sea in his little fishing boat. On days when his luck was good, he would bring back large baskets full of fish which he sold in the village market.

One day, as he was carrying home his load of fish, he saw a group of shouting children. They were gathered around something on the beach and were crying, "Hit him! Poke him!" Taro ran over to see what was the matter, and there on the sand he saw a big brown tortoise. The children were poking it with a long stick and throwing stones at its hard shell.

"Here, here," called Taro. "That's no way to treat him! Why don't you leave him alone, and let him go back to the sea?"

"But we found him," said one of the children. "He belongs to us!"

"Yes, yes, he is ours," cried all the children.

Now, because Urashima Taro was a fair and kindly young man, he said to them, "Suppose I give each of you something in return for the tortoise?" Then he took ten shiny coins out of a small bag of money and gave one to each child. "Now, isn't that a fair bargain?" he asked. "A coin for each of you, and the tortoise for me."

"Yes, yes. Thank you!" called the children, and away they ran to the village candy shop.

"Urashima Taro and the Princess of the Sea." From *The Dancing Kettle and Other Japanese Folk Tales*, copyright, 1949, by Yoshiko Uchida. Reprinted by permission of Harcourt, Brace and Company, Inc.

Taro watched the old tortoise crawl away slowly toward the sea and called, "You'd better stay at home in the sea from now on, old fellow!" Then, smiling happily because he had been able to save the tortoise, he turned to go home. There his mother and father were waiting for him with bowls of steaming rice and soup.

Several days passed, and Taro soon forgot all about the tortoise whom he had saved. One day he was sitting in his boat feeling very sad because he could catch no fish. Suddenly he heard a voice from the sea calling, "Urashima-san! Urashima-san!"

"Now who could be calling me here in the earth! But how can I go to the bottom of the sea, and how can I enter her palace?"

"Just leave everything to me," said the old tortoise. "Hop on my back and I will see that you get there safely. I will also take you into the palace, for I am one of the palace guards."

So Urashima Taro jumped onto the smooth round back of the tortoise, and away they went. Swish, swish . . . the waves seemed to part and make a path for them as the tortoise swam on. Soon Taro felt himself going down . . . down . . . down . . . into the sea, but he wasn't getting wet at all. He heard the waves lapping gently about his ears. "That's strange," thought

middle of the sea?" thought Urashima Taro. He looked high and low, but could see no one. Suddenly, from the crest of a big wave, out popped the head of the old tortoise.

"I came to thank you for saving me the other day," said the tortoise.

"Well, I'm glad you got away safely," said Taro.

"This time I would like to do something for you, Urashima-san," said the tortoise. "How would you like to visit the princess who lives in the Palace of the Sea?"

"The princess of the sea!" shouted Taro. "I have heard often of her beauty, and everyone says her palace is more lovely than any place on

Taro. "This is just like a dream—a nice happy dream."

Before long, they were at the bottom of the big blue sea. Taro could see bright-colored fish playing hide and seek among the long strands of swaying seaweed. He could see clams and other shellfish shyly peeking out at him from their shells. Soon Taro saw something big and shiny looming in the hazy blue water.

"Is that the palace?" he asked anxiously. "It looks very beautiful."

"Oh, no," answered the tortoise. "That is just the outer gate."

They came to a stop and Taro could see that the gateway was guarded by a fish in armor of silver. "Welcome home," the guard called to the tortoise, as he opened the gate for them to enter.

"See whom I have brought back with me," the tortoise answered happily. The guard in the armor of silver turned to Urashima Taro and bowed most politely. Taro just had time to return the bow when he looked up and saw another gate. This one was even larger than the first, and was made of silver stones and pillars of coral. A row of fish in armor of gold was guarding the second gate.

"Now, Urashima-san, if you will get off and wait here, I will tell the princess that you have come," said the tortoise, and he disappeared into the palace beyond the gate. Taro had never seen such a beautiful sight in all his life. The silver stones in the gate sparkled and glittered as though they were smiling at him. Taro had to blink hard.

Soon the tortoise was back at his side telling

him that the princess was waiting to see him. He led Taro through the gate of coral and silver, and up a path of golden stones to the palace. There in front of the palace stood the beautiful princess of the sea with her ladies-in-waiting.

"Welcome to the Palace of the Sea, Urashima Taro," she said, and her voice sounded like the tinkling of little silver bells. "Won't you come with me?" she asked.

Taro opened his mouth to answer, but not a sound would come forth. He could only look at the beautiful princess and the sparkling emeralds and diamonds and rubies which glittered on the walls of the palace. The princess understood how Taro felt, so she just smiled kindly and led him down a hallway paved with smooth, white pearls. Soon they came to a large room, and in the center of the room was an enormous table and an enormous chair. Taro thought they might have been made for a great king.

"Sit down, Urashima-san," said the princess, and as he sat in the enormous chair, the ladies-in-waiting appeared from all sides. They placed on the table plate after plate of all the delicious things that Taro could think of. "Eat well, my friend," said the princess, "and while you dine, my maids will sing and dance for you." Soon there was music and singing and dancing. The room was filled with laughing voices. Taro felt like a king now! He thought surely this was all a dream, and that it would end soon. But no, after he had dined, the princess took him all through the beautiful palace. At the very last, she brought him to a room that looked as though it were made of ice and snow. There were creamy pearls and sparkling diamonds everywhere.

"Now, how would you like to see all the seasons of the year?" whispered the princess.

"Oh, I would like that very much," answered Taro, and as he spoke, the east door of the room opened slowly and quietly. Taro could scarcely believe the sight before his eyes. He saw big clouds of pale pink cherry blossoms and tall green willow trees swaying in the beeze. He could hear bluebirds singing, and saw them fly happily into the sky.

"Ah, that is spring," murmured Taro. "What a lovely sunny day!" But before he could say more, the princess led him further on. As she opened the door to the south, Taro could see white lotus blossoms floating on a still green pond. It was a warm summer day, and he could hear crickets chirping lazily, somewhere in the distance. She opened the door to the west and he saw a hillside of maple trees. Their leaves of crimson and yellow were whirling and dancing down among golden chrysanthemums. He had seen such trees each fall in his own little village. When the princess opened the door to the north, Taro felt a blast of cold air. He shivered, and looked up to see snowflakes tumbling down from gray skies. They were putting white caps on all the fence posts and treetops.

"Now you have seen all the seasons of the year," said the princess.

"They were beautiful!" sighed Taro happily. "I have never seen such wonderful sights in all my life! I wish I could stay here always!"

Taro was having such a very good time that he forgot all about his home in the village. He feasted and danced and sang with his friends in the Palace of the Sea, and before he knew it, three long years had gone by. But to Taro they seemed to be just three short days.

At last Taro said to the princess, "Alas, I have been here much too long. I must go home to see my mother and father so they will not worry about me."

"But you will come back?" asked the princess.

"Oh, yes, yes. I will come back," answered Taro.

"Before you go I have something for you," said the princess, and she gave Taro a small jewel box studded with many precious stones.

"Oh, it is beautiful, Princess," said Taro. "How can I thank you for all you have done for me?"

But the princess went on, "There is just one thing about that box," she said. "You must never, never open it if you ever wish to return to the Palace of the Sea. Can you remember that, Urashima Taro?"

"I will never open it, no matter what happens," promised Taro. Then he said good-bye to all his friends in the palace. Once again he climbed on the back of the old tortoise and they sailed toward his village on the seacoast. The princess and her ladies-in-waiting stood at the coral gate and waved to Taro till he could no longer see them. The tortoise swam on and on,

and one by one all the little bright-colored fish that had been following them began to turn back. Before long, Taro could see the seacoast where he used to go fishing, and soon they were back on the very beach where Taro had once saved the tortoise. Taro hopped off onto the smooth white sand. "Good-bye, old friend," he said. "You have been very good to me. Thank you for taking me to the most beautiful place I have ever seen."

"Farewell, Urashima-san," said the old tortoise. "I hope we may meet again some day." Then he turned and crawled slowly back into the sea.

Now that he was in his own village once more, Taro was most anxious to see his parents. He ran along the path which led to their house with his jewel box tucked securely under his arm. He looked up eagerly at each person whom he passed. He wanted to shout a greeting to them, but each face seemed strange and new. "How odd!" thought Taro. "I feel as though I were in some other village than my own. I don't seem to know anyone. Well, I'll soon see Mother and Father," he said, and hurried on. When he reached the spot where the house should have been, there was no house to be seen. There was just an empty lot full of tall green weeds. Taro couldn't believe his eyes. "Why, what has happened to my home? Where are my parents?" he cried. He looked up and down the dusty path and soon saw an old, old woman coming toward him. "I'll ask her what has happened to my home," thought Taro.

"Old woman, please, can you help me?" asked Taro.

The old woman straightened her bent back and cocked her gray head, "Eh, what did you say?" she asked.

"Can you tell me what happened to Urashima Taro's home? It used to be right here," said Taro.

"Never heard of him," said the old woman, shaking her head.

"But you must have," Taro replied. "He lived right here, on this very spot where you are standing."

"Now let me see," she sighed. "Urashima Taro. Yes, it seems I have heard of him. Oh, I remember now. There is a story that he went out to sea in his fishing boat one day and never came back again. I suppose he was drowned at sea. Well, anyway, that was over three hundred years ago. My great-great-grandfather used to tell me about Urashima Taro when I was just a little girl."

"Three hundred years!" exclaimed Taro. His eyes were like saucers now. "But I don't understand."

"Well, I don't understand what you want with a man who lived three hundred years ago," muttered the old woman, and she trudged on down the road.

"So three years in the Palace of the Sea has really been three hundred years here in my village," thought Taro. "No wonder all my friends are gone. No wonder I can't find my mother or father!" Taro had never felt so lonely or so sad as he did then. "What can I do? What can I do?" he murmured to himself.

Suddenly he remembered the little jewel box which the princess had given him. "Perhaps there is something in there that can help me," he thought, and forgetting the promise he had made to the princess, he quickly opened the box. Suddenly, there arose from it a cloud of white smoke which wrapped itself around Taro so that he could see nothing. When it disappeared, Urashima Taro peered into the empty box, but he could scarcely see. He looked at his hands and they were the hands of an old, old man. His face was wrinkled; his hair was as white as snow. In that short moment Urashima Taro had become three hundred years older. He remembered the promise he had made to the princess, but now it was too late and he knew that he could never visit the Palace of the Sea again. But who knows, perhaps one day the old tortoise came back to the beach once more to help his friend.

A Chinese folk tale

We are just beginning to get some translations of the Chinese folk tales in attractive style. The collection from which this story was taken has some delightful tales for telling to older children.

THE FOX'S DAUGHTER

Nothing is luckier than to be the child of a fox, for, without taking the trouble to learn anything, foxes know as much magic as the man who spends his whole life studying it, and when a fox's child takes human form, as sometimes happens, and becomes a boy or a girl, he knows as much magic as his father.

Liu was a young student who should have been working hard for his examinations, but he was rather idle and much preferred wandering about his father's estate, or sailing in a boat on the river which ran through it, to sitting indoors over his books.

One day, when he was occupied—if it can be called occupied—in this way, he saw the form of a young girl among the reeds which grew upon a little island in the river. Quickly he jumped into

his boat and hurried across the water, and, tying the boat up to a willow tree, he began to search the island for her.

For some time he saw nothing, but he heard mocking laughter to the right and to the left, and, running wildly first in one direction and then in the other, he tore his silk robe and broke the strap of one of his sandals. At last he succeeded in running her down, but she looked so beautiful, leaning against a tree and smiling at him, that even after he had got his breath back he could not speak.

"Alas," said the girl in a clear low voice, looking at his torn robe and flapping sandal, "if

"The Fox's Daughter." From *The Treasure of Li-Po* by Alice Ritchie, copyright, 1949, by Harcourt, Brace and Company, Inc. Published in London by The Hogarth Press Ltd.

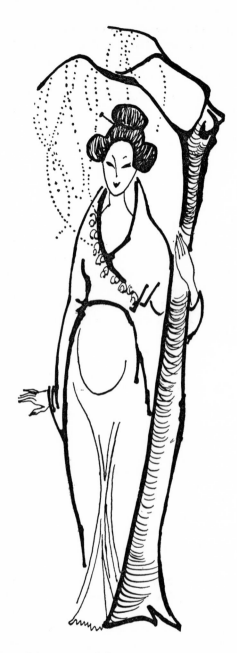

"but as to how I came here, I shall not tell you, and I can go away again as swiftly."

(This was not surprising, because of course she was a fox's daughter, and could appear and disappear at will.) And now she made a movement as if she meant to go, but Liu sprang forward with his hands spread out.

"I beg you to stay," he cried, "or at least tell me where we shall meet again, for you are the most beautiful person I have ever seen."

"Look for me in your books," said the maiden; then, seeing his face become clouded with disappointment, she took a little silver mirror from her girdle and gave it to him. "There," she said, "you shall have something which has belonged to me, but I warn you, you will never see me in it except through your books." And in a moment she had vanished.

Liu went back to his boat feeling very sad, and many times before he reached the house he looked longingly into the silver mirror, but all he saw was the back-view of the beautiful Feng-Lien standing as if she was watching someone going away from her.

As soon as he reached his room, remembering what she had said, he took out the heavy and difficult books which he had never had a mind to study, and laying them on the top of the mirror, he tried to see it through them, but of course he saw nothing, not even its silver handle, buried under those great volumes.

"Feng-Lien meant more than she said," he remarked to himself, and he removed the books from the mirror with a sigh and applied himself earnestly to reading them, refusing to see his friends when they came to the house and not accepting any invitations. After he had spent several days in this way, he looked into the mirror again, and there was Feng-Lien with her face turned towards him, smiling and nodding as if she was pleased.

For a month or more he did nothing but study, looking often into the mirror to be encouraged by the lovely face of Feng-Lien, but presently the fine summer weather came, and he could not force himself to stay in the house. He began once more to wander about the garden and the wild land beside the river, idly enjoying the scent of the newly opened flowers and the sight of the bright birds.

Master Liu pursued his studies with the same zeal as he has pursued me, he would take a high place when the candidates go up to the Examination Hall, and some day he would be a man of great importance—but of course he will do nothing of the sort."

Liu eagerly asked her name and how she happened to know all about him, and also how she came to be upon the island, for he could see no boat except his own.

"My name is Feng-Lien," said the maiden,

"Perhaps I shall see Feng-Lien again," he said. But he did not find her, and in his heart he knew she would not come while he behaved in this way. Then, one evening after he had been on a fishing expedition all day with some friends, when he pulled out the silver mirror he saw Feng-Lien crying bitterly, and the next morning she had her back turned to him.

"It is clear that there is only one thing to be done," he said to himself. "I must make a habit of working all the time."

He took the silver mirror and nailed it on the wall so that whenever he raised his eyes from his difficult reading he would see Feng-Lien's face. She always looked happy now. This went on for two years, and at the end of that time he went up to the Examination Hall and did so well that he took a high place in the final list.

"Now," he said, "at last, I shall surely be allowed to see Feng-Lien herself."

He took up the mirror and looked for a long time at her reflection, at the arched eyebrows and the beautiful eyes and the smiling mouth, until it seemed to him that her lips parted and she spoke, yes, she seemed to be speaking words of welcome and congratulation, and suddenly the mirror dissolved into a drop of dew and instead of her likeness, Feng-Lien herself stood before him.

"Really," she said, bowing very low, "I am quite frightened of this learned young man."

"The success I have had is entirely owing to you," said Liu.

So they were married, and Liu attained to one of the highest positions in China, but Feng-Lien never again had to use the magic she possessed by reason of being a fox's daughter. She found quite simple ways of keeping her husband, who continued to be by nature somewhat lazy, up to the mark.

A Korean folk tale

The Korean tales are full of ghosts and magic. They are often beautiful in style and content and therefore excellent for storytelling.

WHICH WAS WITCH?

Here's a story as witty as its title, and a good tale for Halloween.

There was once a wise and learned man named Kim Su-ik. He lived just inside the south gate of Seoul but he might as well have lived anywhere for all the thought he gave the matter. His mind was entirely taken up with study and books, and one could say of him, as Im Bang said of another scholar, "He used to awake at first cock-crow, wash, dress, take up his book and never lay it aside. On his right were pictures, on his left were books, and he happy between. He rose to be a Prime Minister."

One night Kim Su-ik was absorbed in studying a Chinese classic when he suddenly felt hungry.

"Which Was Witch?" From *Which Was Witch?* by Eleanore M. Jewett. Copyright 1953 by Eleanore M. Jewett. Reprinted by permission of The Viking Press, Inc.

He clapped his hands to summon a servant, and immediately the door of his room opened.

His wife stepped in.

"What does the master of the house desire?" said she.

"Food," he answered briefly, his attention already returned to the book in his lap.

"I have little in the house but a few roasted chestnuts. If that will suffice I will bring them to you myself. The servants have long since gone to their sleeping quarters."

Kim Su-ik grunted his approval and went on with his studies. In a very short time the door opened again and his wife came in bearing a brass bowl full of hot roasted chestnuts. He helped himself to one and was in the act of putting it into his mouth when once more the door opened and in stepped his wife with a brass bowl full of hot roasted chestnuts.

But his wife was already there, standing beside him with the bowl in her hands!

Kim Su-ik, his mouth still open and a chestnut half in it, looked in astonishment from one to the other of the identical women. They were as like as two pins—faces, features, figures, clothes, the way they stood, the way they used their fingers and moved their shoulders. Never were twins more completely alike. Kim Su-ik passed his hands before his eyes. He must have overdone his studying, he thought to himself, read too late and too steadily. His eyes were playing tricks on him, that was all. He was seeing double.

But when he looked again the two women were still there, and what was stranger still, they seemed not to be aware of each other, but stood quietly, gracefully, their eyes fastened on him as if waiting to know his pleasure.

The scholar leaped to his feet, choking back the cry of terror that rose in his throat. He knew, suddenly, without a doubt, what this meant. It was midnight, the moon was at the full, ghosts, evil spirits, witches and goblins would be abroad, filled with power. One of these two creatures standing before him was his wife, known and loved by him all his wedded life—and perhaps not quite fully appreciated, he hastily decided. The other must be a witch, able to change into any form she chose in the twinkling of an eye. But *which was which?* How could he protect his wife and drive this evil double from beside her?

Being a quick thinker as well as a learned one, Kim Su-ik plunged into action. He seized the arm of one of the women with his right hand and before the other could realize what he was about, he had her arm fast in his left hand. They turned mildly reproachful eyes upon him but made no effort to free themselves.

"My dear," said one, "too much study has fevered your brain."

"My dear," said the other, "too much reading of books has affected your mind."

Kim Su-ik looked from one to the other. Not a particle of difference was there to give him a hint as to which was wife and which was witch. He shook them gently. They smiled indulgently as at a child. He shook harder. No resentment, no struggle to get free. He was tempted to relax his grip on the two arms, but he knew he must not for a moment do that, and hung on more firmly than ever.

Minutes went by, then hours, the dull slow moving hours between midnight and cockcrow. The three stood silent, motionless, in the same spot. Kim Su-ik grew weary beyond words. So, too, must his wife be weary, but neither of the two women he held so tightly by the arm said anything or showed by any movement or expression of the face that she was tired, puzzled or angry. His wife would have been tired and puzzled—angry, too, perhaps, but she would not have blustered or scolded. Any other woman would, were she witch or human. But surely his wife would say *something*. What in the world had got into her? Was she bewitched? Or walking in her sleep? Perhaps she was not either one of these two women. He wanted to rush into the other part of the house to see if she was there, thus proving that both of these were witches. But he did nothing, just hung on, grimly, silently.

At long last a cock crowed. Immediately the woman at his left tried to wrench her arm free. The other remained quiet. Kim Su-ik dropped the unresisting one and threw all his strength into a struggle with the other. Like a wild thing the creature fought, biting, snarling, spitting, leaping back and forth. Still the scholar held on to her and would not let go. The arm in his hand shrank and grew hairy. The whole figure dwindled, the eyes grew round and green and blazed with fury.

Another cock crowed and another, and the first gray light of dawn melted the dark shadows out of doors. But Kim Su-ik had no thought or time to notice the coming of day. With a hideous shriek the creature changed before his very eyes into a powerful wildcat. In horror he loosed his hold, and she leaped through the window and was gone.

"I still think you are studying too much," said a quiet, familiar voice behind him, and there stood his wife, pale, trembling a little, but smiling confidently.

"Why didn't you let me know which was which?" demanded Kim Su-ik.

His wife laughed. "I don't know what you are talking about! You behaved very strangely, but then, one never knows what to expect of a scholar. Which was which what?"

"Witch!" said Kim Su-ik.

A Turkish folk tale

*For five centuries the people of Turkey and of all the Near East have
been laughing at Nasr-ed-Din Hodja. He is their Paul Bunyan, their Three Sillies
all in one, their source of wit and pure foolishness.*

HOW MANY DONKEYS?

There was the tinkle of tiny bells, the sharp clip of small hoofs, the throaty drone of a solitary singer. Nasr-ed-Din Hodja was bringing the donkeys back from the mill, their saddlebags filled with freshly ground wheat. The hot Turkish sun beat down on his turbaned head. The brown dust from the donkeys' hoofs puffed about him. The staccato trot of his donkey jiggled him back and forth. But Nasr-ed-Din Hodja was too pleased to be uncomfortable.

"I'll show them," he chuckled. "They gave me plenty of advice about taking care of their donkeys and their wheat. As though I did not know more about donkeys than any man in Ak Shehir."

His eyes rested lazily on the road ahead. At first it followed the brook running away from Mill Valley, the brook that turned the heavy stones to grind the wheat. Then the road disappeared over a hilltop.

"Just over that hill," he mused contentedly, "is Ak Shehir, where they are waiting for their donkeys. There is not a scratch or a bruise on one of the little creatures. No donkeys in all Turkey have had better treatment today than these nine."

Idly he began counting them.

"What?" he gasped. "Eight donkeys?"

He jumped from his donkey and ran hither and yon, looking behind rocks and over hilltops, but no stray donkey could he see. At last he stood beside the donkeys and counted again. This time there were nine. With a sigh of relief he climbed onto his own donkey and went swinging along the road. His long legs in their

"How Many Donkeys?" From *Once the Hodja* by Alice Geer Kelsey, Longmans, Green and Company. Copyright 1943 by Alice Geer Kelsey

baggy pantaloons swung easily back and forth in time to the donkey's trot. Passing through a cluster of trees he thought it time to count the donkeys again.

"One—two—three—" and up to eight he counted, but no ninth donkey was to be seen. Down from his donkey's back he came. Behind all the trees he peered. Not a hair of a donkey could he find.

Again he counted, standing beside his donkeys. There they all were—nine mild little donkeys waiting for orders to move on. Nasr-ed-Din Hodja scratched his poor head in bewilderment. Was he losing his mind or were the donkeys all bewitched? Again he counted. Yes, surely there were nine.

"Ughr-r-r-r," Nasr-ed-Din Hodja gave the low guttural which is Turkish for "Giddap." As he rode on, he looked about him for the evil spirits which must be playing tricks on him. Each donkey wore the blue beads which should drive away the evil spirits. Were there evil spirits abroad stronger even than the blue beads?

He was glad to see a friend coming toward him down the road.

"Oh, Mustapha Effendi," he cried. "Have you seen one of these donkeys? I have lost a donkey and yet I have not lost it."

"What can you mean, Hodja Effendi?" asked Mustapha.

"I left the mill with nine donkeys," explained the Hodja. "Part of the way home there have been nine and part of the way there have been eight. Oh, I am bewitched! Help me! Help me!"

Mustapha was used to the queer ways of the Hodja, but he was surprised. He counted the donkeys silently.

"Let me see you count the donkeys," he ordered the Hodja.

"One—two—three," began the Hodja, pointing at each one as he counted up to eight.

As he said the last number, he stopped and looked at his friend with a face full of helplessness and terror. His terror turned to amazement as Mustapha slapped his knee and laughed until he almost fell from his donkey.

"What is so funny?" asked the Hodja.

"Oh, Hodja Effendi!" Mustapha laughed. "When you are counting your brothers, why, oh why, do you not count the brother on whom you are riding?"

Nasr-ed-Din Hodja was silent for a moment to think through this discovery. Then he kissed the hand of his deliverer, pressed it to his forehead and thanked him a thousand times for his help. He rode, singing, on to Ak Shehir to deliver the donkeys to their owners.

A Costa Rican folk tale

Because of certain references to God and the Saints, the Costa Rican stories should be used with discretion and are better for adult references than for the children's use. The Costa Rican tales include many variants of European, especially Spanish, folk tales.

THE WITCHES' RIDE

Here is as lively a Halloween story as anyone could ask for. It has a familiar theme—the simpleton who comes out on top—but it is extraordinarily eerie. Children may need to know that, according to the story, any sacred name or sign has the power to banish witches or fairies or to put an end to a spell.

Once, in the days of long ago, there lived in Costa Rica a widow who had an only son. Now this son was considered a *bobo,* or simpleton, because he was lazy and, more than that, because in one way or another he muddled everything he set out to do.

One day the bobo's mother was preparing to cook the *chayote* hash and rice which were to be their supper. She went to the shed for wood to burn in the stove, but the shed was empty. So she told the bobo to go to the forest yonder and bring her some sticks for the fire.

Since it was already late afternoon and a chill wind was blowing, the bobo wrapped himself up

"The Witches' Ride." From *The Witches' Ride and Other Tales from Costa Rica* by Lupe de Osma, copyright 1957 by Lupe de Osma, by permission of William Morrow and Company, Inc.

in a coarse old blanket, wearing it like a cape. Then he set off. He soon entered the forest, but there were no broken branches at hand and since he had no machete, or long, sharp knife, with him to cut branches from the trees, he went on farther and farther, from one thicket to another. Before long he was deep in the forest.

Soon it grew dark and he lost the path. As he groped his way through the dense underbrush and hanging vines, not knowing which way to turn, he suddenly came upon a hut. He was glad to find a shelter and knocked a good round knock. No one answered. So he opened the door and went in. Finding the hut deserted, he proceeded to make himself at home. In a corner behind a pile of straw he found an old mat woven of reeds, and there he snuggled down. Soon, in good comfort, he was fast asleep.

He slept and slept till at the hour of midnight he was awakened with a start by the sound of merry voices. He raised his head a wee bit and looked around with one eye.

Through the open window of the hut the moonlight shone on the clay floor, turning it white. There the bobo saw twelve black shadows—the shadows of twelve old witches. They were jesting and laughing and having altogether a merry time as each witch took a sip from a big drinking gourd, then smacked her lips and passed it on.

Meantime, the bobo lay quiet and still behind the pile of straw, scarcely daring to draw his breath lest the witches find him and change him into some bird or beast.

And the riot and revelry went on until the gourd ran dry. Then without any warning at all, a witch cried out in a croaking voice, "Time to be off!" At the same moment she picked up a broom from a pile on the floor, placed herself nimbly upon it, and said these magic words:

"Fly me faster than a fairy,
  Without God—without Saint Mary!"

Away out of the window she flew and soared gracefully up into the air. The others followed quickly—each pouncing upon a broomstick from the pile, then repeating the magic words.

High in the night sky they flew, one behind the other, like a long black waving ribbon. They circled once and again around the big yellow moon and then vanished swiftly from sight beyond the tall mountain peaks.

"A week of Sundays!" cried the bobo in surprise. "Wasn't that neatly done! I wouldn't mind doing it myself! And why not?"

Well, as soon as the last witch had disappeared, up sprang the bobo from the reed mat and straightway went to the corner where the pile of brooms had been. He hoped that the witches might have left one behind. And they had! He snatched it up, and fastening the blanket around his shoulders good and tight, he placed himself upon the stick. Then he shouted with all his might:

"Fly me faster than a fairy,
  Without God—without Saint Mary!"

These words were scarcely out of his mouth when up he shot into the air like a whizzing arrow, and out of the window he flew. Faster and faster he soared, low over the treetops and high toward the moon, like a bird. And he flew and flew and flew, and the higher he went, the more he liked it—so much that every once in a while he would say the magic words again to the broom.

But, alas, he was not called a bobo for nothing. In his great glee he muddled the words, and said to the broomstick:

"Fly me faster than a fairy,
  Fly with God and good Saint Mary!"

No sooner were these words out of his mouth than the broom began to fall. Fast—and faster than fast—it dropped. The poor bobo had no time to think of the right magic words as he tumbled and somersaulted through the air.

Now then, it so happened that some robbers were hiding at the edge of the forest that night. Their booty was spread out on a large cloth, and they were seated around it, counting out each one's share of the treasure by the weak light of their lantern.

"Ho! The Devil himself must have been with us today," cried one of the robbers in delight. "Hope he doesn't take a fancy to drop in for his share!"

And at this very moment the bobo, who was coming down full tilt, saw the group and shouted, "Out of the way! Look out there, all of you! Make way for this poor devil!"

The robbers looked up, each and all of them afraid of the strange sight the bobo made. For his blanket flapped and danced behind him like two big black wings as he plunged down upon them. They sprang up in great fear, thinking they had the Devil on their backs.

"The Devil! The Devil is loose! Here he comes!" they cried in terror. "Run! Let us fly! Away . . . away!" They took to their heels as if they were running a race. And they left their booty behind.

The bobo came down in one enormous swoop upon the pile of riches—*plump!* There he sat, gazing rapturously at the heap of gold and silver coins. "Bless my soul! Bless my little soul!" he cried.

Straightway he jumped up and piled the coins together again in the center of the large cloth. Then he made a bundle out of it, slung it over his shoulder, and hobbled home very happy, humming a merry tune.

And as for the robbers, they were never seen again.

A Canadian folk tale

Natalie Savage Carlson has collected a group of Canadian tales under the title Sashes Red and Blue *and has told them with her usual charm and humor. The Nichet stories are traditional tales but are completely realistic.*

LITTLE NICHET'S

BABY SISTER

That little Nichet, Jean LeBlanc's youngest child, was one to keep his parents as busy as all the other thirteen tied together.

One day the little fellow had a new question for his wise father.

"Papa," said Nichet, "where did the Boulangers get their new baby?"

"That is an easy question," answered Jean LeBlanc. "The good Indians brought her, my little nest egg."

"Did the good Indians bring me to you?" asked Nichet.

"Of course," answered his father. "The good Indians bring all the babies."

Little Nichet thought about this for a while.

"Papa," he asked again, "will the good Indians bring us another baby? I would like to have a little sister like Marie Boulanger."

"*Tatata!*" exclaimed Jean LeBlanc. "Already the good Indians have brought us a houseful. Thirteen brothers and sisters are quite enough for such a little fellow as you. And if we had a new baby, you would no longer be our little nest egg."

But Nichet did not think that thirteen brothers and sisters were enough, especially when they were all older and bigger than he.

One afternoon little Nichet wanted to ask his father more about this. But his father and his mother had driven to town in the two-wheeled cart with his eight sisters squeezed together in back.

It was a lonely day for Nichet because his five brothers were out in the field working. And Grandmère kept falling asleep over the rug she was hooking.

So Nichet bravely decided to go to the Indian village himself and ask the Indians if they didn't have an extra baby for the LeBlancs.

Nichet started out on his own two short legs. He walked down the river road. He walked up the Indian trail.

At last he came to the Indian village with its houses scattered over the ground like half-melons.

The Indian village was deserted. The Indians must have gone to town too. Then Nichet saw a few squaws working among the corn sprouts on the hillside. He started toward them.

But he never got as far as the cornfields. For there, propped against a tree trunk, was exactly what Nichet wanted. It was a little papoose laced to its cradle board.

Nichet was so excited that he could scarcely unlace the baby from the board. He lifted it carefully in his arms. The baby did not cry like the Boulanger's new Marie. Nichet looked at its brown skin and its black eyes and its straight black hair. He tried to decide whether it looked more like his papa or his mamma.

The little baby waved its tiny brown arms at him.

"You are my little sister," said Nichet. "I think you look most like me. I will take you home to your papa and mamma."

Nichet LeBlanc carried the papoose down the trail to the river road. It was a long walk and Nichet was so tired he did not think he would ever get the baby to its home. But his sturdy legs carried them both there at last.

Papa and Mamma and the girls had not returned from town yet. The boys were still in the field. Nichet took the baby to show her to Grandmère, but the old lady was asleep with her mouth open and her glasses on the end of her nose.

So little Nichet carried the baby into his parents' bedroom. He carefully laid it in the middle of the bright quilt. Then he ran down the lane to wait for his mamma and papa. He wanted to be the first one to tell them the news that they had a new baby.

At first his papa and mamma thought that little Nichet had a fever. Then they thought that he had fallen asleep like Grandmère and had had a bad dream. But when they saw the brown baby with the black hair and black eyes lying on the bed, they knew that Nichet had told the truth.

"Where did this baby come from?" cried Mamma LeBlanc.

"The Indians brought her," said little Nichet. "That is, I went and got her myself so they wouldn't give her to someone else."

Then there was a great *tohu-bohu* of chattering among the LeBlancs.

"We will have to take it right back," said Jean LeBlanc. "If the Indians think we have stolen their baby, they might burn down our house."

Little Nichet was brokenhearted. He begged and begged his parents to keep his little brown sister with the black hair and black eyes who looked so much like him.

But back to the Indians went the little sister. Little Nichet held her in his arms all the way there in the two-wheeled cart.

There was another *tohu-bohu* of chattering going on at the Indian village.

"A bear has carried off one of the babies," a young brave explained to Jean LeBlanc.

"We have your baby here," said Jean. "It was carried off by a very little bear."

Nichet cried and cried at the loss of his Indian sister. He began feeling sorry for himself. He began thinking that if his papa and mamma had returned the baby to the Indians, they might do the same with him someday.

Little Nichet began feeling sorrier than ever for himself. He decided to return to the Indians of his own free will. How his parents would cry when they found he was gone! They would come galloping to the Indian village. They would take him home again—and his baby sister too.

He packed his nightshirt and his willow whistle and his lynx tail into a sack and set out for the Indian village once more. He walked all the way down the river road. He followed the trail to the houses that were like half-melons.

"I have come back to stay with my little sister," Nichet told one of the Indians.

Then the Indians were as worried as the Le-Blancs had been.

"If we keep you here," said one of them, "your papa will think that we have stolen you. He will burn down our lodges."

Little Nichet refused to leave. "I want to stay here and be an Indian like my little sister," he said.

The Indians gathered together and talked their *micmac* talk, which Nichet could not understand. Then one of them turned to him.

"Can you shoot a bow and arrow?" he asked in Nichet's talk.

"No," said little Nichet.

"Can you skin a moose?"

"No," said little Nichet.

"Can you build a birch canoe?"

"No," said little Nichet.

"Then you cannot stay with us," said the brave. "An Indian must be able to do all those things."

So little Nichet sadly turned and started away. But another Indian came running to him with something furry in his hands.

"A gift for you," said the Indian. "A trade for the baby you returned to us."

He dropped a tiny baby animal into Nichet's arms. It had the head of a beaver, the body of a bear, and the tail of a rabbit.

"What is it?" asked Nichet.

"Your wise father will have a name for it," said the Indian, then he began talking his *micmac* talk that Nichet could not understand.

Nichet carried the baby animal home happily. All the way his busy mind wondered if it was a fox or a beaver or a mink or what.

All the LeBlancs were happy to see that Nichet was home again. For truth, they didn't even know he had gone away until they saw the furry little animal in his arms.

"It is a little whistler," said his wise father, Jean LeBlanc. "Some people call them woodchucks and some people call them groundhogs. But the people back in France call them marmots."

"What is it good for?" asked Grandmère. "Will it give milk or pull a cart or lay eggs?"

"It is good for a lonesome little boy who needs a companion smaller than himself," said Jean LeBlanc. He leaned over Nichet and smiled at the new baby. "Across the ocean in France," he

said, "chimney sweeps from the mountains keep whistlers for pets. They teach them to do a little dance like a bear's."

"Can I be a chimney sweep when I am bigger?" asked little Nichet.

"You may be a chimney sweep tomorrow," said Jean LeBlanc generously. "I am going to take down the stovepipe for your mamma and you may help me clean the soot out of it."

So little Nichet thought that he had made a very good trade with the Indians. The boy picked out the name of Pierrette for his tiny pet, and his father helped him to teach that whistler to dance.

Whenever Nichet whistled a special tune, Pierrette would sit up on her hindquarters and wave her forepaws from right to left as she did her dance of the bear. And from time to time she would make polite curtsies. You may be sure that Pierrette was as popular at the stay-awake parties as old Michel Meloche, the storyteller.

Variants of European folk tales

in the United States

Kindergarten teachers who tell their children "Epaminondas" have long known that it is a Negro variant of the English "Lazy Jack" or the German "Clever Hans," and they also know that it is a better story than either of these and much more satisfying to the five-year-olds. Now we know that our American "The Gingerbread Boy" is a variant of the Scotch "The Wee Bannock" or perhaps the Norse "The Pancake" or the English "The Johnny Cake." But it has taken recent research to uncover for us the wealth of European folk tales which have been preserved in typically American vernacular and scene. Not all of these are as good as the European originals, but many of them have a style, a turn of phrase, and characters that are exceedingly fresh and droll. Richard Chase's Jack Tales *are especially amusing, and the bibliography lists other sources of homespun heroes with European relatives.*

THE GINGERBREAD BOY

This American variant of "The Pancake" is a favorite in spite of the urban child's unfamiliarity with "threshers" and "mowers." The gay refrain carries the story.

"The Gingerbread Boy." From *St. Nicholas Magazine*, May 1875

Now you shall hear a story that somebody's great-great-grandmother told a little girl ever so many years ago:

There was once a little old man and a little old woman, who lived in a little old house in the edge of a wood. They would have been a very happy old couple but for one thing—they had no little child, and they wished for one very much. One day, when the little old woman was baking gingerbread, she cut a cake in the shape of a little boy, and put it into the oven.

Presently, she went to the oven to see if it was baked. As soon as the oven door was opened, the little gingerbread boy jumped out, and began to run away as fast as he could go.

The little old woman called her husband, and they both ran after him. But they could not catch him. And soon the gingerbread boy came to a barn full of threshers. He called out to them as he went by, saying:

"I've run away from a little old woman,
    A little old man,
    And I can run away from you, I can!"

Then the barn full of threshers set out to run after him. But, though they ran fast, they could not catch him. And he ran on till he came to a field full of mowers. He called out to them:

"I've run away from a little old woman,
    A little old man,
    A barn full of threshers,
    And I can run away from you, I can!"

Then the mowers began to run after him, but they couldn't catch him. And he ran on till he came to a cow. He called out to her:

"I've run away from a little old woman,
    A little old man,
    A barn full of threshers,
    A field full of mowers,
    And I can run away from you, I can!"

But, though the cow started at once, she couldn't catch him. And soon he came to a pig. He called out to the pig:

"I've run away from a little old woman,
    A little old man,
    A barn full of threshers,
    A field full of mowers,
    A cow,
    And I can run away from you, I can!"

But the pig ran, and couldn't catch him. And he ran till he came across a fox, and to him he called out:

"I've run away from a little old woman,
    A little old man,
    A barn full of threshers,
    A field full of mowers,
    A cow and a pig,
    And I can run away from you, I can!"

Then the fox set out to run. Now foxes can run very fast, and so the fox soon caught the gingerbread boy and began to eat him up.

Presently the gingerbread boy said: "Oh, dear! I'm quarter gone!" And then: "Oh, I'm half gone!" And soon: "I'm three-quarters gone!" And at last: "I'm all gone!" and never spoke again.

THE GIFT OF SAINT NICHOLAS

Here is a novel Christmas story with St. Nick in a new character—a bit of a curmudgeon but an enforcer of justice.

Three hundred years ago in the little city of New Amsterdam lived a young cobbler named Claas. A fortunate young fellow indeed was Claas. He had a lovely brick house with a garden, a big pond full of fat white geese, a thriving trade, and a pretty wife whose name was Anitje. He had worked hard for these blessings from the first bleak day when he landed on the shores of the New World, an orphan boy from Holland. He now was a rich man, rich enough to wear eight pairs of breeches at once.

The only dark cloud in his sky was Roeloffsen, the burgomaster, an old miser who had long been in love with Anitje. As the richest old bachelor in the town, he had expected her to marry him without any question. When she married the poor cobbler boy, the burgomaster's pride was hurt. He swore that he should have his revenge. Whenever Claas and Anitje walked out in their Sunday clothes, with their family of fat Dutch children toddling behind them, he hid behind the heavy curtains of his house and said terrible things.

"The Gift of Saint Nicholas." From *American Myths and Legends* by Charles M. Skinner. As adapted in *Yankee Doodle's Cousins*, edited by Anne Malcolmson. Reprinted by permission of and arrangement with Houghton Mifflin Company and Mrs. Clara A. Skinner

At last his ugly thoughts were put into deeds. He taught the village blacksmith to make hobnails for the townspeople's boots. These nails made a dreadful racket as they clattered over the brick streets. But they kept the boots from wearing out. The boots wore so long that poor Claas had very little business as a cobbler. He had a very hard time of it to make ends meet.

This was not enough for the black-hearted burgomaster, however. Claas and his Anitje still lived in their fine brick house and walked out on Sundays in their handsome clothes. Roeloffsen had to think of something else.

Soon he knew what to do. As an officer of the city he ordered a new street to be built. This street ran right through the middle of Claas's pond. The city builders came and drained the pond. Poor Claas had to sell his beloved geese. This was a great blow to him, because the eggs he sold at the marketplace helped make up for the boots he was unable to sell.

But this was not the worst of it. As Claas sat by his fire sorrowing for the loss of his geese, he had visitors. These were men from the city council. Since the road ran through his land, they said, he should pay for its building. They demanded fifty pieces of gold for this purpose. Fifty pieces of gold! That was all Claas had tucked away in his teapot.

Claas and Anitje had to work harder than ever to keep their family fed and clothed. They sold vegetables from their little garden and managed to make themselves a fair living. Then came the jealous burgomaster. He built another road, through the middle of Claas's garden patch this time. Once again the poor cobbler had to rob his teapot of the vegetable money in order to pay for this road.

And so it went. Every time Claas made a little money, the burgomaster built a new road and made him pay for it. Before long, he had to sell his fine house. No longer could he afford to wear eight pairs of breeches, nor Anitje her twelve petticoats. The little family was poor. They had sold all their belongings except a bare few. They lived in a miserable little cottage with only a dirt floor.

The wicked old burgomaster at last was satisfied. He danced with joy when he saw how low the cobbler had fallen. This would show the people of New Amsterdam that no orphan boy could outdo the wealthy Heer Roeloffsen!

On Christmas Eve, as the burgomaster was enjoying his fine dinner, Claas and Anitje and their children sat huddled before the fireplace in their little cottage. The very last log burned on the hearth and gave out little heat at best. Their cupboard, like Old Mother Hubbard's, was bare. After their supper of bread and cheese, not a crumb remained. A poor Christmas this would be. No presents, no blazing fire, not even a dinner!

Of all their possessions, only two treasures remained. One was the Bible which Claas's mother had given him long ago. It was bound in beautiful leather and held shut with silver clasps. Claas was tempted to take off these clasps and sell them. They might bring him enough money to provide a Christmas for his children.

No! said Anitje. To sell the clasps from a Bible would be wicked. He should never think of doing such a thing. Better it would be to starve than to feast on the sale of holy things.

The other treasure which remained was a pipe. This was a special, lovely pure meerschaum pipe which to Claas had a magic meaning. As a little boy, leaving his home for the New World, he had found the pipe in his stocking. Where it had come from he could not tell. He was sure it was a present from the good Saint Nicholas himself.

The thought of selling this treasure nearly broke his heart. Even so, it was better than the thought of selling his mother's silver clasps. He reached down into the family chest and took out his beloved meerschaum. Sadly he rubbed it against his trousers and watched it gleam in the firelight.

As he rubbed it the cottage door swung open and a blast of cold air filled the room. There before the fire stood a fat little stranger, about three feet tall. He was dripping with snow, and icicles hung from his shaggy eyebrows and his long white beard.

"Br-r-r!" muttered the stranger crossly. "It's a wonder you wouldn't answer the door when a traveler knocks. Fine manners, I must say, on a night like this!"

All thoughts of the pipe were forgotten as Claas and Anitje stared at their visitor. The children scrambled to hide under the bed. Only their bright blue eyes shone out from behind the curtains.

"Well, come along! Come along!" went on the visitor, growing more angry every minute. "Don't stand there! The least you can do is to put another log on the fire so that I can warm myself. Can't you see I'm half frozen?"

"I-I-I-I'm very sorry, sir," admitted Claas, finding his tongue at last, "but there is no other log to put on the fire. You're very welcome to warm yourself at our poor hearth."

"Well, then," snapped the stranger, "send one of those ragamuffins out to the woodshed. I'm freezing, I tell you!" He glared at the children, who pushed themselves farther back under the bed hangings.

"Oh, sir!" cried Anitje, "if only we had more wood in the shed we would gladly fetch it for you. But, alas, this is our last stick. We have no more to keep ourselves warm."

"Humph!" snorted the little fellow. "That's very careless of you. But what must be, must be." With that he cracked the fine cane he carried over his knee. It broke into several pieces. These he tossed onto the coals. As they struck the fire, something wonderful happened. Each of the pieces of the cane changed into a big birch log. The dark coals blazed up and soon the room was dancing with the light of a huge fire.

"That's better," muttered the stranger. "Upon my life, I thought I should turn to an icicle for all you cared."

The children crept out from their hiding place to gape at the magic blaze. Claas and Anitje rubbed their eyes.

"And now, I suppose, you're going to let me starve to death, too!" sneered the visitor, looking in the direction of the cupboard. "It's a wonder you wouldn't invite me to have some supper. I haven't eaten since this morning."

Tears came to Anitje's eyes. "Oh, sir, whoever you may be, we should indeed be happy to give you our last crumb. But," she sobbed, "we have nothing to eat in the house. We ate our last scrap of cheese for our evening meal."

"That was certainly rude of you," barked the funny little man. "Here I come, after a hard day's tramp over the mountains, through wind and rain and snow! You say you have no fire to warm me! You say you have no bread to feed me! My dear lady, I know better. Your shelves are heaped with cakes and apples. And if that's not roast goose I smell cooking, I'll eat my beard!"

Without thinking, the whole family stopped to sniff. Why, they did smell roast goose! And cabbage and onion and mince pie and pumpkin! These delicious smells were fairly bursting from the oven door. They looked quickly at the cupboard. Its shelves were groaning under bowls of apples and pears and platters of cakes and cookies. The water jug was filled to the brim with sweet cider.

"Don't stand there, don't stand there like a forest of trees!" shouted the stranger. "Can't you see I'm dying of hunger? Get me something to eat and be quick about it. No food, indeed! Why, there's a whole feast in that oven. Put it on the table."

Not knowing whether to be overjoyed or frightened, Claas and Anitje set the table and drew it before the fire. They opened the wide door of the oven. There indeed were the goose and the vegetables and the pies they smelled.

At the sight of the richly spread table, the children forgot their shyness. Hungrily they feasted. But none of them ate so much as did their visitor. Time and again he passed back his plate for another drumstick. An ordinary goose has only two legs, but this one sprouted a new one whenever the little man passed his plate.

When at last the fat little stranger had had enough and the buttons had begun to burst from Claas's coat, the table was cleared away. No longer did the visitor snap angrily at his hosts. He leaned back in his chair and lit his pipe. A twinkle appeared in his eye and he patted the children's blond heads. For an hour he sat talking pleasantly with the happy family, telling strange and marvelous stories of distant lands. But not once did he tell them who he was.

At the stroke of midnight he got up from his chair. "I must be off!" he exclaimed. "Thank you indeed for a pleasant evening and a delicious dinner." He turned to Claas, "Don't ever sell that pipe!" he shouted.

With that, a gust of wind down the chimney filled the whole room with smoke. Before the family could open their smarting eyes again, the stranger was gone without so much as a good-bye.

In the morning Claas was awakened by a great

hammering at his door. There was Burgomaster Roeloffsen and a party of soldiers. "We have come to arrest you!" they screamed. "You are a wizard, a witch, a magician. You are a disgrace to the city of New Amsterdam."

Poor Claas didn't know what to make of it. Why should anyone call him a wizard? He was nothing but a poor cobbler who had had a lovely dream.

"Come!" roared the burgomaster. "Open the door and let us in. We shall have no wizards in our city!"

As he slowly awakened, Claas looked about him. The wretched little cottage had disappeared. He was standing in the hall of a great house. The walls were hung with silks, and from the cupboards shone silver platters and copper bowls. He looked timidly out of the window. Around him spread wide lawns and gardens and in the distance glimmered the ice of a huge pond.

"Open up, I say," bellowed the burgomaster. "Open up in the name of the law. We have come to take you to jail as you deserve." Claas opened the door. In poured the soldiers.

"Aha!" screamed Heer Roeloffsen, his face red with anger. "Seize him! Seize the witch! He has not only changed his cottage to a fine estate. He has filled his chests with gold."

Before the astonished Claas the burgomaster lifted the lid of a chest. The great box was full to the top with pieces of money.

"You thief! You robber! I'll . . ." But before he could finish his sentence, a pair of invisible hands clapped themselves over his mouth. More hands which could not be seen grabbed the soldiers. Then came an awful wacking and thrashing as the unseen arms paddled the burgomaster and his party with unseen switches.

"Ouch! Help! Stop it!" yelled Roeloffsen. But the paddling went on. The soldiers ran down the path to the main road and headed away from town, crying and yelling and trying to defend themselves from the blows of the unseen paddlers.

That was the last ever seen of the jealous burgomaster. Claas and his family lived on in their fine new home, never wanting for food or warmth. How their good fortune had come they did not know. The only clue they had was a piece of paper slipped under the door. It said simply, "Don't ever sell that pipe."

JACK AND THE ROBBERS

The tens and elevens will readily recognize "The Four Musicians" in this homespun variant with the realistic conclusion. They should hear Richard Chase tell it in the laconic drawl of a mountain man.

This here's another tale about Jack when he was still a small-like boy. He was about twelve, I reckon, and his daddy started tryin' to make him help with the work around the place. But Jack he didn't like workin' much. He would piddle around a little and then he'd go on back to the house, till one day his daddy whipped him. He just tanned Jack good. Jack didn't cry none, but he didn't like it a bit. So early the next mornin' he slipped off without tellin' his mother and struck out down the public road. Thought he'd go and try his fortune somewhere off from home.

"Jack and the Robbers." From *The Jack Tales* edited by Richard C. Chase. Copyright 1943 by Richard C. Chase. Reprinted by permission of and arrangement with Houghton Mifflin Company, the authorized publishers

He got down the road a few miles and there was an old ox standin' in a field by a rail fence, a-bellowin' like it was troubled over somethin'—

"Um-m-muh!
Um-m-m—muh-h-h!"

"Hello!" says Jack. "What's the matter?"

"I'll just tell you," says the old ox. "I'm gettin' too old to plow and I heard the men talkin' about how they'd have to kill me tomorrow and get shet of me."

"Come on down here to the gap," says Jack, "and you can slip off with me."

So the old ox followed the fence to where the gap was at and Jack let the bars down and the old ox got out in front of Jack, and they went on down the public road.

Jack and the ox traveled on, and pretty soon they came where there was an old donkey standin' with his head hangin' down over the gate, a-goin'—

"Wahn-n-n-eh!
Wahn-n-n-eh!
Wahn-n-n-eh!"

"Hello," says Jack. "What's troublin' you?"

"Law me!" says the old donkey. "The boys took me out to haul in wood this mornin' and I'm gettin' so old and weak I couldn't do no good. I heard 'em say they were goin' to kill me tomorrow, get shet of me."

"Come on and go with us," says Jack.

So he let the old donkey out and they pulled on down the public road. The old donkey told Jack to get up on his back and ride.

They went on a piece, came to an old hound dog settin' in a man's yard. He would bark awhile and then howl awhile—

"A-woo! woo! woo!
A-oo-oo-oo!"

—sounded awful lonesome.

"Hello," says Jack. "What you a-howlin' so for?"

"Oh, law me!" says the old dog. "The boys took me coon-huntin' last night, cut a tree where the coon had got up in it. I got hold on the coon all right, but my teeth are all gone and hit got loose from me. They said they were goin' to kill me today, get shet of me."

"Come on, go with us," says Jack.

So the old dog scrouged under the gate.

The old donkey says to him, "Get up on my back and ride, if you want to."

Jack holp the old dog up behind him, and they went on down the public road.

Came to an old tomcat climbin' along the fence. Hit was a-squallin' and meowin', stop ever' now and then, sit down on the top rail—

"Meow-ow!
Meow-ow-ow!"

—sounded right pitiful.

"Hello!" says Jack. "What's the matter you squallin' so?"

"Oh, law!" says the old cat. "I caught a rat out in the barn this mornin', but my teeth are gettin' so old and bad I let him go. I heard 'em talkin' about killin' me to get shet of me, 'cause I ain't no good to catch rats no more."

"Come on and go with us," says Jack.

So the old cat jumped down off the fence.

The old donkey says, "Hop up there on my back and you can ride."

The old cat jumped up, got behind the dog, and they went on down the public road.

Came to where they saw an old rooster settin' on a fence post, crowin' like it was midnight, makin' the awfulest lonesome racket—

"Ur rook-a-roo!
Ur-r-r rook-a-roo-oo-oo!"

"Hello!" says Jack. "What's troublin' you?"

"Law me!" says the old rooster. "Company's comin' today and I heard 'em say they were goin' to kill me, put me in a pie!"

"Come on with us," says Jack.

Old rooster flew on down, got behind the cat, says, "All right, boys. Let's go!"

So they went right on down the highway. That was about all could get on the old donkey's back. The old rooster was right on top its tail and a-havin' a sort of hard time stayin' on. They traveled on, traveled on, till hit got plumb dark.

"Well," says Jack, "we got to get off the road and find us a place to stay tonight."

Directly they came to a little path leadin' off in the woods, decided to take that, see could they find a stayin' place in there. Went on a right smart piece further, and 'way along up late in the night they came to a little house, didn't have no clearin' around it. Jack hollered hello at the fence, but there didn't nobody answer.

"Come on," says the old donkey. "Let's go investigate that place."

Well, there wasn't nobody ever came to the door and there wasn't nobody around back of the house, so directly they went on in. Found a right smart lot of good somethin' to eat in there.

Jack says, "Now, who in the world do you reckon could be a-livin' out here in such a wilderness of a place as this?"

"Well," says the old donkey, "hit's my o-pinion that a gang of highway robbers lives out here."

So Jack says, "Then hit looks like to me we might as well take up and stay here. If they've done stole all these vittles, we got as much right to 'em as they have."

"Yes," says the old dog, "that's exactly what I think, too. But if we stay, I believe we better get fixed for a fight. I expect they'll be comin' back in here about midnight."

"That's just what I was goin' to say," says the old cat. "I bet it's pretty close to midnight right now."

"Hit lacks about a hour," says the old rooster.

"Come on, then," says Jack. "Let's all of us get set to fight 'em."

The ox said he'd stay out in the yard. The old donkey said he'd take up his stand on the porch just outside the door. The dog said he'd get in behind the door and fight from there. The old tomcat got down in the fireplace, and the old rooster flew up on the comb of the roof, says, "If you boys need any help now, just call on me, call on me-e-e!"

They all waited awhile. Heard somebody comin' directly; hit was seven highway robbers. They came on till they got pretty close to the house, then they told one of 'em to go on in and start up a fire so's they could have a light to see to get in and so they could divide out the money they'd stole that day.

One man went on in the house, the other six waited outside the gate.

That man went to the fireplace, got down on his knees to blow up the fire. The cat had his head right down on the hearth-rock and that man thought its eyes was coals of fire. Time he blowed in that old cat's eyes, it reached out its claws right quick and scratched him down both cheeks. The robber hollered and headed for the door. The dog ran out and bit him in the leg. He shook it off and ran on the porch and the old donkey raised up and kicked him on out in the yard. The ox caught him up on its horns and ran to the fence and threw him out in the bresh. About that time the old rooster settin' up there on top of the house started in to crowin' right big.

The other robbers, time they heard all that racket, they put out from there just as fast as they could run. The one they'd sent in the house finally got up and started runnin' like a streak, caught up with 'em in no time. They said to him, says, "What in the world was that in there?"

"Oh, I'm killed! I'm killed!" says the man. "I won't live over fifteen minutes!"

The other said, "Well, 'fore ye die, tell us what it was caused all that racket back yonder."

"Law me! That house is plumb full of men, and they've even got one on the roof. I went to blow up the fire and a man in the fireplace raked me all over the face with an awl. Started to run and a man behind the door took me in the leg with a butcher knife. Time I got out the door, a man out there hit me with a knot-maul, knocked me clean off the porch. A man standin' in the yard caught me on a pitchfork and threw me over the fence. And then that man up on the roof hollered out,

'Chunk him on up here! Chunk him on up here.'

Ain't no use in us goin' back there with all of them men in the house. Let's leave here quick 'fore they come after us."

So them highway robbers ran for their life, and kept on runnin' till they were plumb out the country.

Jack and the ox and the old donkey and the dog and the cat and the rooster, they took possession of that house, and just had 'em a big time.

But the last time I was down that way, Jack had gone on back home to his folks. He was out in the yard a-cuttin' his mother a big pile of stovewood.

FILL, BOWL! FILL!

The old man Jack meets in this tale is strongly reminiscent of the god Odin, gray bearded, with a staff that performs magic deeds.

This here tale's another'n about Jack goin' a-courtin'. And there's some more tales about Jack gettin' married; like that 'un about the doctor's girl, and there was that pretty girl down in Old Fire Dragaman's hole in the ground. 'Course Jack didn't marry all them girls at once. Hit might 'a been one way and hit might 'a been another. There's just different ways of tellin' it.

Well, this time it wasn't no King's girl. There was a farmer lived 'way back in the mountain had two awful pretty girls, and the boys were all crazy about 'em. This farmer, though, he was wealthy, and he didn't want the boys comin' around there, so he fixed up a way to get shet of 'em.

He put out a adver-tize-ment that any boy who wanted one of his girls would have to ketch 'em a wild rabbit and put it in a ring and make it stay there thirty minutes. That was his prop-osition: they would have to bring the rabbit and he'd make a ring ten foot across; then they'd put the rabbit in there and if it stayed thirty minutes, they could have one of the girls. But if the rabbit failed to stay that long, he'd kill the boy that brought the rabbit.

Well, not many went to try, but some did, and the old man cut their heads off. Directly it got so the boys mostly quit goin' down here. That suited the old man fine. But then some boy would get so struck on one of the girls, he'd venture, and get his head cut off. Fin'ly it got so no-body'd go.

Well, Jack he got to studyin' about how he might get one of them girls. His mother told him he better not do that, but Jack said he'd just have to try. So he caught him a rabbit, and put him a little snack of dinner in a poke, and then he got fixed up and started out.

About twelve o'clock in the wilder-ness, Jack met up with an old gray-bearded man. This old man looked like he was about a hundred years old, and he was walkin' with a walkin' stick.

Jack came along, the old man stopped, says, "Howdy do, Jack."

"Howdy do, daddy."

Jack looked at him, says, "I don't believe I know ye."

"No," says the old man. "I know you, though, and I know right where you've started. You're a-fixin' to get killed, now, ain't ye?"

"I might, now," says Jack.

"Are you familiar with what you got to do to get one of them girls?"

"Tol'able familiar," says Jack.

"Don't you think you'd just as well start on back home?"

"Oh, no," says Jack. "I'd never turn back. I'm a-goin' on down there now."

"Well, I might help ye," says the old man, "if ye got any faith. How's your faith, Jack?"

Jack said his faith was pretty good, says, "I'd sure be much obliged was you to help me, daddy."

"Well, if you come down the road a piece with me, I'll test you out a little and we'll see whether you got faith or no."

Got down the road a ways, the old man says, "Now, Jack, you take this stick here and go up there in the woods a ways till you come to a very flush spring. Then you take my stick and stir in that spring till the water turns to wine. And against ye get that done, I'll come up there with somethin' to help ye."

So Jack took that walkin' stick and went on to where there was a very bold spring comin' out the ground. Stuck that stick down in it and com-menced stirrin'.

Jack's faith was sort of weak when he started, but he 'lowed he'd have to keep on tryin'. He stirred right on, stirred right on, and pretty soon it looked like the water *was* turnin' just a little bit pink. So Jack's faith got stronger and stronger and the water got redder and redder.

Well, when that spring turned real red, there was that old man standin' there, says, "Well, Jack, you sure got faith. Now you get out your lunch and we'll eat a little and try some of that and see whether it tastes like wine or not."

So they did, and that water was just as good as any wine.

Then the old man says to Jack, says, "I've done

"Fill, Bowl! Fill!" From *The Jack Tales* edited by Richard C. Chase. Copyright 1943 by Richard C. Chase. Reprinted by permission of and arrangement with Houghton Mifflin Company, the authorized publishers

made ye a drill here, Jack. You can take that and stick it down in the middle of the ring that man'll make and your rabbit'll stay in there till it dies; it don't differ how wild he is."

He gave Jack a drill shaved out of a stick. It was eight-square like a steel drill and about a foot long.

Jack thanked him and started on again.

Got down to that place where the girls were, Jack hollered the old man out and said he'd come to try for one of his girls.

The man told Jack to come around in the yard, and then he marked out a ring, says, "Now, you put your rabbit down in this ring and if it stays in there thirty minutes, you can take whichever girl you want. And if it don't stay in the ring thirty minutes, I'll kill you. You understand now, do ye?"

Jack said he did, made like he was goin' to turn his rabbit loose.

The man says to him, says, "I'll make ye another proposition; if you can make that rabbit stay in there thirty minutes, I'll just let you kill me and take all the money I got."

Jack went and stuck that drill down in the middle of the ring, and dumped the rabbit out the poke he had in it. The rabbit got up on its feet, saw that drill and took out around it hard as it could go, around and around and around.

The old man watched Jack's rabbit a-goin' around in there, and his eyes just stuck out. Walked around the other side the ring, watched it some more. That rabbit ran right on, 'round and 'round the drill. The old man kept takin' out his watch; fin'ly he turned around and went on back in the house.

Told his old woman and the girls, says, "It's my opinion that rabbit is stayin' in there on account of that drill Jack stuck in the ring. One of you go on out there and see can't ye buy that thing off of Jack."

So the oldest girl she went out, says to Jack, "What'll ye take for that drill, Jack?"

Jack says, "I don't know as I'd want to sell it right now."

"I'll give ye a thousand dollars for it."

"No," says Jack, "I'll not sell it."

So she went on back, told her daddy she couldn't make no trade.

Then he sent his youngest girl out.

She came up 'side of Jack, says, "Jack, I'd like awful well to buy that drill."

"Well," says Jack, "you can have it after thirty minutes is up."

"Aw, Jack," she says, "I want it now. I'll pay ye two thousand dollars for it."

"No," says Jack, "you wait till thirty minutes is out, and then we'll trade."

So she saw she couldn't do no good, went on back in the house.

Then the man said to his old lady, says, "You go."

She went out.

"Jack, I'd sure like to trade ye out of that drill. You can have one of the girls, right now; and I'll give ye three thousand dollars and ever'thing on the place."

"No," says Jack, "not till thirty minutes is out."

The old lady went on back, says, "I can't do a thing with him. He won't even talk about sellin'."

The old man looked at his watch, says, "Well, that thirty minutes is about up. I reckon I'll have to go on out and let Jack kill me."

Started out, picked up a big bowl off the table, and took that to Jack, says, "Jack, it looks like your rabbit's goin' to stay in there. You might as well kill me." Says, "'Fore you do, though, I wish you'd sing this bowl full of lies for me."

"All right," says Jack, "I'll try."

"Oh, the oldest daughter she came out
All for to buy my drill.
I fooled a-round her, kissed her well.
Fill, bowl! Fill!"

Says, "Is it full?"

"No," says the old man, "only one drop."

"Oh, the youngest daughter she came out
All for to buy my drill.
I fooled around her, kissed her well.
Fill, bowl! Fill!"

"Is it full yet?"

"Just two drops, Jack."

"Oh, the old lady she came out
All for to buy my drill.
I fooled around her, ki . . ."

"Stop, Jack! Hit's full and runnin' over. Just cut my head off."

North American Indian folk tales

*On the whole, the stories of our American Indians are not particularly
appealing unless they are edited to a considerable degree. They are often overly
long and formless. One folklorist said that they "give one an impression
that their narrators were incapable of even preserving an old tale, to say nothing
of inventing a new one." Perhaps they have suffered by translation, but beyond
the mythlike* why *stories, not many of them are good storytelling material.
Among the various collections, however, there are stories such as the two included
here which are delightful to read or tell.*

LITTLE BURNT-FACE

(Micmac)

*Little Burnt-Face is the scorched face of the
desert in the burning summer. The Great Chief,
whose symbol is the rainbow, is the rain. Invisible for a long time, he comes at last and restores
beauty to the face of the waiting earth child.
This is an interesting variant of the "Cinderella"
theme.*

Once upon a time, in a large Indian village
on the border of a lake, there lived an old man
who was a widower. He had three daughters.
The eldest was jealous, cruel, and ugly; the second was vain; but the youngest of all was very
gentle and lovely.

Now, when the father was out hunting in the
forest, the eldest daughter used to beat the
youngest girl, and burn her face with hot coals;
yes, and even scar her pretty body. So the people
called her "Little Burnt-Face."

When the father came home from hunting he
would ask why she was so scarred, and the eldest
would answer quickly: "She is a good-for-nothing! She was forbidden to go near the fire, and
she disobeyed and fell in." Then the father
would scold Little Burnt-Face and she would
creep away crying to bed.

By the lake, at the end of the village, there
was a beautiful wigwam. And in that wigwam
lived a Great Chief and his sister. The Great

"Little Burnt-Face." From *Red Indian Fairy Book* by
Frances J. Olcott. Copyright 1917, 1945 by Frances J.
Olcott and Houghton Mifflin Company. Reprinted by permission of and arrangement with Houghton Mifflin Company, the authorized publishers

Chief was invisible; no one had ever seen him
but his sister. He brought her many deer and
supplied her with good things to eat from the
forest and lake, and with the finest blankets and
garments. And when visitors came all they ever
saw of the Chief were his moccasins; for when
he took them off they became visible, and his
sister hung them up.

Now, one Spring, his sister made known that
her brother, the Great Chief, would marry any
girl who could see him.

Then all the girls from the village—except
Little Burnt-Face and her sisters—and all the
girls for miles around hastened to the wigwam,
and walked along the shore of the lake with his
sister.

And his sister asked the girls, "Do you see my
brother?"

And some of them said, "No"; but most of
them answered, "Yes."

Then his sister asked, "Of what is his shoulder-strap made?"

And the girls said, "Of a strip of rawhide."

"And with what does he draw his sled?" asked
his sister.

And they replied, "With a green withe."

Then she knew that they had not seen him at
all, and said quietly, "Let us go to the wigwam."

So to the wigwam they went, and when they
entered, his sister told them not to take the seat
next the door, for that was where her brother sat.

Then they helped his sister to cook the supper,
for they were very curious to see the Great Chief
eat. When all was ready, the food disappeared,
and the brother took off his moccasins, and his
sister hung them up. But they never saw the
Chief, though many of them stayed all night.

One day Little Burnt-Face's two sisters put on their finest blankets and brightest strings of beads, and plaited their hair beautifully, and slipped embroidered moccasins on their feet. Then they started out to see the Great Chief.

As soon as they were gone, Little Burnt-Face made herself a dress of white birch-bark, and a cap and leggings of the same. She threw off her ragged garments, and dressed herself in her birch-bark clothes. She put her father's moccasins on her bare feet; and the moccasins were so big that they came up to her knees. Then she, too, started out to visit the beautiful wigwam at the end of the village.

Poor Little Burnt-Face! She was a sorry sight! For her hair was singed off, and her little face was as full of burns and scars as a sieve is full of holes; and she shuffled along in her birch-bark clothes and big moccasins. And as she passed through the village the boys and girls hissed, yelled, and hooted.

And when she reached the lake, her sisters saw her coming, and they tried to shame her, and told her to go home. But the Great Chief's sister received her kindly, and bade her stay, for she saw how sweet and gentle Little Burnt-Face really was.

Then as evening was coming on, the Great Chief's sister took all three girls walking beside the lake, and the sky grew dark, and they knew the Great Chief had come.

And his sister asked the two elder girls, "Do you see my brother?"

And they said, "Yes."

"Of what is his shoulder-strap made?" asked his sister.

"Of a strip of rawhide," they replied.

"And with what does he draw his sled?" asked she.

And they said, "With a green withe."

Then his sister turned to Little Burnt-Face and asked, "Do you see him?"

"I do! I do!" said Little Burnt-Face with awe. "And he is wonderful!"

"And of what is his sled-string made?" asked his sister gently.

"It is a beautiful Rainbow!" cried Little Burnt-Face.

"But, my sister," said the other, "of what is his bow-string made?"

"His bow-string," replied Little Burnt-Face, "is the Milky Way!"

Then the Great Chief's sister smiled with delight, and taking Little Burnt-Face by the hand, she said, "You have surely seen him."

She led the little girl to the wigwam, and bathed her with dew until the burns and scars all disappeared from her body and face. Her skin became soft and lovely again. Her hair grew long and dark like the Blackbird's wing. Her eyes were like stars. Then his sister brought

from her treasures a wedding-garment, and she dressed Little Burnt-Face in it. And she was most beautiful to behold.

After all this was done, his sister led the little girl to the seat next the door, saying, "This is the Bride's seat," and made her sit down.

And then the Great Chief, no longer invisible, entered, terrible and beautiful. And when he saw Little Burnt-Face, he smiled and said gently, "So we have found each other!"

And she answered, "Yes."

Then Little Burnt-Face was married to the Great Chief, and the wedding-feast lasted for days, and to it came all the people of the village. As for the two bad sisters, they went back to their wigwam in disgrace, weeping with shame.

THE TWO-FACES

Here is an authentic Indian story, rich in tribal myths and the everyday activities of a people. It is so long it should probably be read or told to children serially. It will add much to an Indian unit or to a child's understanding of Indian life.

"Now I will tell you a story," said Walks-with-the-wolf when Woodtick had finished.

There was once a tribe of people who had two faces. One was in front where a face ought to be; the other was behind where no face belongs. Nobody knew where their village was; nobody ever saw the Two-faces when they were at home. Old men say they lived somewhere north of here, but nobody knows.

The Two-faces owned a slave who was afraid of them. He was their scout, and they kept him traveling. The Winds were his helpers. He rode them everywhere. No matter which way they were blowing he went along to learn what was going on. After he got there and looked around he waited till a right Wind came along. Then he rode it back to the village of the Two-faces and told their Chief what he had seen and heard. He had to do this, of course, because he was a slave. But he was a very smart Person. He was a Magpie's Feather.

The Two-faces were rich people. They owned many fine lodges, had beautiful clothes and more painted robes than they could use. But they did not work to make any of these things; and they did not steal them. They won everything they possessed by gambling with others. And they kept the Magpie's Feather busy looking for strangers who would play gambling games. He

"The Two-Faces." From *Old Man Coyote* by Frank B. Linderman. The John Day Company, Inc., Publishers. Copyright, 1931, by Frank B. Linderman

would blow into a village, tumble around here and there, into lodges and out again without being noticed, because he was only a Magpie's Feather. But he saw everything everywhere. When he had finished looking and listening he would sleep until the right Wind came blowing along; then he would ride it back to the village of the Two-faces.

The Chief would listen, and if he believed it worth while he would talk things over with the headmen, and if all were agreed, the Chief would give the scout some meat, but never enough! The Magpie's Feather was always hungry!

The next day, if they thought it worth while, the Magpie's Feather would be sent back to the strange village to tell the people there that the Two-faces would visit them and play gambling games, if they were willing. They pretended to be quite polite, always, you see.

Of course all tribes liked to play gambling games. They always listened when the Magpie's Feather came to ask if the Two-faces might come and play games with them, because playing games is friendly. But the tribes did not know that the Two-faces always won, nor that after winning all the property a tribe possessed the Two-faces wagered their lives against the lives of the people they were playing with, so that when the last game was played there was never anybody to tell what had happened. If the tribes had known these things they would not have played with the Two-faces. But you see, no tribe that played with them ever lived to tell the others, because the Two-faces won every game they played. One who gambles must pay if he loses, so that all those who played with the Two-faces paid with their lives in the end.

One day when the North-wind was blowing, the Magpie's Feather rode into the village of the Absanakees. The young men were on the plains hunting, the old men were making weapons and talking of wars, the women were making kettles of Buffalo-paunches, or sewing, or cooking, while the children played. Nobody noticed the black and white Magpie's Feather blowing around.

Four days after this a Person came into the village from the north. Our scouts saw him coming a long time, but he was alone and unarmed, and they let him pass. He was tall and wore a white robe. He spoke softly and was a fine sign-talker. His face was painted, and there was a Magpie's Feather in his hair. He walked straight to the Chief's lodge, and no dogs barked when he passed. After a time men and women saw him leave the Chief's lodge and go out of the village, alone. But nobody, not even the scouts, could tell which way he had gone!

That evening, after the hunters had returned, a crier went about the village saying that four days from then Strangers would visit the Absanakees, and that there would be gambling for four days.

The Absanakees were glad. But when at last the visitors arrived they were not so pleased. The Strangers had *two faces!* No matter which way they turned they were looking at a Person. Nobody could get behind a Two-face, and nobody could be certain that he was in front of him. This would be bad in gambling! Two eyes can never catch all that four eyes can see. Besides this, there were twice as many mouths to feed as there were visitors. But the Absanakees had plenty of meat. And they had invited the Two-faces to their village, or they had told them they might come, which was the same. There was nothing to do about it now.

The Chiefs talked together, and then a crier told the two villages that there would be four games played—one each day for four days. The first was to be the hoop-and-arrow game played twice; once on the first day, and again on the second day. The third day they were to run foot-races, and on the fourth and last day they were to play shinny.

The cunning Two-faces managed things as they had always done. The foolish Absanakees wagered all their property in their lodges against all the property in the lodges of the Two-faces. And the Absanakees lost!

Next day the Absanakees lost all their weapons. The third day the Two-faces won all the lodges of the Absanakees, and on the fourth day —not to be dared by their visitors—the Absanakees bet their lives against the lives of the Two-faces on a game of shinny. The Two-faces won! The Two-faces took the Absanakees' lives, leaving no living thing in the Absanakee village. Yet they did not need all the lodges, and left many standing on the plains when they went back to their own country, wherever it is. They believed that all the Absanakees were dead now.

They did not know that two were still living! One was a middle-aged woman who was away from the village when the Two-faces came. She was far away picking berries. The other was a little boy who had been playing with some puppies in a hole and had gone to sleep there with the baby dogs.

When the Woman came back to the village and found her people dead she did not know what had happened. She was afraid, and she cried among the dead Absanakees, looking to see if any were yet alive. She found the Boy asleep with the puppies in the hole, and together they searched the remaining lodges for property that had been left by the Two-faces. What they found they took, and with the best lodge they saw, they moved up the river to a grove of trees and camped.

The Woman was a good worker and smart. When the Boy grew old enough she made him a bow and arrows and taught him how to use the weapons. He soon became a good hunter. They always had plenty of meat now and skins to make their clothing. The Woman dressed every robe and skin the Boy brought in, so that soon they had more than they needed. They were rich.

One day when the Boy was butchering a Buffalo in a deep coulee a Person came and stood beside him. The Person was tall and wore a white robe. He spoke softly and was a good sign-talker. His face was painted, and there was a Magpie's Feather in his hair.

"Sit down and eat," said the Boy, glad to see anyone. "Eat all you wish."

But the Person did not speak, even after he had eaten all he wished. He did not even say that he was grateful. He only walked away; and when he was gone, the Boy could not tell which way he went.

"Do you ever see anybody when you are hunting?" asked the Woman when the Boy was back in the lodge that night.

"Today when I was butchering a Buffalo a Person came to me," said the Boy.

"How did he look?" she asked, acting afraid.

"He was tall, and wore a white robe. He spoke softly, and was a good sign-talker. His face was painted, and there was a Magpie's Feather in his hair."

"Ha! I know who he is," said the Woman. "He is the scout of the Two-faces—the people who killed all the Absanakees but you and me. If he finds our lodge, and tells the Two-faces, we shall die. Never bring that Person here. Never tell him where we are camped if you do not wish to die."

One windy day the Boy was butchering a Buffalo-cow on the plains when a voice, close behind him, spoke softly. He turned quickly, and there again was the White-robed-person with the Magpie's Feather in his hair.

"Listen, Lives-with-his-grandmother," said the Person, "you were kind to me. You gave me meat —all I could eat—even though I was your enemy. I am the scout of the Two-faces who killed your people, the Absanakees, all but you and one woman. I am their slave and must do as they say. But my heart is bad for the Two-faces, and it is good for you, who gave me meat, all the meat I could eat. The Two-faces give me little to eat. I am always hungry and very tired. I have never had a good sleep in my life."

"Why do you not run away? When you get far off why do you go back?" asked the Boy.

"Because there are Persons who follow: Persons that are never seen, but who would tell the Two-faces where to find me," said the Magpie's Feather. "But I may get away if you will help me," he went on, speaking fast. "First I will help you and the Woman. Then, if I help you, I shall expect you to help me. Will you do this, Lives-with-his-grandmother?"

"Yes, of course I will help you," said the Boy. "What is it you would have me do?"

"This, Lives-with-his-grandmother. The Two-faces know where your lodge is. I told them. I was obliged to tell them. Tomorrow they will come to gamble with you, and you must pretend to be glad. They will play the hoop-and-arrow game twice; one game the first day and another game on the second day. After that they will run a foot-race and play a game of shinny. They have four Medicine-arrows. One is Black, one is Red, one is Yellow, and one is Blue. They will let you choose an arrow for the hoop-and-arrow game. Remember to choose the Black one! Insist that in betting all their property against all your

property they include me, their slave. If you win, you will save me. I will come to your lodge and be your slave. I have spoken."

When the Magpie's Feather had gone the Boy went to his lodge wondering how he could beat the people who had killed all the Absanakees except him and the Woman. Even if he won the first game with the Black arrow what good would this do with the other games to follow? How could the Magpie's Feather help him with the other games? How could any Person help him against the Two-faces?

"Lives-with-his-grandmother! Lives-with-his-grandmother!" Somebody was calling him!

When he raised the lodge-door in stepped Esahcawata, Old-man-coyote. He wore a Wolf's tail tied to each of his moccasins, and he was laughing. "Ha-ha-ha," he cackled like a woman that is very old. "I have come to help my brother, Lives-with-his-grandmother! I have heard that the Two-faces are coming to play gambling games with you. I have come to help. Give me some meat. You have plenty; you are rich!"

"Who told you that the Two-faces are coming here, Esahcawata," asked the Woman, giving him some meat.

"Oh, the Raven, of course; the Raven, and others. I have many friends," said Old-man-coyote, beginning to eat as though he could never get enough to fill his belly. "I'm here in plenty of time, too!" he laughed. "And I've brought my coup-stick. I expect to count some coups here." He showed them a willow-stick to which four small Eagle's feathers were tied. "Oh, it will have more feathers after this, several more," he told them when he saw that the Boy did not think his coup-stick very fine. "You will have to play games with the Two-faces, Lives-with-his-grand-mother," said Old-man-coyote, seriously. "You cannot fight them, so you must play with them and be polite."

The Two-faces were there when the Boy wakened in the morning. Old-man-coyote listened through the lodge-skin while the Boy talked to their Chief, who offered to wager all his people's property, except clothes and lodges, against all the property the Boy owned, except his clothes and his lodge.

"I will do as you say if you will include your slave with your other property," said the Boy, remembering what the Magpie's Feather had told him.

"Good!" agreed the Chief of the Two-faces. "Here are four arrows. Choose one for the first game—any one of them."

The Boy pretended he did not know which arrow to choose, the Red arrow, or the Blue arrow, or the Yellow arrow, or the Black arrow. But he took the Black one.

The village crier ran about among the Two-faces saying, "Everybody stand aside! This Boy has bet all his property, except his lodge and clothing, against all our property, except our lodges and clothing, that he can beat us at the hoop-and-arrow game!"

"Hi-Hi-Hi-Hi!" cried all the Two-faces, as though they were surprised.

"And this is the hoop we shall use!" called the camp crier, holding up a painted hoop that all might see that it was fair; that it had four large sections, and a small circle in its center; that it was like this ⊕ and fair.

Then he rolled the hoop. Their player ran after it on one side, and the Boy ran on the other side, each with his bow and arrow. The Two-face shot first. His arrow, the Blue one, went through the rolling hoop, but not through the small circle in its center.

"Ki-yaah—Ki-yaaaaah!" The Two-faces were glad. They cheered their player. "Ki-yaah—Ki-yaaaaah!"

"Zippp!" went the Boy's arrow, straight through the small circle in the hoop's center! He had won! The hoop was pinned to the ground!

"Hi-Hi! Ha-ha-ha!" Old-man-coyote began to sing and dance, the Wolf-tails dangling at his moccasin-heels. "You Two-faced-persons are playing games against a Boy who has powerful friends," he called, tauntingly, jumping over the hoop. Then he struck it down with his coup-stick, as though the hoop were an enemy in war. "Now I will count coup; tie another Eagle's feather on my coup-stick. Watch me, all you Two-faces!" He reached into a pouch, drew out a ruffled Eagle's feather, and tied it with the others to his willow-stick.

"I told you I would help you, Lives-with-his-grandmother!" said Old-man-coyote to the Boy when they went to their lodge with the Magpie's Feather, after the game. "And I will help you more after this."

"Tomorrow," said the Magpie's Feather, "when they permit you to choose an arrow for the second hoop-and-arrow game, take the Blue one, the arrow the Two-faces used today. Remember this, Lives-with-his-grandmother."

"Yes, that is the best one," said Old-man-coyote, though he knew nothing about the arrows. "That is the best arrow, and I will be thinking of something else to do."

In the morning when the Chief of the Two-faces offered the arrows and said, "Choose," the Boy was a long time deciding. But, of course, he chose the Blue arrow. Then they rolled the hoop again, and again the Boy won. Now he owned all the property of the Two-faces, all their lodges and clothing, and their slave, besides. But he was very unhappy. Tomorrow the game would be a foot-race, and he would be obliged to wager all his winnings against the weapons of the Two-faces. He, himself, was not a swift runner. Old-man-coyote could not run at all, and the Magpie's Feather was a slave. The Two-faces would not play against a slave-person! The Boy was certain of this—and now he was very much afraid.

But Old-man-coyote kept singing and dancing as though there was nothing to fear—as though all things were even between the Two-faces and the Boy. "We are Smart-persons," he kept saying over and over again.

"I am sorry," said the Magpie's Feather that night in the lodge. "I cannot help you further. Tomorrow there will be a foot-race, and the runner for the Two-faces will be The-shadow-of-a-cloud. He is the swiftest Person on this world."

"Oh, no, he isn't—no, he isn't," laughed Old-man-coyote. "No, he isn't. He is fast. But I know some Persons who can beat The-shadow-of-a-cloud, if I can find them."

He stood up. "I will go now, and look for a friend of mine. I may not find him, of course. But remember I will be here in time for the race tomorrow," he said, and went out of the lodge.

The Boy and the Magpie's Feather were asleep when the Woman called them. "Someone is outside," she said, straightening the robes in the lodge.

"Well, I'm back, you see," laughed Old-man-coyote, coming in with a Person. "And I found the Swift-runner, too. Sit down!" he told the Person, as though the lodge were his own.

The Person sat by the fire. He was tall and very thin, and he was white-looking, and there were two heavy stones tied to his feet.

"This Person is fast. One's eyes cannot see him when he runs," said Old-man-coyote. "He must have heavy stones tied to his feet to keep him from running all the time. He cannot walk unless stones are tied to his feet. Tomorrow when we cut them off he will run forever unless we catch him and tie them on again. I guess I am smart enough for those Two-faced-persons."

The race was to be around the edge of the World and back again. The Two-faces had The-shadow-of-a-cloud ready when the Boy brought his runner to the starting place. The Two-faced crier went among the people telling them of the race, and while this was going on the Boy got ready to cut the thongs that held the stones to his runner's feet.

"Ho!" called the Two-faced crier. And the racers were gone! The-shadow-of-a-cloud was behind!

"Hi-Hi-Hi—Ha-ha-ha-ha!" Old-man-coyote began to sing and dance, flipping the Wolf-tails around his heels, and acting silly. The Two-faces were looking at him, and they were scowling, too. But he did not care about their looks, because he could not tell which way they were looking. "Hi-Hi-Hi—Ha-ha-ha-ha! Now get your rope, Lives-with-his-grandmother! Get your rope, and catch your runner when he comes back, or he will run himself to death. He will run forever!" he called.

The Boy got his rope, and when his runner came running back he caught him.

"Hold him! Hold him!" cried Old-man-coyote, tying the heavy stones to the Person's feet. "Now let him up. Ha-ha! We have beaten the Two-faces again."

Night came before The-shadow-of-a-cloud came into the village. He had lost the race around the edge of the World and back again. The Boy had won!

"I'm a pretty smart Person, you'll find," said Old-man-coyote that night in the Boy's lodge. "And you'd better pay attention when I say things to you. Listen now. Tomorrow we play shinny against those Two-faces. It is the last game, and our lives will be wagered on it. Of course they cannot kill me, but they will kill you and the Magpie's Feather and this Woman, if we lose. Go now, and say to the Two-face Chief these words: 'I have played all the games with you, and I have done as you wished in all. Tomorrow when we play shinny I wish to use my own ball.' Say these words, and bring his answer back here. I wish to know it."

The Boy went to the Chief of the Two-faces and said the words Old-man-coyote had spoken. "It is good," answered the Chief. "We will play shinny with your ball. But remember that your lives will be wagered on the game—your lives against ours."

"Hi-Hi! Ha-ha-ha!" laughed Old-man-coyote, when the Boy told him what the Chief had said. "Ha-ha-ha-ha! This game of shinny will be funny! We are to start playing from the center of the World, and put the ball into salt-water east or west. Is this agreed upon, Lives-with-his-grandmother?"

"Yes, Esahcawata, we are to start at the center of the World and knock the ball into salt-water either east or west."

"Good! Good!" chuckled Old-man-coyote. "Who are the swiftest runners that play shinny for the Two-faces?" he asked, counting the feathers on his willow coup-stick.

"Wolf and Coyote," answered Magpie's Feather, uneasily. "But what are we going to use for a shinny-ball?"

"Oh, a good one. One that will do, anyway," laughed Old-man-coyote, rising to go out into the night. "Do not be surprised if the weather turns cold before I come back," he laughed. "I'll be here in time to see the game, remember."

"Why, the snow is falling!" said the Woman, looking up through the smoke-hole of the lodge. "Our lodge is cold!" She put wood on the fire, and drew her robe about her shoulders.

Before morning the snow reached above a man's knees. Then it stopped suddenly, and rain came; then the rain stopped, and the weather turned suddenly cold again and there was a crust on the snow that would bear the weight of a light Person, but not one that was heavy. And now the sky was clear.

"Here I am again; and I've brought a Hot Thing for a shinny-ball." Old-man-coyote came into the lodge with the Morning-star! "This

Person has nothing to do at this time of year," he told them. "The Morning-star does not shine, has no work, until after the Buffalo-calves are born on the plains and stand up. But he will help us. He is the Son of the Sun, and a friend of mine. Now give me some dressed Elk-skin. I shall have to cover this Person so that he will look like a shinny-ball before we use him," he said, beginning to sew Elk-skin around the Morning-star.

The Two-faces were certain they would win the shinny-game and take back their property, even before they killed the Absanakees. But the deep snow worried them a little while they were walking to the center of the World to start the shinny-game. The crust kept breaking. It was only strong enough to hold up the small Persons, like the Fox and the Lynx.

The crier of the Two-faces was ahead. "Here we are! Here we are!" he called, sticking his lance into the snow to mark the place. "This is the center of the World."

The Two-faces gathered around him and his lance that was standing up in the snow just as our people stop to make camp when our Medicine-men stick a lance where our village is to be. "Everybody who desires to play may do so," called out the crier, "but remember the game is for our lives! Our swiftest who will play for us are the Wolf and the Coyote," he finished, stepping back, and waving the people away from the lance in the snow, which was the center of the World.

"And our runners are two Foxes, the Red one and the Silver-cross, first cousins," said Old-man-coyote, who had come up to the lance with the shinny-ball and the Foxes.

There was much talking, and some disputing, over who should first have the Ball. But while this was going on the Ball, in Old-man-coyote's arms, whispered to the Foxes: "Run westward where there are no people at all! I will be there quickly. I will roll under the snow so that they may not see me go. I will melt my way, for I am hot. I will come up out of the snow where you are standing. When you see me, grab me quickly and run west to salt-water. I will not burn you."

The Boy won the Ball, after much talking. "Ho!" called the Two-faced crier. "Play at once!"

Old-man-coyote raised the Ball four times as though he would toss it westward; then, instead, he tossed it eastward where the people were thickest!

There was a mad striking of shinny-clubs! Clubs were so thick there that nobody could see the Ball for flying snow. The Two-faces struck and struck, but not one struck the Ball! It was under the snow and traveling westward.

"Hi-Hi! Ha-ha-ha!" Old-man-coyote ran among the Two-faces, striking frantically, as though he believed the Ball was there. "Do your best, you Two-faces!" he called to them, striking right and left, and making the snow fly. "Remember that we don't love you very much."

They were excited, and all kept striking the snow where Old-man-coyote pretended the Ball was until a Two-face saw the Foxes running away with it, westward. This Person shouted, "There they go! They've got the Ball, and are going westward with it!"

Away went the Wolf and Coyote, their tongues hanging out of their mouths. But they kept breaking through the crust of the snow! They are powerful and swift, but the snow made their work difficult. The rest could not keep up at all.

At length the Wolf and Coyote caught up to the Foxes who were running side by side. The Red-fox was carrying the Ball. The Silver-fox fell back just a little to fool the Wolf and Coyote—to make them believe he was tiring. Then, after a little, he caught up again and the Red-fox passed him the Ball to carry a while. They changed off, you see, and kept running toward the salt-water all the time. Nobody else was near when, out of breath, and very tired, the Red-fox tossed the Ball into the salt-water! The Wolf was reaching for it, too, and nearly took it, but the Red-fox, dodging just when the snow-crust broke with the Wolf, tossed the Ball into the salt-water!

Everybody heard it splash! "Hi-Hi-Hi—Ha-ha-ha!" Old-man-coyote began to laugh. But the Two-faces were crying now.

"Call the Blue-heron," laughed Old-man-coyote. "Call the Blue-heron-person! Let him do this job with his bill. Hi-Hi—Ha-ha-ha! I will call him myself. I planned this thing." He turned his back and sang his Medicine-song.

When the Blue-heron came Old-man-coyote

said, "Brother, kill all these Two-faced ones, and cut off their heads with your bill to make sure your job is well done."

"Boy," he said, "you and this Woman go away from here. Take the Magpie's Feather with you. Do not come back, or even look this way for four days. After four days come back here to your lodge."

The first night the Woman heard men singing back where she and the Boy had left Old-man-coyote. The next night she heard children laughing, and told the Boy. The third night both smelled smoke from many lodges, and the fourth night they could hear war-drums, and people dancing.

The fifth morning they went back. A large village stood where they had left their lodge!

"Welcome—welcome, Lives-with-his-grandmother. Welcome, Woman," many voices were saying. And the words were Absanakee! The Absanakees had come back!

But, of course, Esahcawata, Old-man-coyote, was gone.

"I have finished this story."

Tall tales

England has its giant stories, but the United States of America, with its national symbols a spread eagle and a super-tall figure of a man called "Uncle Sam," has expressed its exuberant sense of bigness in a series of tall tales. Pecos Bill, a western cowboy; Paul Bunyan of the lumber camps; Stormalong, a New England sailor; John Henry, a railroad hand; and some "super-duper" animals like Babe, the Blue Ox, and the Fast Sooner Hound are only a few of our tall tale heroes. Where these stories came from, nobody knows, but they are as indigenous to the United States as its great cornfields, its vast prairies, and its giant trees. These stories voice the philosophy of a new world, a young nation. They say, with tongue in cheek and rare drollery, that our native sons can do anything—"the sky's the limit!" The general formula for these bouncing stories is that the details shall be meticulously realistic and convincing, and the whopping exaggerations shall be told with a straight face and complete gravity. Boys love the stories, and girls like them, too. Told on a picnic, on the beach or around a camp fire, no stories are more fun. But they go almost as well in the home or the classroom, and once the children get the flavor of a series of these hero tales, they want more. Incidentally, when children have caught their style and pattern, they can make up their own tall tales.

THE CAMP
ON THE BIG ONION

With this introduction to Paul Bunyan, the mighty logger, children may want Glen Rounds' delightful book, Ole Paul the Mighty Logger.

That first fall I was workin' for Paul was when he got the big hotcake griddle. Always in the woods in them days the boys was mighty fond of hotcakes—just like men are pretty generally any-

wheres, I guess—and if there was anything could be said for Paul it was that he tried to treat his men right. And so, naturally, he wanted 'em to have hotcakes if there was any way he could fix it, and then besides, the way he ate 'em afterwards, he was more'n a little fond of 'em himself.

Well, in camp before that they hadn't never had hotcakes, because they didn't have no griddle big enough to cook 'em on, and no stove they could of put the griddle on if they'd of had it anyway, and so what they had for breakfast before that and what they was havin' when I went to work for Paul was just sourdough biscuits. And even so the cook used to have to get up

"The Camp on the Big Onion." From *Paul Bunyan,* copyright 1924, 1952 by Esther Shephard. Reprinted by permission of Harcourt, Brace and Company, Inc.

twenty-six hours before daylight to get the biscuits cooked in time because all he had to cook 'em on was one of them there drumhead stoves they used to have and he couldn't only cook but sixty-four drippin' pans full at a time.

But that year Paul made up his mind he was goin' to have hotcakes for the men and he was goin' to have a griddle big enough to cook 'em on. And so he went down to the plow-works at Moline, Illinois, and contracted for 'em to make him one to suit him.

The steel that went into this griddle of Paul's was what would have gone into two hundred and sixty breakin' plows, and when it was done finally, it measured two hundred and thirty-five foot across.

And then the men at the plow-works, of course, didn't have no way to ship it up to Paul and they was out there in the yard at the works figgurin' on how they could build some side-tracks and put several flatcars alongside each other and try to ship it up on them, when Paul happened to come along to see if his griddle wasn't finished yet.

"Never mind that," he says to the men when he seen 'em out there. "Never mind tryin' to build any extra tracks. We couldn't never get enough cars anyway, I don't believe. I'll just raise 'er up on edge and hitch my Blue Ox to 'er, and she'll roll right along."

And so after they'd got out of the way he raised 'er up, and hitched on, and started right out for home.

And when he come to within four or five miles of the camp, like he'd calculated it out beforehand, I guess, he just unhitched the Blue Ox and let the griddle spin on by itself. And here she come, rollin' right along. And when she got to just the right place, where he'd figgured to place her, she begun to spin round and round like spin-the-plate at a play-party and dug a nice big hole for the fire to go in under it, and settled right down and was all ready to go.

Paul had the bull-cooks pile in an acre or two of brush for a good fire, and him and Ole the Blacksmith rigged up a tank for the cook to make his batter in and a flume with a stop-cock in it, so's he could run it out onto the griddle and then shut it off whenever he had enough. Paul got flunkies with slabs of bacon strapped to their feet to skate around on the griddle to keep it greased, and a chicken wire fence all around for 'em to climb up on when the batter come in too thick. We rigged up a kind of block and tackle arrangement to haul the hotcake off with when it was done—that's on that first griddle. Afterwards, like in the camp in North Dakota, Paul, of course, always had donkey engines.

There was four hundred bull-cooks bringin' in the spruce-boughs for the bunks in the big bunkhouse at that first camp I was in; it had eighty tiers of bunks, most of 'em muzzle loaders but the two bottom layers, they was sidewinders. And the men used to go to bed in balloons at night and come down in parachutes in the mornin'.

A pretty sight it used to be to watch 'em comin' down.

"R-o-oo-ool out! Daylight in the swamp!" one of the cookees would yell, and then in a minute or two they'd all be rollin' out of their blankets, and the parachutes would open and they'd all come sailin' down. It sure was a pretty sight—about as fine a show as I ever laid eyes on.

Sometimes in the mornin' I used to stop at the door of the bunkhouse, on my way from the barn, to watch 'em. For Bill and I generally used to be on our way in to breakfast about that time, and Bill'd sometimes take the time to stop for a minute or so.

"I like to see 'em," he'd say to me. "Angus, that's a mighty fine show. They come faster now than they used to when it was just for sourdough biscuits. But we'll have to hustle along and get our hotcakes. We got to get back to the Ox."

That spring on the Big Onion we had an awful lot of trouble with the garlic that growed there where Garlic Crick joins the Big Onion River—a kind of V-shaped tract in there along the loggin' road, that was just full of it. The cook tried to use it all up seasonin' the soup but the Frenchies wouldn't stand for it in their pea-soup after the first week, and even with that he only got the top layer off and then there was four more layers growin' under that one. It beats all how thick that wild garlic can grow when it gets a good start. Everybody that even went by that place was seasoned so strong there wasn't nobody else could live with him and, worst of it, he couldn't stand to live with himself even. And we pretty near just had to break up camp, but then Paul heard that the Italian garlic crop was goin' to fail that year and so we grubbed up the whole piece, every last layer of it, and shipped it all to Italy and that way we got rid of it at last; just in time when a good many of us was goin' on the drive anyway, though.

PECOS BILL

AND HIS BOUNCING BRIDE

Here is one of the children's favorites of all the tall tale heroes. As in moving-picture Westerns, women are an unimportant detail, and certainly Pecos Bill's bride must have been glad to see the last of "the Widow-maker." The children will like Le Grand's tall tale, "Why Cowboys Sing in Texas."

There were two loves in the life of Pecos Bill. The first was his horse Widow-Maker, a beautiful creamy white mustang. The second, was a girl, a pretty, gay creature named Slue-Foot Sue.

Widow-Maker was the wildest pony in the West. He was the son of the White Mustang. Like his father he had a proud spirit which refused to be broken. For many years cowboys and *vaqueros* had tried to capture him. At last Pecos Bill succeeded. He had a terrible time of it. For a whole week he lay beside a water hole before he could lasso the white pony. For another week he had to ride across the prairies, in and out of canyons and briar patches, before he could bring the pony to a walk. It was a wild ride indeed. But after Bill's ride on the cyclone it was nothing.

At last the white stallion gave up the struggle. Pecos patted his neck gently and spoke to him in horse language. "I hope you will not be offended," he began as politely as possible, "but beauty such as yours is rare, even in this glorious state of Texas. I have no wish to break your proud spirit. I feel that together you and I would make a perfect team. Will you not be my partner at the I.X.L. Ranch?"

The horse neighed sadly. "It must be," he

"Pecos Bill and His Bouncing Bride." From *Pecos Bill* by James C. Bowman. As adapted in *Yankee Doodle's Cousins* by Anne Malcolmson. Copyright 1941 by Anne Burnett Malcolmson. Reprinted by permission of Albert Whitman & Company and Houghton Mifflin Company.

sighed. "I must give up my freedom. But since I must, I am glad that you are the man who has conquered me. Only Pecos Bill is worthy to fix a saddle upon the son of the great White Stallion, the Ghost King of the Prairie."

"I am deeply honored," said Pecos Bill, touched in his heart by the compliment.

"It is rather myself who am honored," replied the mustang, taking a brighter view of the situation.

The two of them went on for several hours saying nice things to each other. Before they were through, the pony was begging Pecos to be his master. Pecos was weeping and saying he was not fit to ride so magnificent a beast. In the end, however, Pecos Bill made two solemn promises. He would never place a bit in the pony's mouth. No other human would ever sit in his saddle.

When Bill rode back to I.X.L. with his new mount, the second promise was broken. Old Satan, the former bad man, had not completely recovered from his badness. He was jealous of Bill. When he saw the beautiful white stallion he turned green and almost burst with jealousy. One night he stole out to the corral. Quietly he slipped up beside the horse and jumped into the saddle.

Pegasus, as the horse was called, knew right away that his rider was not Pecos Bill. He lifted his four feet off the ground and bent his back into a perfect semicircle. Old Satan flew off like an arrow from a bow. He flew up into the air, above the moon, and came down with a thud on top of Pike's Peak. There he sat howling with pain and fright until the boys at I.X.L. spotted him.

Bill was angry. He knew, however, that Old Satan had had enough punishment. In his kind heart he could not allow the villain to suffer any more than he had to. So he twirled his lasso around his head, let it fly, and roped Old Satan back to the Texas ranch. The former desperado never tried to be bad again.

The cowhands were so impressed by the pony's bucking they decided to change his name. From that time on they dropped the name of Pegasus and called him Widow-Maker. It suited him better.

The story of Bill's other love, Slue-Foot Sue,

is a long one. It began with the tale of the Perpetual Motion Ranch. Bill had bought a mountain from Paul Bunyan. It looked to him like a perfect mountain for a ranch. It was shaped like a cone, with smooth sides covered with grassy meadows. At the top it was always winter. At the bottom it was always summer. In between it was always spring and fall. The sun always shone on one side; the other was always in shade. The cattle could have any climate they wished.

Bill had to breed a special kind of steer for his ranch. These had two short legs on one side and two long legs on the other. By traveling in one direction around the mountain, they were able to stand up straight on the steep sides.

The novelty wore off, however, and at last Bill sold the Perpetual Motion Ranch to an English duke. The day that the I.X.L. boys moved out, the lord moved in. He brought with him trainload after trainload of fancy English things. He had featherbeds and fine china and oil paintings and real silver and linen tablecloths and silk rugs. The cowboys laughed themselves almost sick when they saw these dude things being brought to a cattle ranch.

Pecos Bill didn't laugh. He didn't even notice the fancy things. All he could see was the English duke's beautiful daughter. She was as pretty as the sun and moon combined. Her hair was silky and red. Her eyes were blue. She wore a sweeping taffeta dress and a little poke bonnet with feathers on it. She was the loveliest creature Pecos Bill had ever seen.

She was as lively and gay as she was pretty. Bill soon discovered that Slue-Foot Sue was a girl of talent. Before anyone could say "Jack Robinson," she changed into a cowboy suit and danced a jig to the tune of "Get Along, Little Dogies."

Bill soon lost all his interest in cowpunching. He spent his afternoons at the Perpetual Motion Ranch, teaching Sue to ride a broncho. Sue could ride as well as anyone, but she pretended to let him teach her. After several months of Bill's lessons, she put on a show. She jumped onto the back of a huge catfish in the Rio Grande River and rode all the way to the Gulf of Mexico, bareback. Bill was proud of her. He thought she had learned her tricks all from him.

Sue's mother was terribly upset by her daugh-

ter's behavior. She didn't care much for Bill. She was very proper. It was her fondest hope that Sue would stop being a tomboy and marry an earl or a member of Parliament.

As soon as she realized that her daughter was falling in love with a cowboy, she was nearly heart-broken. There was nothing she could do about it, however. Slue-Foot Sue was a headstrong girl who always had her own way.

At last the duchess relented. She invited Bill to tea and began to lecture him on English manners. She taught him how to balance a teacup,

how to bow from the waist, and how to eat scones and marmalade instead of beans and bacon. He learned quickly, and soon the duchess was pleased with him. She called him "Colonel."

When the boys from the I.X.L. Ranch saw what was going on they were disgusted. Here was their boss, their brave, big, cyclone-riding Pecos Bill, mooning around in love like a sick puppy. They laughed at his dude manners. They made fun of his dainty appetite. When he dressed up in his finery to call on his girl, they stood in the bunkhouse door. They simpered and raised their eyebrows and said to one another, "La-dee-da, dearie, ain't we fine today!"

But for all their kidding they were broken-hearted. None of them had anything against Sue. They admired the way she rode a horse and played a guitar and danced a jig. But the thought of losing Bill to a woman was too much. Even worse was the thought that Bill might get married and bring a woman home to live with them. That was awful.

In spite of their teasing and the duchess's lessons, Bill asked Slue-Foot Sue to marry him. She accepted before he could back out. Her father, the lord, had always liked Bill and was terribly pleased at the match.

On his wedding day Pecos Bill shone like the sun in his new clothes. His boys were dressed in their finest chaps and boots for the occasion. Half of them were going to be groomsmen. The other half were going to be bridesmen. At first Bill asked them to be bridesmaids, but they refused. They said that was going too far.

They rode to the Perpetual Motion Ranch in a fine procession, Bill at the head on Widow-Maker. The white horse pranced and danced with excitement.

At the ranch house waited the rest of the wedding party. The lord had sent back to England for a bishop to perform the ceremony. There stood His Eminence in his lace robes. On his one hand stood the duke in a cutaway coat. On his other hand stood the duchess in a stiff purple gown right from Paris.

Down the stairs came the bride. She was a vision of beauty. She wore a white satin dress cut in the latest fashion. It had a long lace train, but its chief glory was a bustle. A bustle was a wire contraption that fitted under the back of the dress. It made the skirt stand out and was considered very handsome in those days.

As Slue-Foot Sue danced down the steps even the cowhands forgot their sorrow. They jumped down from their horses and swept their sombreros from their heads. Pecos Bill lost his head. He leapt down from Widow-Maker and ran to meet her. "You are lovely," he murmured. "I promise to grant you every wish you make."

That was a mistake. A devilish gleam twinkled in Sue's eye. For months she had been begging Bill to let her ride Widow-Maker. Bill, of course, had always refused.

Now Sue saw her chance. Before she allowed the wedding to proceed, she demanded that Bill give her one ride on his white mustang.

"No, no!" cried Pecos Bill. Before he could stop her Sue dashed down the drive and placed her dainty foot into the stirrup. The duchess screamed. The bishop turned pale.

Widow-Maker gave an angry snort. This was the second time the promise to him had been broken. He lifted his four feet off the ground and arched his back. Up, up, up shot Slue-Foot Sue. She disappeared into the clouds.

"Catch her, catch her!" roared Bill at the boys. They spread themselves out into a wide circle. Then from the sky came a scream like a siren. Down, down, down fell Sue. She hit the earth with terrible force. She landed on her bustle. The wire acted as a spring. It bounced. Up again she flew.

Up and down, up and down between the earth and sky Sue bounced like a rubber ball. Every time she fell her bustle hit first. Back she bounced. This went on for a week. When at last she came back to earth to stay, she was completely changed. She no longer loved Pecos Bill.

The wedding was called off and the boys returned to the I.X.L. with their unhappy boss. For months he refused to eat. He lost interest in cowpunching. He was the unhappiest man Texas had ever seen.

At last he called his hands together and made a long speech. He told them that the days of real cowpunching were over. The prairie was being fenced off by farmers. These "nesters," as he called them, were ruining the land for the ranchers. He was going to sell his herd.

The I.X.L. had its last roundup. Bill gathered all the prime steers together and put them on the train for Kansas City. Then he divided the cows and calves among his boys. He himself mounted Widow-Maker and rode away.

The boys hated to see him go, but they knew how he felt. "Nesters" or no "nesters," the real reason for his going was his broken heart.

None of them ever saw him again. Some of them thought he had gone back to the coyotes. Others had an idea that Slue-Foot Sue had changed her mind and that she and Bill were setting up housekeeping in some private canyon. But they never knew.

Some years later an old cowhand claimed that Bill had died. The great cowpuncher had met a dude rancher at a rodeo. The dude was dressed up in an outfit he had bought from a movie cowboy. The dude's chaps were made of doeskin. His boots were painted with landscapes and had heels three inches high. The brim of his hat was broad enough to cover a small circus. Bill took a good look at him and died laughing.

THE BOOMER FIREMAN'S
FAST SOONER HOUND

Children will enjoy Virginia Burton's pictures in Jack Conroy's and Arna Bontemps' book The Fast Sooner Hound. *They will also be entertained by that super horse, recorded in verse by Dick Jones and called* Platonia the Pride of the Plain.

In the days of the old railroad trains before diesel engines were ever thought of the fireman was an important man. A Boomer fireman could get him a job most anytime on most any railroad and was never long for any one road. Last year he might have worked for the Frisco, and this year he's heaving black diamonds for the Katy or the Wabash. He travelled light and travelled far and didn't let any grass grow under his feet when they got to itching for the greener pastures on the next road or the next division or maybe on the other side of the mountains. He didn't need furniture and he didn't need many clothes, and goodness knows he didn't need a family or a dog.

One day when one of these Boomer firemen pulled into the roadmaster's office looking for a job, there was that Sooner hound of his loping after him. That hound would sooner run than eat and he'd sooner eat than fight or do something useful like catching a rabbit. Not that a rabbit would have any chance if the Sooner really wanted to nail him, but that crazy hound

"The Boomer Fireman's Fast Sooner Hound," by Jack Conroy. From *A Treasury of American Folklore*, edited by B. A. Botkin. Crown Publishers, New York, 1944. Used with the kind permission of Jack Conroy

dog didn't like to do anything but run and he was the fastest thing on four legs.

"I might use you," said the roadmaster. "Can you get a boarding place for the dog?"

"Oh, he goes along with me," said the Boomer. "I raised him from a pup just like a mother or father and he ain't never spent a night or a day or even an hour far away from me. He'd cry like his poor heart would break and raise such a ruckus nobody couldn't sleep, eat or hear themselves think for miles about."

"Well, I don't see how that would work out," said the roadmaster. "It's against the rules of the road to allow a passenger in the cab, man or beast, or in the caboose and I aim to put you on a freight run so you can't ship him by express. Besides, he'd get the idea you wasn't nowhere about and pester folks out of their wits with his yipping and yowling. You look like a man that could keep a boiler popping off on an uphill grade, but I just don't see how we could work it if the hound won't listen to reason while you're on your runs."

"Why he ain't no trouble," said the Boomer. "He just runs alongside, and when I'm on a freight run he chases around a little in the fields to pass the time away. It's a little bit tiresome on him having to travel at such a slow gait, but that Sooner would do anything to stay close by me, he loves me that much."

"Oh, is that so? Well, don't try to tell that yarn around here," said the roadmaster.

"I'll lay my first paycheck against a fin[1] that he'll be fresh as a daisy and his tongue behind his teeth when we pull into the junction. He'll run around the station a hundred times or so to limber up."

"It's a bet," said the roadmaster.

On the first run the Sooner moved in what was a slow walk for him. He kept looking up into the cab where the Boomer was shoveling in the coal.

"He looks worried," said the Boomer. "He thinks the hog law[2] is going to catch us, we're making such bad time."

The roadmaster was so sore at losing the bet that he transferred the Boomer to a local passenger run and doubled the stakes. The Sooner

[1] Five dollar bill.—J. C.
[2] Rule forbidding excessive over time.—J. C.

speeded up to a slow trot, but he had to kill a lot of time, at that, not to get too far ahead of the engine.

Then the roadmaster got mad enough to bite off a drawbar. People got to watching the Sooner trotting alongside the train and began thinking it must be a mighty slow road. Passengers might just as well walk; they'd get there just as fast. And if you shipped a yearling calf to market, it'd be a bologna bull before it reached the stockyards. Of course, the trains were keeping up their schedules the same as usual, but that's the way it looked to people who saw a no-good mangy Sooner hound beating all the trains without his tongue hanging out an inch or letting out the least little pant.

It was giving the road a black eye, all right. The roadmaster would have fired the Boomer and told him to hit the grit with his Sooner and never come back again, but he was stubborn from the word go and hated worse than anything to own up he was licked.

"I'll fix that Sooner," said the roadmaster. "I'll slap the Boomer into the cab of the Cannon Ball, and if anything on four legs can keep up with the fastest thing on wheels I'd admire to see it. That Sooner'll be left so far behind it'll take nine dollars to send him a post card."

The word got around that the Sooner was going to try to keep up with the Cannon Ball. Farmers left off plowing, hitched up, and drove to the right of way to see the sight. It was like a circus day or the county fair. The schools all dismissed the pupils, and not a factory could keep enough men to make a wheel turn.

The roadmaster got right in the cab so that the Boomer couldn't soldier on the job to let the sooner keep up. A clear track for a hundred miles was ordered for the Cannon Ball, and all the switches were spiked down till after that streak of lightning had passed. It took three men to see the Cannon Ball on that run: one to say, "There she comes," one to say, "There she is," and another to say, "There she goes." You couldn't see a thing for steam, cinders and smoke, and the rails sang like a violin for a half hour after she'd passed into the next county.

Every valve was popping off and the wheels three feet in the air above the roadbed. The Boomer was so sure the Sooner would keep up

that he didn't stint the elbow grease; he wore the hinges off the fire door and fifteen pounds of him melted and ran right down into his shoes. He had his shovel whetted to a nub.

The roadmaster stuck his head out of the cab window, and—whosh!—off went his hat and almost his head. The suction like to have jerked his arms from their sockets as he nailed a-hold of the window seat.

It was all he could do to see, and gravel pinged against his goggles like hailstones, but he let out a whoop of joy.

"THE SOONER! THE SOONER!" he yelled. "He's gone! He's gone for true! Ain't *nowhere* in sight!"

"I can't understand that," hollered the Boomer. "He ain't *never* laid down on me yet. It just ain't like him to lay down on me. Leave me take a peek."

He dropped his shovel and poked out his head. Sure enough, the Sooner was nowhere to be seen. The Boomer's wild and troubled gaze swept far and wide.

"Don't see him, do you?" the roadmaster demanded. "He's at least seventy-six miles behind."

The Boomer didn't answer. He just threw his head back into the cab and began to shovel coal. He shoveled without much spirit, shaking his head sadly. There was no need for hard work, anyhow, for the Cannon Ball was puffing into the station at the end of the run.

Before the wheels had stopped rolling, the roadmaster jumped nimbly to the ground. A mighty cheer was heard from a group of people nearby. The roadmaster beamed as he drew near them.

"Here I am!" he shouted. "Where are the cameras? Do you want to take my picture in the cab?"

"Go way back and sit down!" a man shouted as he turned briefly toward the railroad official. "You might as well scrap that Cannon Ball. The Sooner has been here a good half hour and time has been hanging heavy on his hands. Look at him!"

The Sooner was loping easily around a tree, barking at a cat which had taken refuge in the branches and was spitting angrily. The Sooner didn't look even a mite tired, and his tongue was behind his teeth.

"I'm through! Enough is enough, boys!" the roadmaster sputtered. "The rule about passengers in the cab is a dead duck from now on. Let the Sooner ride in the cab as often and as far as he wants to."

The Cannon Ball chugged out of the station with the Boomer waving his shovel in salute and the Sooner yelping proudly beside him. The people cheered until the train disappeared around a bend.

Stories from "Uncle Remus"

The talking beast tales of Uncle Remus are a priceless treasure of Negro folk tales. Many of them had their origin in India, but undoubtedly most of them traveled to this country from Africa. Joel Chandler Harris, a native of Georgia, recorded them from the lips of Negro storytellers. He had an ear for language and a deep love for the philosophy, the canny understanding of human nature, and the humor of the Negroes. In these tales he has preserved the Negro's unsurpassed gifts for storytelling. The hero of the stories is Brer Rabbit, the weakest of all the animals. He is a trickster, but a lovable one, with no meanness in him, just a delight in playing pranks on his bigger neighbors. Occasionally, they turn the tables on him, but his wit and resourcefulness always save him. Those fortunate people who can read and understand the rich dialect in which these stories are recorded should always read or tell them in that form. But for those who find the dialect an impossible barrier to using the stories, two of the stories have been translated into everyday English with every possible effort to retain, in the process, some of the characteristic turns of speech which give the stories their unique charm. Perhaps the examples of translating the stories will encourage grownups who cannot manage the dialect to try the same process with more of the stories. The collection is too rich for children to miss, and every effort should be made to keep these stories in circulation.

THE WONDERFUL
TAR-BABY STORY

This is the best known of all the stories and a perennial favorite with children.

"Didn't the fox *never* catch the rabbit, Uncle Remus?" asked the little boy the next evening.

"He come mighty nigh it, honey, sho's you born—Brer Fox did. One day atter Brer Rabbit fool 'im wid dat calamus root, Brer Fox went ter wuk en got 'im some tar, en mix it wid some turkentime, en fix up a contrapshun wat he call a Tar-Baby, en he tuck dish yer Tar-Baby en he sot 'er in de big road, en den he lay off in de bushes fer to see what de news wuz gwineter be.

"The Wonderful Tar-Baby Story." From *Uncle Remus, His Songs and His Sayings* by Joel Chandler Harris

En he didn't hatter wait long, nudder, kaze bimeby here come Brer Rabbit pacin' down de road — lippity-clippity, clippity-lippity — dez ez sassy ez a jay-bird. Brer Fox, he lay low. Brer Rabbit come prancin' 'long twel he spy de Tar-Baby, en den he fotch up on his behime legs like he wus 'stonished. De Tar-Baby, she sot dar, she did, en Brer Fox, he lay low.

" 'Mawnin'!' sez Brer Rabbit, sezee—'nice wedder dis mawnin',' sezee.

"Tar-Baby ain't sayin' nothin', en Brer Fox, he lay low.

" 'How duz yo' sym'tums seem ter segashuate?' sez Brer Rabbit, sezee.

"Brer Fox, he wink his eye slow, en lay low, en de Tar-Baby, she ain't sayin' nothin'.

" 'How you come on, den? Is you deaf?' sez Brer Rabbit, sezee. 'Kaze if you is, I kin holler louder,' sezee.

"Tar-Baby stay still, en Brer Fox, he lay low.

" 'Youer stuck up, dat's w'at you is,' says Brer Rabbit, sezee, 'en I'm gwineter kyore you, dat's w'at I'm a gwineter do,' sezee.

"Brer Fox, he sorter chuckle in his stummick, he did, but Tar-Baby ain't sayin' nothin'.

" 'I'm gwineter larn you howter talk ter 'specttubble fokes ef hit's de las' ack,' sez Brer Rabbit, sezee. 'Ef you don't take off dat hat en tell me howdy, I'm gwineter bus' you wide open,' sezee.

"Tar-Baby stay still, en Brer Fox, he lay low.

"Brer Rabbit keep on axin' 'im, en de Tar-Baby, she keep on sayin' nothin', twel present'y Brer Rabbit draw back wid his fis', he did, en blip he tuck 'er side er de head. Right dar's what he broke his merlasses jug. His fis' stuck, en he can't pull loose. De tar hilt 'im. But Tar-Baby, she stay still, en Brer Fox, he lay low.

" 'Ef you don't lemme loose, I'll knock you agin,' sez Brer Rabbit, sezee, en wid dat he fotch 'er a wipe wid de udder han', en dat stuck. Tar-Baby, she ain't sayin' nothin', en Brer Fox, he lay low.

" 'Tu'n me loose, fo' I kick de natal stuffin' outen you,' sez Brer Rabbit, sezee, but de Tar-Baby, she ain't sayin' nothin'. She des hilt on, en den Brer Rabbit lose de use er his feet in de same way. Brer Fox, he lay low. Den Brer Rabbit squall out dat ef de Tar-Baby don't tu'n 'im loose he butt 'er cranksided. En den he butted, en his head got stuck. Den Brer Fox, he sa'ntered fort', lookin' des ez innercent ez one er yo' mammy's mockin'-birds.

" 'Howdy, Brer Rabbit,' sez Brer Fox, sezee. 'You look sorter stuck up dis mawnin',',' sezee, en den he rolled on de groun', en laughed en laughed twel he couldn't laugh no mo'. 'I speck you'll take dinner wid me dis time, Brer Rabbit. I done laid in some calamus root, en I ain't gwineter take no skuse,' sez Brer Fox, sezee."

Here Uncle Remus paused, and drew a two-pound yam out of the ashes.

"Did the fox eat the rabbit?" asked the little boy to whom the story had been told.

"Dat's all de fur de tale goes," replied the old man. "He mout, en den again he moutent. Some say Jedge B'ar come long en loosed 'im—some say he didn't. I hear Miss Sally callin'. You better run 'long."

HOW MR. RABBIT

HOW MR. RABBIT

WAS TOO SHARP FOR MR. FOX

"Uncle Remus," said the little boy one evening, when he had found the old man with little or nothing to do, "did the fox kill and eat the rabbit when he caught him with the Tar-Baby?"

"Law, honey, ain't I tell you 'bout dat?" replied the old darkey, chuckling slyly. "I 'clar ter grashus I ought er tole you dat, but old man Nod wuz ridin' on my eyeleds 'twel a leetle mo'n I'd a dis'member'd my own name, en den on to dat here come yo' mammy hollerin' atter you.

"W'at I tell you w'en I fus' begin? I tole you Brer Rabbit wuz a monstus soon creetur; leas'ways dat's w'at I laid out fer ter tell you. Well, den, honey, don't you go en make no udder calkalashuns, kaze in dem days Brer Rabbit en his fambly wuz at de head er de gang w'en enny racket wuz on han', en dar dey stayed. 'Fo' you begins fer ter wipe yo' eyes 'bout Brer Rabbit, you wait en see whar'bouts Brer Rabbit gwineter fetch up at. But dat's needer yer ner dar.

"W'en Brer Fox fine Brer Rabbit mixt up wid de Tar-Baby, he feel mighty good, en he roll on de groun' en laff. Bimeby he up'n say, sezee:

" 'Well, I speck I got you dis time, Brer Rabbit, sezee; 'maybe I ain't, but I speck I is. You been runnin' roun' here sassin' atter me a mighty long time, but I speck you done come ter de en' er de row. You bin cuttin' up yo' capers en bouncin' 'roun' in dis neighberhood ontwel you come ter b'leeve yo'se'f de boss er de whole gang. En den youer allers some'rs whar you got no bizness,' sez Brer Fox, sezee. 'Who ax you fer ter come en strike up a 'quaintance wid dish yer Tar-Baby? En who stuck you up dar whar you iz? Nobody in de roun' worril. You des tuck en jam yo'se'f on dat Tar-Baby widout waitin' fer enny invite,' sez Brer Fox, sezee, 'en dar you is, en dar you'll stay twel I fixes up a bresh-pile and fires her up, kaze I'm gwineter bobby-cue you dis day, sho,' sez Brer Fox, sezee.

"Den Brer Rabbit talk mighty 'umble.

" 'I don't keer w'at you do wid me, Brer Fox,' sezee, 'so you don't fling me in dat brier-patch.

"How Mr. Rabbit Was Too Sharp for Mr. Fox." From *Uncle Remus, His Songs and His Sayings* by Joel Chandler Harris

Roas' me, Brer Fox,' sezee, 'but don't fling me in dat brier-patch,' sezee.

" 'Hit's so much trouble fer ter kindle a fier,' sez Brer Fox, sezee, 'dat I speck I'll hatter hang you,' sezee.

" 'Hang me des ez high as you please, Brer Fox,' sez Brer Rabbit, sezee, 'but do fer de Lord's sake don't fling me in dat brier-patch,' sezee.

" 'I ain't got no string,' sez Brer Fox, sezee, 'en now I speck I'll hatter drown you,' sezee.

" 'Drown me des ez deep ez you please, Brer Fox,' sez Brer Rabbit, sezee, 'but do don't fling me in dat brier-patch,' sezee.

" 'Dey ain't no water nigh,' sez Brer Fox, sezee, 'en now I speck I'll hatter skin you,' sezee.

" 'Skin me, Brer Fox,' sez Brer Rabbit, sezee, 'snatch out my eyeballs, t'ar out my years by de roots, en cut off my legs,' sezee, 'but do please, Brer Fox, don't fling me in dat brier-patch,' sezee.

"Co'se Brer Fox wanter hurt Brer Rabbit bad ez he kin, so he cotch 'im by de behime legs en slung 'im right in de middle er de brier-patch. Dar wuz a considerbul flutter whar Brer Rabbit struck de bushes, en Brer Fox sorter hang 'roun' fer ter see w'at wuz gwineter happen. Bimeby he hear somebody call 'im, en way up de hill he see Brer Rabbit settin' cross-legged on a chinkapin log koamin' de pitch outen his har wid a chip. Den Brer Fox know dat he bin swop off mighty bad. Brer Rabbit wuz bleedzed fer ter fling back some er his sass, en he holler out:

" 'Bred en bawn in a brier-patch, Brer Fox— bred en bawn in a brier-patch!' en wid dat he skip out des ez lively ez a cricket in de embers."

THE WONDERFUL
TAR-BABY STORY[1]

Brer Fox was always fixing some way to catch Brer Rabbit so, one day Brer Fox went to work and got him some tar, and mixed it with turpentine, and fixed up a contraption that he called a Tar-Baby. He took this here Tar-Baby and sat him in the big road, and then he laid off in the bushes for to see what the news was going to be. He didn't have to wait long, neither, for by and

[1] Adapted by May Hill Arbuthnot from the two preceding stories.

by here came Brer Rabbit pacing down the road —*lippity-clippity, clippity-lippity*—just as sassy as a jay-bird. Brer Fox he lay low. Brer Rabbit came prancing along till he spied the Tar-Baby, and then he fetched up on his hind legs like he was astonished. The Tar-Baby, she sat there, she did, and Brer Fox he lay low.

"Morning!" says Brer Rabbit, says he—"nice weather this morning," says he.

Tar-Baby says nothing, and Brer Fox, he lay low.

"How does your symptoms seem to segashuate?" says Brer Rabbit, says he.

Brer Fox, he winked his eye slow, and lay low, and the Tar-Baby, she says nothing.

"How you come on, then? Are you deaf?" says Brer Rabbit, says he. " 'Cause if you are, I can holler louder," says he.

Tar-Baby stay still, and Brer Fox he lay low.

"You're stuck up, that's what you are," says Brer Rabbit, says he, "and I'm going to cure you, that's what I'm going to do," says he.

Brer Fox, he sort of chuckled in his stomach, he did, but Tar-Baby, she says nothing.

"I'm going to learn you how to talk to respectable folks if it's my last act," says Brer Rabbit, says he. "If you don't take off that hat and tell me howdy, I'm going to bust you wide open," says he.

Tar-Baby stay still, and Brer Fox, he lay low.

Brer Rabbit keeps on asking, and the Tar-Baby, she keep on saying nothing, till presently Brer Rabbit draw back with his fist, he did, and *blip* he took her on the side of the head. Right there's where he broke his molasses jug. His fist stuck, and he can't pull loose. The tar held him. But Tar-Baby, she stay still, and Brer Fox, he lay low.

"If you don't let me loose, I'll knock you again," says Brer Rabbit, says he, and with that he fetched a swipe with the other hand, and that stuck fast. Tar-Baby, she say nothing, and Brer Fox, he lay low.

"Turn me loose, before I kick the natural stuffing out of you," says Brer Rabbit, says he, but Tar-Baby, she say nothing. She just held on, and then Brer Rabbit lose the use of his two feet the same way. Brer Fox, he lay low. Then Brer Rabbit squall out that if the Tar-Baby don't turn him loose, he'll butt her cranksided.

And then he butted, and his head got stuck. And there he was. And Brer Fox he sauntered forth looking just as innocent as a mocking-bird.

"Howdy, Brer Rabbit," says Brer Fox, says he. "You look sort of stuck up this morning," says he, and then he rolled on the ground and he laughed and laughed till he couldn't laugh any more. "Well, I 'spect I got you this time, Brer Rabbit," says he; "maybe I ain't but maybe I is. You've been running round here sassing me for a mighty long time but I 'spect you've come to the end of the row. You've been cutting up capers and bouncing round this neighborhood till you've come to believe you're the boss of the whole gang. And then you're always somewhere where you got no business to be," says Brer Fox, says he. "Who asked you to come and strike up an acquaintance with the Tar-Baby? And who stuck you up there where you are? Nobody in the round world. You just took and jammed yourself on that Tar-Baby without waiting for an invitation," says Brer Fox, says he, "And there's where you are, and there you'll stay, till I fix up a brush pile and fires her up, 'cause I'm going to barbecue you this day, sure," says Brer Fox, says he.

Then Brer Rabbit talked mighty humble.

"I don't care what you do with me, Brer Fox," says he, "just so you don't fling me in that brier-patch. Roast me, Brer Fox," says he, "but don't fling me in that brier-patch," says he.

"It's so much trouble for to kindle a fire," says Brer Fox, says he, "that I 'spect I'll have to hang you," says he.

"Hang me just as high as you please, Brer Fox," says Brer Rabbit, says he, "but for the land sakes, don't fling me in that brier-patch."

"I ain't got any string," says Brer Fox, says he, "and now I 'spect I'll have to drown you," says he.

"Drown me just as deep as you please, Brer Fox," says Brer Rabbit, says he, "but don't fling me in that brier-patch," says he.

"There ain't any water nearby," says Brer Fox, says he, "and now I 'spect I'll have to skin you," says he.

"Skin me, Brer Fox," says Brer Rabbit, says he, "snatch out my eyeballs, tear out my hair by the roots, cut off my legs," says he, "but please, Brer Fox, please don't fling me in that brier-patch," says he.

Of course Brer Fox wanted to hurt Brer Rabbit as bad as he could so he caught him by the hind legs and slung him right in the middle of the brier-patch. There was a considerable flutter where Brer Rabbit struck the bushes, and Brer Fox sort of hung around to see what was going to happen. By and by he heard someone call him, way up the hill, and he saw Brer Rabbit sitting cross-legged on a chinkapin log combing the pitch out of his hair with a chip. Then Brer Fox knew he'd been fooled mighty bad. And

Brer Rabbit was obliged to fling back some of his sass, so he hollered out:

"Bred and born in the brier-patch, Brer Fox —bred and born in the brier-patch!" and with that he skipped out as lively as a cricket in the embers.

"HEYO, HOUSE!"

"I don't think Brother Lion had much sense," remarked the little boy after awhile.

"Yit he had some," responded Uncle Remus. "He bleedz ter had some, but he ain't got much ez Brer Rabbit. Dem what got strenk ain't got so mighty much sense. You take niggers—dey er lots stronger dan what white folks is. I ain't so strong myse'f," remarked the old man, with a sly touch of vanity that was lost on the little boy, "but de common run er niggers is lots stronger dan white folks. Yit I done tuck notice in my time dat what white folks calls sense don't turn out ter be sense eve'y day en Sunday too. I ain't never see de patter-roller what kin keep up wid me. He may go hoss-back, he may go foot-back, it don't make no diffunce ter me. Dey never is kotch me yit, en when dey does, I'll let you know.

"Dat de way wid Brer Rabbit," Uncle Remus went on, after a pause. "De few times what he been outdone he mighty willin' fer ter let um talk 'bout it, ef it'll do um any good. Dem what outdo 'im got de right ter brag, en he ain't make no deniance un it.

"Atter he done make way wid ole Brer Lion, all de yuther creeturs say he sholy is a mighty man, en dey treat 'im good. Dis make 'im feel so proud dat he bleedz ter show it, en so he strut 'roun' like a boy when he git his fust pa'r er boots.

"'Bout dat time, Brer Wolf tuck a notion dat ef Brer Rabbit kin outdo ole Brer Lion, he can't outdo him. So he pick his chance one day whiles ole Miss Rabbit en de little Rabs is out pickin' sallid fer dinner. He went in de house, he did, en wait fer Brer Rabbit ter come home. Brer Rabbit had his hours, en dis wuz one un um, en 'twan't long 'fo' here he come. He got a mighty quick eye, mon, en he tuck notice dat ev'ything

"Heyo, House!" From *Uncle Remus and His Friends* by **Joel Chandler Harris**

mighty still. When he got little nigher, he tuck notice dat de front door wuz on de crack, en dis make 'im feel funny, kaze he know dat when his ole 'oman en de chillun out, dey allers pulls de door shet en ketch de latch. So he went up a little nigher, en he step thin ez a batter-cake. He peep here, en he peep dar, yit he ain't see nothin'. He lissen in de chimbley cornder, en he lissen und' de winder, yit he ain't hear nothin'.

"Den he sorter wipe his mustach en study. He 'low ter hisse'f, 'De pot rack know what gwine on up de chimbley, de rafters know who's in de loft, de bed-cord know who und' de bed. I ain't no pot-rack, I ain't no rafter, en I ain't no bed-cord, but, please gracious! I'm gwine ter fin' who's in dat house, en I ain't gwine in dar nudder. Dey mo' ways ter fin' out who fell in de mill-pond widout fallin' in yo'se'f.'

"Some folks," Uncle Remus went on, "would 'a' rushed in dar, en ef dey had, dey wouldn't 'a' rushed out no mo', kaze dey wouldn't 'a' been nothin' 'tall lef' un um but a little scrap er hide en a han'ful er ha'r.

"Brer Rabbit got better sense dan dat. All he ax anybody is ter des gi' 'im han'-roomance, en dem what kin ketch 'im is mo' dan welly-come ter take 'im. Dat 'zackly de kinder man what Brer Rabbit is. He went off a little ways fum de house en clum a 'simmon stump en got up dar en 'gun ter holler.

"He 'low, 'Heyo, house!'

"De house ain't make no answer, en Brer Wolf, in dar behime de door, open his eyes wide. He ain't know what ter make er dat kinder doin's.

"Brer Rabbit holler, 'Heyo, house! Whyn't you heyo?'

"House ain't make no answer, en Brer Wolf in dar behime de door sorter move roun' like he gittin' restless in de min'.

"Brer Rabbit out dar on de 'simmon stump holler mo' louder dan befo', 'Heyo, house! Heyo!'

"House stan' still, en Brer Wolf in dar behime de door 'gun ter feel col' chills streakin' up and down his back. In all his born days he ain't never hear no gwines on like dat. He peep thoo de crack er de door, but he can't see nothin'.

"Brer Rabbit holler louder, 'Heyo, house! Ain't you gwine ter heyo? Is you done los' what little manners you had?'

"Brer Wolf move 'bout wuss'n befo'. He feel des like some un done hit 'im on de funny-bone.

"Brer Rabbit holler hard ez he kin, but still he ain't git no answer, en den he 'low, 'Sholy sump'n nudder is de matter wid dat house, kaze all de times befo' dis, it been holler'n back at me, Heyo, yo'se'f!'

"Den Brer Rabbit wait little bit, en bimeby he holler one mo' time, 'Heyo, house!'

"Ole Brer Wolf try ter talk like he speck a house 'ud talk, en he holler back, 'Heyo, yo'se'f!'

"Brer Rabbit wunk at hisse'f. He 'low, 'Heyo, house! Whyn't you talk hoarse like you got a bad col'?'

"Den Brer Wolf holler back, hoarse ez he kin, 'Heyo, yo'se'f!'

"Dis make Brer Rabbit laugh twel a little mo' en he'd a drapt off'n dat ar 'simmon stump en hurt hisse'f.

"He 'low, 'Eh-eh, Brer Wolf! dat ain't nigh gwine ter do. You'll hatter stan' out in de rain a mighty long time 'fo' you kin talk hoarse ez dat house!'

"I let you know," continued Uncle Remus, laying his hand gently on the little boy's shoulder, "I let you know, Brer Wolf come a-slinkin' out, en made a break fer home. Atter dat, Brer Rabbit live a long time wid'out any er de yuther creeturs a-pesterin' un 'im!"

BROTHER RABBIT'S
ASTONISHING PRANK

"I 'speck dat 'uz de reas'n w'at make ole Brer Rabbit git 'long so well, kaze he aint copy atter none er de yuther creeturs," Uncle Remus continued, after a while. "W'en he make his disappearance 'fo' um, hit 'uz allers in some bran new place. Dey aint know wharbouts fer ter watch out fer 'im. He wuz de funniest creetur er de whole gang. Some folks moughter call him lucky, en yit, w'en he git in bad luck, hit look lak he mos' allers come out on top. Hit look mighty kuze now, but 'twa'n't kuse in dem days, kaze hit 'uz done gun up dat, strike 'im w'en you might en whar you would, Brer Rabbit wuz de soopless creetur gwine.

"Brother Rabbit's Astonishing Prank." From *Nights with Uncle Remus* by Joel Chandler Harris

"One time, he sorter tuck a notion, ole Brer Rabbit did, dat he'd pay Brer B'ar a call, en no sooner do de notion strike 'im dan he pick hisse'f up en put out fer Brer B'ar house."

"Why, I thought they were mad with each other," the little boy exclaimed.

"Brer Rabbit make he call w'en Brer B'ar en his fambly wuz off fum home," Uncle Remus explained, with a chuckle which was in the nature of a hearty tribute to the crafty judgment of Brother Rabbit.

"He sot down by de road, en he see um go by, —ole Brer B'ar en ole Miss B'ar, en der two twin-chilluns, w'ich one un um wuz name Kubs en de t'er one wuz name Klibs."

The little boy laughed, but the severe seriousness of Uncle Remus would have served for a study, as he continued:

"Ole Brer B'ar en Miss B'ar, dey went 'long ahead, en Kubs en Klibs, dey come shufflin' en scramblin' 'long behime. W'en Brer Rabbit see dis, he say ter hisse'f dat he 'speck he better go see how Brer B'ar gittin' on; en off he put. En 'twa'n't long n'er 'fo' he 'uz ransackin' de premuses same like he 'uz sho' 'nuff patter-roller. W'iles he wuz gwine 'roun' peepin' in yer en pokin' in dar, he got ter foolin' 'mong de shelfs, en a bucket er honey w'at Brer B'ar got hid in de cubbud fall down en spill on top er Brer Rabbit, en little mo'n he'd er bin drown. Fum head ter heels dat creetur wuz kiver'd wid honey; he wa'n't des only bedobble wid it, he wuz des kiver'd. He hatter set dar en let de natal sweetness drip outen he eyeballs 'fo' he kin see he han' befo' 'im, en den, atter he look 'roun' little, he say to hisse'f, sezee:

"'Heyo, yer! W'at I gwine do now? Ef I go out in de sunshine, de bumly-bees en de flies dey'll swom up'n take me, en if I stay yer, Brer B'ar'll come back en ketch me, en I dunner w'at in de name er gracious I gwine do.'

"Ennyhow, bimeby a notion strike Brer Rabbit, en he tip 'long twel he git in de woods, en w'en he git out dar, w'at do he do but roll in de leafs en trash en try fer ter rub de honey off'n 'im dat a-way. He roll, he did, en de leafs dey stick; Brer Rabbit roll, en de leafs dey stick, en he keep on rollin' en de leafs keep on stickin', twel after w'ile Brer Rabbit wuz de mos' owdashus-lookin' creetur w'at you ever sot eyes on.

En ef Miss Meadows en de gals could er seed 'im den en dar, dey wouldn't er bin no mo' Brer Rabbit call at der house; 'deed, en dat dey wouldn't.

"Brer Rabbit, he jump 'roun', he did, en try ter shake de leafs off'n 'im, but de leafs, dey aint gwine ter be shuck off. Brer Rabbit, he shake en he shiver, but de leafs dey stick; en de capers dat creetur cut up out dar in de woods by he own-alone se'f wuz scan'lous—dey wuz dat; dey wuz scan'lous.

"Brer Rabbit see dis wa'n't gwine ter do, en he 'low ter hisse'f dat he better be gittin' on todes home, en off he put. I 'speck you done year talk ez deze yer booggers w'at gits atter bad chilluns," continued Uncle Remus, in a tone so seriously confidential as to be altogether depressing; "well, den, des 'zactly dat a-way Brer Rabbit look, en ef you'd er seed 'im you'd er made sho' he de gran'-daddy er all de booggers. Brer Rabbit pace 'long, he did, en ev'y motion he make, de leafs dey'd go *swishy-swushy, splushy-splishy,* en, fum de fuss he make en de way he look, you'd er tuck 'im ter be de mos' suvvigus varment w'at disap-pear fum de face er de yeth sence ole man Noah let down de draw-bars er de ark en tu'n de creeturs loose; en I boun' ef you'd er struck up long wid 'im, you'd er been mighty good en glad ef you'd er got off wid dat.

"De fus' man w'at Brer Rabbit come up wid wuz ole Sis Cow, en no sooner is she lay eyes on 'im dan she h'ist up 'er tail in de elements, en put out like a pack er dogs wuz atter 'er. Dis make Brer Rabbit laff, kaze he know dat w'en a ole settle' 'oman like Sis Cow run 'stracted in de broad open day-time, dat dey mus' be sump'n' mighty kuse 'bout dem leafs en dat honey, en he keep on a-rackin' down de road. De nex' man w'at he meet wuz a black gal tollin' a whole passel er plantation shotes, en w'en de gal see Brer Rabbit come prancin' 'long, she fling down 'er basket er corn en des fa'rly fly, en de shotes, dey tuck thoo de woods, en sech n'er racket ez dey kick up wid der runnin', en der snortin', en der squealin' aint never bin year in dat settle-ment needer befo' ner since. Hit keep on dis a-way long ez Brer Rabbit meet anybody—dey des broke en run like de Ole Boy wuz atter um.

"C'ose, dis make Brer Rabbit feel monst'us biggity, en he 'low ter hisse'f dat he 'speck he better drap 'roun' en skummish in de neighbor-hoods er Brer Fox house. En w'iles he wuz stannin' dar runnin' dis 'roun' in he min', yer come old Brer B'ar en all er he fambly. Brer Rabbit, he git crossways de road, he did, en he sorter sidle todes um. Ole Brer B'ar, he stop en look, but Brer Rabbit, he keep on sidlin' todes um. Ole Miss B'ar, she stan' it long ez she kin, en den she fling down 'er parrysol en tuck a tree. Brer B'ar look lak he gwine ter stan' his groun', but Brer Rabbit he jump straight up in de a'r en gin hisse'f a shake, en, bless yo' soul, honey! ole Brer B'ar make a break, en dey tells me he to' down a whole panel er fence gittin' 'way fum dar. En ez ter Kubs en Klibs, dey tuck der hats in der han's, en dey went skaddlin' thoo de bushes des same ez a drove er hosses."

"And then what?" the little boy asked.

"Brer Rabbit p'raded on down de road," con-tinued Uncle Remus, "en bimeby yer come Brer Fox en Brer Wolf, fixin' up a plan fer ter nab Brer Rabbit, en dey wuz so intents on der confab dat dey got right on Brer Rabbit 'fo' dey seed 'im; but, gentermens! w'en dey is ketch a glimpse un 'im, dey gun 'im all de room he want. Brer Wolf, he try ter show off, he did, kase he wanter play big 'fo' Brer Fox, en he stop en ax Brer Rabbit who is he. Brer Rabbit, he jump up en down in de middle er de road, en holler out:

" 'I'm de Wull-er-de-Wust. I'm de Wull-er-de-Wust, en youer de man I'm atter!'

"Den Brer Rabbit jump up en down en make lak he gwine atter Brer Fox en Brer Wolf, en de way dem creeturs lit out fum dar wuz a cau-tion.

"Long time atter dat," continued Uncle Re-mus, folding his hands placidly in his lap, with the air of one who has performed a pleasant duty,—"long time atter dat, Brer Rabbit come up wid Brer Fox en Brer Wolf, en he git behime a stump, Brer Rabbit did, en holler out:

" 'I'm de Wull-er-de-Wust, en youer de mens I'm atter!'

"Brer Fox en Brer Wolf, dey broke, but 'fo' dey got outer sight en outer year'n', Brer Rabbit show hisse'f, he did, en laugh fit ter kill hisse'f. Atterwuds, Miss Meadows she year 'bout it, en de nex' time Brer Fox call, de gals dey up en giggle, en ax 'im ef he aint feard de Wull-er-de-Wust mought drap in."

MR. RABBIT
MEETS HIS MATCH AGAIN

"Dere wuz nudder man dat sorter play it sharp on Brer Rabbit," said Uncle Remus, as, by some mysterious process, he twisted a hog's bristle into the end of a piece of thread—an operation which the little boy watched with great interest. "In dem days," continued the old man, "de creeturs kyar'd on marters same ez fokes. Dey went inter fahmin', en I speck ef de troof wuz ter come out, dey kep' sto', en had der camp-meetin' times en der bobbycues' w'en de wedder wuz 'greeble."

Uncle Remus evidently thought that the little boy wouldn't like to hear of any further discomfiture of Brer Rabbit, who had come to be a sort of hero, and he was not mistaken.

"I thought the Terrapin was the only one that fooled the Rabbit," said the little boy, dismally.

"Hit's des like I tell you, honey. Dey ain't no smart man, 'cep' w'at dey's a smarter. Ef ole Brer Rabbit hadn't er got kotch up wid, de nabers 'ud er took 'im for a h'ant, en in dem times dey bu'nt witches 'fo' you could squinch yo' eyeballs. Dey did dat."

"Who fooled the Rabbit this time?" the little boy asked.

When Uncle Remus had the bristle "sot" in the thread, he proceeded with the story.

"One time Brer Rabbit en ole Brer Buzzard 'cluded dey'd sorter go snacks, en crap tergedder. Hit wuz a mighty good year, en de truck tu'n out monstus well, but bimeby, w'en de time come fer dividjun, hit come ter light dat ole Brer Buzzard ain't got nuthin'. De crap wuz all gone, en dey want nuthin' dar fer ter show fer it. Brer Rabbit, he make like he in a wuss fix'n Brer Buzzard, en he mope 'roun', he did, like he fear'd dey gwineter sell 'im out.

"Brer Buzzard, he ain't sayin' nuthin', but he keep up a monstus thinkin', en one day he come 'long en holler en tell Brer Rabbit dat he done fine rich gole-mine des' cross de river.

"'You come en go 'longer me, Brer Rabbit,' sez Brer Tukky Buzzard, sezee. 'I'll scratch en you kin grabble, en 'tween de two un us we'll make short wuk er dat gole-mine,' sezee.

"Brer Rabbit, he wuz high up fer de job, but he study en study, he did, how he gwineter git 'cross de water, kaze ev'y time he git his foot wet all de fambly kotch cole. Den he up'n ax Brer Buzzard how he gwine do, en Brer Buzzard he up'n say dat he kyar Brer Rabbit 'cross, en wid dat ole Brer Buzzard, he squot down, he did, en spread his wings, en Brer Rabbit, he mounted, en up dey riz." There was a pause.

"What did the Buzzard do then?" asked the little boy.

"Dey riz," continued Uncle Remus, "en w'en dey lit, dey lit in de top er de highest sorter pine, en de pine w'at dey lit in wuz growin' on er ilun, en de ilun wuz in de middle er de river, wid de deep water runnin' all 'roun'. Dey ain't mo'n lit 'fo' Brer Rabbit, he know w'ich way de win' 'uz blowin', en by de time ole Brer Buzzard got his-se'f ballunce on a lim', Brer Rabbit, he up'n say, sezee:

"'W'iles we er res'n here, Brer Buzzard, en bein's you bin so good, I got sump'n fer ter tell you,' sezee. 'I got a gole-mine er my own, one w'at I make myse'f, en I speck we better go back ter mine 'fo' we bodder 'longer yone,' sezee.

"Den ole Brer Buzzard, he laff, he did, twel he shake, en Brer Rabbit, he sing out:

"'Hole on, Brer Buzzard! Don't flop yo' wings w'en you laff, kaze den if you duz, sump'n 'ill drap fum up yer, en my gole-mine won't do you no good, en needer will yone do me no good.'

"But 'fo' dey got down fum dar, Brer Rabbit done tole all 'bout de crap, en he hatter promus fer ter 'vide fa'r en squar. So Brer Buzzard, he kyar 'im back, en Brer Rabbit he walk weak in de knees a mont' atterwuds."

"Mr. Rabbit Meets His Match Again." From *Uncle Remus, His Songs and His Sayings* by Joel Chandler Harris

Of all forms of fiction, the fable is the most pedantic and the least appealing to children. It is a lesson in behavior, a kind of sugar-coated moral pill, large doses of which are hard to take. Yet presented occasionally, among other and livelier kinds of stories, fables are not unpalatable. They offer a shrewd appraisal of motives and behavior. Their canny and satiric comments on folly are amusing, and wise behavior is picturesquely presented. Such fables as "The Dog in the Manger," "The Wolf in Sheep's Clothing," "The Fox and the Crow," and "The Hare and the Tortoise" are never forgotten. These and many others have come to occupy a permanent place in our thinking and our speech. Children

OLD MORALITIES: THE FABLES

should know the fables because they contain the distilled wisdom of the ages in striking and memorable form.

Fables might be defined as brief narratives which attempt to make abstract ideas of good or bad, wise or foolish behavior, concrete and sufficiently striking to be understood and remembered. But because they are concerned with abstract ideas of good and evil they are not readily understood by most children until the episodes and their significance have been talked over. Sometimes the characters are men, sometimes, the elements, but chiefly, they are animals. Whatever they are, the characters of a fable are as impersonal and abstract as an algebraic equation. It is never Peter Rabbit with his little brothers and sisters, Flopsy, Mopsy, and Cottontail. It is merely RABBIT and you never care whether RABBIT has a family or is an orphan. He is simply RABBIT. This abstract, impersonal quality of the fable does not appeal to small children, and the obvious intention of teaching a moral lesson grows tiresome if the fables are used too often or with too heavy a hand.

Sources and values

The great fable sources are Aesop, *The Panchatantra,* the *Jatakas,* and La Fontaine,[1] but to most English-speaking people, fables and Aesop are synonymous. A fourteenth-century monk by the name of Planudes added to a collection of fables, supposedly by Aesop, a story of the man's life. Its authenticity is now considered doubtful, and perhaps there never was such a man as the Greek slave Aesop. Picturesque legends about him continued to grow, however, and we like to ascribe those wise and witty stories to some specific source. So, authentic or not, his name goes right on appearing on each new edition and people keep right on hoping that it was an obscure slave, ugly and perhaps deformed as the legends describe him, who collected these priceless tales which mirror man's foibles so relentlessly.

From the time they were collected, translated into Latin in the first or third centuries, and used as a textbook in the medieval schools, the popularity of Aesop's fables has never waned. Undoubtedly adults sensed their teaching values and offered them to children and youth, generation after generation, as guides to wise conduct. Today, there are innumerable beautiful editions of Aesop's fables illustrated by distinguished artists. Appealing as these books are, children should not be expected to sit down and read

[1] See May Hill Arbuthnot, *Children and Books,* pp. 282–288.

them as a whole. They are tiresome when tackled in such a fashion. Fables are for occasional use and they should be presented and discussed with a light touch and the minimum of pedantry. But as carriers of the moral code they are still unforgettable.

Using fables with children

Fables, because they are abstractions, brief sermons on morality, are the least appealing of all story types to children. They are attempting to make abstract ideas striking enough to be understood and remembered.

For young children, five- to nine- or ten-years-old, use anywhere from two to five or six fables a year. Choose those that have the maximum story interest, like "The Lion and the Mouse," and talk the story over without moralizing, just to make sure that the children appreciate the fact that sometimes very small creatures may be useful and helpful and are not to be scorned because they are small and seemingly unimportant.

With older children, the purpose of the fable may be discussed frankly. Then it is fun to have one child read a fable to the whole group and see if the class can make up a pithy moral. Let these upper grade or high school students discover also that fables are still being written. Read them the "Copy-Kitten," p. 281 or "Nothing at All," p. 281 or even Hans Christian Andersen's "The Ugly Duckling," p. 311, to illustrate this point. They will also find it interesting to compare different versions of the same fable, for example, Aesop's "The Fox and the Crow," p. 225 and La Fontaine's version of this tale, p. 232.

When they are still older, children will begin to see how the fable may have grown out of the proverb, which is the most highly condensed commentary on human folly or wisdom, or may develop into an allegory. They will see its similarity to the parable, which also tells a brief story from which a moral truth may be inferred. But in this field of abstract virtues and moral lessons, children are easily bewildered and never too comfortable. The baffled child who defines an allegory as ". . . a story where everything is what it ain't," should be a lesson to grownups. A few fables, a few abstractions go a long way with children.

Aesop's fables

*"The Lion and the Mouse" and "The Town Mouse and the Country
Mouse" are well liked by the five- and six-year-olds because they are simple little
stories and the morals are not too obtrusive. The other fables might
well appear in almost any order you like, three or four a year. Perhaps the moral
of "The Fox and the Grapes," "The Wolf in Sheep's Clothing," "The
Milkmaid and Her Pail," and "The Dog in the Manger" are a little too subtle for
young children and are better reserved for the oldest children. Be
sure to bring from the library some of the illustrated editions of the fables. John
Averill, who illustrated the fables in this section, has stylized the characters with great humor, and after all, the fables are highly stylized stories. It might
be an interesting art project for the oldest children to compare the
fable pictures in three or four major editions and then try some of their own.*

THE HARE WITH MANY FRIENDS

A Hare was very popular with the other beasts who all claimed to be her friends. But one day she heard the hounds approaching and hoped to escape them by the aid of her many friends. So she went to the horse, and asked him to carry her away from the hounds on his back. But he declined, stating that he had important work to do for his master. He felt sure, he said, that all her other friends would come to her assistance. She then applied to the bull, and hoped that he would repel the hounds with his horns. The bull replied: "I am very sorry, but I have an appointment with a lady; but I feel sure that our friend the goat will do what you want." The goat, however, feared that his back might do her some harm if he took her upon it. The ram, he felt sure, was the proper friend to apply to. So she went to the ram and told him the case. The ram replied: "Another time, my dear friend. I do not like to interfere on the present occasion, as hounds have been known to eat sheep as well as hares." The Hare then applied, as a last hope, to the calf, who regretted that he was unable to help her, as he did not like to take the responsibility upon himself, as so many older persons than himself had declined the task. By this time the

"The Hare with Many Friends" and "The Ant and the Grasshopper." From *The Fables of Aesop*, edited by Joseph Jacobs, Macmillan, 1950. By permission of The Macmillan Company, New York and Macmillan & Co. Ltd., London

hounds were quite near, and the Hare took to her heels and luckily escaped.

"He that has many friends has no friends."

THE ANT

AND THE GRASSHOPPER

In a field one summer's day a Grasshopper was hopping about, chirping and singing to its heart's content. An Ant passed by, bearing along with great toil a grain of corn he was taking to the nest.

"Why not come and chat with me," said the Grasshopper, "instead of toiling and moiling in that way?"

"I am helping to lay up food for the winter," said the Ant, "and recommend you to do the same."

"Why bother about winter?" said the Grasshopper. "We have got plenty of food at present." But the Ant went on its way and continued its toil.

When the winter came the Grasshopper had no food, and found itself dying of hunger, while it saw the ants distributing every day corn and grain from the stores they had collected in the summer.

"It is best to prepare for the days of necessity."

THE FOX AND THE CROW

A Fox once saw a Crow fly off with a piece of cheese in its beak and settle on a branch of a tree. "That's for me, as I am a Fox," said Master Reynard, and he walked up to the foot of the tree. "Good-day, Mistress Crow," he cried. "How well you are looking today: how glossy your feathers; how bright your eye. I feel sure your voice must surpass that of other birds, just as your figure does; let me hear but one song from you that I may greet you as the Queen of Birds." The Crow lifted up her head and began to caw her best, but the moment she opened her mouth the piece of cheese fell to the ground, only to be snapped up by Master Fox. "That will do," said he. "That was all I wanted. In exchange for your cheese I will give you a piece of advice for the future——

"Do not trust flatterers."

THE LION AND THE MOUSE

Once when a Lion was asleep a little Mouse began running up and down upon him; this soon wakened the Lion, who placed his huge paw upon him, and opened his big jaws to swallow him. "Pardon, O King," cried the little

"The Fox and the Crow" and "The Lion and the Mouse." From *The Fables of Aesop*, edited by Joseph Jacobs, Macmillan, 1950. By permission of The Macmillan Company, New York, and Macmillan & Co. Ltd., London

Mouse; "forgive me this time, I shall never forget it: who knows but what I may be able to do you a turn some of these days?" The Lion was so tickled at the idea of the Mouse being able to help him, that he lifted up his paw and let him go. Some time after the Lion was caught in a trap, and the hunters, who desired to carry him alive to the King, tied him to a tree while they went in search of a wagon to carry him on. Just then the little Mouse happened to pass by, and seeing the sad plight in which the Lion was, went up to him and soon gnawed away the ropes that bound the King of the Beasts. "Was I not right?" said the little Mouse.

"Little friends may prove great friends."

THE DOG IN THE MANGER

A Dog looking out for its afternoon nap jumped into the Manger of an Ox and lay there cosily upon the straw. But soon the Ox, returning from its afternoon work, came up to the Manger and wanted to eat some of the straw. The Dog in a rage, being awakened from its slumber, stood up and barked at the Ox, and whenever it came near attempted to bite it. At

last the Ox had to give up the hope of getting at the straw, and went away muttering:

"Ah, people often grudge others what they cannot enjoy themselves."

"Hercules and the Waggoner" and "The Dog in the Manger." From *The Fables of Aesop*, edited by Joseph Jacobs, Macmillan, 1950. By permission of The Macmillan Company, New York and Macmillan & Co. Ltd., London

HERCULES AND THE WAGGONER

A waggoner was once driving a heavy load along a very muddy way. At last he came to a part of the road where the wheels sank halfway into the mire, and the more the horses pulled, the deeper sank the wheels. So the Waggoner threw down his whip, and knelt down and prayed to Hercules the Strong. "O Hercules, help me in this my hour of distress," quoth he. But Hercules appeared to him, and said: "Tut, man, don't sprawl there. Get up and put your shoulder to the wheel."

"The gods help them that help themselves."

THE SHEPHERD'S BOY

There was once a young Shepherd Boy who tended his sheep at the foot of a mountain near a dark forest. It was rather lonely for him all day, so he thought upon a plan by which he could get a little company and some excitement. He rushed down towards the village calling out "Wolf, Wolf," and the villagers came out to meet him, and some of them stopped with him for a considerable time. This pleased the boy so much that a few days afterwards he tried the same trick, and again the villagers came to his help. But shortly after this a Wolf actually did come out from the forest, and began to worry the sheep, and the boy of course cried out "Wolf, Wolf," still louder than before. But this time the villagers, who had been fooled twice before, thought the boy was again deceiving them, and nobody stirred to come to his help. So the Wolf made a good meal off the boy's flock, and when the boy complained, the wise man of the village said:

"A liar will not be believed, even when he speaks the truth."

THE TOWN MOUSE

AND THE COUNTRY MOUSE

Now you must know that a Town Mouse once upon a time went on a visit to his cousin in the country. He was rough and ready, this cousin, but he loved his town friend and made him heartily welcome. Beans and bacon, cheese and bread, were all he had to offer, but he offered them freely. The Town Mouse rather turned up his long nose at this country fare, and said: "I cannot understand, Cousin, how you can put up with such poor food as this, but of course you cannot expect anything better in the country; come you with me and I will show you how to live. When you have been in town a week you will wonder how you could ever have stood a country life." No sooner said than done: the two mice set off for the town and arrived at the Town Mouse's residence late at night. "You will want some refreshment after our long journey," said the polite Town Mouse, and took his friend into the grand dining-room. There they found the remains of a fine feast, and soon the two mice were eating up jellies and cakes and all that was nice. Suddenly they heard growling and barking. "What is that?" said the Country Mouse. "It is only the dogs of the house," answered the other. "Only!" said the Country Mouse. "I do not like that music at my dinner." Just at that moment the door flew open, in came two huge mastiffs, and the two mice had to scamper down and run off. "Good-bye, Cousin," said the Country Mouse. "What! going so soon?" said the other. "Yes, he replied;

"Better beans and bacon in peace than cakes and ale in fear."

THE FROG AND THE OX

"Oh father," said a little Frog to the big one sitting by the side of a pool, "I have seen such a terrible monster! It was as big as a mountain, with horns on its head, and a long tail, and it had hoofs divided in two."

"Tush, child, tush," said the old Frog, "that was only Farmer White's Ox. It isn't so big either; he may be a little taller than I, but I could easily make myself quite as broad; just you see." So he blew himself out, and blew himself out, and blew himself out. "Was he as big as that?" asked he.

"Oh, much bigger than that," said the young Frog.

Again the old one blew himself out, and asked the young one if the Ox was as big as that.

"Bigger, father, bigger," was the reply.

So the Frog took a deep breath, and blew and blew and blew, and swelled and swelled and swelled. And then he said: "I'm sure the Ox is not as big as ——" But at this moment he burst.

"Self-conceit may lead to self-destruction."

"The Shepherd's Boy," "The Town Mouse and the Country Mouse," and "The Frog and the Ox." From *The Fables of Aesop*, edited by Joseph Jacobs, Macmillan, 1950. By permission of The Macmillan Company, New York and Macmillan & Co. Ltd., London

BELLING THE CAT

Long ago, the mice held a general council to consider what measures they could take to outwit their common enemy, the Cat. Some said this, and some said that; but at last a young mouse got up and said he had a proposal to make, which he thought would meet the case. "You will all agree," said he, "that our chief danger consists in the sly and treacherous manner in which the enemy approaches us. Now, if we could receive some signal of her approach, we could easily escape from her. I venture, therefore, to propose that a small bell be procured, and attached by a ribbon round the neck of the Cat. By this means we should always know when she was about, and could easily retire while she was in the neighbourhood."

This proposal met with general applause, until an old mouse got up and said: "That is all very well, but who is to bell the Cat?" The mice looked at one another and nobody spoke. Then the old mouse said:

"It is easy to propose impossible remedies."

"Belling the Cat," "The Dog and the Shadow," and "The Wind and the Sun." From *The Fables of Aesop*, edited by Joseph Jacobs, Macmillan, 1950. By permission of The Macmillan Company, New York and Macmillan & Co., Ltd., London

THE DOG AND THE SHADOW

It happened that a Dog had got a piece of meat and was carrying it home in his mouth to eat it in peace. Now on his way home he had to cross a plank lying across a running brook. As he crossed, he looked down and saw his own shadow reflected in the water beneath. Thinking it was another dog with another piece of meat, he made up his mind to have that also. So he made a snap at the shadow in the water, but as he opened his mouth the piece of meat fell out, dropped into the water and was never seen more.

"Beware lest you lose the substance by grasping at the shadow."

THE WIND AND THE SUN

The Wind and the Sun were disputing which was the stronger. Suddenly they saw a traveler coming down the road, and the Sun said: "I see a way to decide our dispute. Whichever of us can cause that traveler to take off his cloak shall be regarded as the stronger. You begin." So the Sun retired behind a cloud, and the Wind began to blow as hard as he could upon the traveler. But the harder he blew the more closely did the traveler wrap his cloak round him, till at last the Wind had to give up in despair. Then the Sun came out and shone in all his glory upon the traveler, who soon found it too hot to walk with his cloak on.

"Kindness effects more than Severity."

THE FOX AND THE GRAPES

One hot summer's day a Fox was strolling through an orchard till he came to a bunch of Grapes just ripening on a vine which had been trained over a lofty branch. "Just the thing to quench my thirst," quoth he. Drawing back a few paces, he took a run and a jump, and just missed the bunch. Turning round again with a One, Two, Three, he jumped up, but with no greater success. Again and again he tried after the tempting morsel, but at last had to give it up, and walked away with his nose in the air, saying: "I am sure they are sour."

"It is easy to despise what you cannot get."

THE CROW AND THE PITCHER

A thirsty Crow found a Pitcher with some water in it, but so little was there that, try as she might, she could not reach it with her beak, and it seemed as though she would die of thirst within sight of the remedy. At last she hit upon a clever plan. She began dropping pebbles into the Pitcher, and with each pebble the water rose a little higher until at last it reached the brim, and the knowing bird was enabled to quench her thirst.

"Necessity is the mother of invention."

"The Fox and the Grapes," "The Crow and the Pitcher," and "The Milkmaid and Her Pail." From *The Fables of Aesop*, edited by Joseph Jacobs, Macmillan, 1950. By permission of The Macmillan Company, New York and Macmillan & Co. Ltd., London

THE MILKMAID AND HER PAIL

A farmer's daughter had been out to milk the cows, and was returning to the dairy carrying her pail of milk upon her head. As she walked along, she fell a-musing after this fashion: "The milk in this pail will provide me with cream, which I will make into butter and take to market to sell. With the money I will buy a number of eggs, and these, when hatched, will produce chickens, and by and by I shall have quite a large poultry-yard. Then I shall sell some of my fowls, and with the money which they will bring in I will buy myself a new gown, which I shall wear when I go to the fair; and all the young fellows will admire it, and come and make love to me, but I shall toss my head and have nothing to say to them." Forgetting all about the pail, and suiting the action to the word, she tossed her head. Down went the pail, all the milk was spilled and all her fine castles in the air vanished in a moment!

"Do not count your chickens before they are hatched."

THE WOLF
IN SHEEP'S CLOTHING

A Wolf found great difficulty in getting at the sheep owing to the vigilance of the shepherd and his dogs. But one day it found the skin of a sheep that had been flayed and thrown aside, so it put it on over its own pelt and strolled down among the sheep. The Lamb that belonged to the sheep, whose skin the Wolf was wearing, began to follow the Wolf in the Sheep's clothing; so, leading the Lamb a little apart, he soon made a meal off her, and for some time he succeeded in deceiving the sheep, and enjoying hearty meals.

"Appearances are deceptive."

THE HARE AND THE TORTOISE

The Hare was once boasting of his speed before the other animals. "I have never yet been beaten," said he, "when I put forth my full speed. I challenge any one here to race with me."

The Tortoise said quietly: "I accept your challenge."

"That is a good joke," said the Hare; "I could dance round you all the way."

"Keep your boasting till you've beaten," answered the Tortoise. "Shall we race?"

So a course was fixed and a start was made. The Hare darted almost out of sight at once, but soon stopped and, to show his contempt for the Tortoise, lay down to have a nap. The Tortoise plodded on and plodded on, and when the Hare awoke from his nap, he saw the Tortoise just near the winning post and could not run up in time to save the race.

"Plodding wins the race."

"The Wolf in Sheep's Clothing" and "The Hare and the Tortoise." From *The Fables of Aesop*, edited by Joseph Jacobs, Macmillan, 1950. By permission of The Macmillan Company, New York and Macmillan & Co. Ltd., London

Fables of Bidpai

The fables in the East Indian collections are much longer and more like stories with morals than they are like the spare little abstractions we know as Aesop's fables. The Panchatantra was really a textbook on "the wise conduct of life" and contained stories within stories. Maude Barrows Dutton retold thirty-four of the best-known tales from The Panchatantra and, with the inimitable illustrations of E. Boyd Smith, made an attractive little book called The Tortoise and the Geese and Other Fables of Bidpai. The other source of Indian fables is the group called the Jatakas, which are stories of Gautama Buddha in his progressive reincarnations in the forms of different animals. When references to the Buddha are omitted, these stories become good talking beast tales, and therefore the selections from the Jatakas are included with the folk tales.

THE PARTRIDGE AND THE CROW

A Crow flying across a road saw a Partridge strutting along the ground.

"What a beautiful gait that Partridge has!" said the Crow. "I must try to see if I can walk like him."

She alighted behind the Partridge and tried for a long time to learn to strut. At last the Partridge turned around and asked the Crow what she was about.

"Do not be angry with me," replied the Crow. "I have never before seen a bird who walks as beautifully as you can, and I am trying to learn to walk like you."

"Foolish bird!" responded the Partridge. "You are a Crow, and should walk like a Crow. You would look silly indeed if you were to strut like a partridge."

But the Crow went on trying to learn to strut, until finally she had forgotten her own gait, and she never learned that of the Partridge.

THE TYRANT WHO BECAME A JUST RULER

In olden times there lived a King, who was so cruel and unjust towards his subjects that he was always called The Tyrant. So heartless was he that his people used to pray night and day that they might have a new king. One day, much to their surprise, he called his people together and said to them,——

"My dear subjects, the days of my tyranny are over. Henceforth you shall live in peace and happiness, for I have decided to try to rule henceforth justly and well."

The King kept his word so well that soon he was known throughout the land as The Just King. By and by one of his favorites came to him and said,——

"Your Majesty, I beg of you to tell me how it was that you had this change of heart towards your people?"

And the King replied,——

"As I was galloping through my forests one afternoon, I caught sight of a hound chasing a fox. The fox escaped into his hole, but not until he had been bitten by the dog so badly that he would be lame for life. The hound, returning home, met a man who threw a stone at him, which broke his leg. The man had not gone far when a horse kicked him and broke his leg. And the horse, starting to run, fell into a hole and broke his leg. Here I came to my senses, and resolved to change my rule. 'For surely,' I said to myself, 'he who doeth evil will sooner or later be overtaken by evil.'"

Fables of La Fontaine

In France the fables were turned into verse by a skilled poet, Jean de La Fontaine, a contemporary of Charles Perrault. The sources used by La Fontaine were Latin versions of Aesop and The Fables of Bidpai, *and the versions of Marie de France, who introduced the fable into France in the twelfth century. La Fontaine's rhymed moralities were so popular in the France of his day that people called him "le fablier," the "fable-teller." To translate his witty French verses into English verse is to lose some of their gaiety and charm, so they are usually translated into prose. "The Grasshopper and the Ant" is an example of a metrical translation and "The Fox and the Crow" and "The Cricket and the Ant" are in the vigorous prose of Margaret Wise Brown. In "The Fox and the Crow" she has used a sing-and-say style that suggests the original verse form but tells the story clearly.*

THE FOX AND THE CROW

Mister Crow sat on the limb of a tree with a big piece of cheese in his mouth.

Old Mister Fox smelled the cheese from a long way off. And he came to the foot of the tree and spoke to the crow.

"Good morning, Mr. Coal Black Crow,
How beautiful and shining your feathers grow,
Black as the night and bright as the sun,
If you sing as well, your fortune is won."

At these words Mr. Crow joyously opened his beak to sing his creaky old crow song.

And the cheese fell down to the ground. The fox snapped it up in his mouth.

As he ran away he called back over his bushy tail, "My dear Mr. Crow, learn from this how every flatterer lives at the expense of anybody who will listen to him. This lesson is well worth the loss of a cheese to you."

THE CRICKET AND THE ANT

All through the summer the cricket sang. He sang in the grass when they planted the seed. And he sang in the grass when the flowers bloomed. Why should a cricket work on a sunny day, when he could sing and dance and play? In the early fall when the seeds were blowing in the air the cricket chirped his song. But when winter came and the cold winds blew, the merry little cricket had nothing to eat and nowhere to go.

So he hopped to the house of his neighbor, the ant, who had worked all summer storing up her food for the winter. He knocked at the door and cried, "Oh, dear! Oh, dear! I am starving, hungry, starving! Kind ant, will you lend me some seeds to live on until spring? And I will give you five seeds in the spring for every seed that you give me today."

But the ant was practical—as ants are.

"What did you do in the summer when the days were warm and the flowers were going to seed?" asked the ant. "What did you do in the early fall when the seeds were blowing through the air?"

"Night and day I sang," said the cricket.

"You sang!" said the ant. "Then now you can dance to your own music. I will eat the seed I gathered and the house I have built will keep me warm. Maybe your dancing will keep you warm in the snow."

THE GRASSHOPPER AND
THE ANT

A grasshopper gay
Sang the Summer away,
And found herself poor
By the winter's first roar.
Of meat and of bread,
Not a morsel she had!
So a-begging she went,
To her neighbour the ant,
  For the loan of some wheat,
  Which would serve her to eat,
Till the season came round.
  "I will pay, you," she saith
  "On an animal's faith,

Double weight in the pound
Ere the harvest be bound."
The ant is a friend
  (And here she might mend)
  Little given to lend.
"How spent you the summer?"
  Quoth she, looking shame
  At the borrowing dame.
"Night and day to each comer
I sang if you please."
  "You sang! I'm at ease;
For 'tis plain at a glance,
Now, Ma'am, you must dance."

Myth and epic are a part of that anonymous stream of folklore which includes the folk tales and the fables. All these helped to weld people together with a body of common beliefs, customs, morals, and finally a hero cult. They were indeed the "cement of society," holding it together with a moral code.

Origin of the myth

Mythological stories strike the modern reader as a kind of grown-up fairy tale, strangely beautiful and unearthly, a world of sky dwellers who

GODS AND MEN: MYTH AND EPIC

leave their bright Olympus, now and then, to visit dazzled earth creatures. Actually, such stories are only a part of the varied tales included in the whole body of myth. Taken as a whole, myth attempts to explain in complex symbols:

(1) cosmic phenomena (e.g., how the earth and sky came to be separated); (2) peculiarities of natural history (e.g., why rain follows the cries or activities of certain birds); (3) the origins of human civilization (e.g., through the beneficent action of a culture-hero like

Prometheus); or (4) the origin of social or religious custom or the nature and history of objects of worship.[1]

The stories range from little *why* stories to the most involved and sometimes unpleasant stories of the gods' ways with man or with each other told in symbols which are incomprehensible to children. In spite of the fact that many of the myths because of their complexity and eroticism are unfit for youngsters, there still remain many excellent stories which are enjoyed by children.

The developmental stages of myth-making are interesting because they not only help to explain the variety of the stories, but also help to guide our selection of those that children are most likely to understand and enjoy. No one knows how myth began, except that man seems always to have had the capacity for wondering about himself and his environment. In an age when nature and society were not areas of objective study in our modern scientific sense, but were, instead, areas of unquestioning acceptance, primitive man simply used his imagination to explain their peculiarities. So, the first stage of myth-making was probably submission to and worship of some inexplicable, impersonal force which caused the crops to grow, the rivers to flow, and man to live and die in his appointed time.

The second stage may have followed hard upon the first—the stage of giving body to this impersonal force, personifying it as an animal or a man. One of our American Indian tribes has "Old Man Coyote" among its nature deities, and, for the ancient Greeks, the god Apollo became the embodiment of all the warmth, power, and beauty of the sun. In this personification stage of myth-making, it was natural for men to attribute to their gods a nature like their own on a magnified scale. So it is the anger of a god which accounts for thunderbolts or causes raging storms at sea, and the god must be propitiated. There were so many phenomena to be explained that the Greeks developed more and more gods, of major and minor importance, until G. K. Chesterton sums up their polytheistic mythology by commenting that "the Greeks could not see trees for dryads."

[1] William Reginald Halliday, "Folklore," *Encyclopaedia Britannica*

This multiplication of deities led to the third stage of myth-making, the development of relationships among the gods and the limitations of the powers of each one. In Greek myth, for example, Zeus (Jove or Jupiter)[2] was all powerful; Hera (Juno) was his wife and a jealous guardian of the marriage state; Poseidon (Neptune) ruled the sea, and so the development of relationships and assignment of special powers continued down to those beguiling little creatures of the supernatural world, the local gods of rivers, springs, and groves, and the little dryads, satyrs, and fawns, who followed in the wake of Pan. Unfortunately, the limitation of godly prerogatives led to the same kind of chicanery, squabbles, and warfare that man himself was busily waging on earth. These mythical creatures displayed weaknesses on a grandiose scale sadly like man's own foibles.

The fourth stage of myth-making began when the powers of each god were extended to include certain abstract virtues, so that the god became less human and more of a symbolic figure. Apollo, for instance, began as a sun god, a beautiful young man who daily drove his fiery chariot across the sky. But in this fourth stage, he became a god of health and healing, the patron of physicians. Then, the idea of healing and health was expanded to rites of purification, and the god became a symbol for the abstract idea of purity.

The conversion of these earthy, man-made gods into symbols of moral virtues gave rise to the last and most advanced stage of myth-making, the development of a priesthood, temples, and a ritual of worship. The Apollo myth and other Greek myths reached this last stage of development, but among less civilized peoples myth-making stops at any one of the earlier stages and their myths remain correspondingly primitive.

Kinds of myth

The varying stories of the gods grew, then, out of the various levels of myth-making. The simplest stories, the *why* or *pourquoi* tales, emerge from that first explanatory stage. "Clytie" is the story of why the sunflower turns to the sun

[2] For a fuller list of the Greek and Roman names of the gods and the special powers of each, see May Hill Arbuthnot, *Children and Books*, p. 297.

and "Arachne" explains why spiders spin. Our American Indians have innumerable stories, such as "Why the Woodpecker Has a Red Head."

In both the Greek and Norse mythologies the *why* stories became more complex as the myth itself developed into its second and third stages and grew steadily more symbolic and abstract. The beautiful Greek story "Demeter and Persephone" (Ceres and Proserpine) tells, in symbols, the story of the changing seasons. Demeter, goddess of agriculture, loses her daughter Persephone, or grain, to Hades, the god who rules the dark underground world. The conclusion of the story explains why there is winter on the earth for half of the year. Children accept this story as a kind of super fairy tale and would certainly never catch its seasonal significance if it were not pointed out to them. This is true of the two similar stories in this volume—the Norse "The Death of Balder" and the desert Indian story "Little Burnt-Face."

As man advanced into later myth-making stages, the *why* stories not only became more symbolic and complex but they turned, presently, into full-fledged allegories. King Midas is the personification of greed for gold, and the allegory shows the punishment that follows this offense. Philemon and Baucis, who stand for simple kindness and goodness, are tenderly rewarded by their visitors from Olympus. At precisely what point the explanatory and symbolic character of the *why* story became pure allegory is not important. The changes merely call attention to the progression in complexity, significance, and difficulty to be found in myth.

Another group of stories concerns *the ways of the gods with men* and includes both tales which are best suited and those least appropriate to children. Such tales as "Midas" and "Baucis and Philemon" are delightful, and their meaning is evident. But stories dealing with the gods' amatory adventures among mortals and the revenge their jealous spouses wreak on their rivals are obviously unsuitable for children's reading fare.

This is also true of many of the stories concerned with *the ways of the gods with other gods*. Repellent tales of the creation, matings of brothers and sisters, matings with monsters, and the birth of more monsters, infidelity, jealousy, revenge, are all to be found in this group of stories.

There are noble stories among them, too, but they are often expressed in erotic symbols or ones too difficult for youngsters. For instance, Prometheus, who dared the wrath of the gods to bring fire to man, is so noble a figure of sacrifice that poets have used the story repeatedly. But its symbolism is at once too meaningful and too difficult for children to grasp.

The value of the myths

There is, then, in myth as in the folk tales a great body of material which is adult in form and concept. The myths selected for this collection are the simpler tales—*why* stories, allegories, and a few tales of gods and men. The Greek and Roman stories predominate not only because they are, on the whole, more interesting but also because they are the source of innumerable allusions which the child will encounter now and later on. The modern child sees Mercury or his winged sandals adorning railroad terminals and automobile advertisements. Minerva and her owl stare down at him in libraries. Venus rising from her seashell appears on advertisements for bath salts, and the child eats his morning cereal, a word which goes back to Ceres. Not to know something of Greek mythology is to be deprived of a rich source of linguistic, literary, artistic, and even commercial reference.

It is hoped that this small selection of myth will send teachers and children to whole books of mythology, to be used in connection with their study of a people or just for delight in the stories themselves. For to know the beauty of Olympus or Valhalla and to encounter the gods at their best is to dream with them some of man's ancient dreams of how splendid life may be for those who dare greatly. And some of these old dreams have come true. Icarus today has mastered the air, and modern Phaetons drive their chariots coolly across the sky and do not perish. These are splendid dreams for children to share, couched in symbols whose meaning will grow with the children's maturity.

Epics and Hero Tales

The great epics of literature are book-size collections of tales, far too long to include in such a volume as this. Instead, "The Curse of Polyphemus" one of the stories from the *Odyssey,* and a hero tale "Little John and the Tanner of Blyth" have been included. These samples will, it is hoped, lead children to the collections from which these stories were taken. For to read an epic is to live, day after day, with greatness, and such an experience is good for young spirits.

The epic grew out of or along with myth and consists of a cycle of stories about some human hero, buffeted by gods and men, who suffers greatly and endures staunchly to the end. Myth is still with us in the early epics, for the gods apparently leave their own affairs in Olympus for the express purpose of interfering with man's adventures on earth. But in epics the center of interest shifts from the gods to the human hero, from Olympus to earth. After both the gods and Olympus had faded from man's dreams, culture heroes still excited man's imagination and gained his belief. Tales of greatness would cluster about a single name until a Roland or a Robin Hood assumed the impressive stature of the epic hero even without the background of warring gods.

The epic is strongly national in its presentation of human character. Odysseus may never have lived, but he is the embodiment of the Greek ideals of manly courage, sagacity, beauty, and endurance. Sigurd is the personification of the Norse code of heroism. King Arthur represents chivalry, and Robin Hood, the English love of freedom and justice as well as the ideal of lusty, jovial manhood. Study the epic hero of a nation and you will learn a great deal about the moral code of that nation and era.

Not all epics are suitable for children, but some of them provide a literary and emotional experience as unforgettable as it is precious. *Robin Hood* is certainly the prime favorite with elementary school children, with the *Odyssey* next in appeal. It is probable that *King Arthur, Roland,* the *Iliad,* and perhaps the *Sigurd Saga* are better postponed for the days of adolescence, although if told to children, the Sigurd stories are well liked and so are many of the Arthur cycle. The personification of a great ideal in one hero, the sweep and excitement of epic action, the continuity of the adventures, and the nobility of the stories—these are epic qualities for which there are no substitutes.

Greek and Roman myth and epic

Myth introduces children to a new world of dreams and magic,
where gods and goddesses replace fairies, and golden Olympus becomes
a "land of heart's desire" on a grand scale. Greek myth has the bright beauty
of a southern country and Norse myth the somber, heroic qualities of the north.
Both are for children of eleven and older, with only a few stories
simple enough for the nines or tens. These stories may be used to intro-
duce children to the field of mythology, or to furnish religious background
of a people, or just for their charm and entertainment values.

CLYTIE

The maiden in the process of transformation is an interest-subject for illustration.

Clytie was a water-nymph and in love with Apollo, who made her no return. So she pined away, sitting all day long upon the cold ground,

"Clytie." From *A Book of Myths,* selections from Bulfinch's *Age of Fable.* Copyright, 1942, by The Macmillan Company and used with their permission

with her unbound tresses streaming over her shoulders. Nine days she sat and tasted neither food nor drink. She gazed on the sun when he rose, and as he passed through his daily course to his setting; she saw no other object, her face turned constantly on him. At last, they say, her limbs rooted in the ground, her face became a flower, which turns on its stem so as always to face the sun throughout its daily course; for it retains to that extent the feeling of the nymph from whom it sprang.

ARACHNE

The gods seem to be especially hard on conceit and boastfulness.

Not among mortals alone were there contests of skill, nor yet among the gods, like Pan and Apollo. Many sorrows befell men because they grew arrogant in their own devices and coveted divine honors. There was once a great hunter, Orion, who outvied the gods themselves, till they took him away from his hunting-grounds and set him in the heavens, with his sword and belt, and his hound at his heels. But at length jealousy invaded even the peaceful arts, and disaster came of spinning!

There was a certain maiden of Lydia, Arachne by name, renowned throughout the country for her skill as a weaver. She was as nimble with her fingers as Calypso, that nymph who kept Odysseus for seven years in her enchanted island. She was as untiring as Penelope, the hero's wife, who wove day after day while she watched for his return. Day in and day out, Arachne wove too. The very nymphs would gather about her loom, naiads from the water and dryads from the trees.

"Maiden," they would say, shaking the leaves or the foam from their hair, in wonder, "Pallas Athena must have taught you!"

But this did not please Arachne. She would not acknowledge herself a debtor, even to that goddess who protected all household arts, and by whose grace alone one had any skill in them.

"I learned not of Athena," said she. "If she can weave better, let her come and try."

The nymphs shivered at this, and an aged woman, who was looking on, turned to Arachne.

"Be more heedful of your words, my daughter," said she. "The goddess may pardon you if you ask forgiveness, but do not strive for honors with the immortals."

Arachne broke her thread, and the shuttle stopped humming.

"Keep your counsel," she said. "I fear not Athena; no, nor anyone else."

As she frowned at the old woman, she was amazed to see her change suddenly into one tall,

"Arachne." From *Old Greek Folk Stories Told Anew* by Josephine Preston Peabody. Houghton, Mifflin Co., 1897

majestic, beautiful—a maiden of gray eyes and golden hair, crowned with a golden helmet. It was Athena herself.

The bystanders shrank in fear and reverence; only Arachne was unawed and held to her foolish boast.

In silence the two began to weave, and the nymphs stole nearer, coaxed by the sound of the shuttles, that seemed to be humming with delight over the two webs,—back and forth like bees.

They gazed upon the loom where the goddess stood plying her task, and they saw shapes and images come to bloom out of the wondrous colors, as sunset clouds grow to be living creatures when we watch them. And they saw that the goddess, still merciful, was spinning, as a warning for Arachne, the pictures of her own triumph over reckless gods and mortals.

In one corner of the web she made a story of her conquest over the sea-god Poseidon. For the first king of Athens had promised to dedicate the city to that god who should bestow upon it the most useful gift. Poseidon gave the horse. But Athena gave the olive,—means of livelihood,—symbol of peace and prosperity, and the city was called after her name. Again she pictured a vain woman of Troy, who had been turned into a crane for disputing the palm of beauty with a goddess. Other corners of the web held similar images, and the whole shone like a rainbow.

Meanwhile Arachne, whose head was quite turned with vanity, embroidered her web with stories against the gods, making light of Zeus himself and of Apollo, and portraying them as birds and beasts. But she wove with marvelous skill; the creatures seemed to breathe and speak, yet it was all as fine as the gossamer that you find on the grass before rain.

Athena herself was amazed. Not even her wrath at the girl's insolence could wholly overcome her wonder. For an instant she stood entranced; then she tore the web across, and three times she touched Arachne's forehead with her spindle.

"Live on, Arachne," she said. "And since it is your glory to weave, you and yours must weave forever." So saying, she sprinkled upon the maiden a certain magical potion.

Away went Arachne's beauty; then her very

human form shrank to that of a spider, and so remained. As a spider she spent all her days weaving and weaving; and you may see something like her handiwork any day among the rafters.

ORPHEUS AND EURYDICE

This story makes an invaluable background for the "Orpheus and Eurydice" music by Gluck.

When gods and shepherds piped and the stars sang, that was the day of musicians! But the triumph of Phoebus Apollo himself was not so wonderful as the triumph of a mortal man who lived on earth, though some say that he came of divine lineage. This was Orpheus, that best of harpers, who went with the Grecian heroes of the great ship *Argo* in search of the Golden Fleece.

After his return from the quest, he won Eurydice for his wife, and they were as happy as people can be who love each other and every one else. The very wild beasts loved them, and the trees clustered about their home as if they were watered with music. But even the gods themselves were not always free from sorrow, and one day misfortune came upon that harper Orpheus whom all men loved to honor.

Eurydice, his lovely wife, as she was wandering with the nymphs, unwittingly trod upon a serpent in the grass. Surely, if Orpheus had been with her, playing upon his lyre, no creature could have harmed her. But Orpheus came too late. She died of the sting, and was lost to him in the Underworld.

For days he wandered from his home, singing the story of his loss and his despair to the helpless passers-by. His grief moved the very stones in the wilderness, and roused a dumb distress in the hearts of savage beasts. Even the gods on Mount Olympus gave ear, but they held no power over the darkness of Hades.

Wherever Orpheus wandered with his lyre, no one had the will to forbid him entrance; and at length he found unguarded that very cave that leads to the Underworld where Pluto rules the

spirits of the dead. He went down without fear. The fire in his living heart found him a way through the gloom of that place. He crossed the Styx, the black river that the gods name as their most sacred oath. Charon, the harsh old ferryman who takes the Shades across, forgot to ask of him the coin that every soul must pay. For Orpheus sang. There in the Underworld the song of Apollo would not have moved the poor ghosts so much. It would have amazed them, like a star far off that no one understands. But here was a human singer, and he sang of things that grow in every human heart, youth and love and death, the sweetness of the Earth, and the bitterness of losing aught that is dear to us.

Now the dead, when they go to the Underworld, drink of the pool of Lethe; and forget-

"Orpheus and Eurydice." From *Old Greek Folk Stories Told Anew* by Josephine Preston Peabody

fulness of all that has passed comes upon them like a sleep, and they lose their longing for the world, they lose their memory of pain, and live content with that cool twilight. But not the pool of Lethe itself could withstand the song of Orpheus; and in the hearts of the Shades all the old dreams awoke wondering. They remembered once more the life of men on Earth, the glory of the sun and moon, the sweetness of new grass, the warmth of their homes, all the old joy and grief that they had known. And they wept.

Even the Furies were moved to pity. Those, too, who were suffering punishment for evil deeds ceased to be tormented for themselves, and grieved only for the innocent Orpheus who had lost Eurydice. Sisyphus, that fraudulent king (who is doomed to roll a monstrous boulder uphill forever), stopped to listen. The daughters of Danaus left off their task of drawing water in a sieve. Tantalus forgot hunger and thirst, though before his eyes hung magical fruits that were wont to vanish out of his grasp, and just beyond reach bubbled the water that was a torment to his ears; he did not hear it while Orpheus sang.

So, among a crowd of eager ghosts, Orpheus came, singing with all his heart, before the king and queen of Hades. And the queen Proserpina wept as she listened and grew homesick, remembering the fields of Enna and the growing of the wheat, and her own beautiful mother, Demeter. Then Pluto gave way.

They called Eurydice and she came, like a young guest unused to the darkness of the Underworld. She was to return with Orpheus, but on one condition. If he turned to look at her once before they reached the upper air, he must lose her again and go back to the world alone.

Rapt with joy, the happy Orpheus hastened on the way, thinking only of Eurydice, who was following him. Past Lethe, across the Styx they went, he and his lovely wife, still silent as a Shade. But the place was full of gloom, the silence weighed upon him, he had not seen her for so long; her footsteps made no sound; and he could hardly believe the miracle, for Pluto seldom relents. When the first gleam of upper daylight broke through the cleft to the dismal world, he forgot all, save that he must know if she still followed. He turned to see her face, and the promise was broken!

She smiled at him forgivingly, but it was too late. He stretched out his arms to take her, but she faded from them, as the bright snow, that none may keep, melts in our very hands. A murmur of farewell came to his ears—no more. She was gone.

He would have followed, but Charon, now on guard, drove him back. Seven days he lingered there between the worlds of life and death, but after the broken promise, Hades would not listen to his song. Back to the Earth he wandered, though it was sweet to him no longer. He died young, singing to the last, and round about the place where his body rested, nightingales nested in the trees. His lyre was set among the stars; and he himself went down to join Eurydice, unforbidden.

Those two had no need of Lethe, for their life on earth had been wholly fair, and now that they are together they no longer own a sorrow.

PROSERPINE

This myth, sometimes called "Demeter and Persephone," the Greek names for the mother and child, is the story of winter and summer, of the grains maturing below ground in darkness.

In the vale of Enna there is a lake embowered in woods, which screen it from the fervid rays of the sun, while the moist ground is covered with flowers, and Spring reigns perpetual. Here Proserpine was playing with her companions, gathering lilies and violets, and filling her basket and her apron with them, when Pluto saw her, loved her, and carried her off. She screamed for help to her mother and companions; and when in her fright she dropped the corners of her apron and let the flowers fall, childlike she felt the loss of them as an addition to her grief.

Pluto urged on his steeds, calling them each by name, and throwing loose over their heads and necks his iron-coloured reins. When he reached the River Cyane, and it opposed his passage, he struck the river-bank with his trident, and the earth opened and gave him a passage to Tartarus.

"Proserpine." From *A Book of Myths,* selections from Bulfinch's *Age of Fable,* Macmillan, 1942

Ceres, Proserpine's mother, sought her daughter all the world over. Bright-haired Aurora, when she came forth in the morning, and Hesperus, when he led out the stars in the evening, found her still busy in the search. But it was all unavailing. At length, weary and sad, she sat down upon a stone, and continued sitting nine days and nights, in the open air, under the sunlight and moonlight and falling showers. It was where now stands the city of Eleusis, then the home of an old man named Celeus.

He was out on the field, gathering acorns and blackberries, and sticks for his fire. His little girl was driving home their two goats, and as she passed the goddess, who appeared in the guise of an old woman, she said to her, "Mother,"—and the name was sweet to the ears of Ceres,—"why do you sit here alone upon the rocks?" The old man also stopped, though his load was heavy, and begged her to come into his cottage, such as it was. She declined, and he urged her. "Go in peace," she replied, "and be happy in your daughter; I have lost mine." As she spoke, tears fell down her cheeks upon her bosom. The compassionate old man and his child wept with her. Then said he, "Come with us, and despise not our humble roof; so may your daughter be restored to you in safety."

"Lead on," she said, "I cannot resist that appeal!" So she rose from the stone and went with them. As they walked he told her that his only son, a little boy, lay very sick, feverish, and sleepless. She stooped and gathered some poppies. As they entered the cottage, they found all in great distress, for the boy seemed past hope of recovery. Metanira, his mother, received her kindly, and the goddess stooped and kissed the lips of the sick child. Instantly the paleness left his face, and healthy vigour returned to his body. The whole family were delighted—that is, the father, mother, and little girl, for they were all; they had no servants.

They spread the table, and put upon it curds and cream, apples, and honey in the comb. While they ate, Ceres mingled poppy juice in the milk of the boy. When night came and all was still, she arose, and taking the sleeping boy, moulded his limbs with her hands, and uttered over him three times a solemn charm, then went and laid him in the ashes. His mother, who had been watching what her guest was doing, sprang forward with a cry and snatched the child from the fire.

Then Ceres assumed her own form, and a divine splendour shone all around. While they were overcome with astonishment, she said, "Mother, you have been cruel in your fondness to your son. I would have made him immortal, but you have frustrated my attempt. Nevertheless, he shall be great and useful. He shall teach men the use of the plough, and the rewards which labour can win from the cultivated soil." So saying, she wrapped a cloud about her, and mounting her chariot rode away.

Ceres continued her search for her daughter, passing from land to land, and across the seas and rivers, till at length she returned to Sicily, whence she at first set out, and stood by the banks of the River Cyane, where Pluto made himself a passage with his prize to his own dominions. The river nymph would have told the goddess all she had witnessed, but dared not, for fear of Pluto; so she only ventured to take up the girdle which Proserpine had dropped in her flight, and waft it to the feet of the mother.

Ceres, seeing this, was no longer in doubt of her loss, but she did not yet know the cause, and laid the blame on the innocent land. "Ungrateful soil," said she, "which I have endowed with fertility and clothed with herbage and nourishing grain, no more shall you enjoy my favours." Then the cattle died, the plough broke in the furrow, the seed failed to come up; there was too much sun, there was too much rain; the birds stole the seeds—thistles and brambles were the only growth.

Seeing this, the fountain Arethusa interceded for the land. "Goddess," said she, "blame not the land; it opened unwillingly to yield a passage to your daughter. I can tell you of her fate, for I have seen her. When I passed through the lower parts of the earth, I saw your Proserpine. She was sad, but no longer showing alarm in her countenance. Her look was such as became a queen—the queen of Erebus; the powerful bride of the monarch of the realms of the dead."

When Ceres heard this, she stood for a while like one stupified; then turned her chariot towards heaven, and hastened to present herself before the throne of Jove. She told the story of her bereavement, and implored Jupiter to interfere to procure the restitution of her daughter. Jupiter consented on one condition, namely, that Proserpine should not during her stay in the lower world have taken any food; otherwise, the Fates forbade her release.

Accordingly, Mercury was sent, accompanied by Spring, to demand Proserpine of Pluto. The wily monarch consented; but, alas! the maiden had taken a pomegranate which Pluto offered her, and had sucked the sweet pulp from a few of the seeds. This was enough to prevent her complete release; but a compromise was made, by which she was to pass half the time with her mother, and the rest with her husband Pluto.

Ceres allowed herself to be pacified with this arrangement, and restored the earth to her favour.

ICARUS AND DAEDALUS

Among all those mortals who grew so wise that they learned the secrets of the gods, none was more cunning than Daedalus.

He once built, for King Minos of Crete, a wonderful Labyrinth of winding ways so cunningly tangled up and twisted around that, once inside, you could never find your way out again without a magic clue. But the king's favor veered with the wind, and one day he had his master architect imprisoned in a tower. Daedalus managed to escape from his cell; but it seemed impossible to leave the island, since every ship that came or went was well guarded by order of the king.

At length, watching the sea-gulls in the air—the only creatures that were sure of liberty—he thought of a plan for himself and his young son Icarus, who was captive with him.

Little by little, he gathered a store of feathers great and small. He fastened these together with thread, moulded them in with wax, and so fashioned two great wings like those of a bird. When they were done, Daedalus fitted them to his own shoulders, and after one or two efforts, he found that by waving his arms he could winnow the air and cleave it, as a swimmer does the sea. He

"Icarus and Daedalus." From *Old Greek Folk Stories Told Anew* by Josephine Preston Peabody

held himself aloft, wavered this way and that with the wind, and at last, like a great fledgling, he learned to fly.

Without delay, he fell to work on a pair of wings for the boy Icarus, and taught him carefully how to use them, bidding him beware of rash adventures among the stars. "Remember," said the father, "never to fly very low or very high, for the fogs about the earth would weigh you down, but the blaze of the sun will surely melt your feathers apart if you go too near."

For Icarus, these cautions went in at one ear and out by the other. Who could remember to be careful when he was to fly for the first time? Are birds careful? Not they! And not an idea remained in the boy's head but the one joy of escape.

The day came, and the fair wind that was to set them free. The father bird put on his wings, and, while the light urged them to be gone, he waited to see that all was well with Icarus, for the two could not fly hand in hand. Up they rose, the boy after his father. The hateful ground of Crete sank beneath them; and the country folk, who caught a glimpse of them when they were high above the tree-tops, took it for a vision of the gods—Apollo, perhaps, with Cupid after him.

At first there was a terror in the joy. The wide vacancy of the air dazed them—a glance downward made their brains reel. But when a great wind filled their wings, and Icarus felt himself sustained, like a halcyon-bird in the hollow of a wave, like a child uplifted by his mother, he forgot everything in the world but joy. He forgot Crete and the other islands that he had passed over: he saw but vaguely that wingèd thing in the distance before him that was his father Daedalus. He longed for one draught of flight to quench the thirst of his captivity: he stretched out his arms to the sky and made towards the highest heavens.

Alas for him! Warmer and warmer grew the air. Those arms, that had seemed to uphold him, relaxed. His wings wavered, drooped. He fluttered his young hands vainly—he was falling—and in that terror he remembered. The heat of the sun had melted the wax from his wings; the feathers were falling, one by one, like snowflakes; and there was none to help.

He fell like a leaf tossed down the wind, down, down, with one cry that overtook Daedalus far away. When he returned, and sought high and low for the poor boy, he saw nothing but the bird-like feathers afloat on the water, and he knew that Icarus was drowned.

The nearest island he named Icaria, in memory of the child; but he, in heavy grief, went to the temple of Apollo in Sicily, and there hung up his wings as an offering. Never again did he attempt to fly.

CUPID AND PSYCHE

The theme of this beautiful story is similar to that of "East o' the Sun" and other stories of maidens who doubt and lose their loves but search for them faithfully and successfully.

Once upon a time, through that Destiny that overrules the gods, Love himself gave up his immortal heart to a mortal maiden. And thus it came to pass.

There was a certain king who had three beautiful daughters. The two elder married princes of great renown; but Psyche, the youngest, was so radiantly fair that no suitor seemed worthy of her. People thronged to see her pass through the city, and sang hymns in her praise, while strangers took her for the very goddess of beauty herself.

This angered Venus, and she resolved to cast down her earthly rival. One day, therefore, she called hither her son Love (Cupid, some name him), and bade him sharpen his weapons. He is an archer more to be dreaded than Apollo, for Apollo's arrows take life, but Love's bring joy or sorrow for a whole life long.

"Come, Love," said Venus. "There is a mortal maid who robs me of my honors in yonder city. Avenge your mother. Wound this precious Psyche, and let her fall in love with some churlish creature mean in the eyes of all men."

Cupid made ready his weapons, and flew down to earth invisibly. At that moment Psyche was asleep in her chamber; but he touched her heart with his golden arrow of love, and she opened her eyes so suddenly that he started (forgetting

"Cupid and Psyche." From *Old Greek Folk Stories Told Anew* by Josephine Preston Peabody

that he was invisible), and wounded himself with his own shaft. Heedless of the hurt, moved only by the loveliness of the maiden, he hastened to pour over her locks the healing joy that he ever kept by him, undoing all his work. Back to her dream the princess went, unshadowed by any thought of love. But Cupid, not so light of heart, returned to the heavens, saying not a word of what had passed.

Venus waited long; then, seeing that Psyche's heart had somehow escaped love, she sent a spell upon the maiden. From that time, lovely as she was, not a suitor came to woo; and her parents, who desired to see her a queen at least, made a journey to the Oracle, and asked counsel.

Said the voice: "The princess Psyche shall never wed a mortal. She shall be given to one who waits for her on yonder mountain; he overcomes gods and men."

At this terrible sentence the poor parents were half distraught, and the people gave themselves up to grief at the fate in store for their beloved princess. Psyche alone bowed to her destiny. "We have angered Venus unwittingly," she said, "and all for sake of me, heedless maiden that I am! Give me up, therefore, dear father and mother. If I atone, it may be that the city will prosper once more."

So she besought them, until, after many unavailing denials, the parents consented; and with a great company of people they led Psyche up the mountain,—as an offering to the monster of whom the Oracle had spoken,—and left her there alone.

Full of courage, yet in a secret agony of grief, she watched her kindred and her people wind down the mountain-path, too sad to look back, until they were lost to sight. Then, indeed, she wept, but a sudden breeze drew near, dried her tears, and caressed her hair, seeming to murmur comfort. In truth, it was Zephyr, the kindly West Wind, come to befriend her; and as she took heart, feeling some benignant presence, he lifted her in his arms, and carried her on wings as even as a sea-gull's, over the crest of the fateful mountain and into a valley below. There he left her, resting on a bank of hospitable grass, and there the princess fell asleep.

When she awoke, it was near sunset. She looked about her for some sign of the monster's approach; she wondered, then, if her grievous trial had been but a dream. Near by she saw a sheltering forest, whose young trees seemed to beckon as one maid beckons to another; and eager for the protection of the dryads, she went thither.

The call of running waters drew her farther and farther, till she came out upon an open place, where there was a wide pool. A fountain fluttered gladly in the midst of it, and beyond there stretched a white palace wonderful to see. Coaxed by the bright promise of the place, she drew near, and, seeing no one, entered softly. It was all kinglier than her father's home, and as she stood in wonder and awe, soft airs stirred about her. Little by little the silence grew murmurous like the woods, and one voice, sweeter than the rest, took words. "All that you see is yours, gentle high princess," it said. "Fear nothing; only command us, for we are here to serve you."

Full of amazement and delight, Psyche followed the voice from hall to hall, and through the lordly rooms, beautiful with everything that could delight a young princess. No pleasant thing was lacking. There was even a pool, brightly tiled and fed with running waters, where she bathed her weary limbs; and after she had put on the new and beautiful raiment that lay ready for her, she sat down to break her fast, waited upon and sung to by the unseen spirits.

Surely he whom the Oracle had called her husband was no monster, but some beneficent power, invisible like all the rest. When daylight waned, he came, and his voice, the beautiful voice of a god, inspired her to trust her strange destiny and to look and long for his return. Often she begged him to stay with her through the day, that she might see his face; but this he would not grant.

"Never doubt me, dearest Psyche," said he. "Perhaps you would fear if you saw me, and love is all I ask. There is a necessity that keeps me hidden now. Only believe."

So for many days Psyche was content; but when she grew used to happiness, she thought once more of her parents mourning her as lost, and of her sisters who shared the lot of mortals while she lived as a goddess. One night she told her husband of these regrets, and begged that her sisters at least might come to see her. He sighed, but did not refuse.

"Zephyr shall bring them hither," said he. And on the following morning, swift as a bird, the West Wind came over the crest of the high mountain and down into the enchanted valley, bearing her two sisters.

They greeted Psyche with joy and amazement, hardly knowing how they had come hither. But when this fairest of the sisters led them through her palace and showed them all the treasures that were hers, envy grew in their hearts and choked their old love. Even while they sat at feast with her, they grew more and more bitter; and hoping to find some little flaw in her good fortune, they asked a thousand questions.

"Where is your husband?" said they. "And why is he not here with you?"

"Ah," stammered Psyche. "All the day long— he is gone, hunting upon the mountains."

"But what does he look like?" they asked; and Psyche could find no answer.

When they learned that she had never seen him, they laughed her faith to scorn.

"Poor Psyche," they said. "You are walking in a dream. Wake, before it is too late. Have you forgotten what the Oracle decreed,—that you were destined for a dreadful creature, the fear of gods and men? And are you deceived by this show of kindliness? We have come to warn you. The people told us, as we came over the mountain, that your husband is a dragon, who feeds you well for the present, that he may feast the better, some day soon. What is it that you trust? Good words! But only take a dagger some night, and when the monster is asleep go, light a lamp, and look at him. You can put him to death easily, and all his riches will be yours—and ours."

Psyche heard this wicked plan with horror. Nevertheless, after her sisters were gone, she brooded over what they had said, not seeing their evil intent; and she came to find some wisdom in their words. Little by little, suspicion ate, like a moth, into her lovely mind; and at nightfall, in shame and fear, she hid a lamp and a dagger in her chamber. Toward midnight, when her husband was fast asleep, up she rose, hardly daring to breathe; and coming softly to his side, she uncovered the lamp to see some horror.

But there the youngest of the gods lay sleeping,—most beautiful, most irresistible of all immortals. His hair shone golden as the sun, his face was radiant as dear Springtime, and from his shoulders sprang two rainbow wings.

Poor Psyche was overcome with self-reproach. As she leaned toward him, filled with worship, her trembling hands held the lamp ill, and some burning oil fell upon Love's shoulder and awakened him.

He opened his eyes, to see at once his bride and the dark suspicion in her heart.

"O doubting Psyche!" he exclaimed with sudden grief,—and then he flew away, out of the window.

Wild with sorrow, Psyche tried to follow, but she fell to the ground instead. When she recovered her senses, she stared about her. She was alone, and the place was beautiful no longer. Garden and palace had vanished with Love. Over mountains and valleys Psyche journeyed alone until she came to the city where her two envious sisters lived with the princes whom they had married. She stayed with them only long enough to tell the story of her unbelief and its penalty. Then she set out again to search for Love.

As she wandered one day, travel-worn but not hopeless, she saw a lofty palace on a hill near by, and she turned her steps thither. The place seemed deserted. Within the hall she saw no human being,—only heaps of grain, loose ears of corn half torn from the husk, wheat and barley, alike scattered in confusion on the floor. Without delay, she set to work binding the sheaves together and gathering the scattered ears of corn in seemly wise, as a princess would wish to see them. While she was in the midst of her task, a voice startled her, and she looked up to behold Demeter herself, the goddess of the harvest, smiling upon her with good will.

"Dear Psyche," said Demeter, "you are worthy of happiness, and you may find it yet. But since you have displeased Venus, go to her and ask her favor. Perhaps your patience will win her pardon."

These motherly words gave Psyche heart, and she reverently took leave of the goddess and set out for the temple of Venus. Most humbly she offered up her prayer, but Venus could not look at her earthly beauty without anger.

"Vain girl," said she, "perhaps you have come to make amends for the wound you dealt your husband; you shall do so. Such clever people can always find work!"

Then she led Psyche into a great chamber

heaped high with mingled grain, beans, and lintels (the food of her doves), and bade her separate them all and have them ready in seemly fashion by night. Heracles would have been helpless before such a vexatious task; and poor Psyche, left alone in this desert of grain, had not courage to begin. But even as she sat there, a moving thread of black crawled across the floor from a crevice in the wall; and bending nearer, she saw that a great army of ants in columns had come to her aid. The zealous little creatures worked in swarms, with such industry over the work they like best, that, when Venus came at night, she found the task completed.

"Deceitful girl!" she cried, shaking the roses out of her hair with impatience, "this is my son's work, not yours. But he will soon forget you. Eat this black bread if you are hungry, and refresh your dull mind with sleep. To-morrow you will need more wit."

Psyche wondered what new misfortune could be in store for her. But when morning came, Venus led her to the brink of a river, and, pointing to the wood across the water, said, "Go now to yonder grove where the sheep with the golden fleece are wont to browse. Bring me a golden lock from every one of them, or you must go your ways and never come back again."

This seemed not difficult, and Psyche obediently bade the goddess farewell, and stepped into the water, ready to wade across. But as Venus disappeared, the reeds sang louder and the nymphs of the river, looking up sweetly, blew bubbles to the surface and murmured: "Nay, nay, have a care, Psyche. This flock has not the gentle ways of sheep. While the sun burns aloft, they are themselves as fierce as flame; but when the shadows are long, they go to rest and sleep, under the trees; and you may cross the river without fear and pick the golden fleece off the briers in the pasture."

Thanking the water-creatures, Psyche sat down to rest near them, and when the time came, she crossed in safety and followed their counsel. By twilight she returned to Venus with her arms full of shining fleece.

"No mortal wit did this," said Venus angrily. "But if you care to prove your readiness, go now, with this little box, down to Proserpina and ask her to enclose in it some of her beauty,

for I have grown pale in caring for my wounded son."

It needed not the last taunt to sadden Psyche. She knew that it was not for mortals to go into Hades and return alive; and feeling that Love had forsaken her, she was minded to accept her doom as soon as might be.

But even as she hastened toward the descent, another friendly voice detained her. "Stay, Psyche, I know your grief. Only give ear and you shall learn a safe way through all these trials." And the voice went on to tell her how one might avoid all the dangers of Hades and come out unscathed. (But such a secret could not pass from mouth to mouth, with the rest of the story.)

"And be sure," added the voice, "when Proserpina has returned the box, not to open it, however much you may long to do so."

Psyche gave heed, and by this device, whatever it was, she found her way into Hades safely, and made her errand known to Proserpina, and was soon in the upper world again, wearied but hopeful.

"Surely Love has not forgotten me," she said. "But humbled as I am and worn with toil, how shall I ever please him? Venus can never need all the beauty in this casket; and since I use it for Love's sake, it must be right to take some." So saying, she opened the box, heedless as Pandora! The spells and potions of Hades are not for mortal maids, and no sooner had she inhaled the strange aroma than she fell down like one dead, quite overcome.

But it happened that Love himself was recovered from his wound, and he had secretly fled from his chamber to seek out and rescue Psyche. He found her lying by the wayside; he gathered into the casket what remained of the philter, and awoke his beloved.

"Take comfort," he said, smiling. "Return to our mother and do her bidding till I come again."

Away he flew; and while Psyche went cheerily homeward, he hastened up to Olympus, where all the gods sat feasting, and begged them to intercede for him with his angry mother.

They heard his story and their hearts were touched. Zeus himself coaxed Venus with kind words till at last she relented, and remembered that anger hurt her beauty, and smiled once more. All the younger gods were for welcoming Psyche at once, and Hermes was sent to bring her hither. The maiden came, a shy newcomer among those bright creatures. She took the cup that Hebe held out to her, drank the divine ambrosia, and became immortal.

Light came to her face like moonrise, two radiant wings sprang from her shoulders; and even as a butterfly bursts from its dull cocoon, so the human Psyche blossomed into immortality.

Love took her by the hand, and they were never parted any more.

ATALANTA'S RACE

Even if Prince Meleager had lived, it is doubtful if he could ever have won Atalanta to be his wife. The maiden was resolved to live unwed, and at last she devised a plan to be rid of all her suitors. She was known far and wide as the swiftest runner of her time; and so she said that she would only marry that man who could outstrip her in the race, but that all who dared to try and failed must be put to death.

This threat did not dishearten all of the suitors, however, and to her grief, for she was not cruel, they held her to her promise. On a certain day the few bold men who were to try their fortune made ready, and chose young Hippomenes as judge. He sat watching them before the word was given, and sadly wondered that any brave man should risk his life merely to win a bride. But when Atalanta stood ready for the contest, he was amazed by her beauty. She looked like Hebe, goddess of young health, who is a glad serving-maiden to the gods when they sit at feast.

The signal was given, and, as she and the suitors darted away, flight made her more enchanting than ever. Just as a wind brings sparkles to the water and laughter to the trees, haste fanned her loveliness to a glow.

Alas for the suitors! She ran as if Hermes had lent her his wingèd sandals. The young men, skilled as they were, grew heavy with weariness and despair. For all their efforts, they seemed to

"Atalanta's Race." From *Old Greek Folk Stories Told Anew* by Josephine Preston Peabody

lag like ships in a calm, while Atalanta flew before them in some favoring breeze—and reached the goal!

To the sorrow of all on-lookers, the suitors were led away; but the judge himself, Hippomenes, rose and begged leave to try his fortune. As Atalanta listened, and looked at him, her heart was filled with pity, and she would willingly have let him win the race to save him from defeat and death; for he was comely and younger than the others. But her friends urged her to rest and make ready, and she consented, with an unwilling heart.

Meanwhile Hippomenes prayed within himself to Venus: "Goddess of Love, give ear, and send me good speed. Let me be swift to win as I have been swift to love her."

Now Venus, who was not far off,—for she had already moved the heart of Hippomenes to love, —came to his side invisibly, slipped into his hand three wondrous golden apples, and whispered a word of counsel in his ear.

The signal was given; youth and maiden started over the course. They went so like the wind that they left not a footprint. The people cheered on Hippomenes, eager that such valor should win. But the course was long, and soon fatigue seemed to clutch at his throat, the light shook before his eyes, and, even as he pressed on, the maiden passed him by.

At that instant Hippomenes tossed ahead one of the golden apples. The rolling bright thing caught Atalanta's eye, and full of wonder she stooped to pick it up. Hippomenes ran on. As he heard the flutter of her tunic close behind him, he flung aside another golden apple, and another moment was lost to the girl. Who could pass by such a marvel? The goal was near and Hippomenes was ahead, but once again Atalanta caught up with him, and they sped side by side like two dragon-flies. For an instant his heart failed him; then, with a last prayer to Venus, he flung down the last apple. The maiden glanced at it, wavered, and would have left it where it had fallen, had not Venus turned her head for a second and given her a sudden wish to possess it. Against her will she turned to pick up the golden apple, and Hippomenes touched the goal.

So he won that perilous maiden; and as for

Atalanta, she was glad to marry such a valorous man. By this time she understood so well what it was like to be pursued, that she had lost a little of her pleasure in hunting.

BAUCIS AND PHILEMON

On a certain hill in Phrygia stand a linden tree and an oak, enclosed by a low wall. Not far from the spot is a marsh, formerly good habitable land, but now indented with pools, the resort of fen-birds and cormorants.

Once upon a time Jupiter, in human shape, visited this country, and with him his son Mercury without his wings. They presented themselves, as weary travellers, at many a door, seeking rest and shelter, but found all closed, for it was late and the inhospitable inhabitants would not rouse themselves to open for them. At last a humble cottage received them, where Baucis, a pious old dame, and her husband, Philemon, had grown old together. Not ashamed of their poverty, they made it endurable by their modest desires and kind dispositions.

When the two heavenly guests crossed the humble threshold and bowed their heads to pass under the low door, the old man placed a seat, on which Baucis, bustling and attentive, spread a cloth, and begged them to sit down. Then she raked out the coals from the ashes and kindled up a fire, fed it with leaves and dry bark, and with her scanty breath blew it into a flame. She brought out of a corner split sticks and dry branches, broke them up, and placed them under the small kettle.

Her husband collected some pot-herbs in the garden, and she shred them from the stalks and prepared them for the pot. He reached down with a forked stick a flitch of bacon hanging in the chimney, cut a small piece, and put it in the pot to boil with the herbs, setting away the rest for another time. A bowl was filled with warm water, so the guests might wash. While all was doing, they beguiled the time with conversation.

On the bench designed for the guests was laid a cushion stuffed with sea-weed; and a cloth, only produced on great occasions, but ancient

"Baucis and Philemon." From *A Book of Myths*, selections from Bulfinch's *Age of Fable*, Macmillan, 1942

and coarse enough, was spread over that. The old lady, with her apron on, with trembling hand set the table. One leg was shorter than the rest, but a piece of slate put under brought it level. When fixed, she rubbed the table down with some sweet-smelling herbs. Upon it she set some olives, some cornel berries preserved in vinegar, and added radishes and cheese, with eggs lightly cooked in the ashes. All were served in earthen dishes, and an earthenware pitcher, with wooden cups, stood beside them. When all was ready, the stew, smoking hot, was set on the table. Some wine, not of the oldest, was added; and for dessert, apples and wild honey. Over and above all, there were friendly faces and a simple, but hearty welcome.

Now, while the meal was being eaten, the old folks were astonished to see that the wine, as fast as it was poured out, renewed itself in the pitcher, of its own accord. Struck with terror, Baucis and Philemon recognized their heavenly guests, fell on their knees, and with clasped hands implored forgiveness for their poor entertainment. There was an old goose, which they kept as the guardian of their humble cottage, and they bethought them to make this a sacrifice in honour of their guests.

But the goose, too nimble with the aid of feet and wings, eluded them and at last took shelter between the gods themselves. They forbade it to be slain and spoke these words: "We are gods. This inhospitable village shall pay the penalty of its impiety; you alone shall go free from punishment. Leave your house and come with us to the top of yonder hill."

They hastened to obey, and, staff in hand, toiled up the steep ascent. They had reached to within an arrow's flight of the top when, turning their eyes below, they beheld all the country sunk in a lake, only their own house left standing. While they gazed with wonder at the sight and lamented the fate of their neighbours, that old house of theirs was changed into a temple. Columns took the place of the corner posts, the thatch grew into a gilded roof, the floors became marble, the doors were enriched with carving and ornaments of gold.

Then spoke Jupiter: "Excellent old man, and woman worthy of such a husband, speak, tell us your wishes; what favour have you to ask of us?"

Philemon took counsel with Baucis a few moments; then they declared to the gods their wish. "We ask to be priests and guardians of your temple; and since we have passed our lives here in love and agreement, we wish that one and the same hour may take us both from life, that I may not live to see her grave nor be laid in my own by her."

Their prayer was granted. They were the keepers of the temple as long as they lived. When grown very old, as they stood one day before the steps of the building and were telling the story of the place, Baucis saw Philemon begin to put forth leaves, and old Philemon saw Baucis changing in the same manner. And now a leafy crown had grown over their heads. They exchanged parting words as long as they could speak. "Farewell, dear spouse," they said together, and at the same moment the bark closed over their mouths. The Tyanean shepherd still shows the two trees, standing side by side, made out of the two good old people.

PEGASUS AND THE CHIMAERA

When Perseus cut off Medusa's head, the blood sinking into the earth produced the winged horse Pegasus. Minerva caught and tamed him and presented him to the Muses. The fountain Hippocrene, on the Muses' mountain Helicon, was opened by a kick from his hoof.

The Chimaera was a fearful monster, breathing fire. The fore part of its body was a compound of the lion and the goat, and the hind part a dragon's. It made great havoc in Lycia, so that the king, Iobates, sought for some hero to destroy it. At that time there arrived at his court a gallant young warrior, whose name was Bellerophon. He brought letters from Proetus, the son-in-law of Iobates, recommending Bellerophon in the warmest terms as an unconquerable hero, but added at the close a request to his father-in-law to put him to death. The reason was that Proetus was jealous of him, suspecting that his wife Antea looked with too much admiration on the young warrior.

Iobates, on perusing the letters, was puzzled

"Pegasus and the Chimaera." From *A Book of Myths,* selections from Bulfinch's *Age of Fable,* Macmillan, 1942

what to do, not willing to violate the claims of hospitality, yet wishing to oblige his son-in-law. A lucky thought occurred to him, to send Bellerophon to combat with the Chimaera. Bellerophon accepted the proposal, but before proceeding to the combat consulted a soothsayer, who advised him to procure if possible the horse Pegasus for the conflict.

For this purpose he directed him to pass the night in the temple of Minerva. He did so, and as he slept Minerva came to him and gave him a golden bridle. When he awoke the bridle remained in his hand. Minerva also showed him Pegasus drinking at the well of Pirene, and at the sight of the bridle the winged steed came willingly and suffered himself to be taken. Bellerophon mounted him, rose with him into the air, soon found the Chimaera, and gained an easy victory over the monster.

After the conquest of the monster Bellerophon was exposed to further trials and labours by his unfriendly host, but by the aid of Pegasus he triumphed in them all, till at length Iobates, seeing that the hero was a special favourite of the gods, gave him his daughter in marriage and made him his successor on the throne. At last Bellerophon by his pride and presumption drew upon himself the anger of the gods; it is said he even attempted to fly up into heaven on his winged steed, but Jupiter sent a gadfly which stung Pegasus and made him throw his rider, who became lame and blind in consequence. After this Bellerophon wandered lonely through the Aleian field, avoiding the paths of men, and died miserably.

MIDAS

This is the meager source (in translation) from which Hawthorne spun the better-known version which follows.

Bacchus, in return for a kindness done him, offered King Midas his choice of a reward, whatever he might wish. Midas asked to have everything he should touch changed into gold. Bacchus consented, though sorry he had not made a better choice. Midas went his way, rejoicing in his new-acquired power, which he hastened to put to the test. He could scarcely believe his eyes when he found a twig of an oak, which he plucked from the branch, become gold in his hand. He took up a stone; it turned to gold. He touched a sod; it did the same. He took an apple from the tree; you would have thought he had robbed the garden of the Hesperides.

His joy knew no bounds, and as soon as he reached home, he ordered the servants to set a splendid feast on the table. Then he found to his dismay that whenever he touched bread, it hardened in his hand, or put a morsel to his lips,

"Midas." From *A Book of Myths*, selections from Bulfinch's *Age of Fable*, Macmillan, 1942

it defied his teeth. He took a glass of wine, but it flowed down his throat like melted gold.

Worried by this affliction, he tried to get rid of the power; he hated the gift he had lately coveted. But all in vain. Starvation seemed to await him. He raised his arms, all shining with gold, in prayer to Bacchus, begging to be delivered from his glittering destruction. Bacchus, merciful deity, heard and consented. "Go," he said, "to the River Factolus, trace the stream to its source, and there plunge your head and body in and wash away your fault and its punishment."

He did so, and scarcely had he touched the waters before the gold-creating power passed into them, and the river sands were changed into gold, as they remain to this day.

Henceforth Midas, hating wealth and splendour, lived in the country and became a worshipper of Pan, the god of the fields. On a certain occasion Pan dared to compare his music with that of Apollo, and to challenge the god of the lyre to a trial of skill. Tmolus, the mountain god, was chosen umpire. He took his seat and cleared away the trees from his ears to listen. At a given signal, Pan blew on his pipes and with his melody gave great satisfaction to himself and his faithful follower, Midas. Then Tmolus turned his head toward the sun-god, and all his trees turned with him.

Apollo rose, his brow wreathed with Parnassian laurel, while his robe of Tyrian purple swept the ground. In his left hand he held the lyre, and with his right hand struck the strings. Ravished with the harmony, Tmolus at once awarded the victory to Apollo, and all but Midas acquiesced in the judgement. He dissented and questioned the justice of the award. Apollo would not suffer such a depraved pair of ears any longer to wear human form, but caused them to increase in length, grow hairy within and without, and become movable at their roots; in short, the perfect pattern of those of an ass.

Mortified enough was King Midas at this mishap; but he consoled himself with the thought that it was possible to hide his misfortune, which he attempted to do by means of an ample turban or head-dress. But his hair-dresser of course knew the secret. He was charged not to mention it, and threatened with dire punishment if he presumed to disobey. But he found it too much to keep such a secret. He went out into the meadow, dug a hole in the ground, and stooping down, whispered the story and covered it up. Before long, a thick bed of reeds sprang up in the meadow, and as soon as it had gained its growth, began whispering the story and has continued to do so from that day to this, every time a breeze passes over the place.

THE GOLDEN TOUCH

Once upon a time, there lived a very rich king whose name was Midas; and he had a little daughter, whom nobody but myself ever heard of, and whose name was Marygold.

This King Midas was fonder of gold than of anything else in the world. He valued his royal crown chiefly because it was composed of that precious metal. If he loved anything better, or half so well, it was the one little maiden who played so merrily around her father's footstool. But the more Midas loved his daughter, the more did he desire and seek for wealth. He thought, foolish man! that the best thing he could possibly do for this dear child would be to bequeath her the immensest pile of yellow, glistening coin, that had ever been heaped together since the world was made. Thus, he gave all his thoughts and all his time to this one purpose. If ever he happened to gaze for an instant at the gold-tinted clouds of sunset, he wished that they were real gold, and that they could be squeezed safely into his strong box. When little Marygold ran to meet him, with a bunch of buttercups and dandelions, he used to say, "Poh, poh, child! If these flowers were as golden as they look, they would be worth the plucking!"

And yet, in his earlier days, before he was so entirely possessed of this insane desire for riches, King Midas had shown a great taste for flowers. He had planted a garden, in which grew the biggest and beautifullest and sweetest roses that any mortal ever saw or smelt. These roses were still growing in the garden, as large, as lovely, and as fragrant, as when Midas used to pass whole hours in gazing at them, and inhaling

"The Golden Touch." From *A Wonder Book for Girls and Boys* by Nathaniel Hawthorne

their perfume. But now, if he looked at them at all, it was only to calculate how much the garden would be worth if each of the innumerable rose-petals were a thin plate of gold. And though he once was fond of music the only music for poor Midas, now, was the chink of one coin against another.

At length Midas had got to be so exceedingly unreasonable, that he could scarcely bear to see or touch any object that was not gold. He made it his custom, therefore, to pass a large portion of every day in a dark and dreary apartment, under ground, at the basement of his palace. It was here that he kept his wealth. To this dismal hole —for it was little better than a dungeon—Midas betook himself, whenever he wanted to be particularly happy. Here, after carefully locking the door, he would take a bag of gold coin, or a gold cup as big as a washbowl, or a heavy golden bar, or a peck-measure of gold-dust, and bring them from the obscure corners of the room into the one bright and narrow sunbeam that fell from the dungeon-like window. He valued the sunbeam for no other reason but that his treasure would not shine without its help. And then would he reckon over the coins in the bag, toss up the bar, and catch it as it came down; sift the gold-dust through his fingers; look at the funny image of his own face, as reflected in the burnished circumference of the cup; and whisper to himself, "O Midas, rich King Midas, what a happy man art thou!"

Midas was enjoying himself in his treasure-room, one day, as usual, when he perceived a shadow fall over the heaps of gold; and, looking suddenly up, what should he behold but the figure of a stranger, standing in the bright and narrow sunbeam! It was a young man, with a cheerful and ruddy face. Whether it was that the imagination of King Midas threw a yellow tinge over everything, or whatever the cause might be, he could not help fancying that the smile with which the stranger regarded him had a kind of golden radiance in it. Certainly, although his figure intercepted the sunshine, there was now a brighter gleam upon all the piled-up treasure than before. Even the remotest corners had their share of it, and were lighted up, when the stranger smiled, as with tips of flame and sparkles of fire.

As Midas knew that he had carefully turned the key in the lock, and that no mortal strength could possibly break into his treasure-room, he, of course, concluded that his visitor must be something more than mortal. Midas had met such beings before now, and was not sorry to meet one of them again.

The stranger gazed about the room; and when his lustrous smile had glistened upon all the golden objects that were there, he turned again to Midas.

"You are a wealthy man, friend Midas!" he observed. "I doubt whether any other four walls, on earth, contain so much gold as you have contrived to pile up in this room."

"I have done pretty well,—pretty well," answered Midas, in a discontented tone. "But, after all, it is but a trifle, when you consider that it has taken me my whole life to get it together. If one could live a thousand years, he might have time to grow rich!"

"What!" exclaimed the stranger. "Then you are not satisfied?"

Midas shook his head.

"And pray what would satisfy you?" asked the stranger. "Merely for the curiosity of the thing, I should be glad to know."

Midas paused and meditated. He felt a presentiment that this stranger, with such a golden lustre in his good-humored smile, had come hither with both the power and the purpose of gratifying his utmost wishes. Now, therefore, was the fortunate moment, when he had but to speak, and obtain whatever possible, or seemingly impossible thing, it might come into his head to ask. So he thought, and thought, and thought, and heaped up one golden mountain upon another, in his imagination, without being able to imagine them big enough. At last, a bright idea occurred to King Midas. It seemed really as bright as the glistening metal which he loved so much.

Raising his head, he looked the lustrous stranger in the face.

"Well, Midas," observed his visitor, "I see that you have at length hit upon something that will satisfy you. Tell me your wish."

"It is only this," replied Midas. "I am weary of collecting my treasures with so much trouble, and beholding the heap so diminutive, after I have done my best. I wish everything that I touch be changed to gold!"

The stranger's smile grew so very broad, that it seemed to fill the room like an outburst of the sun, gleaming into a shadowy dell, where the yellow autumnal leaves—for so looked the lumps and particles of gold—lie strewn in the glow of light.

"The Golden Touch!" exclaimed he. "You certainly deserve credit, friend Midas, for striking out so brilliant a conception. But are you quite sure that this will satisfy you?"

"How could it fail?" said Midas.

"And will you never regret the possession of it?"

"What could induce me?" asked Midas. "I ask nothing else, to render me perfectly happy."

"Be it as you wish, then," replied the stranger, waving his hand in token of farewell. "To-morrow, at sunrise, you will find yourself gifted with the Golden Touch."

The figure of the stranger then became exceedingly bright, and Midas involuntarily closed his eyes. On opening them again, he beheld only one yellow sunbeam in the room, and all around him, the glistening of the precious metal which he had spent his life in hoarding up.

Whether Midas slept as usual that night, the story does not say. At any rate, day had hardly peeped over the hills, when King Midas was broad awake, and stretching his arms out of bed, began to touch the objects that were within reach. He was anxious to prove whether the Golden Touch had really come, according to the stranger's promise. So he laid his finger on a chair by the bedside, and on various other things, but was grievously disappointed to perceive that they remained of exactly the same substance as before. Indeed, he felt very much afraid that he had only dreamed about the lustrous stranger, or else that the latter had been making game of him. And what a miserable affair would it be, if after all his hopes, Midas must content himself with what little gold he could scrape together by ordinary means, instead of creating it by a touch!

All this while, it was only the gray of the morning, with but a streak of brightness along the edge of the sky, where Midas could not see it. He lay in a very disconsolate mood, regretting the downfall of his hopes, and kept growing sadder and sadder, until the earliest sunbeam shone through the window, and gilded the ceiling over his head. It seemed to Midas that this bright yellow sunbeam was reflected in rather a singular way on the white covering of the bed. Looking more closely, what was his astonishment and delight, when he found that this linen fabric had been transmuted to what seemed a woven texture of the purest and brightest gold! The Golden Touch had come to him with the first sunbeam!

Midas started up, in a kind of joyful frenzy, and ran about the room, grasping at everything that happened to be in his way. He seized one of the bed-posts, and it became immediately a fluted golden pillar. He pulled aside a window-curtain, in order to admit a clear spectacle of the wonders which he was performing; and the tassel grew heavy in his hand,—a mass of gold. He took up a book from the table. At his first touch, it assumed the appearance of such a splendidly bound and gilt-edged volume as one often meets with, now-adays; but, on running his fingers through the leaves, behold! It was a bundle of thin golden plates, in which all the wisdom of the book had grown illegible. He hurriedly put on his clothes, and was enraptured to see himself in a magnificent suit of gold cloth, which retained its flexibility and softness, although it burdened him a little with its weight. He drew out his handkerchief, which little Marygold had hemmed for him. That was likewise gold, with the dear child's neat and pretty stitches running all along the border, in gold thread!

Somehow or other, this last transformation did not quite please King Midas. He would rather that his little daughter's handiwork should have remained just the same as when she climbed his knee and put it into his hand.

But it was not worth while to vex himself about a trifle. Midas now took his spectacles from his pocket, and put them on his nose, in order that he might see more distinctly what he was about. In those days, spectacles for common people had not been invented, but were already worn by kings; else, how could Midas have had any? To his great perplexity, however, excellent as the glasses were, he discovered that he could not possibly see through them. But this was the most natural thing in the world; for, on taking them off, the transparent crystals turned out to be plates of yellow metal, and, of course, were worthless as spectacles, though valuable as gold. It struck Midas as rather inconvenient that, with all his wealth, he could never again be rich enough to own a pair of serviceable spectacles.

"It is no great matter, nevertheless," said he to himself, very philosophically. "We cannot expect any great good, without its being accompanied with some small inconvenience. The Golden Touch is worth the sacrifice of a pair of spectacles, at least, if not of one's very eyesight. My own eyes will serve for ordinary purposes, and little Marygold will soon be old enough to read to me."

King Midas went down stairs, and smiled, on observing that the balustrade of the staircase became a bar of burnished gold, as his hand passed over it, in his descent. He lifted the door-latch (it was brass only a moment ago, but golden when his fingers quitted it), and emerged into the garden. Here, as it happened, he found a great number of beautiful roses in full bloom, and others in all the stages of lovely bud and blossom. Very delicious was their fragrance in the morning breeze. Their delicate blush was one of the fairest sights in the world; so gentle, so modest, and so full of sweet tranquillity, did these roses seem to be.

But Midas knew a way to make them far more precious, according to his way of thinking, than roses had ever been before. So he took great pains in going from bush to bush, and exercised his magic touch most indefatigably; until every individual flower and bud, and even the worms at the heart of some of them, were changed to gold. By the time this good work was completed, King Midas was summoned to breakfast; and as the morning air had given him an excellent appetite, he made haste back to the palace.

On this particular morning, the breakfast consisted of hot cakes, some nice little brook-trout, roasted potatoes, fresh boiled eggs, and coffee, for King Midas himself, and a bowl of bread and milk for his daughter Marygold.

Little Marygold had not yet made her appearance. Her father ordered her to be called, and, seating himself at table, awaited the child's coming, in order to begin his own breakfast. To do Midas justice, he really loved his daughter, and loved her so much the more this morning, on account of the good fortune which had befallen him. It was not a great while before he heard her coming along the passageway crying bitterly. This circumstance surprised him, because Marygold was one of the cheerfullest little people whom you would see in a summer's day, and hardly shed a thimbleful of tears in a twelvemonth. When Midas heard her sobs, he determined to put little Marygold in better spirits, by an agreeable surprise; so, leaning across the table, he touched his daughter's bowl (which was a China one, with pretty figures all around it), and transmuted it to gleaming gold.

Meanwhile, Marygold slowly and disconsolately opened the door, and showed herself with her apron at her eyes, still sobbing as if her heart would break.

"How now, my little lady!" cried Midas. "Pray what is the matter with you, this bright morning?"

Marygold, without taking the apron from her eyes, held out her hand, in which was one of the roses which Midas had so recently transmuted.

"Beautiful!" exclaimed her father. "And what is there in this magnificent golden rose to make you cry?"

"Ah, dear father!" answered the child, as well as her sobs would let her; "it is not beautiful, but the ugliest flower that ever grew! As soon as I was dressed I ran into the garden to gather some roses for you; because I know you like them. But, oh dear, dear me! What do you think has happened? Such a misfortune! All the beautiful roses, that smelled so sweetly and had so many lovely blushes, are blighted and spoilt! They are grown quite yellow, as you see this one, and have no longer any fragrance! What can have been the matter with them?"

"Poh, my dear little girl,—pray don't cry about it!" said Midas, who was ashamed to confess that he himself had wrought the change which so greatly afflicted her. "Sit down and eat your bread and milk! You will find it easy enough to exchange a golden rose like that (which will last hundreds of years) for an ordinary one which would wither in a day."

"I don't care for such roses as this!" cried Marygold, tossing it contemptuously away. "It has no smell, and the hard petals prick my nose!"

The child now sat down to table, but was so occupied with her grief for the blighted roses that she did not even notice the wonderful transmutation of her China bowl. Perhaps this was all the better; for Marygold was accustomed to take pleasure in looking at the queer figures, and strange trees and houses, that were painted on the circumference of the bowl; and these ornaments were now entirely lost in the yellow hue of the metal.

Midas, meanwhile, had poured out a cup of coffee, and, as a matter of course, the coffee-pot, whatever metal it may have been when he took it up, was gold when he set it down. He thought to himself, that it was rather an extravagant style of splendor, in a king of his simple habits, to breakfast off a service of gold, and began to be puzzled with the difficulty of keeping his treasures safe. The cupboard and the kitchen would no longer be a secure place of deposit for articles so valuable as golden bowls and coffee-pots.

Amid these thoughts, he lifted a spoonful of coffee to his lips, and, sipping it, was astonished to perceive that, the instant his lips touched the liquid, it became molten gold, and, the next moment, hardened into a lump!

"Ha!" exclaimed Midas, rather aghast.

"What is the matter, father?" asked little Marygold, gazing at him, with the tears still standing in her eyes.

"Nothing, child, nothing!" said Midas. "Eat your milk, before it gets quite cold."

He took one of the nice little trouts on his plate, and, by way of experiment, touched its tail with his finger. To his horror, it was immediately transmuted from an admirably fried brook-trout into a gold-fish. A very pretty piece of work, as you may suppose; only King Midas, just at that moment, would much rather have had a real trout in his dish than this elaborate and valuable imitation of one.

"I don't quite see," thought he to himself, "how I am to get any breakfast!"

He took one of the smoking-hot cakes, and had scarcely broken it, when, to his cruel mortification, though, a moment before, it had been of the whitest wheat, it assumed the yellow hue of Indian meal. Almost in despair, he helped himself to a boiled egg, which immediately underwent a change similar to those of the trout and the cake. The egg, indeed, might have been mistaken for one of those which the famous goose, in the story-book, was in the habit of laying; but King Midas was the only goose that had had anything to do with the matter.

"Well, this is a quandary!" thought he, leaning back in his chair, and looking quite enviously at little Marygold, who was now eating her bread and milk with great satisfaction. "Such a costly breakfast before me, and nothing that can be eaten."

Hoping that, by dint of great dispatch, he might avoid what he now felt to be a considerable inconvenience, King Midas next snatched a hot potato, and attempted to cram it into his mouth, and swallow it in a hurry. But the Golden Touch was too nimble for him. He found his mouth full, not of mealy potato, but of solid metal, which so burnt his tongue that he roared aloud, and, jumping up from the table, began to dance and stamp about the room, both with pain and affright.

"Father, dear father!" cried little Marygold, who was a very affectionate child, "pray what is the matter? Have you burnt your mouth?"

"Ah, dear child," groaned Midas, dolefully, "I don't know what is to become of your poor father!"

Already, at breakfast, Midas was excessively hungry. Would he be less so by dinner-time? And how ravenous would be his appetite for supper, which must undoubtedly consist of the same sort of indigestible dishes as those now before him.

These reflections so troubled wise King Midas, that he began to doubt whether, after all, riches are the one desirable thing in the world. But this was only a passing thought. So fascinated was Midas with the glitter of the yellow metal, that he would still have refused to give up the Golden Touch for so paltry a consideration as a breakfast.

Nevertheless, so great was his hunger, and the perplexity of his situation, that he again groaned aloud, and very grievously too. Our pretty Marygold could endure it no longer. She sat, a moment, gazing at her father, and trying, with all the might of her little wits, to find out what was the matter with him. Then, with a sweet and sorrowful impulse to comfort him, she started from her chair, and, running to Midas, threw

her arms affectionately about his knees. He bent down and kissed her. He felt that his little daughter's love was worth a thousand times more than he had gained by the Golden Touch.

"My precious, precious Marygold!" cried he.

But Marygold made no answer.

Alas, what had he done? The moment the lips of Midas touched Marygold's forehead, a change had taken place. Her sweet, rosy face, so full of affection as it had been, assumed a glittering yellow color, with yellow tear-drops, congealing on her cheeks. Her beautiful brown ringlets took the same tint. Her soft and tender little form grew hard and inflexible within her father's encircling arms. Oh, terrible misfortune! The victim of his insatiable desire for wealth, little Marygold was a human child no longer, but a golden statue!

Yes, there she was, with the questioning look of love, grief, and pity, hardened into her face. It was the prettiest and most woeful sight that ever mortal saw. All the features and tokens of Marygold were there; even the beloved little dimple remained in her golden chin. But, the more perfect was the resemblance, the greater was the father's agony at beholding this golden image, which was all that was left him of a daughter. It had been a favorite phrase of Midas, whenever he felt particularly fond of the child, to say that she was worth her weight in gold. And now the phrase had become literally true. And now, at last, when it was too late, he felt how infinitely a warm and tender heart, that loved him, exceeded in value all the wealth that could be piled up betwixt the earth and sky!

Midas, in the fulness of all his gratified desires, began to wring his hands and bemoan himself; and how he could neither bear to look at Marygold, nor yet to look away from her. Except when his eyes were fixed on the image, he could not possibly believe that she was changed to gold. But, stealing another glance, there was the precious little figure, with a yellow tear-drop on its yellow cheek, and a look so piteous and tender, that it seemed as if that very expression must needs soften the gold, and make it flesh again. This, however, could not be.

While Midas was in this tumult of despair, he suddenly beheld a stranger standing near the door. Midas bent down his head, without speaking; for he recognized the same figure which had appeared to him, the day before, in the treasure-room, and had bestowed on him this disastrous faculty of the Golden Touch. The stranger's countenance still wore a smile, which seemed to shed a yellow lustre all about the room, and gleamed on little Marygold's image, and on the other objects that had been transmuted by the touch of Midas.

"Well, friend Midas," said the stranger, "pray how do you succeed with the Golden Touch?"

Midas shook his head.

"I am very miserable," said he.

"Very miserable, indeed!" exclaimed the stranger. "And how happens that? Have I not faithfully kept my promise with you? Have you not everything that your heart desired?"

"Gold is not everything," answered Midas. "And I have lost all that my heart really cared for."

"Ah! So you have made a discovery, since yesterday?" observed the stranger. "Let us see, then. Which of these two things do you think is really worth the most,—the gift of the Golden Touch, or one cup of clear cold water?"

"O blessed water!" exclaimed Midas. "It will never moisten my parched throat again!"

"The Golden Touch," continued the stranger, "or a crust of bread?"

"A piece of bread," answered Midas, "is worth all the gold on earth!"

"The Golden Touch," asked the stranger, "or your own little Marygold, warm, soft, and loving as she was an hour ago?"

"Oh, my child, my dear child!" cried poor Midas, wringing his hands. "I would not have given that one small dimple in her chin for the power of changing this whole big earth into a solid lump of gold!"

"You are wiser than you were, King Midas!" said the stranger, looking seriously at him. "Your own heart, I perceive, has not been entirely changed from flesh to gold. Were it so, your case would indeed be desperate. But you appear to be still capable of understanding that the commonest things, such as lie within everybody's grasp, are more valuable than the riches which so many mortals sigh and struggle after. Tell me, now, do you sincerely desire to rid yourself of this Golden Touch?"

"It is hateful to me!" replied Midas.

A fly settled on his nose, but immediately fell to the floor; for it, too, had become gold. Midas shuddered.

"Go, then," said the stranger, "and plunge into the river that glides past the bottom of your garden. Take likewise a vase of the same water, and sprinkle it over any object that you may desire to change back again from gold into its former substance. If you do this in earnestness and sincerity, it may possibly repair the mischief which your avarice has occasioned."

King Midas bowed low; and when he lifted his head, the lustrous stranger had vanished.

You will easily believe that Midas lost no time in snatching up a great earthen pitcher (but, alas me! it was no longer earthen after he touched it), and hastening to the river-side. As he scampered along, and forced his way through the shrubbery, it was positively marvellous to see how the foliage turned yellow behind him, as if the autumn had been there, and nowhere else. On reaching the river's brink, he plunged head-long in, without waiting so much as to pull off his shoes.

"Poof! poof! poof!" snorted King Midas, as his head emerged out of the water. "Well, this is really a refreshing bath, and I think it must have quite washed away the Golden Touch. And now for filling my pitcher!"

As he dipped the pitcher into the water, it gladdened his very heart to see it change from gold into the same good, honest earthen vessel which it had been before he touched it. He was conscious, also, of a change within himself. A cold, hard, and heavy weight seemed to have gone out of his bosom. Perceiving a violet, that grew on the bank of the river, Midas touched it with his finger, and was overjoyed to find that the delicate flower retained its purple hue, instead of undergoing a yellow blight. The curse of the Golden Touch had, therefore, really been removed from him.

King Midas hastened back to the palace; and, I suppose, the servants knew not what to make of it when they saw their royal master so carefully bringing home an earthen pitcher of water. But that water, which was to undo all the mischief that his folly had wrought, was more precious to Midas than an ocean of molten gold could have been. The first thing he did, as you need hardly be told, was to sprinkle it by handfuls over the golden figure of little Marygold.

No sooner did it fall on her than you would have laughed to see how the rosy color came back to the dear child's cheek! And how she began to sneeze and sputter!—and how astonished she was to find herself dripping wet, and her father still throwing more water over her!

"Pray do not, dear father!" cried she. "See how you have wet my nice frock, which I put on only this morning!"

For Marygold did not know that she had been a little golden statue; nor could she remember anything that had happened since the moment when she ran with outstretched arms to comfort poor King Midas.

Her father did not think it necessary to tell his beloved child how very foolish he had been, but contented himself with showing how much wiser he had now grown. For this purpose, he led little Marygold into the garden, where he sprinkled all the remainder of the water over the rose-bushes, and with such good effect that above five thousand roses recovered their beautiful bloom. There were two circumstances, however, which as long as he lived, used to put King Midas in mind of the Golden Touch. One was, that the sands of the river sparkled like gold; the other, that little Marygold's hair had now a golden tinge, which he had never observed in it before she had been transmuted by the effect of his kiss.

When King Midas had grown quite an old man, and used to trot Marygold's children on his knee, he was fond of telling them this marvellous story, pretty much as I have now told it to you. And then would he stroke their glossy ringlets, and tell them that their hair, likewise, had a rich shade of gold, which they had inherited from their mother.

"And to tell you the truth, my precious little folks," quoth King Midas, diligently trotting the children all the while, "ever since that morning, I have hated the very sight of all other gold, save this!"

THE CURSE OF POLYPHEMUS

This excerpt from the great Greek epic, the Odyssey, *is one of the most interesting episodes in the life of the hero Odysseus, whose wanderings lasted for ten years.*

Of all the heroes that wandered far and wide before they came to their homes again after the fall of Troy, none suffered so many hardships as Odysseus. Ten years did he fight against Troy, but it was ten years more before he came to his

"The Curse of Polyphemus." From *Old Greek Folk Stories Told Anew* by Josephine Preston Peabody home and his wife Penelope and his son Telemachus.

Odysseus set out from Troy with twelve good ships. He touched first at Ismarus, where his first misfortune took place, and in a skirmish with the natives he lost a number of men from each ship's crew.

A storm then drove them to the land of the Lotus-Eaters, a wondrous people, kindly and content, who spend their lives in a day-dream and care for nothing else under the sun. No sooner had the sailors eaten of this magical lotus than they lost all their wish to go home, or to see their wives and children again. By main force, Odysseus drove them back to the ships and saved them from the spell.

Thence they came one day to a beautiful strange island, a verdant place to see, deep with soft grass and well watered with springs. Here they ran the ships ashore, and took their rest and feasted for a day. But Odysseus looked across to the mainland, where he saw flocks and herds, and smoke going up softly from the homes of men; and he resolved to go across and find out what manner of people lived there. Accordingly, next morning, he took his own ship's company and they rowed across to the mainland.

Now, fair as the place was, there dwelt in it a race of giants, the Cyclopes, great rude creatures, having each but one eye, and that in the middle of his forehead. One of them was Polyphemus, the son of Poseidon. He lived by himself as a shepherd, and it was to his cave that Odysseus came, by some evil chance. It was an enormous grotto, big enough to house the giant and all his flocks, and it had a great courtyard without. But Odysseus, knowing nought of all this, chose out twelve men, and with a wallet of corn and a goatskin full of wine they left the ship and made a way to the cave, which they had seen from the water.

Much they wondered who might be the master of this strange house. Polyphemus was away with his sheep, but many lambs and kids were penned there, and the cavern was well stored with goodly cheeses and cream and whey.

Without delay, the wearied men kindled a fire and sat down to eat such things as they found, till a great shadow came dark against the doorway, and they saw the Cyclops near at hand, returning with his flocks. In an instant they fled into the darkest corner of the cavern.

Polyphemus drove his flocks into the place and cast off from his shoulders a load of young trees for firewood. Then he lifted and set in the entrance of the cave a gigantic boulder of a doorstone. Not until he had milked the goats and ewes and stirred up the fire did his terrible one eye light upon the strangers.

"What are ye?" he roared then, "robbers or rovers?" And Odysseus alone had heart to answer.

"We are Achaens of the army of Agamemnon," said he. "And by the will of Zeus we have lost our course, and are come to you as strangers. Forget not that Zeus has a care for such as we, strangers and suppliants."

Loud laughed the Cyclops at this. "You are a witless churl to bid me heed the gods!" said he. "I spare or kill to please myself and none other. But where is your cockle-shell that brought you hither?"

Then Odysseus answered craftily: "Alas, my ship is gone! Only I and my men escaped alive from the sea."

But Polyphemus, who had been looking them over with his one eye, seized two of the mariners and dashed them against the wall and made his evening meal of them, while their comrades stood by helpless. This done, he stretched himself through the cavern and slept all night long, taking no more heed of them than if they had been flies. No sleep came to the wretched seamen, for, even had they been able to slay him, they were powerless to move away the boulder from the door. So all night long Odysseus took thought how they might possibly escape.

At dawn the Cyclops woke, and his awakening was like a thunderstorm. Again he kindled the fire, again he milked the goats and ewes, and again he seized two of the king's comrades and served them up for his terrible repast. Then the savage shepherd drove his flocks out of the cave, only turning back to set the boulder in the doorway and pen up Odysseus and his men in their dismal lodging.

But the wise king had pondered well. In the sheepfold he had seen a mighty club of olive-wood, in size like the mast of a ship. As soon as the Cyclops was gone, Odysseus bade his men cut off a length of this club and sharpen it down to a point. This done, they hid it away under the earth that heaped the floor; and they waited in fear and torment for their chance of escape.

At sundown, home came the Cyclops. Just as he had done before, he drove in his flocks, barred the entrance, milked the goats and ewes, and made his meal of two more hapless men, while their fellows looked on with burning eyes. Then Odysseus stood forth, holding a bowl of the wine that he had brought with him; and, curbing his horror of Polyphemus, he spoke in friendly fashion: "Drink, Cyclops, and prove our wine, such as it was, for all was lost with our ship save this. And no other man will ever bring you more, since you are such an ungentle host."

The Cyclops tasted the wine and laughed with delight so that the cave shook. "Ho, this is a rare drink!" said he. "I never tasted milk so good, nor whey, nor grape-juice either. Give me the rest, and tell me your name, that I may thank you for it."

Twice and thrice Odysseus poured the wine and the Cyclops drank it off; then he answered: "Since you ask it, Cyclops, my name is Noman."

"And I will give you this for your wine, Noman," said the Cyclops; "you shall be eaten last of all!"

As he spoke his head drooped, for his wits were clouded with drink, and he sank heavily out of his seat and lay prone, stretched along the floor of the cavern. His great eye shut and he fell asleep.

Odysseus thrust the stake under the ashes till it was glowing hot; and his fellows stood by him, ready to venture all. Then together they lifted the club and drove it straight into the eye of Polyphemus and turned it around and about.

The Cyclops gave a horrible cry, and, thrusting away the brand, he called on all his fellow-giants near and far. Odysseus and his men hid in the uttermost corners of the cave, but they heard the resounding steps of the Cyclopes who were roused, and their shouts as they called, "What ails thee, Polyphemus? Art thou slain? Who has done thee any hurt?"

"Noman!" roared the blinded Cyclops; "Noman is here to slay me by treachery."

"Then if no man hath hurt thee," they called again, "let us sleep." And away they went to their homes once more.

But Polyphemus lifted away the boulder from the door and sat there in the entrance, groaning with pain and stretching forth his hands to feel if any one were near. Then, while he sat in double darkness, with the light of his eye gone out, Odysseus bound together the rams of the flock, three by three, in such wise that every three should save one of his comrades. For underneath the mid ram of each group a man clung, grasping his shaggy fleece; and the rams on each side guarded him from discovery. Odysseus himself chose out the greatest ram and laid hold of his fleece and clung beneath his shaggy body, face upward.

Now, when dawn came, the rams hastened out to pasture, and Polyphemus felt of their backs as they huddled along together; but he knew not that every three held a man bound securely. Last of all came the kingly ram that was dearest to his rude heart, and he bore the king of Ithaca. Once free of the cave, Odysseus and his fellows loosed their hold and took flight, driving the rams in haste to the ship, where, without delay, they greeted their comrades and went aboard.

But as they pushed from shore, Odysseus could not refrain from hailing the Cyclops with taunts, and at the sound of that voice Polyphemus came forth from his cave and hurled a great rock after the ship. It missed and upheaved the water like an earthquake. Again Odysseus called, saying: "Cyclops, if any shall ask who blinded thine eye, say that it was Odysseus son of Laertes of Ithaca."

Then Polyphemus groaned and cried: "An Oracle foretold it, but I waited for some man of might who should overcome me by his valor—not a weakling! And now"—he lifted his hands and prayed—"Father, Poseidon, my father, look upon Odysseus, the son of Laertes of Ithaca, and grant me this revenge—let him never see Ithaca again! Yet, if he must, may he come late, without a friend, after long wandering, to find evil abiding by his hearth!"

So he spoke and hurled another rock after them, but the ship outstripped it, and sped by to the island where the other good ships waited for Odysseus. Together they put out from land and hastened on their homeward voyage.

But Poseidon, who is lord of the sea, had heard the prayer of his son, and that homeward voyage was to wear through ten years more, with storm and irksome calms and misadventure.

HOW THOR FOUND HIS HAMMER

The Norse myths are on a grand scale with little humor. This story is an exception, but even in this ludicrous situation the grandeur of the great god Thor is never forgotten.

The frost-giants were always trying to get into Asgard. For more than half the year they held the world in their grasp, locking up the streams in their rocky beds, hushing their music and the music of the birds as well, and leaving nothing but a wild waste of desolation under the cold sky. They hated the warm sunshine which stirred the wild flowers out of their sleep, and clothed the steep mountains with verdure, and set all the birds a-singing in the swaying tree-tops. They hated the beautiful god Balder, with whose presence summer came back to the ice-bound earth, and, above all, they hated Thor, whose flashing hammer drove them back into Jotunheim, and guarded the summer sky with its sudden gleamings of power. So long as Thor had his hammer Asgard was safe against the giants.

One morning Thor started up out of a long, deep sleep, and put out his hand for the hammer; but no hammer was there. Not a sign of it could be found anywhere, although Thor anxiously searched for it. Then a thought of the giants came suddenly in his mind; and his anger rose till his eyes flashed like great fires, and his red beard trembled with wrath.

"Look, now, Loke," he shouted, "they have stolen Mjolner by enchantment, and no one on earth or in heaven knows where they have hidden it."

"We will get Freyja's falcon-guise and search for it," answered Loke, who was always quick to get into trouble or to get out of it again. So they went quickly to Folkvang and found Freyja surrounded by her maidens and weeping tears of pure gold, as she had always done since her husband went on his long journey.

"The hammer has been stolen by enchant-

"How Thor Found His Hammer." Reprinted from *Norse Stories* by Hamilton Wright Mabie by permission of Dodd, Mead & Company

ment," said Thor. "Will you lend me the falcon-guise that I may search for it?"

"If it were silver, or even gold, you should have it and welcome," answered Freyja, glad to help Thor find the wonderful hammer that kept them all safe from the hands of the frost-giants.

So the falcon-guise was brought, and Loke put it on and flew swiftly out of Asgard to the home of the giants. His great wings made broad shadows over the ripe fields as he swept along, and the reapers, looking up from their work, wondered what mighty bird was flying seaward. At last he reached Jotunheim, and no sooner had he touched ground and taken off the falcon-guise than he came upon the giant Thrym, sitting on a hill twisting golden collars for his dogs and stroking the long manes of his horses.

"Welcome, Loke," said the giant. "How fares it with the gods and the elves, and what has brought you to Jotunheim?"

"It fares ill with both gods and elves since you stole Thor's hammer," replied Loke, guessing quickly that Thrym was the thief; "and I have come to find where you have hidden it."

Thrym laughed as only a giant can when he knows he has made trouble for somebody.

"You won't find it," he said at last. "I have buried it eight miles under ground, and no one shall take it away unless he gets Freyja for me as my wife."

The giant looked as if he meant what he said, and Loke, seeing no other way of finding the hammer, put on his falcon-guise and flew back to Asgard. Thor was waiting to hear what news he brought, and both were soon at the great doors of Folkvang.

"Put on your bridal dress, Freyja," said Thor bluntly, after his fashion, "and we will ride swiftly to Jotunheim."

But Freyja had no idea of marrying a giant just to please Thor; and, in fact, that Thor should ask her to do such a thing threw her into such a rage that the floor shook under her angry tread, and her necklace snapped in pieces.

"Do you think I am a weak lovesick girl, to follow you to Jotunheim and marry Thrym?" she cried indignantly.

Finding they could do nothing with Freyja, Thor and Loke called all the gods together to talk over the matter and decide what should be done to get back the hammer. The gods were very much alarmed, because they knew the frost-giants would come upon Asgard as soon as they knew the hammer was gone. They said little, for they did not waste time with idle words, but they thought long and earnestly, and still they could find no way of getting hold of Mjolner once more. At last Heimdal, who had once been a Van, and could therefore look into the future, said: "We must have the hammer at once or Asgard will be in danger. If Freyja will not go, let Thor be dressed up and go in her place. Let keys jingle from his waist and a woman's dress fall about his feet. Put precious stones upon his breast, braid his hair like a woman's, hang the necklace around his neck, and bind the bridal veil around his head."

Thor frowned angrily. "If I dress like a woman," he said, "you will jeer at me."

"Don't talk of jeers," retorted Loke; "unless that hammer is brought back quickly, the giants will rule in our places."

Thor said no more, but allowed himself to be dressed like a bride, and soon drove off to Jotun-heim with Loke beside him disguised as a serv-ant-maid. There was never such a wedding journey before. They rode in Thor's chariot and the goats drew them, plunging swiftly along the way, thunder pealing through the mountains and the frightened earth blazing and smoking as they passed. When Thrym saw the bridal party coming he was filled with delight.

"Stand up, you giants," he shouted to his companions; "spread cushions upon the benches and bring in Freyja, my bride. My yards are full of golden-horned cows, black oxen please my gaze whichever way I look, great wealth and many treasures are mine, and Freyja is all I lack."

It was evening when the bride came driving into the giant's court in her blazing chariot. The feast was already spread against her coming, and with her veil modestly covering her face she was seated at the great table, Thrym fairly beside himself with delight. It wasn't every giant who could marry a goddess!

If the bridal journey had been so strange that any one but a foolish giant would have hesitated to marry a wife who came in such a turmoil of fire and storm, her conduct at the table ought certainly to have put Thrym on his guard; for never had a bride such an appetite before. The great tables groaned under the load of good things, but they were quickly relieved of their burden by the voracious bride. She ate a whole ox before the astonished giant had fairly begun to enjoy his meal. Then she devoured eight large salmon, one after the other, without stopping to take breath; and having eaten up the part of the feast specially prepared for the hungry men, she turned upon the delicacies which had been made for the women, and especially for her own fastidious appetite.

Thrym looked on with wondering eyes, and at last, when she had added to these solid foods three whole barrels of mead, his amazement was so great that, his astonishment getting the better of his politeness, he called out, "Did any one ever see such an appetite in a bride before, or know a maid who could drink so much mead?"

Then Loke, who was playing the part of a serving-maid, thinking that the giant might have some suspicions, whispered to him, "Freyja was so happy in the thought of coming here that she has eaten nothing for eight whole days."

Thrym was so pleased at this evidence of affection that he leaned forward and raised the veil as gently as a giant could, but he instantly dropped it and sprang back the whole length of the hall before the bride's terrible eyes.

"Why are Freyja's eyes so sharp?" he called to Loke. "They burn me like fire."

"Oh," said the cunning serving-maid, "she has not slept for a week, so anxious has she been to come here, and that is why her eyes are so fiery."

Everybody looked at the bride and nobody envied Thrym. They thought it was too much like marrying a thunder-storm.

The giant's sister came into the hall just then, and seeing the veiled form of the bride sitting there went up to her and asked for a bridal gift. "If you would have my love and friendship give me those rings of gold upon your fingers."

But the bride sat perfectly silent. No one had yet seen her face or heard her voice.

Thrym became very impatient. "Bring in the hammer," he shouted, "that the bride may be consecrated, and wed us in the name of Var."

If the giant could have seen the bride's eyes when she heard these words he would have sent her home as quickly as possible, and looked somewhere else for a wife.

The hammer was brought and placed in the bride's lap, and everybody looked to see the marriage ceremony; but the wedding was more strange and terrible than the bridal journey had been. No sooner did the bride's fingers close round the handle of Mjolner than the veil which covered her face was torn off and there stood Thor, the giant-queller, his terrible eyes blazing with wrath.

The giants shuddered and shrank away from those flaming eyes, the sight of which they dreaded more than anything else in all the worlds; but there was no chance of escape. Thor swung the hammer round his head and the great house rocked on its foundations. There was a vivid flash of lightning, an awful crash of thunder, and the burning roof and walls buried the whole company in one common ruin.

Thrym was punished for stealing the hammer, his wedding guests got crushing blows instead of bridal gifts, and Thor and Loke went back to Asgard, where the presence of Mjolner made the gods safe once more.

THE DEATH OF BALDER

Here is the Norse equivalent of the Greek myth of Demeter and Persephone. Balder, the sun, drifts away in the fiery flames of autumn, leaving the world to darkness.

There was one shadow which always fell over Asgard. Sometimes in the long years the gods almost forgot it, it lay so far off, like a dim cloud in a clear sky; but Odin saw it deepen and widen as he looked out into the universe, and he knew that the last great battle would surely come, when the gods themselves would be destroyed and a long twilight would rest on all the worlds; and now the day was close at hand. Misfortunes never come singly to men, and they did not to the gods. Idun, the beautiful goddess of youth, whose apples were the joy of all Asgard, made a resting place for herself among the massive branches of Ygdrasil, and there every evening came Brage, and sang so sweetly that the birds stopped to listen, and even the Norns, those implacable sisters at the foot of the tree, were softened by the melody. But poetry cannot change the purposes of fate, and one evening no song was heard of Brage or birds, the leaves of the world-tree hung withered and lifeless on the branches, and the fountain from which they had daily been sprinkled was dry at last. Idun had fallen into the dark valley of death, and when Brage, Heimdal, and Loke went to question her about the future she could answer them only with tears. Brage would not leave his beautiful wife alone amid the dim shades that crowded the dreary valley, and so youth and genius vanished out of Asgard forever.

Balder was the most god-like of all the gods, because he was the purest and the best. Wherever he went his coming was like the coming of sunshine, and all the beauty of summer was but the shining of his face. When men's hearts were white like the light, and their lives clear as the day, it was because Balder was looking down upon them with those soft, clear eyes that were open windows to the soul of God. He had always

"The Death of Balder." Reprinted from *Norse Stories* by Hamilton Wright Mabie by permission of Dodd, Mead & Company

lived in such a glow of brightness that no darkness had ever touched him; but one morning, after Idun and Brage had gone, Balder's face was sad and troubled. He walked slowly from room to room in his palace Breidablik, stainless as the sky when April showers have swept across it because no impure thing had ever crossed the threshold, and his eyes were heavy with sorrow. In the night terrible dreams had broken his sleep, and made it a long torture. The air seemed to be full of awful changes for him, and for all the gods. He knew in his soul that the shadow of the last great day was sweeping on; as he looked out and saw the worlds lying in light and beauty, the fields yellow with waving grain, the deep fiords flashing back the sunbeams from their clear depths, the verdure clothing the loftiest mountains, and knew that over all this darkness and desolation would come, with silence of reapers and birds, with fading of leaf and flower, a great sorrow fell on his heart.

Balder could bear the burden no longer. He went out, called all the gods together, and told them the terrible dreams of the night. Every face was heavy with care. The death of Balder would be like the going out of the sun, and after a long, sad council the gods resolved to protect him from harm by pledging all things to stand between him and any hurt. So Frigg, his mother, went forth and made everything promise, on a solemn oath, not to injure her son. Fire, iron, all kinds of metal, every sort of stone, trees, earth, diseases, birds, beasts, snakes, as the anxious mother went to them, solemnly pledged themselves that no harm should come near Balder. Everything had promised, and Frigg thought she had driven away the cloud; but fate was stronger than her love, and one little shrub had not sworn.

Odin was not satisfied even with these precautions, for whichever way he looked the shadow of a great sorrow spread over the worlds. He began to feel as if he were no longer the greatest of the gods, and he could almost hear the rough shouts of the frost-giants crowding the rainbow bridge on their way into Asgard. When trouble comes to men it is hard to bear, but to a god who had so many worlds to guide and rule it was a new and terrible thing. Odin thought and thought until he was weary, but no gleam of

light could he find anywhere; it was thick darkness everywhere.

At last he could bear the suspense no longer, and saddling his horse he rode sadly out of Asgard to Niflheim, the home of Hel, whose face was as the face of death itself. As he drew near the gates, a monstrous dog came out and barked furiously, but Odin rode a little eastward of the shadowy gates to the grave of a wonderful prophetess. It was a cold, gloomy place, and the soul of the great god was pierced with a feeling of hopeless sorrow as he dismounted from Sleipner, and bending over the grave began to chant weird songs, and weave magical charms over it. When he had spoken those wonderful words which could waken the dead from their sleep, there was an awful silence for a moment, and then a faint ghost-like voice came from the grave.

"Who are thou?" it said. "Who breaketh the silence of death, and calleth the sleeper out of her long slumbers? Ages ago I was laid at rest here, snow and rain have fallen upon me through myriad years; why dost thou disturb me?"

"I am Vegtam," answered Odin, "and I come to ask why the couches of Hel are hung with gold and the benches strewn with shining rings?"

"It is done for Balder," answered the awful voice; "ask me no more."

Odin's heart sank when he heard these words; but he was determined to know the worst.

"I will ask thee until I know all. Who shall strike the fatal blow?"

"If I must, I must," moaned the prophetess. "Hoder shall smite his brother Balder and send him down to the dark home of Hel. The mead is already brewed for Balder, and the despair draweth near."

Then Odin, looking into the future across the open grave, saw all the days to come.

"Who is this," he said, seeing that which no mortal could have seen,— "who is this that will not weep for Balder?"

Then the prophetess knew that it was none other than the greatest of the gods who had called her up.

"Thou art not Vegtam," she exclaimed, "thou art Odin himself, the king of men."

"And thou," answered Odin angrily, "art no prophetess, but the mother of three giants."

"Ride home, then, and exult in what thou has discovered," said the dead woman. "Never shall my slumbers be broken again until Loke shall burst his chains and the great battle come."

And Odin rode sadly homeward knowing that already Niflheim was making itself beautiful against the coming of Balder.

The other gods meanwhile had become merry again; for had not everything promised to protect their beloved Balder? They even made sport of that which troubled them, for when they found that nothing could hurt Balder, and that all things glanced aside from his shining form, they persuaded him to stand as a target for their weapons; hurling darts, spears, swords, and battle-axes at him, all of which went singing through the air and fell harmless at his feet. But Loke, when he saw these sports, was jealous of Balder, and went about thinking how he could destroy him.

It happened that as Frigg sat spinning in her house Fensal, the soft wind blowing in at the windows and bringing the merry shouts of the gods at play, an old woman entered and approached her.

"Do you know," asked the newcomer, "what they are doing in Asgard? They are throwing all manner of dangerous weapons at Balder. He stands there like the sun for brightness, and against his glory, spears and battle-axes fall powerless to the ground. Nothing can harm him."

"No," answered Frigg joyfully; "nothing can bring him any hurt, for I have made everything in heaven and earth swear to protect him."

"What!" said the old woman, "has everything sworn to guard Balder?"

"Yes," said Frigg, "everything has sworn except one little shrub which is called Mistletoe, and grows on the eastern side of Valhal. I did not take an oath from that because I thought it was too young and weak."

When the old woman heard this a strange light came into her eyes; she walked off much faster than she had come in, and no sooner had she passed beyond Frigg's sight than this same old feeble woman grew suddenly erect, shook off her woman's garments, and there stood Loke himself. In a moment he had reached the slope east of Valhal, and plucked a twig of the unsworn Mistletoe, and was back in the circle of the gods, who were still at their favourite pastime with Balder. Hoder was standing silent and alone outside the noisy throng, for he was blind. Loke touched him.

"Why do you not throw something at Balder?"

"Because I cannot see where Balder stands, and have nothing to throw if I could," replied Hoder.

"If that is all," said Loke, "come with me. I will give you something to throw, and direct your aim."

Hoder, thinking no evil, went with Loke and did as he was told.

The little sprig of Mistletoe shot through the air, pierced the heart of Balder, and in a moment the beautiful god lay dead upon the field. A shadow rose out of the deep beyond the worlds and spread itself over heaven and earth, for the light of the universe had gone out.

The gods could not speak for horror. They stood like statues for a moment, and then a hopeless wail burst from their lips. Tears fell like rain from eyes that had never wept before, for Balder, the joy of Asgard, had gone to Niflheim and left them desolate. But Odin was saddest of all, because he knew the future, and he knew that peace and light had fled from Asgard forever, and that the last day and the long night were hurrying on.

Frigg could not give up her beautiful son, and when her grief had spent itself a little, she asked who would go to Hel and offer her a rich ransom if she would permit Balder to return to Asgard.

"I will go," said Hermod; swift at the word of Odin Sleipner was led forth, and in an instant Hermod was galloping furiously away.

Then the gods began with sorrowful hearts to make ready for Balder's funeral. When the once beautiful form had been arrayed in grave-clothes they carried it reverently down to the deep sea, which lay, calm as a summer afternoon, waiting for its precious burden. Close to the water's edge lay Balder's Ringhorn, the greatest of all the ships that sailed the seas, but when the gods tried to launch it they could not move it an inch. The great vessel creaked and groaned, but no one could push it down to the water. Odin walked about it with a sad face, and the gentle ripple of the little waves chasing each other over the rocks seemed a mocking laugh to him.

"Send to Jotunheim for Hyrroken," he said at last; and a messenger was soon flying for that mighty giantess.

In a little time, Hyrroken came riding swiftly on a wolf so large and fierce that he made the gods think of Fenrer. When the giantess had alighted, Odin ordered four Berserkers of mighty strength to hold the wolf, but he struggled so angrily that they had to throw him on the ground before they could control him. Then Hyrroken went to the prow of the ship and with one mighty effort sent it far into the sea, the rollers underneath bursting into flame, and the whole earth trembling with the shock. Thor was so angry at the uproar that he would have killed the giantess on the spot if he had not been held back by the other gods. The great ship floated on the sea as she had often done before, when Balder, full of life and beauty, set all her sails and was borne joyfully across the tossing seas. Slowly and solemnly the dead god was carried on board, and as Nanna, his faithful wife, saw her husband borne for the last time from the earth which he had made dear to her and beautiful to all men, her heart broke with sorrow, and they laid her beside Balder on the funeral pyre.

Since the world began no one had seen such a funeral. No bells tolled, no long procession of mourners moved across the hills, but all the worlds lay under a deep shadow, and from every quarter came those who had loved or feared Balder. There at the very water's edge stood Odin himself, the ravens flying about his head, and on his majestic face a gloom that no sun would ever lighten again; and there was Frigg, the desolate mother, whose son had already gone so far that he would never come back to her; there was Frey standing sad and stern in his chariot; there was Freyja, the goddess of love, from whose eyes fell a shining rain of tears; there, too, was Heimdal on his horse Goldtop; and around all these glorious ones from Asgard crowded the children of Jotunheim, grim mountain-giants seamed with scars from Thor's hammer, and frost-giants who saw in the death of Balder the coming of that long winter in which they should reign through all the worlds.

A deep hush fell on all created things, and every eye was fixed on the great ship riding near the shore, and on the funeral pyre rising from the deck crowned with the forms of Balder and Nanna. Suddenly a gleam of light flashed over the water; the pile had been kindled, and the flames, creeping slowly at first, climbed faster and faster until they met over the dead and rose skyward. A lurid light filled the heavens and shone on the sea, and in the brightness of it the gods looked pale and sad, and the circle of giants grew darker and more portentous. Thor struck the fast burning pyre with his consecrating hammer, and Odin cast into it the wonder ring Draupner. Higher and higher leaped the flames, more and more desolate grew the scene; at last they began to sink, the funeral pyre was consumed. Balder had vanished forever, the summer was ended, and winter waited at the doors.

Meanwhile Hermod was riding hard and fast on his gloomy errand. Nine days and nights he rode through valleys so deep and dark that he could not see his horse. Stillness and blackness and solitude were his only companions until he came to the golden bridge which crosses the river Gjol. The good horse Sleipner, who had carried Odin on so many strange journeys, had never travelled such a road before, and his hoofs rang drearily as he stopped short at the bridge, for in front of him stood its porter, the gigantic Modgud.

"Who are you?" she asked, fixing her piercing eyes on Hermod. "What is your name and parentage? Yesterday five bands of dead men rode across the bridge, and beneath them all it did not shake as under your single tread. There is no colour of death in your face. Why ride you hither, the living among the dead?"

"I come," said Hermod, "to seek for Balder. Have you seen him pass this way?"

"He has already crossed the bridge and taken his journey northward to Hel."

Then Hermod rode slowly across the bridge that spans the abyss between life and death, and found his way at last to the barred gates of Hel's dreadful home. There he sprang to the ground, tightened the girths, remounted, drove the spurs deep into the horse, and Sleipner, with a mighty leap, cleared the wall. Hermod rode straight to the gloomy palace, dismounted, entered, and in a moment was face to face with the terrible queen of the kingdom of the dead. Beside her, on a beautiful throne, sat Balder, pale and wan, crowned with a withered wreath of flowers, and close at hand was Nanna, pallid as her husband, for whom she had died. And all night long, while ghostly forms wandered restless and sleepless through Helheim, Hermod talked with Balder and Nanna. There is no record of what they said, but the talk was sad enough, doubtless, and ran like a still stream among the happy days in Asgard when Balder's smile was morning over the earth and the sight of his face the summer of the world.

When the morning came, faint and dim, through the dusky palace, Hermod sought Hel, who received him as cold and stern as fate.

"Your kingdom is full, O Hel!" he said, "and without Balder, Asgard is empty. Send him back to us once more, for there is sadness in every heart and tears are in every eye. Through heaven and earth all things weep for him."

"If that is true," was the slow, icy answer, "if every created thing weeps for Balder, he shall return to Asgard; but if one eye is dry he remains henceforth in Helheim."

Then Hermod rode swiftly away, and the decree of Hel was soon told in Asgard. Through all the worlds the gods sent messengers to say that all who loved Balder should weep for his return, and everywhere tears fell like rain. There was weeping in Asgard, and in all the earth there was nothing that did not weep. Men and women and little children, missing the light that had once

fallen into their hearts and homes, sobbed with bitter grief; the birds of the air, who had sung carols of joy at the gates of the morning since time began, were full of sorrow; the beasts of the fields crouched and moaned in their desolation; the great trees, that had put on their robes of green at Balder's command, sighed as the wind wailed through them; and the sweet flowers, that waited for Balder's footstep and sprang up in all the fields to greet him, hung their frail blossoms and wept bitterly for the love and the warmth and the light that had gone out. Throughout the whole earth there was nothing but weeping, and the sound of it was like the wailing of those storms in autumn that weep for the dead summer as its withered leaves drop one by one from the trees.

The messengers of the gods went gladly back to Asgard, for everything had wept for Balder; but as they journeyed they came upon a giantess, called Thok, and her eyes were dry.

"Weep for Balder," they said.

"With dry eyes only will I weep for Balder," she answered. "Dead or alive, he never gave me gladness. Let him stay in Helheim."

When she had spoken these words a terrible laugh broke from her lips, and the messengers looked at each other with pallid faces, for they knew it was the voice of Loke.

Balder never came back to Asgard, and the shadows deepened over all things, for the night of death was fast coming on.

An English hero tale

"Little John and the Tanner of Blyth." From *The Merry Adventures of Robin Hood* by Howard Pyle

LITTLE JOHN
AND THE TANNER OF BLYTH

Here is a sample of the Robin Hood hero cycle which children should not miss. The Robin Hood stories may lead into the ballads (see Time for Poetry) *or a medieval unit—or may be used for illustration or dramatization or for pure enjoyment.*

It often comes about in this world that unlucky happenings fall upon one in such measure that it seems, as the saying is, that every cat that one strokes flies into one's face. Thus it was with Robin Hood and Little John one bright day in the merry Maytime; so listen and you shall hear how Dame Luck so buffeted them that their bones were sore for many a day thereafter.

One fine day, not long after Little John had left abiding with the Sheriff and had come back, with his worship's cook, to the merry greenwood, as has just been told, Robin Hood and a few chosen fellows of his band lay upon the soft sward beneath the greenwood tree where they dwelt. The day was warm and sultry, so that whilst most of the band were scattered through the forest upon this mission and upon that, these few stout fellows lay lazily beneath the shade of the tree, in the soft afternoon, passing jests among themselves and telling merry stories, with laughter and mirth.

All the air was laden with the bitter fragrance of the May, and all the bosky shades of the woodlands beyond rang with the sweet song of birds, —the throstle-cock, the cuckoo, and the wood-pigeon,—and with the song of birds mingled the cool sound of the gurgling brook that leaped out of the forest shades, and ran fretting amid its rough, gray stones across the sunlit open glade before the trysting tree. And a fair sight was that halfscore of tall, stout yeomen, all clad in Lincoln green, lying beneath the broad-spreading branches of the great oak tree, amid the quivering leaves of which the sunlight shivered and fell in dancing patches upon the grass.

The good old times have gone by when such men grow as grew then; when sturdy quarterstaff and longbow toughened a man's thews till they were like leather. Around Robin Hood that day there lay the very flower of English yeomanrie. Here the great Little John, with limbs as tough as the gnarled oak, yet grown somewhat soft from good living at the Sheriff's house in Nottingham Town; there Will Stutely, his face as brown as a berry from sun and wind, but, for all that, the comeliest yeoman in the mid-country, only excepting Allan a Dale the minstrel, of whom you shall hear anon. Beside these was Will Scathelock, as lank as a greyhound, yet as fleet of foot as a buck of three years' growth; young David of Doncaster, with great stout limbs only less than those of Little John in size, the tender beard of early youth now just feathering his chin, and others of great renown both far and near.

Suddenly Robin Hood smote his knee.

"By Saint Dunstan," quoth he, "I had nigh forgot that quarter-day cometh on apace, and yet no cloth of Lincoln green in all our store. It must be looked to, and that in quick season. Come, busk thee, Little John! stir those lazy bones of thine, for thou must get thee straight-way to our good gossip, the draper, Hugh Long-shanks of Ancaster. Bid him send us straightway twentyscore yards of fair cloth of Lincoln green; and mayhap the journey may take some of the fat from off thy bones, that thou hast gotten from lazy living at our dear Sheriff's."

"Nay," muttered Little John (for he had heard so much upon this score that he was sore upon the point), "nay, truly, mayhap I have more flesh upon my joints than I once had, yet, flesh or no flesh, I doubt not that I could still hold my place and footing upon a narrow bridge against e'er a yeoman in Sherwood, or Nottinghamshire, for the matter of that, even though he had no more fat about his bones than thou hast, good master."

At this reply a great shout of laughter went up, and all looked at Robin Hood, for each man knew that Little John spake of a certain fight that happened between their master and himself, through which they first became acquainted.

"Nay," quoth Robin Hood, laughing louder than all, "Heaven forbid that I should doubt thee, for I care for no taste of thy staff myself, Little John. I must needs own that there are those of my band can handle a seven-foot staff more deftly than I; yet no man in all Nottinghamshire can draw gray-goose shaft with my fingers. Nevertheless, a journey to Ancaster may not be ill for thee; so go thou, as I bid, and thou hadst best go this very evening, for since thou hast abided at the Sheriff's many know thy face, and if thou goest in broad daylight, thou mayest get thyself into a coil with some of his worship's men-at-arms. Bide thou here till I bring thee money to pay our good Hugh. I warrant he hath no better customers in all Nottinghamshire than we." So saying, Robin left them and entered the forest.

Not far from the trysting tree was a great rock in which a chamber had been hewn, the entrance being barred by a massive oaken door two palms' breadth in thickness, studded about with spikes, and fastened with a great padlock. This was the treasure-house of the band, and thither Robin Hood went, and, unlocking the door, entered the chamber, from which he brought forth a bag of gold, which he gave to Little John, to pay Hugh Longshanks withal, for the cloth of Lincoln green.

Then up got Little John, and, taking the bag of gold, which he thrust into his bosom, he strapped a girdle about his loins, took a stout pikestaff full seven feet long in his hand, and set forth upon his journey.

So he strode whistling along the leafy forest path that led to Fosse Way, turning neither to the right hand nor the left, until at last he came to where the path branched, leading on the one hand onward to Fosse Way, and on the other, as well Little John knew, to the merry Blue Boar Inn. Here Little John suddenly ceased whistling, and stopped in the middle of the path. First he looked up and then he looked down, and then, tilting his cap over one eye, he slowly scratched the back part of his head. For thus it was: at the sight of these two roads, two voices began to alarum within him, the one crying, "There lies the road to the Blue Boar Inn, a can of brown October, and a merry night with sweet companions such as thou mayst find there"; the other, "There lies the way to Ancaster and the duty thou art sent upon." Now the first of these two voices was far the louder, for Little John had grown passing fond of good living through abiding at the Sheriff's house; so, presently, looking up into the blue sky, across which bright clouds were sailing like silver boats, and swallows skimming in circling flight, quoth he, "I fear me it will rain this evening, so I'll e'en stop at the Blue Boar till it passes by, for I know my good master would not have me wet to the skin." So, without more ado, off he strode down the path that lay the way of his likings. Now there was no sign of any foul weather, but when one wishes to do a thing, as Little John did, one finds no lack of reasons for the doing.

Four merry wags were at the Blue Boar Inn; a butcher, a beggar, and two barefoot friars. Little John heard them singing from afar, as he walked through the hush of the mellow twilight that was now falling over hill and dale. Right glad were they to welcome such a merry blade as Little John. Fresh cans of ale were brought, and with jest and song and merry tales the hours slipped away on fleeting wings. None thought of time or tide till the night was so far gone that Little John put by the thought of setting forth upon his journey again that night, and so bided at the Blue Boar Inn until the morrow.

Now it was an ill piece of luck for Little John that he left his duty for his pleasure, and he paid a great score for it, as we are all apt to do in the same case, as you shall see.

Up he rose at the dawn of the next day, and, taking his stout pikestaff in his hand, he set forth upon his journey once more, as though he would make up for lost time.

In the good town of Blyth there lived a stout tanner, celebrated far and near for feats of strength and many tough bouts at wrestling and the quarterstaff. For five years he had held the mid-country champion belt for wrestling, till the great Adam o' Lincoln cast him in the ring and broke one of his ribs; but at quarterstaff he had never yet met his match in all the country about. Beside all this, he dearly loved the longbow, and a sly jaunt in the forest when the moon was full and the dun deer in season; so that the King's rangers kept a shrewd eye upon him and his doings, for Arthur a Bland's house was apt to have a plenty of meat in it that was more like venison than the law allowed.

Now Arthur had been to Nottingham Town the day before Little John set forth on his errand, there to sell a halfscore of tanned cowhides. At the dawn of the same day that Little John left the Inn, he started from Nottingham, homeward for Blyth. His way led, all in the dewy morn, past the verge of Sherwood Forest, where the birds were welcoming the lovely day with a great and merry jubilee. Across the Tanner's shoulders was slung his stout quarterstaff, ever near enough to him to be gripped quickly, and on his head was a cap of double cowhide, so tough that it could hardly be cloven even by a broadsword.

"Now," quoth Arthur a Bland to himself, when he had come to that part of the road that cut through a corner of the forest, "no doubt at this time of year the dun deer are coming from the forest depths nigher to the open meadow lands. Mayhap I may chance to catch a sight of the dainty brown darlings thus early in the morn." For there was nothing he loved better than to look upon a tripping herd of deer, even when he could not tickle their ribs with a clothyard shaft. Accordingly, quitting the path, he went peeping this way and that through the underbrush, spying now here and now there, with all the wiles of a master woodcraft, and of one who had more than once donned a doublet of Lincoln green.

Now as Little John stepped blithely along, thinking of nothing but of such things as the sweetness of the hawthorn buds that bedecked the hedgerows, or the crab trees that stood here and there all covered with fair pink blossoms, or gazing upward at the lark, that, springing from the dewy grass, hung aloft on quivering wings in the yellow sunlight, pouring forth its song that fell like a falling star from the sky, his luck led him away from the highway, not far from the spot where Arthur a Bland was peeping this way and that through the leaves of the thickets. Hearing a rustling of the branches, Little John stopped, and presently caught sight of the brown cowhide cap of the Tanner moving amongst the bushes.

"I do much wonder," quoth Little John to himself, "what yon knave is after, that he should go thus peeping and peering about. I verily believe that yon scurvy varlet is no better than a thief, and cometh here after our own and the good King's dun deer." For by much roving in the forest, Little John had come to look upon all the deer in Sherwood as belonging to Robin Hood and his band as much as to good King Harry. "Nay," quoth he again, after a time, "this matter must e'en be looked into." So, quitting the highroad, he also entered the thickets, and began spying around after stout Arthur a Bland.

So for a long time they both of them went hunting about, Little John after the Tanner, and the Tanner after the deer. At last Little John trod upon a stick, which snapped under his foot, whereupon, hearing the noise, the Tanner turned quickly and caught sight of the yeoman. Seeing that the Tanner had spied him out, Little John put a bold face upon the matter.

"Hilloa," quoth he, "what art thou doing here, thou naughty fellow? Who art thou that comest ranging Sherwood's paths? In very sooth thou hast an evil cast of countenance, and I do think, truly, that thou art no better than a thief, and comest after our good King's deer."

"Nay," quoth the Tanner boldly,—for, though taken by surprise, he was not a man to be frightened by big words,—"thou liest in thy teeth. I am no thief, but an honest craftsman. As for my countenence, it is what it is; and for the matter

of that, thine own is none too pretty, thou saucy fellow."

"Ha!" quoth Little John, in a great loud voice, "wouldst thou give me backtalk? Now I have a great part of mind to crack thy pate for thee. I would have thee know, fellow, that I am, as it were, one of the King's foresters. Leastwise," muttered he to himself, "I and my friends do take good care of our good sovereign's deer."

"I care not who thou art," answered the bold Tanner, "and unless thou hast many more of thy kind by thee, thou canst never make Arthur a Bland cry 'A mercy.'"

"Is that so?" cried Little John in a rage. "Now, by my faith, thou saucy rogue, thy tongue hath led thee into a pit thou wilt have a sorry time getting out of; for I will give thee such a drubbing as ne'er hast thou had in all thy life before. Take thy staff in thy hand, fellow, for I will not smite an unarmed man."

"Marry come up with a murrain!" cried the Tanner, for he, too, had talked himself into a fume. "Big words ne'er killed so much as a mouse. Who art thou that talkest so freely of cracking the head of Arthur a Bland? If I do not tan thy hide this day as ne'er I tanned a calf's

hide in all my life before, split my staff into skewers for lamb's flesh and call me no more brave man! Now look to thyself, fellow!"

"Stay!" said Little John; "let us first measure our cudgels. I do reckon my staff longer than thine, and I would not take vantage of thee by even so much as an inch."

"Nay, I pass not for length," answered the Tanner. "My staff is long enough to knock down a calf; so look to thyself, fellow, I say again."

So, without more ado, each gripped his staff in the middle, and, with fell and angry looks, they came slowly together.

Now news had been brought to Robin Hood how that Little John, instead of doing his bidding, had passed by duty for pleasure, and so had stopped over night with merry company at the Blue Boar Inn, instead of going straight to Ancaster. So, being vexed to his heart by this, he set forth at dawn of day to seek Little John at the Blue Boar, or at least to meet the yeoman on the way, and ease his heart of what he thought of the matter. As thus he strode along in anger, putting together the words he would use to chide Little John, he heard, of a sudden, loud and angry voices, as of men in a rage, passing fell words back and forth from one to the other. At this, Robin Hood stopped and listened. "Surely," quoth he to himself, "that is Little John's voice, and he is talking in anger also. Methinks the other is strange to my ears. Now Heaven forfend that my good trusty Little John should have fallen into the hands of the King's rangers. I must see to this matter, and that quickly."

Thus spoke Robin Hood to himself, all his anger passing away like a breath from the window-pane, at the thought that perhaps his trusty right-hand man was in some danger of his life. So cautiously he made his way through the thickets whence the voices came, and, pushing aside the leaves, peeped into the little open space where the two men, staff in hand, were coming slowly together.

"Ha!" quoth Robin to himself, "here is merry sport afoot. Now I would give three golden angels from my own pocket if yon stout fellow would give Little John a right sound drubbing! It would please me to see him well thumped for having failed in my bidding. I fear me, though, there is but poor chance of my seeing such a pleasant sight." So saying, he stretched himself at length upon the ground, that he might not only see the sport the better, but that he might enjoy the merry sight at his ease.

As you may have seen two dogs that think to fight, walking slowly round and round each other, neither cur wishing to begin the combat, so those two stout yeomen moved slowly around, each watching for a chance to take the other unaware, and so get in the first blow. At last Little John struck like a flash, and, "rap," the Tanner met the blow and turned it aside, and then smote back at Little John, who also turned the blow; and so this mighty battle began. Then up and down and back and forth they trod, the blows falling so thick and fast that, at a distance, one would have thought that half a score of men were fighting. Thus they fought for nigh a half an hour, until the ground was all ploughed up with the digging of their heels, and their breathing grew labored like the ox in the furrow. But Little John suffered the most, for he had become unused to such stiff labor, and his joints were not as supple as they had been before he went to dwell with the Sheriff.

All this time Robin Hood lay beneath the bush, rejoicing at such a comely bout of quarterstaff. "By my faith!" quoth he to himself, "never had I thought to see Little John so evenly matched in all my life. Belike, though, he would have overcome yon stout fellow before this had he been in his former trim."

At last Little John saw his chance, and, throwing all the strength he felt going from him into one blow that might have felled an ox, he struck at the Tanner with might and main. And now did the Tanner's cowhide cap stand him in good stead, and but for it he might never have held staff in hand again. As it was, the blow he caught beside the head was so shrewd that it sent him staggering across the little glade, so that, if Little John had had the strength to follow up his vantage, it would have been ill for stout Arthur. But he regained himself quickly, and at arm's length, struck back a blow at Little John, and this time the stroke reached its mark, and down went Little John at full length, his cudgel flying from his hand as he fell. Then, raising his staff, stout Arthur dealt him another blow upon the ribs.

"Hold!" roared Little John. "Wouldst thou strike a man when he is down?"

"Ay, marry would I," quoth the Tanner, giving him another thwack with his staff.

"Stop!" roared Little John. "Help! hold, I say! I yield me! I yield me, I say, good fellow!"

"Hast thou had enough?" asked the Tanner, grimly, holding his staff aloft.

"Ay, marry, and more than enough."

"And thou dost own that I am the better man of the two?"

"Yea, truly, and a murrain seize thee!" said Little John, the first aloud and the last to his beard.

"Then thou mayst go thy ways; and thank thy patron saint that I am a merciful man," said the Tanner.

"A plague o' such mercy as thine!" said Little John, sitting up and feeling his ribs where the Tanner had cudgelled him. "I make my vow, my ribs feel as though every one of them were broken in twain. I tell thee, good fellow, I did think there was never a man in all Nottinghamshire could do to me what thou hast done this day."

"And so thought I, also," cried Robin Hood, bursting out of the thicket and shouting with laughter till the tears ran down his cheeks. "O man, man!" said he, as well as he could for his mirth, " 'a didst go over like a bottle knocked from a wall. I did see the whole merry bout, and never did I think to see thee yield thyself so, hand and foot, to any man in all merry England. I was seeking thee, to chide thee for leaving my bidding undone; but thou hast been paid all I owed thee, full measure, pressed down and overflowing, by this good fellow. Marry, 'a did reach out his arm full length whilst thou stood gaping at him, and, with a pretty rap, tumbled thee over as never have I seen one tumbled before." So spoke bold Robin, and all the time Little John sat upon the ground, looking as though he had sour curds in his mouth. "What may be thy name, good fellow?" said Robin, next, turning to the Tanner.

"Men do call me Arthur a Bland," spoke up the Tanner, boldly; "and now what may be thy name?"

"Ha, Arthur a Bland!" quoth Robin, "I have heard thy name before, good fellow. Thou didst break the crown of a friend of mine at the fair at Ely last October. The folk there call him Jock o' Nottingham; we call him Will Scathelock. This poor fellow whom thou hast so belabored is counted the best hand at the quarterstaff in all merry England. His name is Little John, and mine Robin Hood."

"How!" cried the Tanner, "art thou indeed the great Robin Hood, and is this the famous Little John? Marry, had I known who thou art, I would never have been so bold as to lift my hand against thee. Let me help thee to thy feet, good Master Little John, and let me brush the dust from off thy coat."

"Nay," quoth Little John, testily, at the same time rising carefully, as though his bones had been made of glass, "I can help myself, good fellow, without thy aid; and, let me tell thee, had it not been for that vile cowskin cap of thine, it would have been ill for thee this day."

At this Robin laughed again, and, turning to the Tanner, he said, "Wilt thou join my band, good Arthur? for I make my vow thou art one of the stoutest men that ever mine eyes beheld."

"Will I join thy band?" cried the Tanner, joyfully; "ay, marry, will I! Hey for a merry life!" cried he, leaping aloft and snapping his fingers, "and hey for the life I love! Away with tanbark and filthy vats and foul cowhides! I will follow thee to the ends of the earth, good master, and not a herd of dun deer in all the forest but shall know the sound of the twang of my bowstring."

"As for thee, Little John," said Robin, turning to him and laughing, "thou wilt start once more for Ancaster, and we will go part way with thee, for I will not have thee turn again to either the right hand or the left till thou hast fairly gotten away from Sherwood. There are other inns that thou knowest yet, hereabouts." Thereupon, leaving the thickets, they took once more to the highway, and departed upon their business.

Modern fairy tales are said to begin with Hans Christian Andersen, but actually, they began around 1700 when Mme. d'Aulnoy wrote "The White Cat," "Graciosa and Percinet," "The Yellow Dwarf," and other fairy tales which delighted the French court. Some fifty years later, Mme. de Beaumont composed her famous "Beauty and the Beast," a story similar in theme to the Norse folk tale "East o' the Sun and West o' the Moon" and the German "Bearskin," and so successfully done in folk tale style that, like Robert Southey's "Three Bears," it is generally grouped with the folk tales. If grownups are not

NEW MAGIC: MODERN FANCIFUL TALES

always consistent in their classifications of old and new stories, children are even less so. They don't care whether a fairy tale is traditional and anonymous or recently composed by a well-known author. Magic is magic to them, and they demand their favorites from ancient tales like "Snow-White and the Seven Dwarfs" and "The Fisherman and His Wife" to modern science fiction like William Pène du Bois' *Twenty-One Balloons*. Old or new, they love these figments of the imagination which they call "fairy tales."

Hans Christian Andersen

Hans Christian Andersen (1805–1875) did, however, give fresh impetus to the writing of modern fanciful tales. He began by retelling old folk tales and then went on to write new stories in folk tale style. Soon his creative genius was inventing new forms, so fresh and beautiful that they became enormously popular in his own day and pointed the way for writers of a later age. It is interesting to note the types of stories he wrote and to trace some of their modern descendants. Many examples of each could be given, but a few will suffice to indicate relationships:

1. *Retelling of old tales:* Andersen, "The Wild Swans."—Wanda Gág, *Gone Is Gone.*
2. *Original stories in folk tale style:* Andersen, "Thumbelisa."—John Ruskin, *King of the Golden River.* Richard Bennett, *Shawneen and the Gander.*
3. *Inanimate objects personified:* Andersen, "The Steadfast Tin Soldier."—Lorenzini, *Pinocchio.* Virginia Burton, *Mike Mulligan and His Steam Shovel.*
4. *Humorous tales, drolls:* Andersen, "The Emperor's New Clothes."—Theodore Seuss Geisel, *The 500 Hats of Bartholomew Cubbins.*
5. *Talking beasts:* Andersen, "The Ugly Duckling."—Rudyard Kipling, "The Elephant's Child." Marjorie Flack, *Ask Mr. Bear.*
6. *Allegory:* Andersen, "The Real Princess."—Phyllis McGinley, *The Plain Princess.*
7. *Fantasy:* Andersen, "The Snow Queen."—Lewis Carroll, *Alice's Adventures in Wonderland.* Ruth Stiles Gannett, *Elmer and the Dragon.*

To be sure, many of Andersen's stories, and other people's too, will fall under two or more of these groupings. Andersen's "The Emperor's New Clothes" is both a droll and an allegory, "The Ugly Duckling" both a talking beast story and an allegory. Here lies one of the chief difficulties of Andersen's tales for children. Most of them have double meanings which the children sense vaguely but do not understand because the stories are so often satires directed against the foibles of the adult world. The emperor stands for pompous pretentiousness in high places. "The Swineherd" lampoons false values—a preference for the artificial rather than the real and simple things in life. "The Real Princess" makes fun of adult snobbery, the myth of blue-blooded superiority. Fortunately, children usually miss the adult significance of these social satires. If, in discussing one of Andersen's tales, children eleven- or twelve-years-old show any signs of catching the social implications of the stories, by all means amplify the meanings and discuss their application to our world today. Otherwise, let the children enjoy the stories happily, just as stories—funny or fantastic, sad or gay, but invariably beautiful and moving.

The six tales selected for this volume show Andersen's versatility and power. Since many of the tales are quite long, you may wish to cut some of the lengthy descriptions, as you read them aloud, and that is easily done. But this sampling of his stories should send some children to the library for the whole collection of the Andersen *Fairy Tales.* Their simple goodness is armor against the continual impact of banality and brutality to which the modern child is exposed. When Andersen shows the children cruelty, sorrow, and even death, he does it so gently and with such beauty that they are neither shocked nor hurt. He dares to show them fools and rogues, too, and makes children laugh at the absurdities of these pompous knaves. Then, he writes tenderly about the loving, humble folk in the world and paints unforgettable pictures of their kindness, sincerity, and faith in God. It is, indeed, the spiritual overtones in Andersen's stories that make them valuable. Paul Hazard said of them:

> It is this inner life that gives the Tales their deep quality. From it also comes that exaltation which spreads through the soul of the readers. . . . Their mission is to bring to the world a renewal of faith and hope.[1]

Andersen's successors

After Andersen's *Fairy Tales* had captured the imagination of children and adults all over the world, other writers were inspired to try their

[1] *Books, Children and Men,* pp. 104–105.

hands at tales of magic. In England, in 1851, John Ruskin, philosopher and art critic, put aside his adult writing long enough to create for children *The King of the Golden River*. This is an original story in the old fairy tale form, strongly reminiscent of Andersen. It has the same somber, frightening air and the same strange beauty. The fiery little King of the Golden River, who emerges from the melting golden mug and helps to save Gluck from his evil brothers, is a never-to-be-forgotten figure.

But neither this story nor anything in the Andersen tales can account for the daft gaiety and originality of England's great fantasy— Lewis Carroll's *Alice's Adventures in Wonderland*. The story of what happened to Alice after she followed the White Rabbit down the rabbit hole is interspersed with nonsense verses as mad and merry as the prose narrative. Sometimes the words don't even make sense, but they sing in your head when worthier words are forgotten.

Alice broke upon the astonished world in 1851 and has continued to charm each generation ever since. At least, it charms those who like it, but it is not universally popular. There is a great controversy over the proper age to introduce *Alice* to children. Some adults say they loved it before they were ten years old. But upon investigation, that usually means *Alice* was read to them by some grownup who thoroughly enjoyed it himself. Others say they disliked it heartily as children but somewhere around high school age found it exceedingly funny. Extreme points of view are the usual thing where tales of magic are concerned. One child's delight is another child's boredom, and each is entitled to his point of view. In the case of Alice and her fantastic wonderland, perhaps the best advice to grownups is to try it out with your children if you yourself like it. Read the first chapter of it aloud or the famous excerpt included here, "A Mad Tea-Party." If the children like it, go on with the readings. If they reject it firmly, don't be too discouraged; they will probably discover it later with delight.

During the 1870's *The Peterkin Papers* were appearing in the United States. They are direct descendants of the folk tale sillies and are the ancestors of Hope Newell's *Little Old Woman Who Used Her Head*. The stories about the Peterkin family are a bit dated perhaps, but still funny. When Mrs. Peterkin puts salt in her morning coffee instead of sugar, and the chemist and the herb woman make it worse and worse, the omniscient "lady from Philadelphia" merely suggests that they throw it out and make a fresh cup, and all is well. Eleven- and twelve-year-old children will readily see the relationship of these drolls to the more recent moron stories.

Howard Pyle, also in the United States, published his retelling of the hero cycle, *The Merry Adventures of Robin Hood*, in 1883. This still remains the finest modern source of these stories, and Howard Pyle's own illustrations add greatly to the charm of the book. In 1886 he published his collection of amusing stories in folk tale style, *Pepper and Salt*. These are excellent and are still in continuous use as storytelling sources.

In England around the turn of the century, the publication of two tiny books opened up a new era in writing for children under six years old. These books are *Little Black Sambo* by Helen Bannerman, 1900, and *The Tale of Peter Rabbit* by Beatrix Potter, 1900. These stories, along with their delightful pictures inseparable from the tales themselves, still delight children. They launched the modern picture-story type of book for young children which has continued to multiply from that day to this. The picture-story means, as its name implies, a story in which the pictures are an integral part of the book and in which pictures and text are synchronized and inseparable. Both *Little Black Sambo* and *The Tale of Peter Rabbit* are in folk tale style or pattern but they are told in terms of a four- or five-year-old's imaginary adventures. *Little Black Sambo* is a first-rate hero tale. Sambo encounters danger in the jungle, he uses his wits, gets back all his fine clothes from the tigers, and returns safely to his loving parents, with whom he shares a prodigious number of pancakes. Here's just the kind of conquering hero every child dreams of being.

Peter Rabbit might be any disobedient child, but it is less embarrassing to talk about naughty Peter's adventures, his narrow escape, and his punishment, than to dwell on one's own five-year-old's mistakes. Both stories end on a note of warm security within the family, a reassurance which all small children need. Both stories have a simple, vigorous style that is a model of what good writing for young children should be—no whimsey and no double meanings. Beatrix Potter's little water-color illustrations are exquisite. And in storytelling style, appealing plots, overtones of emotional security, these two small books have not been surpassed and they continue to charm each new generation. Andersen never reached down to the nursery. It took two women to produce the perfect picture-stories for the delight of the small child.

After these epoch-making books at the beginning of the twentieth century, good writing for children increased with astonishing rapidity and diversity. Kipling's *Jungle Book*, preceding them by a few years, appeared in 1894, a strangely convincing story of Mowgli, the boy raised by a wolf pack in the jungle. This was followed in 1902 by Kipling's *Just So Stories*, which pretends, with tongue-in-cheek, to explain such matters as "How the Tiger Got His Spots," "How the Elephant Got His Trunk." The funny sounding words and sonorous sentences in these tales make them most effective when they are read aloud.

The most beautiful of all talking beast stories is probably Kenneth Grahame's *The Wind in the Willows*, published in England in 1908. It is the story of Ratty, Badger, Mole, and the irrepressible playboy, Toad of Toad Hall. These small denizens of the river bank are, of course, prototypes of human beings and, like the Three Little Pigs or Peter Rabbit or Mickey Mouse, they are funnier or more poignant for being animals. Children and adults have apparently always chuckled over the antics of animals used as caricatures of human foibles, and the popularity of the animated cartoons testifies to the permanence of this taste. But Kenneth Grahame's animals are kindly little creatures, loyal friends, patient and forgiving. They succor each other in need, look after the young things, and reclaim sinners from their own misdeeds. The book is full of an earthy delight in sensory pleasures— hot sunshine, moonlight on the river, a warm fire and sizzling bacon after a bitter storm. But it has also spiritual and aesthetic values which children should not miss. Not every child will like it. Long descriptions and British whimsey make it hard reading for average children, but they may enjoy it if it is read aloud by a grownup who knows and loves it and takes the time to savor it slowly, enjoying both its humor and its beauty.

In 1892 English-speaking children acquired a translation of the Italian story *Pinocchio* by Carlo Lorenzini. This droll account of a puppet which came to life and progressed from one misdeed to another captivated youngsters, probably because Pinocchio does some of the outrageous things they too have yearned to do. The punishments of the puppet are as fantastic and amusing as his adventures, and when he finally reforms and turns into a decent sort of real boy, he is still cocky and on top of the world. This is a face-saving triumph that is seldom possible for the repentant child but always to be hoped for.

Looking over the contribution of these early writers who followed Hans Christian Andersen, we realize that however much the modern fairy tale may owe to Andersen's beautiful innovations, his successors soon broke away from his style, mood, and content. Double meanings, overtones of fable and allegory, so prevalent in Andersen's tales, are also to be found in some of these later writings. In fact, these characteristics seldom seem completely absent from children's fairy stories. But where Andersen's tales are predominantly somber or downright melancholy, Carroll, Hale, Pyle, Bannerman, Potter, Kipling, and Lorenzini introduced gaiety, humor, and nonsense. The content of their stories is also easier for children to understand and much of their writing is simpler. The long descriptions are gone from most of their stories, and Helen Bannerman and Beatrix Potter made enormous strides toward a vigorous, direct style of writing for young children. These are the chief contributions of the early moderns to the development of the fanciful story: a new note of gaiety and the picture-story for children under six written in simple, forthright style.

Modern writers of fanciful tales

Recent writers have added many innovations to the fanciful tales, but most of their stories can be classified under the types listed for Andersen, page 273. In the folk tale section of this book, there are admirable examples of modern *retellings of old tales*. Arthur Ransome, for example, retold the Russian folk tales as he heard them from Russian soldiers in World War I. Andrew Lang has retold "Aladdin" and innumerable other traditional stories. Marie Shedlock's delightful version of "The Hare That Ran Away" and Parker Fillmore's Czech stories illustrate the fascination these old tales have for modern writers. However, in this section our chief concern is with original inventions in the field of the imaginative.

Writing *original stories in folk tale style* has appealed to writers from Andersen, Ruskin, and Pyle to the moderns. Wanda Gág, for instance, heard the folk stories told by family storytellers throughout her childhood. With this background it is not surprising that when she began to write and illustrate her own stories for children, she fell into the folk tale style. Her stories have good plots, a beautiful cadenced rhythm, both in text and pictures, and something of the homely quality of the old tales. Yet nothing could be fresher or more original than the plots of her *Millions of Cats, Snippy and Snappy, The Funny Thing,* and *Nothing at All,* which is included in this book. Each of these is a picture-story with action, suspense, and a satisfying conclusion. They have the fable quality which is characteristic of many of the folk tales, and their quiet humor sets the children to chuckling.

Irish writers and those of Irish descent seem always to have a background of the old tales heard from Irish storytellers whose art is remarkable. Richard Bennett, Arthur Mason, Ella Young, and Eileen O'Faolain show their folk tale heritage in the richness of their own fairy tale invention. Yet they do not write alike nor do their stories have many qualities in common.

Richard Bennett's *Shawneen and the Gander* begins quite realistically. An everyday kind of a child yearns for a trumpet and whoosh! Everything begins to happen. It is soon evident that you can't tamper with leprechauns without getting into hot water. It is the impinging of this strange world of fairy upon everyday mortals that makes these stories convincing to children who have never before heard of leprechauns. This is true also of Arthur Mason's *Wee Men of Ballywooden.* The big wind that blew the Wee Men out to sea also played hob with various humans whose lives were more or less tied up with the Little People. Besides the amusing inci-

dents and characters in these modern Irish fairy tales, it is the continual entanglement of mortals and Wee Men that gives the stories their casual air of veracity. Perhaps no other writers can do this as well as the Irish, brought up on fairylore. Their pookas and leprechauns, their trooping fairies and fairy horses open up a new and strange world to American children, not as readily accepted as other types of make-believe, perhaps, but with a humor, a wonderment, and a poetic quality that seem to explain some of the strangeness of events in everyday life.

Personification of inanimate objects was Andersen's special invention and delight. The Fir Tree, the Darning Needle, the Steadfast Tin Soldier, and other objects which he endowed with a life of their own, are vividly alive to the reader, but all too often they meet with a melancholy end. Not so their modern descendants. From that rascally puppet, Pinocchio, to the most recent tales of inanimate objects which come gaily to life, such personifications make lively and joyous stories, usually of the picture-story type for children four- to eight-years-old.

One of the most successful creators of this type of tale is Virginia Burton, author-artist of *Choo Choo,* a runaway train; *Mike Mulligan and His Steam Shovel,* a story about an intrepid shovel, Mary Anne; and *The Little House* (a Caldecott Award), which tells with pictures and text the fate of a little house which finds itself caught in the evolution of a city. These three picture-stories are not only popular with children five- to eight-years-old, but they have unusual social significance. Virginia Burton, who is Mrs. Demetrios, tells us that her books grew out of the intense interest of her small sons in all sorts of machinery. After hearing *Mike Mulligan* read and poring over the pictures, a second-grade child came dashing into her classroom one morning with the news that "Mary Anne" was working over on the next street. And sure enough, there was a steam shovel labeled "41" but to that child it was indubitably "Mary Anne!"

A. A. Milne's *Winnie-the-Pooh* grew out of his son's personification of his toys. The adventures of Christopher Robin with Pooh, his teddy bear "of little brain"; Eeyore, the old donkey; Kanga and Little Roo, the kangaroos; and Tigger, the tiger, are full of British whimsey but are inexhaustibly funny, once the children catch the pattern of their absurdity. Because the grownup quality of British whimsey is often hard for American children to appreciate fully, the Pooh stories should unquestionably be read aloud to children, with any explanations that seem necessary for enjoyment. The way Christopher walks into his world of fantasy, in which he and the toys get into and out of various difficulties, on the same plane of aliveness, is unique. At the end of the story, Pooh is once more a toy that Christopher Robin carries off to bed. The Pooh books are both fantasy and personifications of inanimate objects and altogether delightful. Their distinctive style is made to order for reading aloud.

Adults may talk about *drolls,* but children call them *"funny stories,"* and their demand for "funny books" never wanes. Looking at a group of modern drolls, we see at once that in this category again there is a greater variety than the folk tales presaged or Andersen developed. The sillies are still with us from "Clever Elsie" to Andersen's "Emperor's New Clothes," Hale's *Peterkin Papers,* and Hope Newell's *Old Woman Who Used Her Head* stories. Hope Newell's tales do not have the literary quality of the Hale stories, but the situations are more modern and therefore more understandable to children today.

Some people might also classify Carl Sandburg's *Rootabaga Stories* as drolls. But if you read the tales aloud and study them, it becomes clear that these are a new type of nonsense. Their repetitious phrases, their airy flights of fancy, and their haunting undertones of almost-making-sense have nothing in common with the drolls of the folk tales or the logical illogic of the *Peterkin Papers.* They are poetic nonsense as light as a puff of cloud and as gay as a spring song. Whether or not children are going to enjoy many of them will depend upon the gaiety with which they are presented. But they are Americana and unique. Certainly, children should have samples of them.

So it is with other modern humorous tales for children. They are fresh inventions, they refuse to be typed, and they fall into almost every category of story writing, but especially fantasy. Indeed all of the stories in this collection which qualify as fantasies are also drolls. Mr. Popper,

in *Mr. Popper's Penguins,* the *Elmer and the Dragon* books, *The Magic Bed-Knob,* and all the others are fantastic nonsense, as funny as they are fantastic and as impossible as *Alice's Adventures in Wonderland.* This type of drollery requires a grave, straight-faced sort of writing that suddenly brings the listener up gasping. In the midst of a realistic setting, it asks its audience to accept one impossible, ridiculous premise, and after that, the story develops easily and convincingly. But the nonsense depends upon this continual admixture of the actual and the wildly absurd.

The books of Theodore Seuss Geisel are fantasies of astonishing originality and variety, but to children they are preëminently "funny books." Grownups find in some of them a rare gift for storytelling and a rhythmic style that is repeated in his illustrations. The books are of two varieties. First there is the accumulative, nonsense narrative, in story style but with no plot, which spins along getting bigger and wilder until it returns to its beginning. *McElligot's Pool,* with its beautiful pictures, is one of the most appealing of this type; *And to Think That I Saw It on Mulberry Street* is the funniest. Such picture narratives are a kind of imaginative play both with words and illustrations, which the children like to carry on, drawing their own candidates for McElligot's pool full of weird fish. The second type of Dr. Seuss book is the plot picture-story of which *The 500 Hats of Bartholomew Cubbins* is probably the best known and the most beloved. Bartholomew has a wistful charm that makes much more of an emotional appeal than the heroes of most nonsense tales, perhaps because we tend to identify ourselves with this harried hero who is always earnestly trying to do the right thing and is forever in the wrong. This droll has grace both in the text and the pictures. It is nonsense-fantasy with beauty. Once children have been introduced to the Dr. Seuss books, they will want to see them all.

These examples suffice to show how far the droll has traveled from the patterns of Andersen and the folk tales. It is today an expertly written tale of great variety and fresh inventiveness.

The allegory with its double meanings and its frankly moral lessons has never been so popular with young children as other types of stories. But when it is lightly written, with humor and charm, it may have considerable appeal. Small children, four- to six-years-old, delight in the *Copy-Kitten,* one of a series of little books by Helen and Alf Evers in fable style. *Nothing at All,* which reads like a folk tale but has a strong allegorical flavor, tells its readers that if you are nothing at all, you have to get dizzy getting busy and the first thing you know you'll be something after all. A plainer lesson could hardly be presented, and yet the story is so amusing and so appealing that children enjoy it without any reservations.

Phyllis McGinley handles the allegory with rare artistry. Her *Plain Princess* will appeal to all little girls who begin to suspect that they are not among the world's beauties. The story is well told, and children seem to take the moral in their stride. Actually, children probably don't mind the moralistic as much as adults have thought. Such stories can be genuinely helpful, and when they are also good entertainment, children accept them readily.

From the time the ass spoke to his obtuse master Balaam and delivered a brief but effective rebuke, *talking beast stories* have been popular and show no signs of becoming less so. They hold up the mirror to human foibles either in derision or for the purpose of teaching morals. From Aesop to Donald Duck and Bugs Bunny they interest, they preach, and they teach.

Robert Lawson's *Rabbit Hill* (Newbery Award), seems to be a direct descendant of *The Wind in the Willows,* but for younger children. To be sure, the small denizens of Rabbit Hill are concerned with the human beings who impinge on their lives, but otherwise they are much like Kenneth Grahame's river creatures, rugged individualists and prototypes of human beings. Mr. Lawson's wonderful drawings add much to the charm of this story which remains a continuous favorite.

Ben and Me, also by Robert Lawson, is the absurd biography of Benjamin Franklin, supposedly written by Amos, the mouse. Amos considers himself well qualified as a biographer, for he admits that it is to him Franklin owes his many successes. A ludicrous series of misadventures qualifies the book as a droll although it is also a hilarious example of the talking beast type of story.

Ask Mr. Bear by Marjorie Flack could also be grouped in either of two categories. It is in the style of the accumulative folk tale and is also an example of a talking beast story. Its modern plot —a little boy looking for a birthday present for his mother, its repetitional style and the surprise ending, also modern, have endeared it to thousands of pre-school children.

Hugh Lofting's stories about the redoubtable *Dr. Dolittle,* who understood the language of birds and beasts and embarked with them on an endless series of adventures, have been exceedingly popular with children. In this collection *The Story of Mrs. Tubbs* will introduce the younger children—seven-, eight-, or nine-years-old—to Hugh Lofting's amusing and enterprising animals.

In all of these tales and dozens more, the talking beast story is pursuing its habitual pattern, with the animals as prototypes of human beings, behaving well or foolishly, teaching morals or playing a moral part, sometimes seriously, sometimes with gay absurdity.

Alice's Adventures in Wonderland set the stage for *fantasy,* by which is meant the whimsical illusory tale. *Pinocchio, Winnie-the-Pooh,* and all of the Dr. Seuss books might well be included in this category. Once the reader accepts its magical premise, he is off to a dream world where anything may happen and strange and curious experiences are guaranteed. This dream world of fantasy ranges from the extremes of make-believe in *Alice's Adventures in Wonderland* to the convincing realism of some of the pseudo-science stories today.

Children five to nine are charmed with the three books about Elmer Elevator and his dragon. Elmer's adventures are as fantastic as Alice's but more easily understood because they are completely modern, for example, Elmer's casual raiding of the refrigerator on his return home after his adventures with the dragon. This same quality of modern situations and action helps children to accept the hilarious escapades of Mr. Popper and his penguins. This story sounds so realistic that the reader must pinch himself to realize that, after all, no one could be quite as penguin-mad as Mr. Popper. The realistic quality of the adventures makes its humor. It is partly the absence of a familiar, modern world setting that makes some of the fantasies of Andersen and Carroll harder for children to follow.

The development of pseudo-scientific fiction is one of the most interesting in the field of fantasy. Older children who begin to read science fiction are completely captivated, and it is hard to get them to read anything else while the interest holds. These stories in modern setting are backed up with all the imposing ramifications of science. In William Pène du Bois' *Twenty-One Balloons* the adventures of a weary ex-professor of mathematics on a mysterious island of diamonds, which finally blows up, are fantastic and absorbing. The action develops with all the serious details of a travel diary. Mr. du Bois' books are all beautifully written and illustrated and *Twenty-One Balloons*, the Newbery Award winner for 1948, is one of the best.

Robert Heinlein's scientific fantasies are more genuinely scientific. It is said that he checks all of the situations in his books for scientific plausibility or even possibility and as a result his books read like factual adventures—*in space*, to be sure, but factual. *Space Cadet* or *Boy on Mars* may sound like a possible story, but it is as much a fantasy as Jules Verne's *Twenty Thousand Leagues under the Sea*, from which it is descended. But no matter how the adventures in space are reinforced with scientific data, the stories are still figments of the imagination and to the average reader they are as fantastic as Professor Sherman's explosive island.

In conclusion, it is well to remind ourselves again that in the field of the folk and fanciful tales, children's tastes differ widely and violently. Some children never enjoy this field of fiction. They remain uneasily conscious of the make-believe or they may reject the magic scornfully. But these young literalists may need exposure to it, nevertheless. The drolleries, the poetry, the high adventures, the moral overtones, the romance and absurdities of modern fairy tales are wholesome antidotes for a too tight literalness which may fossilize young spirits too early.

On the other hand, some children take to the fanciful like ducks to water, and they may begin to reject other types of reading. When this happens, it may mean that the dream world is providing these children with compensation for the drabness or the fearfulness of real life. Up to a point, this is good, but when a child wants nothing but fairy tales he needs help. Look gently into his personal problems first, and then try to balance his reading.

With literary fare as with foods, a varied diet is best. So, don't use the stories in this book in a long series. Intersperse them with poetry, biography, realistic fiction, and science books. But when you use these fanciful stories don't be heavy handed with them and don't label them untrue. It is simply a world of make-believe. If some young realist pins you down with an incredulous—"But that never happened, did it?" you may reply gaily, "Well, maybe it didn't, but wouldn't it be fun if it could happen?"

The modern fanciful tales

ASK MR. BEAR

Marjorie Flack

Although this little story is written like an accumulative tale of talking beasts, the child and the surprise ending are delightfully modern. It is one of the favorites of preschool children.

"Ask Mr. Bear," by Marjorie Flack. Copyright 1932 by The Macmillan Company and used with their permission

Once there was a boy named Danny. One day Danny's mother had a birthday.

Danny said to himself,

"What shall I give my mother for her birthday?"

So Danny started out to see what he could find. He walked along, and he met a Hen.

"Good morning, Mrs. Hen," said Danny.

"Can you give me something for my mother's birthday?"

"Cluck, cluck," said the Hen. "I can give you a nice fresh egg for your mother's birthday."

"Thank you," said Danny, "but she has an egg."

"Let's see what we can find then," said the Hen.

So Danny and the Hen skipped along until they met a Goose.

"Good morning, Mrs. Goose," said Danny. "Can you give me something for my mother's birthday?"

"Honk, honk," said the Goose. "I can give you some nice feathers to make a fine pillow for your mother's birthday."

"Thank you," said Danny, "but she has a pillow."

"Let's see what we can find then," said the Goose.

So Danny and the Hen and the Goose all hopped along until they met a Goat.

"Good morning, Mrs. Goat," said Danny. "Can you give me something for my mother's birthday?"

"Maa, maa," said the Goat. "I can give you milk for making cheese."

"Thank you," said Danny, "but she has some cheese."

"Let's see what we can find then," said the Goat.

So Danny and the Hen and the Goose and the Goat all galloped along until they met a Sheep.

"Good morning, Mrs. Sheep," said Danny. "Can you give me something for my mother's birthday?"

"Baa, baa," said the Sheep. "I can give you some wool to make a warm blanket for your mother's birthday."

"Thank you," said Danny, "but she has a blanket."

"Let's see what we can find then," said the Sheep.

So Danny and the Hen and the Goose and the Goat and the Sheep all trotted along until they met a Cow.

"Good morning, Mrs. Cow," said Danny. "Can you give me something for my mother's birthday?"

"Moo, moo," said the Cow. "I can give you some milk and cream."

"Thank you," said Danny, "but she has some milk and cream."

"Then ask Mr. Bear," said the Cow. "He lives in the woods over the hill."

"All right," said Danny, "let's go and ask Mr. Bear."

"No," said the Hen.

"No," said the Goose.

"No," said the Goat.

"No," said the Sheep.

"No—no," said the Cow.

So Danny went alone to find Mr. Bear. He ran and he ran until he came to the hill, and he walked and he walked until he came to the woods and there he met—Mr. Bear.

"Good morning, Mr. Bear," said Danny. "Can you give me something for my mother's birthday?"

"Hum, hum," said the Bear. "I have nothing to give you for your mother's birthday, but I can tell you something you can give her."

So Mr. Bear whispered a secret in Danny's ear.

"Oh," said Danny. "Thank you, Mr. Bear!"

Then he ran through the woods and he

skipped down the hill and he came to his house.

"Guess what I have for your birthday!" Danny said to his mother.

So his mother tried to guess.

"Is it an egg?"

"No, it isn't an egg," said Danny.

"Is it a pillow?"

"No, it isn't a pillow," said Danny.

"Is it a cheese?"

"No, it isn't a cheese," said Danny.

"Is it a blanket?"

"No, it isn't a blanket," said Danny.

"Is it milk or cream?"

"No, it isn't milk or cream," said Danny.

His mother could not guess at all. So—Danny gave his mother a Big Birthday Bear Hug.

COPY-KITTEN

Helen and Alf Evers

A few modern fables, like this one, are popular with small children, but too many of them become monotonous.

No one knew what the Copy-Kitten really looked like—

Because he always tried to look like some other animal.

Sometimes he copied the pigs—

Sometimes he copied the chickens—

But he never copied his mother—

As the other kittens did—

And his mother was worried about him.

One day—

The circus came to town.

The kitten stole away to watch. He crawled under the big tent.

First he looked at the elephant—

The elephant was easy to copy.

Next he saw the monkey—

The Copy-Kitten swung from a bar like the monkey.

Copying the lion was easy, because the kitten looked a little like a lion anyway.

But when the Copy-Kitten came to the giraffe—

And tried to stretch his neck to look like HIM—

He couldn't do it, although he tried and tried.

He stretched his neck, he twisted his head—

He pushed his head with his paws—

But he just couldn't look a bit like the giraffe.

The poor kitten stopped trying—

He had never felt so sad in his life.

He was so sad and disappointed that he made up his mind never to copy anyone again.

When he was home again everyone was very glad to see him—

And everyone was even more glad, because the Copy-Kitten wasn't copying anyone.

But his mother was still worried about him—

Because he wouldn't copy her, as the other kittens did.

All the other young animals copied their mothers—

But the Copy-Kitten was too happy, just being himself at last, to copy anyone at all!

NOTHING AT ALL

Wanda Gág

Wanda Gág not only heard stories well told when she was a child, but she grew up in a family where the father was an artist and every child could and did draw on every scrap of paper he could collect. The Gágs were poor, but Wanda managed to earn enough money to study art even after both parents were gone and she was the head of the family. Her famous Millions of Cats she made up on the spur of the moment in answer to a child's demand for a cat story. She told it over and over until its rhythm suited her. Then, she made the pictures to go with it. All of her picture-stories have this rhythm of pictures and text, and all of them reflect the style of the old storytellers. Nothing at All is a little allegory, but to children it is just an unusual story.

Once upon a time there were three little orphan dogs. They were brothers. They lived in a far forgotten corner of an old forgotten farm in three forgotten kennels which stood there in a row.

One of the kennels had a pointed roof and in it lived Pointy, the dog with pointed ears.

Another kennel had a curly roof and in it lived Curly, the dog with curly ears.

The middle kennel had a roundish roof and in it lived the third dog, but whether he had round ears nobody knew, for he was a dog whom no one could see. He was invisible.

> He was not very tall
> Nor yet very small;
> He looked like nothing,
> Like nothing at all.

And that was his name—Nothing-at-all.

Nothing-at-all was happy enough, for although no one could see him, he had just as much fun as any other dog.

He could jump and run and eat. He could hear and see and smell. He could bark and romp and play with his two little puppy brothers.

And Pointy said to Nothing-at-all, "We love you even if we can't see you."

And Curly said, "We know you are a really truly dog even if we can't see you. We can't see the wind either but the wind is real. And we can't see smells but smells are *very* real."

And Nothing-at-all said, "Oh, I suppose it takes all kinds of dogs to make a world, both see-able and unsee-able ones, so why should I worry?"

And he was as happy as any dog could be until there came a day when something happened.

It was a warm and drowsy day. Pointy was lying in his pointed kennel, Curly was lying in his curly kennel, and Nothing-at-all was lying in his roundish kennel. They were dozing, all three, when the sound of voices roused them from their dreams.

"Oh look!" cried a boy-voice. "Here are some dog kennels in this far forgotten corner of the old forgotten farm."

"With dogs in them?" asked a girl-voice.

The boy looked into one kennel and said, "Yes! There's a curly-eared dog in here."

Next he looked into another kennel and said, "And a pointy-eared dog in here!"

Then he looked into the middle kennel, but since only invisible Nothing-at-all was in there, he saw nothing. "The roundish kennel is empty," he said. "Nothing in it at all."

Gently and carefully the girl reached for Pointy; gently and carefully the boy reached for Curly, but the two little dogs were frightened and began to whimper.

"Don't cry, little pointy-eared dog," said the girl. "We won't hurt you. We'll adopt you both and give you milk to drink and bones to nibble."

And the boy said, "Don't cry, little curly-eared dog. We'll be kind to you. We won't ever hit you or kick you, or pick you up by your neck or your tail, or with your legs dangling down."

When Pointy and Curly heard this, they knew they would be safe and happy, so they snuggled into the children's arms and went back to sleep.

And then they were carried away to a new and happy home, while poor little Nothing-at-all was left behind. But do you think he sat down and cried? Oh no—he had a plan!

"I'll just be very quiet and go with them," he thought. "After a while they'll get used to me and find out I'm a really truly dog even though they can't see me. Then they'll adopt me too. And they'll never hurt me but will give me milk to drink. And bones to nibble. I think I will like it very much!"

Those were his thoughts as he trotted after the boy and the girl and his two puppy brothers.

But it was a long long road, and soon his little invisible legs felt so weary and his big invisible eyes felt so blinky that he had to sit down and rest. His eyes blinked once and twice and thrice, and then he was fast asleep. When he awoke he was all alone.

"Oh, where is everybody?" he cried. "I must run and find them!"

He ran to the puddle pond. No one was there.

He ran round the blossom bushes. No one was there.

He ran past the poppy patch. No one was there.

Back and forth he went, in and out, over and under, in twists and curves and zigzags, but no one was anywhere.

At last he found a hollow tree which looked something like a kennel. He crept into it—and because he felt so lonely and so very much like nothing, he murmured sadly to himself:

> "Oh, I'm not very tall
> And not very small;
> I look like nothing,
> Like nothing at all!"

As he finished, a voice said, "I can't see you, but aren't you that empty space in the tree trunk?" It was a bird who spoke.

"Yes," said the little dog. "My name is Nothing-at-all, and that's what I look like too. I never minded it before, but now I long to look like other dogs so the boy and the girl can see me, and so they'll give me milk to drink and bones to nibble, and never pick me up by my neck or

my tail, but adopt me for their pet as they did my two puppy brothers."

The bird laughed.

"That's a long speech for an empty space to make!" he said. "But I can understand how you feel, and I might be able to help you."

"But you're only a bird," said Nothing-at-all. "How can you help me?"

"I am a JACKDAW," said the bird proudly, "and as such it is my task to carry home everything I see. Once I even found a Book of Magic—wait! I'll be right back," and the bird was gone.

When he returned, the jackdaw said, "It's just as I thought. In the Book of Magic there is a chapter called NOTHINGNESS AND SOMETHINGNESS. And it says that he who is Nothingy, yet wishes to be Somethingy, must get up at sunrise and whirl around and around and around. While whirling thus, he must say this magic chant:

> I'm busy
> Getting dizzy.

This, says the book, he must do nine days in a row at sunrise, and he shall see what he shall see. Goodbye, I'm off!" and the bird was gone.

The next morning before sunrise Nothing-at-all was wide awake and ready to try his magic. As soon as the sun peeped over the hilltop, he began whirling and twirling and swirling, and he said:

> "I'm busy
> Getting dizzy
> I'm busy
> Getting dizzy."

After he had stopped whirling, what do you suppose had happened?

Do you think he was a dog whom anyone could see? No he wasn't. He still looked Nothingy but now his Nothingness had a shape! When he held up his paw, he couldn't see the paw but he could see a paw-shaped space, and he was very happy about that.

"Well done!" cried a voice which was the jackdaw's. "You are a pleasant-looking shape, I must say. Keep it up!" and the bird was gone.

The next day Nothing-at-all worked at his magic as before. As soon as the sun peeped over the hilltop, he whirled and twirled and swirled, and said:

"I'm busy
Getting dizzy
I'm busy
Getting dizzy."

When he stopped, the jackdaw came and said, "Yes, the magic is working well. That's a fine black spot you have on your back now. Keep it up!" and the bird was gone.

The third morning at sunrise Nothing-at-all whirled and twirled and swirled, and said:

"I'm busy
Getting dizzy
I'm busy
Getting dizzy
I'm busy
Getting dizzy."

When he sat down to rest, the jackdaw came and said, "You're doing better than I expected. You've added quite a few spots today. Goodbye!" and the bird was gone.

The fourth day, after Nothing-at-all had whirled and twirled and swirled and repeated his busy-dizzy chant, the jackdaw came and said, "You are certainly working hard at your magic task. That black tail-tip is a beauty, I must say!"

The little dog was so pleased that he wagged his tail wildly, and although the *tail* was still invisible, its black tip showed the wagging plainly enough. The jackdaw laughed at this and then disappeared.

By the fifth day, Nothing-at-all's eyes were visible.

By the sixth day, his nose and mouth could be seen.

On the seventh day his tongue was visible.

On the eighth day his ears and paws could be seen.

And then came the ninth day.

Nothing-at-all whirled and twirled and swirled as he had never done before, and he said:

"I'm busy
Getting dizzy
I'm busy
Getting dizzy
I'm busy
Getting dizzy
I'm busy
Getting dizzy,"

until he was so dizzy that the whole world seemed to swirl around with him.

When he stopped to rest, the jackdaw came.

"Good work!" he cried. "Now you are SOME-THING after all—a really truly see-able dog! And a most lovable round-eared puppy you are, to be sure. Good luck! Goodbye!" and the jackdaw flew away.

Now the little dog was so happy that he jumped to his feet and barked and picked up sticks and tore about wildly.

Round and round in a circle he ran.

With leaps and bounds and somersaults he ran.

In twists and curves and zigzags he ran.

Back and forth, in and out, over and under, around blossom bushes and puddle ponds and poppy patches he ran.

And then he stopped . . . for——

There in front of him were the boy and the girl. They were coming from the far forgotten corner of the old forgotten farm, and were pulling a long red cart on which were:
the pointed kennel
the curly kennel
and the roundish kennel, all in a row!

With a run and a jump, the round-eared puppy hopped into his roundish kennel, and now he too was taken to a new and happy home. All along the way he wagged his black-tipped tail, and with joyful barks he said:

"I've always been small
And not very tall;
I used to look like nothing at all.
I'm still rather small
And not a bit tall,
But now I'm a see-able dog after all!"

But the boy and the girl didn't know what the little dog was saying. Nor did they know what Pointy and Curly were saying when they met their long-lost brother again.
But maybe,
perhaps,
almost surely, they said:
"How happy we'll be, all three of us here; with our dear old kennels to live in, and the two kind children to play with. And oh, little Something-after-all, it *is* so nice to SEE you!"

SONNY-BOY SIM

Elizabeth W. Baker

This delightful tall tale sounds as traditional as "Little Freddy with His Fiddle" and as droll as The Jack Tales. *Sonny-Boy reads aloud as gaily as a jig and the laughing refrain rises like contagious giggles.*

Once a long time ago there was a little log house 'way off in the piney woods. Right through the middle of the house was the dog-trot. The dog-trot was a wide breezeway, like a hall open at each end, with steps at each end to go in and out.

On one side of the breezeway was a long room with a big fireplace in it, and on the other side were three little bedrooms, each with a bed and a chair.

And three people lived in the little log house in the piney woods.

The first person that lived in the little log house in the piney woods was Grandma. She cooked three meals a day at the big fireplace in the long room. She could make the best corn pone you ever ate. She could roast potatoes in the ashes, and barbecue a turkey on a spit in the fireplace until it would melt in your mouth.

And she kept the wide planks in the floor scrubbed with water and wood ashes till they were white, almost, as the lacy bedspreads that she knit.

But in the evenings she liked to pull her rocking chair out into the dog-trot and sit there and rock and rest, and knit on a new bedspread. There she would rock and knit, rock and knit, till the moon came up behind the piney woods.

The second person that lived in the little log house in the piney woods was Grandpappy. All day long Grandpappy plowed the corn or hoed the cotton in the fields. In the fall he cut firewood for the big fireplace, and made sweet cider at the cider mill out back of the house.

But in the evenings he liked to pull his high-backed chair out into the dog-trot, and tilt it back against the wall, and rest while he played the fiddle. He was the champion fiddler of all

that part of the country. He would cross his knees and play that fiddle, and play that fiddle, till the moon went down behind the piney woods.

The third and last person that lived in the little log house in the piney woods was Sonny-Boy Sim. Sonny-Boy Sim roamed the woods all day with his hound-dog, Homer, chasing a bear or a deer, or sometimes maybe just a black-faced coon.

But in the evenings he liked to go out into the dog-trot and dance to the tune of Grandpappy's fiddle. He could bend and turn and leap and clap his hands and lift his feet quicker and lighter than anybody else in all that part of the country. And he would dance to the tune of Grandpappy's fiddle till the moon was sailing through the thin white clouds far above the trees in the dark piney woods.

One day when Sonny-Boy Sim and Homer the hound-dog were out roaming through the piney woods, they came across the biggest black-faced coon they had ever seen.

And Homer the hound-dog opened his mouth and let out a note like a deep-toned bell. And Sonny-Boy Sim and Homer the hound-dog lit out after that coon and chased him clear down to the bayou. And that coon plunged into the water with Homer the hound-dog right after him, close behind.

But just when Homer the hound-dog thought he had that coon, here came a pine stump just showing above the water, and that coon climbed out of the water onto the pine stump.

And when Homer the hound-dog got right up close to the stump all ready to catch that coon, that black-faced coon put out his little black hand and pushed that hound-dog's head right down under the water.

When Homer the hound-dog came up again, he turned around and swam back to where he had started from. And when he had climbed onto the bank and shaken off the water and looked back, that black-faced coon was sitting on the stump, laughing fit to kill.

Then Sonny-Boy Sim remembered that it was just about dinnertime anyway, so he and Homer the hound-dog ran home to get some of Grandma's good corn pone.

One day Sonny-Boy Sim put on a new straw hat that Grandpappy had bought for him at the store, and he and Homer the hound-dog went off into the piney woods. And the first thing you know they ran across a little black bear cub. But as soon as it saw them coming, it climbed right up into a pine tree and sat in the crotch of a limb and looked down at them.

Now, Sonny-Boy Sim wanted that bear cub for a pet. So he said to himself, "I'll climb that tree and catch that bear cub by the tail, and drop it down to Homer the hound-dog, and we'll take it home and make a pet of it."

So he started climbing up that pine tree.

And when Sonny-Boy Sim got nearly up to where that bear cub was sitting in the crotch of a limb, he reached out his hand to take it by the tail.

But all of a sudden that bear cub opened its mouth and showed all its sharp teeth, and stretched out its long claws and snatched that new straw hat right off Sonny-Boy Sim's head. And Sonny-Boy Sim shinned down that tree a good deal faster than he had climbed up. And when he looked back, that bear cub had Sonny-Boy Sim's new straw hat on its head, and it was laughing fit to kill.

About that time Sonny-Boy Sim thought of that good sweet apple cider that Grandpappy made, and he and Homer the hound-dog ran home to get some.

Another time when Sonny-Boy Sim and Homer the hound-dog were roaming through the piney woods, they came across a beautiful deer with wide-branching horns. And Homer the hound-dog opened his mouth and let out a note like a deep-toned bell. And he and Sonny-Boy Sim lit out after that deer and chased him till they had him cornered against a high bank of rocks along a creek.

Sonny-Boy Sim thought, "I'll catch the deer and take its horns and make Grandpappy a hat-rack out of 'em."

So while Homer the hound-dog barked at the deer's heels, Sonny-Boy Sim reached out to catch that deer by the horns.

But all of a sudden, that deer lowered its head, and with its beautiful wide-branching horns caught Sonny-Boy Sim by his suspenders and threw him right up onto a limb of a big pine tree.

And then it caught Homer the hound-dog and threw him on top of the bank of rock where a thick grapevine made a soft bed of green. Then the deer stood there for a minute looking at them, laughing fit to kill.

And as it disappeared into the piney woods, Sonny-Boy Sim got to thinking of that good barbecue that Grandma was cooking, and he and Homer the hound-dog climbed down and ran home to get some.

Not long after that, the coon and the deer and the bear cub met 'way out in the piney woods. And they stopped to talk together.

The deer said, "I'm tired of being chased by Sonny-Boy Sim and his hound-dog Homer."

"So'm I!" said the black-faced coon.

"Me too!" said the bear cub.

"Then," said the deer, "I'll tell you what let's do. Let's get all our sisters and brothers and aunts and uncles and cousins, and go up to that little log house tonight, and show 'em how it feels to be chased about. Let's be there just as the moon is coming up through the piney woods."

That night Grandma pulled her rocking chair out into the dog-trot and got out her knitting. And Grandpappy brought out his high-backed chair and tilted it back against the wall, and began to fiddle. And Sonny-Boy Sim came out and began dancing.

And just as the moon came up behind the piney woods, Homer the hound-dog lifted his head and let out a note like a deep-toned bell.

Sonny-Boy Sim ran to the end of the dog-trot to see who was coming.

Then they heard him call, "Grandma! Grandpappy! Come quick!"

So Grandma and Grandpappy ran to the end of the dog-trot where Sonny-Boy Sim was standing. And there they saw a black-faced coon, and a deer with beautiful wide-branching horns, and a black bear cub, all standing out in the yard. And all around them were more coons and deer and bears—brothers and sisters and aunts and uncles and cousins.

And you can just better believe that Grandma and Grandpappy and Sonny-Boy Sim were scared!

And when they ran to the other end of the dog-trot and saw more deer and coons and bears lined up, they were scared worse than ever.

And Grandpappy said, "Well, they've got us all hemmed in. If they've come here to eat us up, we might as well have one more good time while we can."

So Grandpappy picked up his fiddle and struck up a lively tune, and Grandma ran back and rolled out a barrel of that good sweet cider.

And Sonny-Boy Sim began to dance, and Homer the hound-dog got up and danced all around Sonny-Boy Sim.

And all those deer and bears and black-faced coons came crowding closer and closer, listening to the music and watching Sonny-Boy Sim and Homer the hound-dog dance.

The music got faster and faster, and Sonny-Boy Sim and Homer the hound-dog flung their feet higher and higher.

And presently, all those deer and bears and black-faced coons began to sway from side to side in the moonlight, and the first thing you know, they were all dancing together to the tune of Grandpappy's fiddle.

Then Grandma filled a big tub with that good sweet cider, and set it out where they could all drink as much as they liked. And they all danced to the tune of Grandpappy's fiddle till the moon went down behind the piney woods.

And a soft white mist came up from the bayou, and it wrapped itself about all those deer and bears and black-faced coons, until, the first thing you know, they all went back into the dark piney woods, laughing fit to kill.

MIKE MULLIGAN
AND HIS STEAM SHOVEL

Virginia Burton

This book fits city units and will satisfy every child's interest in modern machines, and will lead children into Virginia Burton's other books, which should be seen as well as heard. The children will like to know that her books were written for her own sons, who criticized them if any detail was omitted or seemed to be wrong. Mike Mulligan reaches down to the youngest children.

Mike Mulligan had a steam shovel, a beautiful red steam shovel. Her name was Mary Anne. Mike Mulligan was very proud of Mary Anne. He always said that she could dig as much in a day as a hundred men could dig in a week, but he had never been quite sure that this was true.

Mike Mulligan and Mary Anne had been digging together for years and years. Mike Mulligan took such good care of Mary Anne she never grew old.

It was Mike Mulligan and Mary Anne and some others who dug the great canals for the big boats to sail through.

It was Mike Mulligan and Mary Anne and some others who cut through the high mountains so that trains could go through.

It was Mike Mulligan and Mary Anne and some others who lowered the hills and straightened the curves to make the long highways for the automobiles.

It was Mike Mulligan and Mary Anne and some others who smoothed out the ground and filled in the holes to make the landing fields for the airplanes.

And it was Mike Mulligan and Mary Anne and some others who dug the deep holes for the cellars of the tall skyscrapers in the big cities. When people used to stop and watch them, Mike Mulligan and Mary Anne used to dig a little faster and a little better. The more people stopped, the faster and better they dug. Some days they would keep as many as thirty-seven trucks busy taking away the dirt they had dug.

"Mike Mulligan and His Steam Shovel." Reprinted by permission of and arrangement with Houghton, Mifflin Company, the authorized publishers

Then along came the new gasoline shovels and the new electric shovels and the new Diesel motor shovels and took all the jobs away from the steam shovels. Mike Mulligan and Mary Anne were VERY SAD.

All the other steam shovels were being sold for junk, or left out in old gravel pits to rust and fall apart. Mike loved Mary Anne. He couldn't do that to her. He had taken such good care of her that she could still dig as much in a day as a hundred men could dig in a week; at least he thought she could but he wasn't quite sure. Everywhere they went the new gas shovels and the new electric shovels and the new Diesel motor shovels had all the jobs. No one wanted Mike Mulligan and Mary Anne any more.

Then one day Mike read in a newspaper that the town of Popperville was going to build a new town hall.

"We are going to dig the cellar of that town hall," said Mike to Mary Anne, and off they started.

They left the canals and the railroads and the highways and the airports and the big cities where no one wanted them any more and went away out in the country. They crawled along slowly up the hills and down the hills till they came to the little town of Popperville.

When they got there they found the selectmen were just deciding who should dig the cellar for the new town hall. Mike Mulligan spoke to Henry B. Swap, one of the selectmen.

"I heard," he said, "that you are going to build a new town hall. Mary Anne and I will dig the cellar for you in just one day."

"What!" said Henry B. Swap. "Dig a cellar in a day! It would take a hundred men at least a week to dig the cellar for our new town hall."

"Sure," said Mike, "but Mary Anne can dig as much in a day as a hundred men can dig in a week." Though he had never been quite sure that this was true. Then he added, "If we can't do it, you won't have to pay."

Henry B. Swap thought that this would be an easy way to get part of the cellar dug for nothing, so he smiled in rather a mean way and gave the job of digging the cellar of the new town hall to Mike Mulligan and Mary Anne.

They started in early the next morning just as the sun was coming up. Soon a little boy came along. "Do you think you will finish by sundown?" he said to Mike Mulligan.

"Sure," said Mike, "if you stay and watch us. We always work faster and better when someone is watching us."

So the little boy stayed to watch.

Then Mrs. McGillicuddy, Henry B. Swap, and the Town Constable came over to see what was happening, and they stayed to watch.

Mike Mulligan and Mary Anne dug a little faster and a little better.

This gave the little boy a good idea. He ran off and told the postman with the morning mail, the telegraph boy on his bicycle, the milkman with his cart and horse, the doctor on his way home, and the farmer and his family coming into town for the day, and they all stopped and stayed to watch.

That made Mike Mulligan and Mary Anne dig a little faster and a little better.

They finished the first corner neat and square . . . but the sun was getting higher.

Clang! Clang! Clang! The Fire Department arrived. They had seen the smoke and thought there was a fire.

Then the little boy said, "Why don't you stay and watch?"

So the Fire Department of Popperville stayed to watch Mike Mulligan and Mary Anne.

When they heard the fire engine, the children in the school across the street couldn't keep their eyes on their lessons. The teacher called a long recess and the whole school came out to watch. That made Mike Mulligan and Mary Anne dig still faster and still better.

They finished the second corner neat and square, but the sun was right up in the top of the sky.

Now the girl who answers the telephone called up the next towns of Bangerville and Bopperville and Kipperville and Kopperville and told them what was happening in Popperville. All the people came over to see if Mike Mulligan and his steam shovel could dig the cellar in just one day. The more people came, the faster Mike Mulligan and Mary Anne dug. But they would have to hurry. They were still only halfway through and the sun was beginning to go down.

They finished the third corner . . . neat and square.

Never had Mike Mulligan and Mary Anne had so many people to watch them; never had they dug so fast and so well; and never had the sun seemed to go down so fast.

"Hurry, Mike Mulligan! Hurry! Hurry!" shouted the little boy. "There's not much more time!"

Dirt was flying everywhere, and the smoke and steam were so thick that the people could hardly see anything.

But listen!

Bing! Bang! Crash! Slam!

LOUDER AND LOUDER, FASTER AND FASTER.

Then suddenly it was quiet. Slowly the dirt settled down. The smoke and steam cleared away, and there was the cellar all finished.

Four corners . . . neat and square; four walls . . . straight down, and Mike Mulligan and Mary Anne at the bottom, and the sun was just going down behind the hill.

"Hurray!" shouted the people. "Hurray for Mike Mulligan and his steam shovel! They have dug the cellar in just one day."

Suddenly the little boy said, "How are they going to get out?"

"That's right," said Mrs. McGillicuddy to Henry B. Swap. "How is he going to get his steam shovel out?"

Henry B. Swap didn't answer but he smiled in rather a mean way.

Then everybody said, "How are they going to get out? Hi! Mike Mulligan! How are you going to get your steam shovel out?"

Mike Mulligan looked around at the four square walls and four square corners, and he said, "We've dug so fast and we've dug so well that we've quite forgotten to leave a way out!"

Nothing like this had ever happened to Mike Mulligan and Mary Anne before, and they didn't know what to do.

Nothing like this had ever happened before in Popperville. Everybody started talking at once, and everybody had a different idea, and everybody thought that his idea was the best. They talked and they talked and they argued and they fought till they were worn out, and still no one knew how to get Mike Mulligan and Mary Anne out of the cellar they had dug.

Then Henry B. Swap said, "The job isn't fin-ished because Mary Anne isn't out of the cellar, so Mike Mulligan won't get paid." And he smiled again in a rather mean way.

Now the little boy, who had been keeping very quiet, had another good idea. He said, "Why couldn't we leave Mary Anne in the cellar and build the new town hall above her? Let her be the furnace for the new town hall and let Mike Mulligan be the janitor. Then you wouldn't have to buy a new furnace, and we could pay Mike Mulligan for digging the cellar in just one day."

"Why not?" said Henry B. Swap, and smiled in a way that was not quite so mean.

"Why not?" said Mrs. McGillicuddy.

"Why not?" said the Town Constable.

"Why not?" said all the people.

So they found a ladder and climbed down into the cellar to ask Mike Mulligan and Mary Anne.

"Why not?" said Mike Mulligan. So it was decided, and everybody was happy.

They built the new town hall right over Mike Mulligan and Mary Anne. It was finished before winter. Every day the little boy goes over to see Mike Mulligan and Mary Anne, and Mrs. McGillicuddy takes him nice hot apple pies. As for Henry B. Swap he spends most of his time in the cellar of the new town hall listening to the stories that Mike Mulligan has to tell and smiling in a way that isn't mean at all.

Now when you go to Popperville, be sure to go down in the cellar of the new town hall. There they'll be, Mike Mulligan and Mary Anne . . . Mike in his rocking chair smoking his pipe, and Mary Anne beside him, warming up the meetings in the new town hall.

THE STORY OF MRS. TUBBS

Hugh Lofting

This amusing little story should prepare small children to enjoy Hugh Lofting's famous Dr. Dolittle books when they are a little older. They may also like Marie Ets' Mister Penny, another story of enterprising animals who help their human friend.

"The Story of Mrs. Tubbs" by Hugh Lofting. J. B. Lippincott Company, Philadelphia, 1923. Used with the kind permission of Mrs. Hugh Lofting

Once upon a time, many many years ago, there lived a very old woman and her name was Mrs. Tubbs. She lived on a little farm, way off in the country. Her little house stood on the edge of the woods, not very far from a village with a little church, and a little river with a little bridge over it, flowed close by the house. There was a barn too for cows and horses, only the woman hadn't any cows or horses; she lived all alone with a dog and a duck and a pig. The dog's name was Peter Punk, the duck's name was Polly Ponk, and the pig's name was Patrick Pink. The old woman called them Punk, Ponk and Pink for short.

Punk and Ponk had known one another for many years and were very good friends. The pig they treated as a baby because they said he was very young and hadn't much sense.

The old woman did not own the farm although she had lived on it so long. The farm belonged to a man up in London who never came there at all. This man, one fine day at the end of summer when the leaves were beginning to fall in the woods, sent his nephew, a very silly young man with a red face, down from London to live in the farm-house instead of Mrs. Tubbs.

Punk, Ponk and Pink and the old woman were all dreadfully sad at having to leave the home where they had been so happy together for so many years.

As the sun was going down behind the little church one evening at the end of Summer when the leaves were beginning to fall in the woods, they all left the farm together. Punk in front, then Pink, then Ponk and Mrs. Tubbs behind.

They walked a long, long way along the edge of the woods and at last when they saw a seat under a tree they all sat down to rest.

"Oh dear, oh dear," Mrs. Tubbs kept saying, "now I have no home, no place to sleep. And me an old woman. To be turned off the farm after all these years! What shall I do, where shall I go? Oh dear, oh dear!"

Then she stopped talking. Peter Punk and Polly Ponk both understood what she said because they had lived with her so long. Pink couldn't understand because he was only a baby and he kept saying in animal language:—"Let's go on. I don't like this place. There's nothing to eat here."

"I do think it's a shame," Polly Ponk said to Punk, "that the old woman should be turned out. Did you see the way that stupid man slammed the door after we had gone? I'd like to see him turn *me* out of *my* house that way. I'd give him such a peck on his red nose he wouldn't try it again! But of course she is old, very old. I often wonder how old she really is."

"She is over a hundred, I know," said Punk. "Yes, it is a shame she should have to go for that stupid booby. 'Beefsteak-and-Onions' I call him. But it isn't altogether his fault. He's only sent here from London by his uncle who owns the farm."

"Well, what are we going to do with the old lady?" asked Ponk. "She can't stay here."

"We will wait till she falls asleep," said Punk. "Then we'll go into the woods and find a cave for her to spend the night in and cook something to eat."

"Isn't she asleep now?" asked Ponk. "Her eyes are shut."

"No," said the dog, "she's crying. Can't you feel the seat shaking? She always shuts her eyes and shakes when she cries."

Presently the old lady and the pig began to snore together. So they waked poor Pink up and all three went into the woods. They set Pink digging truffles and Polly Ponk went off to the river and caught a fine trout while Punk got sticks together and made a fire.

"Now who's going to do the cooking?" asked Punk.

"Oh, I'll do that," said Ponk.

"Can you cook?" asked the dog.

"Indeed I can," said Polly Ponk. "My Aunt Deborah used to cook at a hotel and she showed me how. You get the fire burning and I'll soon have the fish fried."

So very soon they had a nice meal ready of fried trout and truffles for the old lady.

"Now," said Punk, "we must go into the cave and get a bed ready for Mrs. Tubbs."

So they went into the cave and made a fine, soft bed of leaves.

"What shall we do for a pillow," said Punk. "Shall we use the pig, he would be nice and soft?"

"No," said Ponk, "I'm going to use him as a hot-water bottle. It's very important to keep the old lady's feet warm. But I have some feathers back home which will make a fine pillow. They are some of my own which I kept last moulting season."

"What did you do that for?" asked Punk.

"Well," said the duck, standing first on one foot then on the other, "the fact is I'm not getting any younger myself and I thought that if, when I am very old, I should get bald, I could have them stuck on with glue or something. I'll fly over to the farm and fetch them. I know just where I put them: they're in the left-hand drawer of my bureau under my lavendar bonnet."

With a flap of her wings she flew over the tree-tops to the farm and in a minute was back again with the feathers in a bag.

When they had everything ready they went and fetched Mrs. Tubbs and showed her the supper they had prepared. But the old woman would not eat anything but kept saying,

"Oh dear, oh dear! What shall I do? I am turned out of house and home, and me an old woman!"

So they put her to bed in the cave, covered her over with leaves and placed Pink at her feet as a hot-water bottle. And presently she cried herself to sleep.

Punk and Ponk now began to worry over what they should do with the old woman next.

"She can't stay here," said Ponk. "That's certain. You see, Punk, she isn't eating anything. She is so upset and she is so old. What we've got to do is to find some way to turn that booby out of the farm so she can go back and live there."

"Well, what shall we do?" said the dog.

"I don't just know yet," Polly Ponk answered. "But in the morning before she wakes up, we must go back to the farm and see what can be done."

So next morning, while the old woman was still asleep, off they all went as the sun was getting up behind the woods. Just before they got to the farm as they were crossing the bridge over the stream, they saw Tommy Squeak, the King of the Water-rats coming down for his morning bath in the river.

"Catch him!" said Ponk. "Perhaps he'll be able to help." And they all started running as hard as they could after the water-rat. Poor Tommy Squeak was dreadfully frightened at see-ing a dog and a pig and a duck coming after him, and he made off for the river as fast as his legs would carry him. When he came to the river he jumped in with a splash and disappeared. Punk and Pink sat down on the grass and said, "We've lost him!"

But Polly Ponk, running up behind, never stopped but dived into the river, swam under the water and just caught poor Mr. Squeak as he was popping into a hole way down at the bottom of the river. She pulled him up by his tail, carried him to the shore and put him on the grass. Then they all gathered round him so he couldn't run away.

"Now," said the duck, "don't be frightened. Stay where you are and do as you are told and we won't hurt you. Listen. Do you remember, last summer, when you were stealing cheese from the pantry up at the farm, and you fell into a bucket of water and Mrs. Tubbs came and caught you? Do you remember?"

"Yes," said Tommy Squeak, shaking the water off his whiskers, still very frightened.

"And she didn't hurt you or give you to the cat. Do you remember?"

"Yes," said Tommy Squeak.

"She let you go and told you never to come back again. Did she not?"

"Yes," said Tommy Squeak.

"You know that she is the kindest woman to animals in all the world, don't you?"

"Yes," said Tommy Squeak.

"Allright," said Polly. "Now listen. A red-faced booby from London Town has been sent down here to turn Mrs. Tubbs out of her house. She is terribly old, as you know; we have taken her up into the woods. But she won't eat her food, she is so sad, and we can't do a thing with her. The Winter is coming on and we must get her back into the farm somehow. Now you are the king of the water-rats and this is what you must do: Call all the rats of the river together—every one of them—thousands of them and take them to the farm. Then worry the booby every way you can think of. Rattle the pans in the kitchen at night so he can't sleep. Pull the stuffing out of the chairs. Eat holes in his best hat. Do everything you can to drive him out. Then, if he goes back to London Town, we can put Mrs. Tubbs back on the farm."

"Allright," said Tommy Squeak. "I'll do my best for the old woman. She certainly ought to be put back on the farm."

Then he stood up on his hind legs by the river-bank and facing up the stream, he gave a long, loud, wonderful squeak. Then he turned and facing down the stream he gave another.

And presently there was a rustling sound in the grasses all around and a whispering sound in the bushes and a splashing sound from the water. And everywhere rats appeared, hopping and jumping towards him—big ones and little ones, black ones, grey ones, brown ones, piebald ones —families of them, hundreds of them—thousands—millions. And they gathered round Tommy Squeak the King-Rat in a great, great big circle. Their beady, black eyes looked very frightened when they saw a dog there but they didn't run away because the king had called them.

Then Tommy Squeak stood up to speak to them and they all stopped cleaning their whiskers to listen.

"Rats," he said, "we have a job of work to do. Follow me." And waving his paw to Punk, Ponk and Pink, he led the way to the farm.

For a whole day and a night the rats worked very hard, trying to turn the man out. They rattled the pans in the kitchens at night. They pulled the stuffing out of his chair. They ate holes in his new, green hat. They stopped the clock. They pulled the curtains down upon the floor. But the man sent to London Town and got three wagon-loads of cats and the rats were all driven back to the river. Tommy Squeak came to Punk, Pink and Ponk on the second day and said,

"I am sorry. We did our best, but we couldn't move him."

So Ponk said to Punk, "Well, we must try something else." And they left the old woman in the woods and started off again.

As they were crossing the river this time before they got to the farm, they saw Tilly Twitter, the Queen of the Swallows, sitting on the corner of the bridge.

"Good-morning!" said Tilly. "You all look very sad."

"Oh, Tilly," said Punk, with tears in his eyes, "Mrs. Tubbs has been turned out of house and home."

"Good gracious!" cried Tilly. "You don't say! Who turned her out?"

"A man from London," said Punk. "I call him 'Beefsteak-and-Onions.' Do you think you can do anything to help us get her back to the farm?"

"Certainly I'll do my best," said Tilly, pushing her crown further back on her head. "I have built my nest over the old woman's door for three Springs now. I would hate to have her leave the farm for good. I'll see what I can do."

Then she flew up into the air going round and round in circles. Higher and higher she flew and all the time she sang a beautiful song at the top of her voice.

And this is the song she sang:

"The leaves are falling in the woods.
Go get your travelling rugs and hoods.
The Summer's gone; the snow'll soon be here.
It's time to fly; but we'll come back next year."

Now every year when all the swallows heard Tilly Twitter sing this song they knew it was time for them to get together to fly to Africa because they don't like the winter's cold in England. So now when they heard it they got their children together and snatching up their bags and bundles, they all flew towards Mrs. Tubb's farm. So many of them came that the sky grew dark and people thought the night was come. And the farm-boys in the country around stopped their plough-horses and said, "There go the swallows, getting ready to fly to Africa. The frost will soon be here."

For five hours they kept coming, more and more and more of them. They gathered around Tilly, sitting on the house, on the barn and the railings, on the gates, on the bridge and on the stones. But never on the trees. Swallows never sit on trees. So many of them came that the whole land seemed covered with the blue of their wings and the white of their breasts.

And when they had all arrived Tilly got up and spoke.

"Swallows," she said, "many years ago, when I first built my mud nest under the eaves of this farm, I had five children in my nest. They were my first family and I was very proud of them. That was before I became the Queen of the Swallows. And being a very inexperienced mother I built the nest too small. When my children grew up there was not proper room for them. Philip—a very strong child—was always twisting and turning in the nest and one day he fell out. He bumped his nose badly on the ground but it was not far to fall and he was not much hurt. I was just going to fly down and try to pick him up when I saw a large weasel coming across the farm-yard to get him. My feathers stood up on the top of my head with fright. I flew to the farm-house window and beat upon the glass with my wings. An old woman came out. When she saw Philip on the ground and the weasel coming to get him she threw her porridge-spoon at the weasel, picked Philip up and put him back in my nest. That old woman's name was Mrs. Tubbs. She has now been turned out of her house and a very stupid red-faced man is living on the farm in her place. We have got to do our best to turn him out and put Mrs. Tubbs back in her house, the same as she put my child back in his nest. So I have called you all together a week earlier than usual this year for our long journey to Africa, and before we leave England we have got to see what we can do. The first thing we'll do is to stop up his chimney so his fire won't burn. Then put mud all over the windows so the light will not come in. Bring all the straw from the barn and fill his bed-room with it. Take his best neck-tie and drop it in the river. And do everything you can to drive him out."

So the swallows set to work and Punk, Ponk and Pink went back to the old woman in the woods.

But after two days Tilly came to them and said, "I am very sorry, but I have not succeeded. The cats have driven my swallows away. He has a thousand cats in the place. What can one do?"

So Punk said to Ponk, "We must go out and try something else."

But Polly Ponk answered,

"No, you go alone this time. The old woman is getting a cold and I must stay and look after her."

So Peter Punk went off with his tail dragging on the ground. He hung about the farm and was very sad and wondered what he could do to drive Beefsteak-and-Onions out of the house.

Presently, feeling hungry, he remembered he had hidden a ham-bone in the trunk of a tree behind the house some weeks ago and he went off to see if it was still there. When he got to the tree he stood up on his hind-legs and looked into the hole. A wasp flew out and stung him on the nose. He sat down on the grass and watched the tree for a minute and saw many wasps coming in and going out through the hole. Then he understood what had happened. Thousands of wasps had made a nest in the hollow tree.

So he thought of a plan. He went and got a big stick and threw it into the hole in the tree. Then all the wasps came flying out and tried to sting him. He went running towards the house with the wasps after him and ran in through the back door of the house. The wasps kept following him—though a few stopped to sting some of the cats that were hanging about the back door. Then he ran up the stairs by the front staircase, into the bedrooms and down by the backstairs. In the hall he found Beefsteak-and-Onions, who had just come in from digging potatoes, with a spade in his hand. Punk ran between his legs and out through the front door.

When the wasps could not find Punk any more they thought the man had hidden him somewhere so they set upon him and stung him. And the rest of them stung all the cats they could find in the house and drove them away across the fields.

Poor Beefsteak-and-Onions ran out into the yard and shut himself up in the barn to get away from the wasps. Then he laid down his spade and put on his coat and said,

"I'll leave this house today. My uncle can come and live here himself if he wants to. But I'm going back to London Town. I didn't want to turn the old lady out anyway. I do not believe my uncle knew anyone was living here at all. I am going today."

Punk was listening outside the door and heard him, so he ran off at once back to the woods. When he got to Ponk and Pink he started dancing on his hind-legs.

"What's the matter?" asked Ponk. "Have you gone crazy?"

But all he answered was:

"Hooray, Hooray!
He's going away,
Old Beefsteak-and-Onions
Is going today."

Then he told them how he had at last succeeded and they both thought he was a very clever dog.

It was now getting late in the evening so they went and got Mrs. Tubbs and they all walked back to the farm by moonlight.

And the old woman was so happy to get back to her little house that she made them all a very fine supper. And Pink said,

"I am glad to get back. There is something to eat here."

And so when the leaves were all fallen in the woods, and the trees stood bare waiting for the snow, they used to sit round the warm fire in the evenings toasting chestnuts and telling stories while the kettle steamed upon the hob and the wind howled in the chimney above. And they never had to leave the farm again and they all lived happily ever after.

HOW SHE KEPT

HER GEESE WARM

Hope Newell

There are two books of these "Little Old Woman" stories, and children seem to like them both. With the eights and nines it might be fun to read them "Clever Elsie" and one of the Peterkin stories to see if they will notice the similarity.

One cold winter night, the Little Old Woman was out in the barn putting her geese to bed. She gave them some corn and took off their little red coats. Then she brushed each little coat with a whisk-broom and carefully shook out the wrinkles.

As she was folding the coats in a neat pile, she thought:

"My poor geese must be very cold at night. I have my cozy fire and my feather bed. But they have not even a blanket to keep them warm."

After the geese had eaten their corn, they began to go to roost.

"Honk, honk!" said the big gander, and he hopped up on the roost.

"How She Kept Her Geese Warm." From *The Little Old Woman Who Used Her Head* by Hope Newell. Thomas Nelson & Sons. Used by permission

"Honk, honk!" said the grey goose, and she hopped up on the roost.

"Honk, honk!" said all the other geese, and they hopped up on the roost.

Then the Little Old Woman closed the barn door and went into the house. When she went to bed, she lay awake worrying about the geese. After a while she said to herself:

"I cannot sleep a wink for thinking how cold the geese must be. I had better bring them in the house where it is warm."

So the Little Old Woman dressed herself and went out to the barn to fetch the geese. She shooed them off the roost and put on their little red coats. She picked up two geese, and tucking one under each arm, she carried them into the house.

Then she went out to the barn and picked up two more geese. She tucked one goose under each arm and carried them into the house.

When the Little Old Woman had brought all the geese into the house, she said to herself:

"Now I must get them ready for bed again."

She took off their little red coats and gave the geese some corn. Then she brushed each little coat with a whisk-broom and carefully shook out all the wrinkles.

As she was folding the coats in a neat pile, she thought:

"It was very clever of me to bring the geese into the house. Now they will be warm, and I shall be able to sleep."

Then the Little Old Woman undressed herself again and went to bed.

After the geese had eaten their corn, they began to roost.

"Honk, honk!" said the gander, and he hopped up on the foot of the Little Old Woman's bed.

"Honk, honk!" said the grey goose, and she hopped up on the foot of the Little Old Woman's bed.

"Honk, honk!" said all the other geese, and they tried to hop up on the foot of the Little Old Woman's bed.

But it was not a very big bed, and there was not enough room for all the geese to roost. They began to fight. They pushed and shoved each other. They hissed and squawked and flapped their wings.

All night long the geese pushed and shoved each other. All night long they hissed and squawked and flapped their wings.

They made so much noise that the Little Old Woman did not sleep a wink.

"This will never do," she said. "When they were in the barn, I did not sleep for thinking how cold they must be. When they are in the house, I cannot sleep because they make so much noise. Perhaps if I use my head, I shall know what to do."

The Little Old Woman tied a wet towel around her forehead. Then she sat down with her forefinger against her nose and shut her eyes.

She used her head and used her head, and after a while she knew what to do.

"I will move the roost into the house," she said. "The geese will have the cozy fire to keep them warm. Then I will move my bed out into the barn. My feather bed will keep me warm, and I will not be worrying about the geese. They will not keep me awake with their noise. I shall sleep very comfortably in the barn."

The Little Old Woman moved the roost into the house, and she moved her bed out into the barn.

When night came again, she brought the geese into the house. After she had fed them some corn, she took off their little red coats. Then they all hopped up on the roost, and the Little Old Woman went out to the barn to sleep.

Her feather bed kept her as warm as toast. She was not worried about the geese, because she knew that they were warm too. So she slept as sound as a top all night long.

HOW SHE MADE

THE BABY ELEPHANT HAPPY

Hope Newell

When the Little Old Woman came in sight of her house, she saw something gray and round and fat running around her garden.

As she came near enough to get a good look at it, she saw that it was a baby elephant.

"Mercy on me!" she said. "This is a great day indeed. First, I see the circus come to town and now I find a baby elephant in my garden."

As she watched the baby elephant running about the garden, and pulling up carrots and cabbages and turnips with his trunk, she thought: "It is not often that I find an elephant eating my vegetables. Indeed, so far as I can recall, I have never seen one in my garden before.

"I wonder where he came from. I could use my head and find out, of course. But this is no time to use my head. The main thing is that he

"How She Made the Baby Elephant Happy." From *More About the Little Old Woman Who Used Her Head* by Hope Newell. Thomas Nelson & Sons. Used by permission

is here, and I must make him happy so that he will not run away."

The baby elephant kept running about the garden pulling up cabbages and carrots and turnips with his trunk and eating them.

"I do not need to worry about feeding him," said the Little Old Woman. "He is feeding himself very well. However, I must find him a house, so that he can have a roof over his head."

"He could live in my house," she thought. "Then he could have my roof over his head. But his feet are so big he might step on the rats.

"Or, he might live in the barn," she said. "Then he could have the barn roof over his head. But, if I put him in the barn, he might step on the geese. I had better build him a little shed and then he will have his own roof over his head."

As soon as she had fed the geese and the rats, the Little Old Woman set to work building a shed for the baby elephant. When the shed was finished she coaxed him into it by feeding him peanuts. She nailed a board across the front of it so that he would stay inside. Then she began to weed her garden.

The baby elephant started running after her and dragging the shed with him.

"What a funny elephant," said the Little Old Woman. "He likes to move his shed around with him."

But the shed was not easy to move. The posts dragged on the ground and made the baby elephant stumble. He did not like this so he lifted up his trunk and squealed. He squealed and squealed.

"Dear me!" said the Little Old Woman. "It is very sad to hear a baby elephant squeal. I must use my head and try to figure out how he can move his shed around without stumbling."

The Little Old Woman went into the house, and tied a wet towel around her head. Then she sat down with her forefinger against her nose and shut her eyes.

She used her head and used her head. Before long she had figured out how the baby elephant could move his shed around without stumbling.

"I will put a wheel on the bottom of each post," she said. "Then he can move his shed around very easily."

The Little Old Woman took the wheels off the little wagon that she used for hauling firewood in the winter. She put a wheel on the bottom of each post of the baby elephant's shed.

Then she went on weeding her garden. The baby elephant started running after her. The posts did not drag on the ground and he moved the shed very easily.

"It was very clever of me to think of putting wheels on his shed," said the Little Old Woman. "Now he can move it wherever he wants to and he will not stumble."

All day the Little Old Woman pulled weeds out of her garden. All day, the baby elephant followed her and pulled up carrots and cabbages and turnips with his trunk and ate them.

When the geese went for their evening swim in the nearby pond, the baby elephant went with them. He waded into the pond and filled his trunk with water. He blew water over the top of his shed, and he blew water on the geese.

He was very happy.

After supper the Little Old Woman took her mending and sat down in her rocking-chair on the porch.

The baby elephant had come back from the pond. He was running about the garden, pulling up carrots and cabbages and turnips with his trunk and eating them.

"I like this baby elephant very much," said the Little Old Woman. "However, I hope no more baby elephants come to live with me. I have no more wood to make sheds and they would have no roofs over their heads.

"Moreover, I would not have enough vegetables to feed them. As it is, this baby elephant will have eaten everything in the garden by morning. Then I shall have to use my head to find out how to feed him."

Just then the Little Old Woman heard a great noise in the distance. Wagon wheels were rumbling, men were shouting, and horses' hoofs were going "plack-plack" over the cobblestones.

"Dear me," said the Little Old Woman. "That must be the circus leaving town."

The baby elephant heard the noise, too. When the Little Old Woman went around to the back of her house where she could watch the circus going over the distant hill, the baby elephant went with her.

They watched the big animal wagons go over

the hill. They watched the camels and they watched the big white circus horses, and the little Shetland ponies.

When the baby elephant saw the big elephants walking slowly over the hill, he dropped the carrot he was eating and his big ears started waving back and forth. Then he lifted up his trunk and squealed. He squealed and squealed and squealed.

One of the big elephants dropped the tail of the elephant in front of her. She lifted up her trunk, and rumbled as loud as thunder.

Before the Little Old Woman could wink her eye, the baby elephant started running in his little shed. When he reached the fence he did not stop. He broke right through the fence and kept on running. He reached the hill just as the big cook-wagon went over its top.

The baby elephant ran up the hill and in a few seconds he too disappeared over the top.

"Dear me," said the Little Old Woman, "I do believe the baby elephant belonged to the circus. The big elephant who rumbled so loudly must have been his mother. Now he has gone back to her and I have no baby elephant."

She went back to the porch and sat down in her rocking chair.

"I shall miss the baby elephant very much," she thought.

"However, perhaps it is just as well that he has gone back to his mother. If he ate as much every day as he did today, I would have to use my head very hard to find out how to feed him.

"I am glad that I made him a little shed so that he will always have a roof over his head. It is a very useful thing to know how to make a shed for an elephant. If ever I find another elephant in my garden, I will know just how to go about it. I am a very wise old woman indeed."

WILLIE'S BAD NIGHT

Robert Lawson

Rabbit Hill was the name of Robert Lawson's own house in the country, and the multitude of small animals that inhabited the place gave him his idea for the story. Undoubtedly the four-footed denizens of the Hill approved of Mr. Lawson's generous theory that "there is enough for all," but Mr. Lawson confessed that in spite of "enough," the moles were a problem.

It was Bluegrass that almost proved the undoing of Willie Fieldmouse. He was on the window sill, as usual, watching and listening to the Folks. This evening, having finished their gardening plans, they were talking of grass seed. Willie was not especially interested and was only half listening when he was suddenly electrified by a familiar word.

"This book," the Man was saying, "recommends a mixture of Red Top, White Clover and Kentucky Bluegrass."

Bluegrass! Kentucky Bluegrass! Wouldn't Father Rabbit be pleased! He must be told at once!

Haste and excitement made Willie inexcusably careless. He should have remembered that the lid of the rainwater barrel was old and rotted, that there were several dangerous holes in it. He did not, and his leap from the window sill landed him squarely in one of the holes. He grabbed frantically as he went through, but the rotten wood crumbled under his claws and with a sickening shock he plunged into the icy water.

He came up gasping. The cold seemed to have driven all the air from his lungs but he managed one wild squeak for help before the water closed over him again. He was very feeble when he came up this time. He struggled weakly toward the side of the barrel but the walls were slippery with moss and his paws too numbed to get a hold. Faintly he squeaked once more—why didn't someone help him—Father or Little Georgie or Phewie? As the water closed over him for the last time he was dimly conscious of a noise and a brilliant glare of light. Then the light went out, everything went out.

A long time later, he never knew how long, Willie's eyes fluttered open. He dimly realized that he was still wet, that uncontrollable fits of shivering shook him. He seemed to be lying in a nest of some soft white stuff, that was very comfortable, he could see the glow of dancing flames and feel a gentle warmth. Then he closed his eyes again.

Later they opened and he saw the faces of the Folks bending over his bed. It was terrifying to see Folks this close. They looked enormous, like something in a nightmare. He tried to burrow into the soft cotton when his nose suddenly caught the smell of warm milk. Someone was holding a medicine dropper before his face—on the end of it a white drop hung. Weakly, Willie licked at it—it was delicious. There was something else in the milk, something that coursed hotly through all his body. He felt stronger already and sucked at the dropper until it was completely empty. Ah, that was better! His stomach was swollen with the comforting warm food, his eyelids drooped and again he slept.

There was consternation among the Animals when Willie failed to report to the group waiting at the burrow. Father and Uncle Analdas immediately organized a searching party but were unable to find any trace of him.

Phewie, who had been enjoying the freedom of the garbage pail, reported that he had heard a mouse-cry, had seen the Folks emerge from the house with flashlights and do something at the rain barrel. Just what, he did not know.

Willie's oldest cousin climbed to the window sill but found the window closed. The Gray Squirrel was wakened and sent to the roof to investigate. He listened at all the upstairs windows without discovering anything unusual.

"It's that dingblasted old Cat," shouted Uncle Analdas. "The sneakin', deceitful, hypocritical scoundrel, makin' out he's old and harmless. Wish I'd kicked him in the face like I planned to."

Porkey was inclined to blame Tim McGrath. "It's him and his traps," he argued. "Always talkin' traps he is, and poisons. Likely he led them Folks into settin' a trap fer Willie."

Father said little, but all the night through he, Uncle Analdas and Little Georgie coursed the Hill like setter dogs, searching every inch of field and wall, looking under every shrub and bush. Not till dawn approached did they admit defeat and return wearily to the burrow where Mother, very red-eyed and sniffly, had a hot breakfast waiting for them.

But of all the Animals the Mole's rage and grief were the most moving. His pal, his Eyes, were lost and he was helpless to join in the search!

"I'll fix 'em," he said grimly. "I'll fix 'em. There won't never a blade of grass take root on this place—never! Never a bulb or a shrub stay set neither. I'll tear 'em up and I'll root 'em out, I'll dig and I'll heave and I'll burrow, I'll fetch in every friend and relation from here to Danbury way and tear this place apart till they wish they'd never—"

His threats were muffled as he plunged frantically into the neatly rolled front lawn. All night the other Animals could hear his grunting, could see the surface of the ground ripple and heave like troubled waters.

It was gray dawn when Willie woke again. The room was chilly but on the hearth a few embers still smouldered and the bricks gave out a comforting warmth. He eased himself out of the cardboard box where he had slept and drew closer to the glowing coals. All his muscles felt stiff and sore, he was still a little wobbly but otherwise he felt very well. He bathed a bit and stretched himself, feeling better all the time. That warm milk and whatever was in it had certainly tasted good. He wished he had some more. He ought to be getting along home but there was no way out—the doors and windows were all closed.

The sun had risen before he heard footsteps approaching through the house. He caught a whiff of the Man's pipe smell, heard the soft pad of Mr. Muldoon's paws. Wildly he looked for a hiding place but no good one offered. On either side of the fireplace bookshelves extended from floor to ceiling and in desperation he leaped to the top of the first row of books and crouched back into the darkest corner just as the door opened.

The Folks came in and at once inspected the box. "Well, well, he's gone," said the Man. "Must be feeling better. Wonder where he is?"

The Lady did not answer. She was watching Mr. Muldoon who had wandered idly over to the bookshelves.

Willie backed as far into the corner as he could squeeze, his heart pounding wildly as the great cat drew closer and closer. The head seemed huge now, the mouth was opening, two rows of white fangs showed, his eyes were gleaming yellow coals. Willie, petrified with fear, could only watch helplessly as the red jaws opened wider and wider. He could feel the hot breath, strong with the odor of canned salmon.

Then Mr. Muldoon sneezed.

"There he is," the Lady said quietly, "on the books, in the corner. Come, Mullie, don't worry the poor little thing. He's had enough trouble already." She seated herself and the cat strolled stiffly over, leaped to her lap and settled down for a nap. The Man opened the outside door and also sat down.

It was some time before Willie's breath came back and his heart returned to normal. When it did he ventured forth, an inch at a time. Nothing happened, so he began the long circuit of the room, staying close to the wall and pausing under each piece of furniture. He was almost to the doorway now and gave one quick survey before the final dash.

The Lady still continued to sit quietly, her fingers slowly stroking Mr. Muldoon's jowls. He snored faintly, with a sound not unlike the steady, gurgling wheeze of the Man's pipe.

One wild scurry and Willie burst out into the sunlight. Across the terrace he went, but even in the excitement of his newly won freedom he was forced to pause at the appearance of the front lawn. The smoothly rolled surface was striped and circled and crisscrossed with a perfect crazy-quilt pattern of mole runs, scarcely a foot of it undisturbed. He skipped to the nearest run, made two digs and plunged beneath the surface.

"Mole! Mole!" he cried as he galloped through the echoing tunnel. "Here I am, Mole, it's me—Little Willie."

Tim McGrath, hands on hips, stood on the front lawn surveying the wreckage of his careful labor. His jaws were a deep, purplish red, his neck seemed swollen with suppressed rage.

"Look at it!" he sputtered, *"Just look at it! What did I tell you about them moles? But no. No traps, of course not. No poison, oh dear me, no! Now look!"*

The Man sucked on his pipe rather apologetically. "It is quite a mess, isn't it?" he admitted. "I guess we'll just have to roll it down again."

Tim McGrath gazed at the sky and whispered softly. *"We'll* have to roll it again! *We'll have to roll it again!* Oh Lord, give me strength." Wearily he trudged away to fetch the rake and roller.

PIPPI PLAYS TAG WITH
SOME POLICEMEN

Astrid Lindgren

This is one chapter in a book about the remarkable child Pippi Longstocking. Pippi, who is prodigiously strong, lives all alone except for her monkey and her horse. She is the superchild every child would like to be.

It soon became known throughout the little town that a nine-year-old girl was living all by herself in Villa Villekulla, and all the ladies and gentlemen in the town thought this would never do. All children must have someone to advise them, and all children must go to school to learn the multiplication tables. So the ladies and gentlemen decided that the little girl in Villa Ville-kulla must immediately be placed in a children's home.

One lovely afternoon Pippi had invited Tommy and Annika over for afternoon coffee and *pepparkakor*. She had spread the party out on the front steps. It was so sunny and beautiful there, and the air was filled with the fragrance of the flowers in Pippi's garden. Mr. Nilsson climbed around on the porch railing, and every now and then the horse stuck out his head so that he'd be invited to have a cooky.

"Oh, isn't it glorious to be alive?" said Pippi, stretching out her legs as far as she could reach.

Just at that moment two police officers in full uniform came in through the gate.

"Hurray," said Pippi, "this must be my lucky day too! Policemen are the very best things I know. Next to rhubarb pudding." And with her face beaming she went to meet them.

"Is this the girl who has moved into Villa Villekulla?" asked one of the policemen.

"Quite the contrary," said Pippi. "This is a tiny little auntie who lives on the third floor at the other end of the town."

She said that only because she wanted to have a little fun with the policemen, but they didn't think it was funny at all.

They said she shouldn't be such a smarty. And then they went on to tell her that some nice people in the town were arranging for her to get into a children's home.

"I already have a place in a children's home," said Pippi.

"What?" asked one of the policemen. "Has it been arranged already then? What children's home?"

"This one," said Pippi haughtily. "I am a child and this is my home; therefore it is a children's home, and I have room enough here, plenty of room."

"Dear child," said the policeman, smiling, "you don't understand. You must get into a real children's home and have someone look after you."

"Is one allowed to bring horses to your children's home?" asked Pippi.

"No, of course not," said the policeman.

"That's what I thought," said Pippi sadly. "Well, what about monkeys?"

"Of course not. You ought to realize that."

"Well then," said Pippi, "you'll have to get kids for your children's home somewhere else. I certainly don't intend to move there."

"But don't you understand that you must go to school?"

"Why?"

"To learn things, of course."

"What sort of things?" asked Pippi.

"All sorts," said the policeman. "Lots of useful things—the multiplication tables, for instance."

"I have got along fine without any pluttifika-tion tables for nine years," said Pippi, "and I guess I'll get along without it from now on, too."

"Yes, but just think how embarrassing it will be for you to be so ignorant. Imagine when you grow up and somebody asks you what the capital of Portugal is, and you can't answer!"

"Oh, I can answer all right," said Pippi. "I'll answer like this: 'If you are so bound and determined to find out what the capital of Portugal is, then, for goodness' sakes, write directly to Portugal and ask.'"

"Yes, but don't you think that you would be sorry not to know it yourself?"

"Oh, probably," said Pippi. "No doubt I should lie awake nights and wonder and wonder, 'What in the world is the capital of Portugal?' But one can't be having fun all the time," she continued, bending over and standing on her hands for a change. "For that matter, I've been in Lisbon with my papa," she added, still standing upside down, for she could talk that way too.

But then one of the policemen said that Pippi certainly didn't need to think she could do just as she pleased. She must come to the children's home, and immediately. He went up to her and took hold of her arm, but Pippi freed herself quickly, touched him lightly, and said, "Tag!" Before he could wink an eye she had climbed up on the porch railing and from there onto the balcony above the porch. The policemen couldn't quite see themselves getting up the same way, and so they rushed into the house and up the stairs, but by the time they had reached the balcony Pippi was halfway up the roof. She climbed up the shingles almost as if she were a little monkey herself. In a moment she was up on the ridgepole and from there jumped easily to the chimney. Down on the balcony stood the two policemen, scratching their heads, and on the lawn stood Tommy and Annika, staring at Pippi.

"Isn't it fun to play tag?" cried Pippi. "And weren't you nice to come over. It certainly *is* my lucky day today too."

When the policemen had stood there a while wondering what to do, they went and got a ladder, leaned it against one of the gables of the house and then climbed up, first one policeman and then the other, to get Pippi down. They looked a little scared when they climbed out on the ridgepole and, carefully balancing themselves, went step by step, toward Pippi.

"Don't be scared," cried Pippi. "There's nothing to be afraid of. It's just fun."

When the policemen were a few steps away from Pippi, down she jumped from the chimney and, screeching and laughing, ran along the ridgepole to the opposite gable. A few feet from the house stood a tree.

"Now I'm going to dive," she cried and jumped right down into the green crown of the tree, caught fast hold of a branch, swung back and forth a while, and then let herself fall to the ground. Quick as a wink she dashed around to the other side of the house and took away the ladder.

The policemen had looked a little foolish when Pippi jumped, but they looked even more so when they had balanced themselves backward along the ridgepole and were about to climb down the ladder. At first they were very angry at Pippi, who stood on the ground looking up at them, and they told her in no uncertain terms to get the ladder and be quick about it, or she would soon get something she wasn't looking for.

"Why are you so cross at me?" asked Pippi reproachfully. "We're just playing tag, aren't we?"

The policemen thought a while, and at last one of them said, "Oh, come on, won't you be a good girl and put the ladder back so that we can get down?"

"Of course I will," said Pippi and put the ladder back instantly. "And when you get down we can all drink coffee and have a happy time."

But the policemen were certainly tricky, because the minute they were down on the ground again they pounced on Pippi and cried, "Now you'll get it, you little brat!"

"Oh, no, I'm sorry. I haven't time to play any longer," said Pippi. "But it was fun."

Then she took hold of the policemen by their belts and carried them down the garden path, out through the gate, and onto the street. There she set them down, and it was quite some time before they were ready to get up again.

"Wait a minute," she cried and ran into the kitchen and came back with two cooky hearts. "Would you like a taste?" she asked. "It doesn't matter that they are a little burned, does it?"

Then she went back to Tommy and Annika, who stood there wide-eyed and just couldn't get over what they had seen. And the policemen hurried back to the town and told all the ladies and gentlemen that Pippi wasn't quite fit for an orphanage. (They didn't tell that they had been up on the roof.) And the ladies and gentlemen decided that it would be best after all to let Pippi remain in Villa Villekulla, and if she wanted to go to school she could make the arrangements herself.

But Pippi and Tommy and Annika had a very pleasant afternoon. They went back to their interrupted coffee party. Pippi stuffed herself with fourteen cookies and then she said, "They weren't what I mean by real policemen. No sirree! Altogether too much talk about children's home and pluttifikation and Lisbon."

Afterward she lifted the horse down on the ground and they rode on him, all three. At first Annika was afraid and didn't want to, but when she saw what fun Tommy and Pippi were having, she let Pippi lift her up on the horse's back. The horse trotted round and round in the garden, and Tommy sang, "Here come the Swedes with a clang and a bang."

When Tommy and Annika had gone to bed that night Tommy said, "Annika, don't you think it's good that Pippi moved here?"

"Oh, *yes*," said Annika.

"I don't even remember what we used to play before she came, do you?"

"Oh, sure, we played croquet and things like that," said Annika. "But it's lots more fun with Pippi around, I think. And with horses and things."

THE REAL PRINCESS

Hans Christian Andersen

This is an allegory, a satire on the absurdity of believing in the special delicacy of blue-bloodedness. But children take it literally as a funny story. They enjoy illustrating the princess atop her twenty mattresses.

There was once a prince, and he wanted a princess, but then she must be a *real* princess. He travelled right round the world to find one, but there was always something wrong. There were plenty of princesses, but whether they were real princesses he had great difficulty in discovering; there was always something which was not quite right about them. So at last he had to come home again, and he was very sad because he wanted a real princess so badly.

One evening there was a terrible storm; it thundered and lightened and the rain poured down in torrents; indeed it was a fearful night.

In the middle of the storm somebody knocked at the town gate, and the old King himself went to open it.

It was a princess who stood outside, but she was in a terrible state from the rain and the storm. The water streamed out of her hair and her clothes, it ran in at the top of her shoes and out at the heel, but she said that she was a real princess.

"Well, we shall soon see if that is true," thought the old Queen, but she said nothing. She went into the bedroom, took all the bedclothes off and laid a pea on the bedstead; then she took twenty mattresses and piled them on the top of the pea, and then twenty feather beds on the top of the mattresses. This was where the princess was to sleep that night. In the morning they asked her how she had slept.

"Oh, terribly badly!" said the princess. "I have hardly closed my eyes the whole night! Heaven knows what was in the bed. I seemed to be lying upon some hard thing, and my whole body is black and blue this morning. It is terrible!"

They saw at once that she must be a real prin-

"The Real Princess." From *Fairy Tales* by Hans Christian Andersen, translated by Mrs. Edgar Lucas, Everyman's Library, E. P. Dutton & Co., Inc., New York. By permission also of J. M. Dent & Sons, Ltd., London

cess when she had felt the pea through twenty mattresses and twenty feather beds. Nobody but a real princess could have such a delicate skin.

So the prince took her to be his wife, for now he was sure that he had found a real princess, and the pea was put into the Museum, where it may still be seen if no one has stolen it.

Now this is a true story.

THE PLAIN PRINCESS

Phyllis McGinley

Phyllis McGinley invariably creates something fresh and original when she writes for children. Look up her alphabet rhymes in Time For Poetry *and then, if they are available, show the children her books with Helen Stone's beautiful pictures. The sixes will like her alphabet book,* All Around the Town, *and the eights and nines will thoroughly enjoy* The Most Wonderful Doll in the World.

Once upon a time, in a distant kingdom, there lived a Princess who was an only child. Her name was Esmeralda and in every way save one she was the most fortunate of young persons.

Her father, the King, was rich and powerful, and the pockets of his waistcoat were always filled with treats. The Queen was an amiable and affectionate mother who dearly loved planning birthday parties and surprises for Esmeralda; and frequently let her dress up in the crown jewels on rainy afternoons.

The Princess's nursery was painted a charming color of her own choosing. In her closet hung dozens of dresses, each more splendid than the other. The court poets composed verses for Esmeralda which were set to enchanting music by the court musicians and sung to her at bedtime.

Did she arrive at the age for roller skates? A skilful workman hurried immediately to his workshop and contrived for her the finest pair to be found in the kingdom. When she outgrew her tricycle and mentioned a two-wheeler, a del-

egation of bicycle experts was dispatched to fetch her the handsomest bicycle possible, with a silver basket attached to the handlebars.

The castle boasted velvety lawns where she might play croquet; there was a pond with ducks to which she could throw bread at feeding time; and from numberless great trees hung swings for her pleasure. (The King employed a tall gardener whose sole duty it was to give her run-unders so that she might swing into the topmost branches.)

Two cooks toiled ceaselessly in the kitchen preparing delicious food—puddings and ice cream and enticing salads to tempt her appetite.

She even owned a pony of her own, with a white and crimson saddle made to her measure.

Nevertheless, Esmeralda was *not* the most fortunate Princess in the world and it was on account of her one lack that the whole kingdom mourned.

For Esmeralda was plain.

There weren't two ways about it—the girl had no beauty, and in a royal Princess that is a serious flaw.

"What," the courtiers used to whisper to each other in the corridors, "will happen when Her Highness comes of age? How can she hope to win the affections of Prince Charles Michael who is destined to share her throne?"

And the prettier maids-in-waiting would smooth their hair before the long mirrors, thinking smugly, "We may not be of royal blood but we're luckier than *some* people we could mention, at that."

Aunts and uncles and other relatives spoke frankly.

"Poor child," they'd cluck, shaking their heads, "Heaven knows where she gets her plainness. Not from *our* side of the family, certainly."

Even the King and the Queen, much as they loved their daughter, had to admit that as good looks went, Esmeralda's were nothing to boast about. And as "Esmeralda the Plain" she began to be known throughout the kingdom.

It wasn't her hair. Esmeralda's hair grew golden as the corn and her handmaiden brushed it a hundred times in the morning (so that it shone like silk) and a hundred times at night again, while singing the Princess's favorite lullaby, which went like this:

NIGHT SONG

Now dark comes creeping,
    Now owls awake,
But the swan is sleeping
    Upon the lake,
The thrushes drowse,
    The wood-folk rest
Under the boughs,
    In hole and nest.
The flower buds furl
    Their petals fast
And the busiest girl
    Must nod at last.
Sleep, Little princess, sleep.

Over your bed
    Night's handmaids hover.
The sky has spread
    You a royal cover—
Laid, unwrinkled
    Between the bars
A counterpane sprinkled
    With sapphire stars.
And the moon (with a curve
    To its silver handle)
Waits to serve
    As your bedside candle.
Sleep, Esmeralda, sleep.

It wasn't Esmeralda's complexion, either. The court physicians saw to that. She was fed on the most Scientific Diet, containing just the proper number of calories and exactly the right amount of vitamins, and nobody ever forgot her cod-liver oil or her wholesome fruit. So there were always roses in her cheeks.

Governesses attended to her posture, insisting that she walk eleven times daily about the nursery with a book balanced on her head. Dancing masters taught her grace, and the royal dentist fashioned golden braces for her teeth so they would grow straight and even.

No—it wasn't any of these things which marred the loveliness of Esmeralda. It was something odd about her face. Her nose went up where it should have gone down, and her mouth went down where it should have gone up, and her eyes—her otherwise nice blue eyes—had no Glow. And since in that particular kingdom upward-tilting mouths and downward-tilting

noses and eyes with a glow and a twinkle to them were generally admired, Esmeralda grew plainer and plainer and the hearts of the King and the Queen grew heavier and heavier.

For a long while the Princess was kept in ignorance of her misfortune. Because she had always been waited on and petted, she had become by the time she was seven years old quite vain and haughty and fancied herself superior to all other young ladies. But on her eighth birthday something rather terrible happened.

The Queen issued invitations to a birthday fête and among those asked was the neighboring Prince, Charles Michael. It was a very elegant party with a cake of seven layers and jeweled gifts for every person present.

Esmeralda sat at the head of the table with her mouth turned down and her nose turned up at an unusually plain angle, and next to her they put the Prince. At least his name was written in gilt letters on the card. But alas! his chair was vacant. He had vanished immediately after pinning the tail on the donkey in the state drawing-room, and when the footmen announced supper he did not come running with the rest. Esmeralda was very cross. She wished Charles Michael to admire the paper crown she had pulled from her snapper; but though the servants scoured the castle, no Prince could they find.

It was only after the feast had been finished that they discovered him down by the duck pond, and with him the daughter of the duck-keeper, who had not been invited to the party at all.

"Your Highness," reproved his tutor after Charles Michael had been fetched in and had made his goodbyes to the King and Queen. "Why ever did you run away from the Princess's fête?"

Charles Michael was a polite boy but he was also honest.

"Because," he answered (and the court could not help but overhear), "I liked the duck-keeper's daughter better. She has a mouth prettily turned up and a nose charmingly tilted down and her eyes have the merriest twinkle in the world."

Well, you can imagine Esmeralda's chagrin! She burst into tears and had to be carried away like a baby by her governess. The King and Queen, casting down their eyes, retired unhappily to their rooms. As for the court, they looked at one another knowingly and murmured, "Just goes to show, doesn't it? It'll be hard, later on, to be ruled over by such a very plain Princess."

All night Esmeralda wept and no one could comfort her. Her father and mother were in despair. They called a consultation of the royal physicians but those sages had little to offer.

"In such cases as this, Your Majesty," said the oldest and wisest of them, "we seldom operate. Tonsils we can take out, but there would be no improvement in cutting off Her Highness's nose. Pills would have no effect upon the shape of her mouth. As for the glow of the royal eye— all the drugs in the kingdom would not bring it there."

"Have you nothing at all to suggest?" asked the King. He looked at the doctors severely, so that they shifted from one foot to the other and fingered their stethoscopes. Finally one of the youngest cleared his throat.

"Your Majesty," he said nervously, "why not try magic?"

"Useless!" snapped the King. "We've been all over that with the Wizard of State."

"Offer a reward," bravely continued the young physician. "In this great country there must be someone who knows the right enchantment."

"We-l-l," meditated the King, "we will take it under our royal consideration." And he dismissed the doctors.

The next day in the newspapers appeared a large advertisement stamped with the King's seal. It went like this:

REWARD

Anyone capable of Transforming a Plain Young Lady into a Beautiful Young Lady will be Given a Purse of Gold. Results must be Guaranteed. Those Failing will Lose Their Heads.

That wasn't a very tactful advertisement, it must be confessed, for the King had thought it up himself without consulting his Royal Board of Public Relations. And for a week no one came forward to seek the reward, since, naturally, few persons wanted to risk having their heads cut off.

Then on the last day of the week there came knocking at the castle gate a strange visitor. It was neither a wizard in a tall hat nor a great doctor in a black robe. It was a woman and an unfashionable one at that, but she clutched a copy of the newspaper in her hand and smiled quite cheerfully at the King when she was admitted to his presence.

Dropping an agreeable curtsey, she said, "Your Majesty, I have come in answer to your advertisement."

The King looked at her in astonishment.

"Nonsense!" he cried, somewhat rudely. "My good woman, I was expecting a powerful magician."

She did not seem one whit abashed.

"The oddest people make magic nowadays," she answered. "Besides, Your Majesty, I am a widow and on practically no income at all I have fed, clothed and educated five daughters. I claim that in these days, taxes being what they are, that takes a magician of sorts."

And she looked so serenely at the King that he was impressed in spite of himself.

"Certainly, you're the only one brave enough to answer my advertisement," he mused. "Perhaps you have some power I have not heard of."

Remembering to be businesslike, he added, "What references can you show from your former empl—I mean, have you any proof of your magic?"

The woman fumbled in her purse and drew out a photograph.

"These are my five daughters," she said. "Not a plain one among them."

Truly the King had to admit, as he scanned the picture, that five handsomer girls he had never seen. Every nose tilted daintily down, every mouth turned up, and the photographer had caught the twinkle in every pair of eyes.

"Nice, very nice," murmured the King. "But could you do the same for a young lady who *wasn't* your daughter?"

"Give me thrice three months," said the woman quietly. "I think I could do it in that time. *If* I have a free hand and no interference."

"You realize you'll lose your head if the magic fails?"

"I'm willing to chance it for your sake, Your Majesty, and for the sake of the poor plain little

Princ—" She stopped suddenly and clapped her hand over her mouth but the King only said sadly, "Never mind. Everybody knows about Esmeralda. Come, now, Mrs.—er—"

"Goodwit. Dame Goodwit."

"Come, then, Dame Goodwit. I am inclined to trust you. I like your courage and I like your manners. Let us but see the Queen, speak to the Princess, and then you can at once take up your residence in the castle."

"Oh," cried the Dame, "that is one thing I cannot do, Your Majesty. Unless Her Highness go with me and live as one of my daughters, the magic is of no avail."

"What!" roared the King. "Esmeralda leave her home and her comforts to live with you in —no offense meant, madam—what is bound to be a style to which she is unaccustomed?"

The Dame was calm but firm.

"Those are my conditions, Your Majesty," she replied. "Your advisers may examine my home. You may keep watch from afar during the Princess's stay. But come with me she must; and what is more she must take little with her. Not one silken gown or jeweled plaything may she bring if my magic is to be effective."

Well, the King argued and he argued but he got nowhere; and finally he gave in. So did the Queen. For once in their lives, also, they were firm with Esmeralda (who did not take kindly to the idea of going away from home with so common a woman) and insisted she try the power of Dame Goodwit.

The very next day, after the royal emissaries had turned in a report that the Dame lived in respectable though very humble circumstances, off they packed her in a hired coach. (For Dame Goodwit had insisted that the journey begin with no royal fanfare.)

Not one thing, either, was Esmeralda permitted to bring along which might remind her of her exalted state—not her bicycle with the silver basket, nor her roller skates, nor her dolls with their numberless costumes, nor her pony, nor any of her beautiful frocks. The Dame went through her closet and selected two or three of the very plainest dresses and a couple of pinafores and a warm coat and hat. Only in one matter did she relent. She permitted Esmeralda to wear about her neck a little trinket, a pearl locket which had been given her by her Godmother and which, though of slight value, the Princess had worn since babyhood. Esmeralda was still clutching tightly to the locket as she rode weeping away in an ordinary coach to the house of Dame Goodwit and her five daughters.

For three hours they rode—out of the city, through a dim forest, into a meadow, and at last the coachman drew up before a small and shabby cottage. The roof was peaked, the shutters a faded blue, the windows insignificant. Flowers of early spring nodded beside the walk, and near the picket fence flamed beds of crocuses. But Esmeralda saw only the shabbiness and the smallness.

"Oh," she sobbed, "to be shut away here in this horrid spot! How can there be magic in such a place?" And she would have run back to the coach if it had not already galloped away.

Dame Goodwit took no notice of her tears and merely said, "Trot along in, my dear, and take a look around." Then, raising her voice, she called, "Come out, daughters, to greet our guest."

Immediately the little front door popped open and out hurried five handsome girls, all beaming at Esmeralda.

"Esmeralda, these are my daughters," said the Dame. "Their names are Annabelle, Christabelle, Dulcibelle, Floribelle, and Echo. Four belles and an echo, you see. Children, Esmeralda will be living with us for a while. You, Annabelle, take her bag. Christabelle, show her where she will sleep. Fetch her, Dulcibelle, something warm to drink, while you, Flory, put on an egg for her supper. And Echo, my pet, give her the kiss of welcome."

Like five stair steps they were, from a very little girl to a very tall girl, and they all smiled shyly at the Princess and ran to assist her. However, it was as if they were greeting a friend instead of a Princess, for not one of them curtsied or kissed her hand. But Esmeralda found no breath to chide them, so briskly did they bundle her in, every damsel talking at once. Her tears, however, began afresh when she saw the tiny cubicle that held her bed, the rough cup out of which she was supposed to drink, the simple kitchen where supper was prepared. Everything was clean as a scrubbed turnip, but to Esmeralda's eyes, dazzled so long by riches, her surroundings seemed too dreary to bear.

Instead of eating the fresh egg which Floribelle obligingly broke for her, she flung herself on the floor, kicking her heels, and indulged, regrettably, in a temper tantrum. At the castle, ten handmaids would have bustled about with spirits of ammonia and soothing words. But Dame Goodwit said only, "Let her be, girls. Esmeralda is possibly homesick. She'll feel better in the morning." And the six of them sat down to eat their wholesome supper. Then they cleared away, stepping neatly around Esmeralda, who was still stretched out on the linoleum.

After a while, since no one paid any attention to her, she left off weeping and kicking, arose, and stated, "I'm hungry."

"Christabelle, see if there's any soup left," instructed the Dame.

Christabelle filled a bowl and set it before Esmeralda, who drank it greedily.

"I am also sleepy," the Princess announced. "Ask one of your daughters, Dame, to attend me to bed."

"People," said that lady cheerfully, "attend themselves here. That is part of the magic." So for the first time in her life, Esmeralda took off her own clothes, turned down her own covers and smoothed her own pillow. She did it with bad grace and clumsily, but she managed, and weary as she was, fell asleep quickly even on the hard mattress.

That was the beginning of a strange life for the Princess. Whatever spells Dame Goodwit knew, they were not, at once, evident. She never said "Abracadabra" or "Hocus Pocus," and there wasn't a single wand anywhere about the cottage. And though Esmeralda looked earnestly in the cracked mirror each day, she could see no improvement in her plainness. In fact, she was, if anything, plainer, for her eyes were continually red from weeping over her lot. No one seemed to recall that she was a royal child, entitled to the privileges of her birth. Only the pearl locket, hung around her neck, reminded her; and that she treasured and fingered constantly, to reassure herself that the castle was not a dream.

The Dame treated her kindly but with no more ceremony than she gave to her own daughters. Esmeralda found, to her horror, that she was even expected to assist with the housework.

"We won't ask you to do much at first," said the Dame. "You'd be only a hindrance. But you aren't really stupid; you'll learn."

"Stupid, indeed!" Esmeralda was outraged.

But as time went on, the Princess secretly discovered that the Dame had been no more than right. Compared to Christabelle and Annabelle and the rest, she *was* quite dull. All the things they could do! They could out-run her at races. They could play innumerable games she had never heard of. Even little Echo could climb into the gnarled apple trees more spryly than she. And at housewifely tasks they were incredibly deft. They sewed and patched and darned and embroidered and whipped up delicate puddings out of practically nothing, while she could scarcely pour water without spilling it.

Not that she tried, at first. She demanded to be waited on. But no one ran to do her bidding. If she neglected to make her bed in the morning, she must sleep that night in rumpled sheets. If she refused to help with the table-setting, no place was laid for her. When she forgot to hang up her clothes, they grew creased and wrinkled and nobody pressed them for her.

What amazed her most was how little the Dame's five daughters minded their humble surroundings. When she wasn't sulking she would spin them long tales of how elegantly she had lived at home, or what tempting meals had been served in her royal nursery, or how remarkably well she rode her pony. But Annabelle and Christabelle and Dulcibelle and Floribelle would mumble politely, "How nice for you," or "Wasn't that pleasant?" and go on digging in the garden or ironing a napkin.

Once, after Esmeralda had regaled them with an especially tedious story of her grand life, good-tempered Dulcy said abruptly (for her), "You may have been a Princess but you never learned to jump rope like us or spell so well or sew a decent seam. You hadn't even any sisters or playmates. What good is it, anyhow, being rich and royal?"

Only little Echo listened attentively to her recountings and followed her about like a shadow. And Esmeralda, who had loved nothing except herself, grew excessively fond of the pretty child, taking comfort in her affection.

After the first bitter weeks, she even stopped being scornful of some of the menial tasks she was called upon to perform. She began to envy the clever hands of Floribelle as she beat up a sponge cake. She noticed what satisfaction Christabelle took in embroidering a pocket on her smock. How awkwardly her own fingers held a needle or wielded a spoon on her rare attempts to compete! Into her mind crept the suspicion that perhaps simply being born a Princess did not make her a really superior person. And one day when the first three months were nearly up, she said grudgingly (watching Floribelle taking delicious gingerbread from the oven), "I wish, Flory, that I could be as clever as you."

At that moment a bird sang loudly, a rainbow appeared in the sky though there had been no rain, and Esmeralda felt a strange sensation. Something odd was happening to her. She ran to the mirror and peered into it. And what do you think?

No longer did Esmeralda's nose turn plainly up. It tilted so charmingly down that she cried out with delight. And with what excitement the generous family gathered 'round to compliment her, for it was indeed an improvement.

"The magic is working!" shouted Esmeralda. "Dame Goodwit, you are an enchantress after all!"

But the Dame only smiled. "That is as may be," she said mildly. "Certainly your nose is more attractive, child. But perhaps that is because you have stopped turning it up at the world in general. Perhaps you have found out there are people just as clever and just as fortunate in their own way, as you."

But Esmeralda was sure it was magic and she began to relent in her feeling toward the Dame and the life of the cottage. Its meanness still irked her and at night she still fondled the pearl locket. But her manners improved and she joined the rest of the girls more frequently in their games and at their chores.

She hung up her clothes, nightly, quite by habit. "Let me gather the eggs," she would sometimes ask at evening when it was time to search the hen-house. Almost humbly she followed at the heels of Christabelle or Floribelle while, singing, they swept or dusted or scoured the hearth. Dame Goodwit gave her a tiny plot of ground for her to plant and she grew reasonably adept at coaxing the seeds to climb up into the sunlight. She burned her thumbs trying to make cookies, she scratched her knees blackberrying, she made up stories for Echo which had nothing to do with how important she had been at the castle.

Then, when save for a day and a night another three months had sped, the second magic came to pass.

It happened on an afternoon when a soft rain was falling. The house was quiet, for the Dame and her daughters were resting after a busy morning. Only Esmeralda was awake, standing by the window watching the drops roll down the pane and thinking with a pang of homesickness about her own nursery at tea-time. She remembered how the lamps would have been lighted and it would have been time for muffins to come up on a tray. She was not sad—merely wistful—but she was seized with a sudden desire to taste again those muffins, so hot, so crisp, so buttery. "Why not make some?" she thought daringly. "Goodness knows I've watched the Dame turn out enough hot breads, and I know exactly where she keeps the cook book."

Without more ado, she crept quietly into the little kitchen, found an apron, and set about her task. The Dame and her daughters must have napped well that day, for Esmeralda made more noise than she had counted on, what with beating the eggs and measuring the sugar and dropping things and opening up drawers and testing the oven to see if it was hot enough. But the batter got itself mixed at last and popped into the stove and, just at the moment the family aroused itself and came looking for Esmeralda, that proud young lady was taking out a batch of crusty, golden-brown muffins.

You can imagine what a stir it created in the house. They may not have been the *best* muffins ever baked—perhaps they were just a bit doughy at the center and a trifle lopsided at the edges if you looked closely—but Esmeralda could not have been more pleased had they been perfection. The Dame praised her, the daughters praised her, and Echo kissed her on both cheeks. And Esmeralda just beamed and beamed. Then suddenly a rose beside the door unfolded its petals, a cricket chirped, and Floribelle cried out, "Esmeralda, your mouth! It turns up!"

Sure enough, when the excited Princess flew to the mirror, she saw a wonderful transformation. Beneath her dainty new nose, her mouth—her drooping, sullen little mouth—turned up as sweetly as that of Echo.

"I'm prettier! I'm growing prettier!" cried Esmeralda.

"She's growing prettier!" sang the sisters and they threw their arms about her and hugged her joyously.

"It was the muffins," said Echo.

"It was the magic," bubbled Esmeralda.

But Dame Goodwit merely smiled and said, "That is as may be. Perhaps your mouth turned down because life was dull. Never before, I think, have you known what it was to be proud of the work of your own hands."

After that famous occurrence, Esmeralda forgot to count the days till her exile ended. She grew happier in the cottage than she had been in the castle—except, of course, for missing her father and mother. She forgot about her pony in caring for the brown hens. She forgot about the tall swings, with clambering up the old apple trees for fruit. She left off yearning for

her usual luxuries in the pleasure of playing Hop Scotch with Floribelle or of beating Christabelle at races or of doing well at household tasks. She tidied her room; she polished the tin pots until they shone bright as copper; she learned to make gingerbread men with raisins for eyes. The pearl locket lay in a drawer of her rickety dresser and although she looked at it each day, its touch was not now her only consolation. The good Dame was well pleased with Esmeralda and remarked it so frequently that the Princess's turned-up smile got quite dimply with happiness.

Autumn waned. The last three months spent themselves in a haze of soft skies and flaming leaves. Light snow fell. In early December the cottage rocked with whisperings and giggles, for little Echo was to have a birthday.

All the sisters were planning surprises for the child—stitching away, after she had gone to bed, on cloth dolls, embroidering aprons and jolly bonnets. Only Esmeralda looked castdown, for she had been able to contrive no gift for her favorite. She couldn't sew as well as Annabelle or knit like Christabelle, or do fine cross-stitch like Dulcy, or twist yarn into cunning toys like Floribelle. There was no use her baking cookies—Dame Goodwit was already frosting an impressive cake. So for the first time in a long while she felt sad and left out.

"Never mind, Esmeralda," Dulcy soothed her. "Echo knows you love her and would give her something if you could."

Yet on the night before the birthday, Esmeralda let fall a salt tear into her pillow. She thought of her thousand riches at home and of how little they helped her now. Her hands, alone, tomorrow would be empty.

Yet need they be? There was her locket. True, it was what she treasured most of all. Without it she might forget altogether that she was the daughter of the King. But Echo had been her admirer, her comforter, her dear friend.

In the darkness, Esmeralda felt for the locket, fitted her hand about it as if in farewell, then fell peacefully to sleep.

At dawn she awoke, found a piece of paper and tied the pearled bauble gaily with a bit of red string from the grocery bundles. When Echo came to the breakfast table, greeted by the

"Happy Birthdays" of the household, there was Esmeralda's present on top of the pile. Echo opened it curiously. Then she cried out, "The locket!" threw herself headlong into Esmeralda's arms, and they both burst into happy tears.

"It was all I had to give you," gulped the Princess. "Wear it for me."

At that moment a gleam of light from the winter morning glittered brightly upon her head, somewhere far off a bell pealed, and Floribelle looked up with amazement.

"Esmeralda," she sang out. "Your eyes! They are glowing like stars."

Once more Esmeralda sped to the cracked mirror and with overwhelming happiness beheld her countenance. What a pair of eyes twinkled back at her, glowing, indeed, like stars!

"The magic," she said softly. "It is complete. I am no longer plain."

Then she turned to Dame Goodwit.

"My father the King will reward you well. You are a powerful enchantress."

"That is as may be," said the Dame placidly. "Perhaps your eyes glow because for the first time in your life you have done an unselfish thing. I am well pleased with you, Esmeralda."

In the midst of the rejoicing there came a rattle of wheels, the sound of horses' hoofs along the frosty road, and someone smote heavily on the door.

It was the King himself, come to fetch his daughter. For thrice three months were gone.

"Come in, Your Majesty, and welcome," spoke the Dame graciously. She dropped a dignified curtsey.

Esmeralda would have run to him but shyness held her and it was only when he called out, "Esmeralda, my child! My lovely child! Is it really you?" that she fled to his embrace.

"Let me look at you," he commanded, holding her at arm's length. "I can scarcely believe it. A mouth like mine, a nose like your mother's, and your eyes, my dear! Such splendid, glowing eyes."

Turning to the Dame, he said, "Well do you deserve the purse of gold which my messengers will shortly bring. I was fearful, very fearful, the magic might not avail. It would have been a sad thing to behead so worthy a widow as yourself."

"The women of my family, Your Majesty," answered the Dame serenely, "seldom lose their heads. As for the purse of gold, I do not want it. Esmeralda herself worked the enchantment."

And try as he would, no reward could he persuade the remarkable woman to accept.

Esmeralda, after bidding a tender goodbye to the Dame and to Annabelle and Christabelle and Dulcibelle and Floribelle and especially to little Echo, stepped into the carriage and was driven away. Strangely enough, as she pressed her face to the coach window, waving her hand as long as the cottage was in sight, her heart seemed almost as heavy as it had been on the journey which had carried her there.

Excitement, however, awaited her at the castle, for the King's messengers had run ahead with the glad news, and now the whole kingdom rejoiced. Flags flew from battlements, cannons fired salutes, and for the occasion the court poets hurried to compose a magnificent ode of fifty verses entitled, simply, *To Esmeralda.*

As the Princess walked gracefully between the silken ropes which had been stretched on either side of the castle steps, an audible gasp arose from all the servants and courtiers and guards of honor who were lined up there in their best livery.

"Is it really Esmeralda?" they whispered. "What poise, what charm, what sparkling eyes!"

The aunts and uncles and cousins nodded their heads complacently, observing, "Gets her looks from our side of the family."

The maids-in-waiting glanced furtively into their hand-mirrors and sighed with envy.

And the court physicians murmured, "Miraculous. We must get the case history."

Only Esmeralda herself kept her composure and was so modest and quiet that the Queen thought she must be ill and insisted she take a spoonful of cod-liver oil at once.

But modest she remained, although pleased with her welcome. And the first thing she did, when the flurry died down, was to persuade the King and Queen to remodel one of the gardener's houses into a comfortable dwelling (with telephone and all modern conveniences) and to send for the Dame and her family. They were naturally reluctant to leave their own home, but when the Queen pointed out what advantages the daughters would enjoy in the matter of schools and of acquiring suitable husbands, she consented finally to move into the cozy residence.

Esmeralda spent much of her time there, keeping up her skill at cookie-making, at climbing apple trees, and at excelling in games of Prisoner's Base.

And she lent her bicycle to Christabelle and her pony to Echo and her roller skates to Dulcy whenever they expressed a wish to try them.

Prince Charles Michael at the next castle party did not run down to the duck pond but paid marked attention to the Princess, helping her adjust her paper crown at the table.

As she grew older she became known far and wide not as "Esmeralda the Plain," but as "Esmeralda the Beautiful." And everyone lived happily ever after—or at least as happily as is possible in this mortal world.

THE UGLY DUCKLING

Hans Christian Andersen

Here is the old "Cinderella" theme of the misunderstood, scorned, and humble creature who finally comes into his own after much suffering. Children eight- or nine-years-old who hear the story read sometimes find it almost unbearably sad. The tens and elevens take it better and will be interested to know that it is much like Andersen's own life. Here is an allegory they can see illustrated in Constance Burnett's life of Andersen, The Shoemaker's Son. *They will also enjoy Will Nickless' illustrated edition of* The Ugly Duckling.

The country was lovely just then; it was summer! The wheat was golden and the oats still green; the hay was stacked in the rich low-lying meadows, where the stork was marching about on his long red legs, chattering Egyptian, the language his mother had taught him.

Round about field and meadow lay great

"The Ugly Duckling." From *Fairy Tales* by Hans Christian Andersen, translated by Mrs. Edgar Lucas, Everyman's Library, E. P. Dutton & Co., Inc., New York. By permission also of J. M. Dent & Sons, Ltd., London

woods, in the midst of which were deep lakes. Yes, the country certainly was delicious. In the sunniest spot stood an old mansion surrounded by a deep moat, and great dock leaves grew from the walls of the house right down to the water's edge; some of them were so tall that a small child could stand upright under them. In amongst the leaves it was as secluded as in the depths of a forest; and there a duck was sitting on her nest. Her little ducklings were just about to be hatched, but she was nearly tired of sitting, for it had lasted such a long time. Moreover, she had very few visitors, as the other ducks liked swimming about in the moat better than waddling up to sit under the dock leaves and gossip with her.

At last one egg after another began to crack. "Cheep, cheep!" they said. All the chicks had come to life, and were poking their heads out.

"Quack! quack!" said the duck; and then they all quacked their hardest, and looked about them on all sides among the green leaves; their mother allowed them to look as much as they liked, for green is good for the eyes.

"How big the world is to be sure!" said all the young ones; for they certainly had ever so much more room to move about, than when they were inside in the eggshell.

"Do you imagine this is the whole world?" said the mother. "It stretches a long way on the other side of the garden, right into the parson's field; but I have never been as far as that! I suppose you are all here now?" and she got up. "No! I declare I have not got you all yet! The biggest egg is still there; how long is it going to last?" and then she settled herself on the nest again.

"Well, how are you getting on?" said an old duck who had come to pay her a visit.

"This one egg is taking such a long time," answered the sitting duck, "the shell will not crack; but now you must look at the others; they are the finest ducklings I have ever seen! they are all exactly like their father, the rascal! he never comes to see me."

"Let me look at the egg which won't crack," said the old duck. "You may be sure that it is a turkey's egg! I have been cheated like that once, and I had no end of trouble and worry with the creatures, for I may tell you that they are afraid of the water. I could not get them into it, I quacked and snapped at them, but it was no good. Let me see the egg! Yes, it is a turkey's egg! You just leave it alone and teach the other children to swim."

"I will sit on it a little longer, I have sat so long already, that I may as well go on till the Midsummer Fair comes round."

"Please yourself," said the old duck, and she went away.

At last the big egg cracked. "Cheep, cheep!" said the young one and tumbled out; how big and ugly he was! The duck looked at him.

"That is a monstrous big duckling," she said; "none of the others looked like that; can he be a turkey chick? well we shall soon find that out; into the water he shall go, if I have to kick him in myself."

Next day was gloriously fine, and the sun shone on all the green dock leaves. The mother duck with her whole family went down to the moat.

Splash, into the water she sprang. "Quack, quack!" she said, and one duckling plumped in after the other. The water dashed over their heads, but they came up again and floated beautifully; their legs went of themselves, and they were all there, even the big ugly gray one swam about with them.

"No, that is no turkey," she said; "see how beautifully he uses his legs and how erect he holds himself: he is my own chick! after all, he is not so bad when you come to look at him properly. Quack, quack! Now come with me and I will take you into the world, and introduce you to the duckyard; but keep close to me all the time, so that no one may tread upon you, and beware of the cat!"

Then they went into the duckyard. There was a fearful uproar going on, for two broods were fighting for the head of an eel, and in the end the cat captured it.

"That's how things go in this world," said the mother duck, and she licked her bill for she wanted the eel's head herself.

"Use your legs," said she; "mind you quack properly, and bend your necks to the old duck over there! She is the grandest of them all; she has Spanish blood in her veins and that accounts for her size, and, do you see? she has a red rag round her leg; that is a wonderfully fine thing, and the most extraordinary mark of distinction any duck can have. It shows clearly that she is not to be parted with, and that she is worthy of recognition both by beasts and men! Quack now! don't turn your toes in, a well brought up duckling keeps his legs wide apart just like father and mother; that's it, now bend your necks, and say quack!"

They did as they were bid, but the other ducks round about looked at them and said, quite loud; "Just look there! now we are to have that tribe! just as if there were not enough of us already, and, oh dear! how ugly that duckling is, we won't stand him!" and a duck flew at him at once and bit him in the neck.

"Let him be," said the mother; "he is doing no harm."

"Very likely not, but he is so ungainly and queer," said the biter; "he must be whacked."

"They are handsome children that mother has," said the old duck with the rag round her leg; "all good looking except this one, and he is not a good specimen; it's a pity you can't make him over again."

"That can't be done, your grace," said the mother duck; "he is not handsome, but he is a thorough good creature, and he swims as beautifully as any of the others; nay, I think I might venture even to add that I think he will improve as he goes on, or perhaps in time he may grow smaller! he was too long in the egg, and so he has not come out with a very good figure." And then she patted his neck and stroked him down. "Besides, he is a drake," said she; "so it does not matter so much. I believe he will be very strong, and I don't doubt but he will make his way in the world."

"The other ducklings are very pretty," said the old duck. "Now make yourselves quite at home, and if you find the head of an eel you may bring it to me!"

After that they felt quite at home. But the poor duckling which had been the last to come out of the shell, and who was so ugly, was bitten, pushed about, and made fun of both by the ducks and the hens. "He is too big," they all said; and the turkey-cock, who was born with his spurs on, and therefore thought himself quite an emperor, puffed himself up like a vessel in full sail, made for him, and gobbled and gobbled till he became quite red in the face. The poor duckling was at his wit's end, and did not know which way to turn; he was in despair because he was so ugly, and the butt of the whole duckyard.

So the first day passed, and afterwards matters grew worse and worse. The poor duckling was chased and hustled by all of them, even his brothers and sisters ill-used him; and they were always saying, "If only the cat would get hold of you, you hideous object!" Even his mother said, "I wish to goodness you were miles away." The ducks bit him, the hens pecked him, and the girl who fed them kicked him aside.

Then he ran off and flew right over the hedge, where the little birds flew up into the air in a fright.

"That is because I am so ugly," thought the poor duckling, shutting his eyes, but he ran on all the same. Then he came to a great marsh where the wild ducks lived; he was so tired and miserable that he stayed there the whole night.

In the morning the wild ducks flew up to inspect their new comrade.

"What sort of a creature are you?" they inquired, as the duckling turned from side to side and greeted them as well as he could. "You are frightfully ugly," said the wild ducks; "but that does not matter to us, so long as you do not marry into our family!" Poor fellow! he had no thought of marriage, all he wanted was permission to lie among the rushes, and to drink a little of the marsh water.

He stayed there two whole days, then two wild geese came, or rather two wild ganders, they were not long out of the shell, and therefore rather pert.

"I say, comrade," they said, "you are so ugly that we have taken quite a fancy to you; will you join us and be a bird of passage? There is another marsh close by, and there are some charming wild geese there; all sweet young ladies, who can say quack! You are ugly enough to make your fortune among them." Just at that moment, bang! bang! was heard up above, and both the wild geese fell dead among the reeds, and the water turned blood red. Bang! bang! went the guns, and whole flocks of wild geese flew up from the rushes and the shot peppered among them again.

There was a grand shooting party, and the sportsmen lay hidden round the marsh, some even sat on the branches of the trees which overhung the water; the blue smoke rose like clouds among the dark trees and swept over the pool.

The water-dogs wandered about in the swamp, splash! splash! The rushes and reeds bent beneath their tread on all sides. It was terribly alarming to the poor duckling. He twisted his head round to get it under his wing and just at that moment a frightful, big dog appeared close beside him; his tongue hung right out of his mouth and his eyes glared wickedly. He opened his great chasm of a mouth close to the duckling, showed his sharp teeth—and—splash—went on without touching him.

"Oh, thank Heaven!" sighed the duckling, "I am so ugly that even the dog won't bite me!"

Then he lay quite still while the shot whistled among the bushes, and bang after bang rent the air. It only became quiet late in the day, but even then the poor duckling did not dare to get up; he waited several hours more before he looked about and then he hurried away from the marsh as fast as he could. He ran across fields and meadows, and there was such a wind that he had hard work to make his way.

Toward night he reached a poor little cottage; it was such a miserable hovel that it could not make up its mind which way to fall even, and so it remained standing. The wind whistled so fiercely round the duckling that he had to sit on his tail to resist it, and it blew harder and harder; then he saw that the door had fallen off one hinge and hung so crookedly that he could creep into the house through the crack and by this means he made his way into the room. An old woman lived there with her cat and her hen. The cat, which she called "Sonnie," could arch his back, purr, and give off electric sparks, that is to say if you stroked his fur the wrong way. The hen had quite tiny short legs and so she was called "Chuckie low-legs." She laid good eggs, and the old woman was as fond of her as if she had been her own child.

In the morning the strange duckling was discovered immediately, and the cat began to purr and the hen to cluck.

"What on earth is that!" said the old woman

looking round, but her sight was not good and she thought the duckling was a fat duck which had escaped. "This is a capital find," said she; "now I shall have duck's eggs if only it is not a drake! we must find out about that!"

So she took the duckling on trial for three weeks, but no eggs made their appearance. The cat was the master of the house and the hen the mistress, and they always spoke of "we and the world," for they thought that they represented the half of the world, and that quite the better half.

The duckling thought there might be two opinions on the subject, but the hen would not hear of it.

"Can you lay eggs?" she asked.

"No!"

"Will you have the goodness to hold your tongue then!"

And the cat said, "Can you arch your back, purr, or give off sparks?"

"No."

"Then you had better keep your opinions to yourself when people of sense are speaking!"

The duckling sat in the corner nursing his ill-humour; then he began to think of the fresh air and the sunshine, an uncontrollable longing seized him to float on the water, and at last he could not help telling the hen about it.

"What on earth possesses you?" she asked; "you have nothing to do, that is why you get these freaks into your head. Lay some eggs or take to purring, and you will get over it."

"But it is so delicious to float on the water," said the duckling; "so delicious to feel it rushing over your head when you dive to the bottom."

"That would be a fine amusement," said the hen. "I think you have gone mad. Ask the cat about it, he is the wisest creature I know; ask him if he is fond of floating on the water or diving under it. I say nothing about myself. Ask our mistress yourself, the old woman, there is no one in the world cleverer than she is. Do you suppose she has any desire to float on the water, or to duck underneath it?"

"You do not understand me," said the duckling.

"Well, if we don't understand you, who should? I suppose you don't consider yourself cleverer than the cat or the old woman, not to mention me. Don't make a fool of yourself, child, and thank your stars for all the good we have done you! Have you not lived in this warm room, and in such society that you might have learnt something? But you are an idiot, and there is no pleasure in associating with you. You may believe me I mean you well, I tell you home truths, and there is no surer way than that of knowing who are one's friends. You just see about laying some eggs, or learn to purr, or to emit sparks."

"I think I will go out into the wide world," said the duckling.

"Oh, do so by all means," said the hen.

So away went the duckling, he floated on the water and ducked underneath it, but he was looked askance at by every living creature for his ugliness. Now the autumn came on, the leaves in the woods turned yellow and brown; the wind took hold of them, and they danced about. The sky looked very cold, and the clouds hung heavy with snow and hail. A raven stood on the fence and croaked Caw! Caw! from sheer cold; it made one shiver only to think of it, the poor duckling certainly was in a bad case.

One evening, the sun was just setting in wintry splendour, when a flock of beautiful large birds appeared out of the bushes; the duckling had never seen anything so beautiful. They were dazzlingly white with long waving necks; they were swans, and uttering a peculiar cry they spread out their magnificent broad wings and flew away from the cold regions to warmer lands and open seas. They mounted so high, so very high, and the ugly little duckling became strangely uneasy, he circled round and round in the water like a wheel, craning his neck up into the air after them. Then he uttered a shriek so piercing and so strange, that he was quite frightened by it himself. Oh, he could not forget those beautiful birds, those happy birds, and as soon as they were out of sight he ducked right down to the bottom, and when he came up again he was quite beside himself. He did not know what the birds were, or whither they flew, but all the same he was more drawn towards them than he had ever been by any creatures before. He did not envy them in the least, how could it occur to him even to wish to be such a marvel of beauty; he would have been thankful if only the ducks would have tolerated him among them—the poor ugly creature!

The winter was so bitterly cold that the duckling was obliged to swim about in the water to keep it from freezing, but every night the hole in which he swam got smaller and smaller. Then it froze so hard that the surface ice cracked, and the duckling had to use his legs all the time, so that the ice should not close in round him; at last he was so weary that he could move no more, and he was frozen fast into the ice.

Early in the morning a peasant came along and saw him; he went out on to the ice and hammered a hole in it with his heavy wooden shoe, and carried the duckling home to his wife. There it soon revived. The children wanted to play with it, but the duckling thought they were going to ill-use him, and rushed in his fright into the milk pan, and the milk spurted out all over the room. The woman shrieked and threw up her hands, then it flew into the butter cask, and down into the meal tub and out again. Just imagine what it looked like by this time! The woman screamed and tried to hit it with the tongs, and the children tumbled over one another in trying to catch it, and they screamed with laughter—by good luck the door stood open, and the duckling flew out among the bushes and the new fallen snow—and it lay there thoroughly exhausted.

But it would be too sad to mention all the privation and misery it had to go through during that hard winter. When the sun began to shine warmly again, the duckling was in the marsh, lying among the rushes; the larks were singing and the beautiful spring had come.

Then all at once it raised its wings and they flapped with much greater strength than before, and bore him off vigorously. Before he knew where he was, he found himself in a large garden where the apple trees were in full blossom, and the air was scented with lilacs, the long branches of which overhung the indented shores of the lake. Oh! the spring freshness was so delicious!

Just in front of him he saw three beautiful white swans advancing towards him from a thicket; with rustling feathers they swam lightly over the water. The duckling recognized the majestic birds, and he was overcome by a strange melancholy.

"I will fly to them, the royal birds, and they will hack me to pieces, because I, who am so ugly, venture to approach them! But it won't matter; better be killed by them than be snapped at by the ducks, pecked by the hens, or spurned by the henwife, or suffer so much misery in the winter."

So he flew into the water and swam towards the stately swans; they saw him and darted toward him with ruffled feathers.

"Kill me, oh, kill me!" said the poor creature, and bowing his head towards the water he awaited his death. But what did he see reflected in the transparent water?

He saw below him his own image, but he was no longer a clumsy dark gray bird, ugly and ungainly, he was himself a swan! It does not matter in the least having been born in a duckyard, if only you come out of a swan's egg!

He felt quite glad of all the misery and tribulation he had gone through; he was the better able to appreciate his good fortune now, and all the beauty which greeted him. The big swans swam round and round him, and stroked him with their bills.

Some little children came into the garden with corn and pieces of bread, which they threw into the water; and the smallest one cried out: "There is a new one!"

The other children shouted with joy, "Yes, a new one has come!" And they clapped their hands and danced about, running after their father and mother. They threw the bread into the water, and one and all said that "the new one was the prettiest; he was so young and handsome." And the old swans bent their heads and did homage before him.

He felt quite shy, and hid his head under his wing; he did not know what to think; he was so very happy, but not at all proud; a good heart never becomes proud. He thought of how he had been pursued and scorned, and now he heard them all say that he was the most beautiful of all beautiful birds. The lilacs bent their boughs right down into the water before him, and the bright sun was warm and cheering, and he rustled his feathers and raised his slender neck aloft, saying with exultation in his heart: "I never dreamt of so much happiness when I was the Ugly Duckling!"

THE 500 HATS
OF BARTHOLOMEW CUBBINS

Dr. Seuss

"Dr. Seuss," who is really Theodore Seuss Geisel, lives on a mountain, in a tall house called "The Tower." When he draws, he looks out of a window to the sea, where the whales go by every spring. When he writes, he can go up to the top of his tower and see mountains in Mexico or mountains in his own state. Sometimes when the fog rolls in from the sea, mountains and land and sea are all hidden and "The Tower" seems to be perched on clouds. Perhaps all this accounts for the wonderful fantasies he has written for children and perhaps the twinkle in his eye explains why children always say his picture-stories are "funny books," the funniest books of all.

In the beginning, Bartholomew Cubbins didn't have five hundred hats. He had only one hat. It was an old one that had belonged to his father and his father's father before him. It was probably the oldest and the plainest hat in the whole Kingdom of Didd, where Bartholomew Cubbins lived. But Bartholomew liked it—especially because of the feather that always pointed straight up in the air.

The Kingdom of Didd was ruled by King Derwin. His palace stood high on the top of the mountain. From his balcony he looked down over the houses of all his subjects—first over the spires of the noblemen's castles, across the broad roofs of the rich men's mansions, then over the little houses of the townsfolk, to the huts of the farmers far off in the fields.

It was a mighty view and it made King Derwin feel mighty important.

Far off in the fields, on the edge of a cranberry bog, stood the hut of the Cubbins family. From the small door Bartholomew looked across the huts of the farmers to the houses of the townsfolk, then to the rich men's mansions and the noblemen's castles, up to the great towering palace of the King. It was exactly the same view that King Derwin saw from his balcony, but Bartholomew saw it backward.

It was a mighty view, but it made Bartholomew Cubbins feel mighty small.

Just after sunrise one Saturday morning Bartholomew started for town. He felt very happy. A pleasant breeze whistled through the feather in his hat. In his right hand he carried a basket of cranberries to sell at the market. He was anxious to sell them quickly and bring the money back home to his parents.

He walked faster and faster till he got to the gates of the town.

The sound of silver trumpets rang through the air. Hoof beats clattered on the cobbled streets.

"Clear the way! Clear the way! Make way for the King!"

All the people rushed for the sidewalks. They drove their carts right up over the curbstones. Bartholomew clutched his basket tighter.

Around the corner dashed fifty trumpeters on yellow-robed horses. Behind them on crimson-robed horses came the King's Own Guards.

"Hats off to the King!" shouted the Captain of the King's Own Guards.

On came the King's carriage—white and gold and purple. It rumbled like thunder through the narrow street.

It swept past Bartholomew. Then suddenly its mighty brakes shrieked. It lurched—and then it stopped. The whole procession stood still.

Bartholomew could hardly believe what he saw. Through the side window of the carriage, the King himself was staring back—straight back at him! Bartholomew began to tremble.

"Back up!" the King commanded the Royal Coachman.

The Royal Coachman shouted to the royal horses. The King's Own Guards shouted to their crimson-robed horses. The trumpeters shouted to their yellow-robed horses. Very slowly the whole procession backed down the street, until the King's carriage stopped right in front of Bartholomew.

The King leaned from his carriage window and fixed his eyes directly on Bartholomew Cubbins. "Well . . . ? Well . . . ?" he demanded.

Bartholomew shook with fright. "I ought to say something," he thought to himself. But he could think of nothing to say.

"Well?" demanded the King again. "Do you

or do you *not* take off your hat before your King?"

"Yes, indeed, Sire," answered Bartholomew, feeling greatly relieved. "I *do* take off my hat before my King."

"Then take it off this very instant," commanded the King more loudly than before.

"But, Sire, my hat *is* off," answered Bartholomew.

"Such impudence!" shouted the King, shaking an angry finger. "How dare you stand there and tell me your hat is off!"

"I don't like to say you are wrong, Sire," said Bartholomew very politely, "but you see my hat *is* off." And he showed the King the hat in his hand.

"If that's your hat in your hand," demanded the King, "what's that on your head?"

"On my head?" gasped Bartholomew. There *did* seem to be something on his head. He reached up his hand and touched a hat!

The face of Bartholomew Cubbins turned very red. "It's a hat, Sire," he stammered, "but it *can't* be mine. Someone behind me must have put in on my head."

"I don't care *how* it got there," said the King. "You take it off." And the King sat back in his carriage.

Bartholomew quickly snatched off the hat. He stared at it in astonishment. It was exactly the same as his own hat—the same size, the same color. And it had exactly the same feather.

"By the Crown of my Fathers!" roared the King, again leaning out of the carriage window. "Did I or did I *not* command you to take off your hat?"

"You did, Sire . . . I took it off . . . I took it off twice."

"Nonsense! There is still a hat upon your head."

"Another hat?" Again Bartholomew reached up his hand and touched a hat.

"Come, come, what is the meaning of all this?" demanded the King, his face purple with rage.

"I don't know, Sire," answered Bartholomew. "It never happened to me before."

The King was now shaking with such fury that the carriage rocked on its wheels and the Royal Coachman could hardly sit in his seat.

"Arrest this impudent trickster," shouted the King to the Captain of the King's Own Guards. "We'll teach him to take off his hat."

The Royal Coachman cracked his long whip. The King's carriage swung forward up the street toward the palace.

But the Captain of the King's Own Guards leaned down from his big brass saddle and grabbed Bartholomew Cubbins by his shirt. Away flew Bartholomew's basket! The cranberries bounced over the cobblestones and rolled down into the gutter.

With a jangling of spurs and a clatter of horseshoes, the Captain and Bartholomew sped up the winding street toward the palace. Out of the narrow streets, on up the hill! Bartholomew clung to the Captain's broad back. On and on they galloped, past the bright gardens of the wealthy merchants. Higher and higher up the mountain, on past the walls of the noblemen's castles. . . .

Flupp! . . . the sharp wind whisked off Bartholomew's hat. *Flupp Flupp* . . . two more flew off. *Flupp Flupp Flupp* flew another . . . and another. ". . . 4 . . . 5 . . . 6 . . . 7 . . ." Bartholomew kept counting as the hats came faster and faster. Lords and ladies stared from the windows of their turrets, wondering what the strange stream of hats could mean.

Over the palace drawbridge they sped— through the great gates, and into the courtyard. The Captain pulled in his reins.

"His Majesty waits in the Throne Room," said a guard, saluting the Captain.

"The Throne Room!" The Captain dropped Bartholomew to the ground. "I'd certainly hate to be in your shoes," he said, shaking his head sadly.

For a moment Bartholomew was terribly frightened. "Still," he thought to himself, "the King can do nothing dreadful to punish me, because I really haven't done anything wrong. It would be cowardly to feel afraid."

Bartholomew threw back his shoulders and marched straight ahead into the palace. "Follow the black carpet," said the guard at the door. All through the long hallway Bartholomew could hear the muttering of voices behind heavy doors. "He won't take off his hat?" "No, he won't take off his hat."

Bartholomew walked on till he stood in the very middle of the Throne Room. The King, in a long scarlet robe, was sitting on his throne. Beside him stood Sir Alaric, Keeper of the King's Records. He wore in his belt, instead of a sword, a long silver ruler. Lords and noblemen of the court stood solemn and silent.

The King looked down at Bartholomew severely. "Young man, I'll give you one more chance. Will you take off your hat for your King?"

"Your Majesty," said Bartholomew as politely as he possibly could, "I will—but I'm afraid it won't do any good." And he took off his hat—and it didn't do any good. Another hat sat on Bartholomew's head. He took off hat after hat after hat after hat until he was standing in the middle of a great pile of hats.

The lords and noblemen were so astonished they couldn't even speak. Such a thing had never happened in the Throne Room before.

"Heavens!" said Sir Alaric, Keeper of the Records, blinking behind his triangular spectacles. "He's taken off 45!"

"And there were 3 more down in the town," said the King.

"And you must add on 87 more that blew off my head as we galloped up the hill," said Bartholomew, trying to be helpful.

"One hundred and thirty-five hats! Most unusual," said Sir Alaric, writing it down on a long scroll.

"Come, come," said the King impatiently. "Sir Alaric, what do you make of all this nonsense?"

"Very *serious* nonsense, Your Majesty," answered Sir Alaric. "I advise you to call in an expert on hats."

"Excellent," agreed the King. "Ho, Guard! Fetch in Sir Snipps, maker of hats for all the fine lords."

Into the Throne Room marched the smallest man, wearing the tallest hat that Bartholomew had ever seen. It was Sir Snipps. Instead of a sword, he wore at his side a large pair of scissors.

"Take a look at this boy's hat," commanded the King. Sir Snipps looked at Bartholomew Cubbins' hat and sniffed in disgust. Then he turned to the King and bowed stiffly. "Your Majesty, I, Sir Snipps, am the maker of hats for all the fine lords. I make hats of cloth of gold,

fine silks and gems and ostrich plumes. You ask *me* what I think of *this* hat? Pooh! It is the most ordinary hat I ever set eyes on."

"In that case," said the King, "it should be very simple for you to take it off."

"Simple, indeed," mumbled Sir Snipps haughtily, and, standing on his tiptoes, he pushed his pudgy thumb at Bartholomew's hat and knocked it to the floor. Immediately another appeared on Bartholomew's head.

"Screebees!" screamed Sir Snipps, leaping in the air higher than he was tall. Then he turned and ran shrieking out of the Throne Room.

"Dear me!" said the King, looking very puzzled. "If Snipps can't do it, this *must* be more than an ordinary hat."

"One hundred and thirty-six," wrote Sir Alaric, wrinkling his brow. "Your Majesty, I advise that you call in your Wise Men."

"A fine idea!" said the King. "Ho, Guard! bring me Nadd. Nadd knows about everything in all my kingdom."

In came an old, old man. He looked at the hat on Bartholomew's head, and he looked at the pile of hats on the floor.

"Nadd, my Wise Man, can you take off his hat?" asked the King. Nadd shook his head solemnly—solemnly no.

"Then fetch me the Father of Nadd," commanded the King. "He knows about everything in all my kingdom and in all the world beyond."

In came an even older man. But when he looked at Bartholomew's hats, the Father of Nadd merely locked his fingers across his beard and said nothing.

"Then bring me the Father of the Father of Nadd!" ordered the King. "He knows about everything in all my kingdom, in all the world beyond, and in all other worlds that may happen to be."

Then came the oldest man of them all. But he just looked at Bartholomew and nibbled nervously at the end of his beard.

"Does this mean there is *no one* in my whole kingdom who can take off this boy's hat?" bellowed the King in a terrifying voice.

A small voice came up through the balcony window. "What's the matter, Uncle Derwin?" To Bartholomew, it sounded like the voice of a boy.

The King stepped out on the balcony and leaned over the marble railing. "There's a boy in here . . . just about your age," the King said. "He won't take off his hat."

Bartholomew tiptoed up behind the King and looked down. There stood a boy with a big lace collar—a very proud little boy with his nose in the air. It was the Grand Duke Wilfred, nephew of the King.

"You send him down here," said the Grand Duke Wilfred. "*I'll* fix him."

The King thought for a minute. He pushed back his crown and scratched his head. "Well . . . maybe you can. There's no harm trying."

"Take him to the Grand Duke Wilfred!" commanded the King. And two of the King's Own Guards led Bartholomew out of the Throne Room.

"Pooh!" said the Grand Duke Wilfred, looking at Bartholomew's hat and laughing meanly. "*That* hat won't come off? You stand over there." He pointed to a corner where the wall curved out. "I need a little target practise with my bow and arrow."

When Bartholomew saw that the Grand Duke Wilfred had only a child's bow he didn't feel frightened. He spoke up proudly, "I can shoot with my father's big bow."

"My bow's plenty big enough for shooting hats—especially hats like yours," answered Wilfred. And he let fly an arrow. zZZ! . . . it grazed Bartholomew's forehead and nipped off his hat. Away it blew, and over the parapet. But another hat appeared on his head. zZZ! . . . zZZ! . . . zZZ! . . . the arrows flew . . . till the Grand

Duke's whole bagful of arrows was gone. And still a hat sat upon Bartholomew's head.

"It's not fair," cried the Grand Duke. "It's not fair!" He threw down his bow and stamped upon it.

"One hundred and fifty-four hats!" gulped Sir Alaric.

"These hats are driving me mad!" The King's voice rang out through all the palace. "Why waste time with a *child's* bow and arrow. Fetch me the mightiest bow and arrow in all my realm—fetch the Yeoman of the Bowmen!"

"Yeoman of the Bowmen," echoed all the lords and noblemen of the court.

A gigantic man strode out across the terrace. His bow was as big as the branch of a tree. The arrow was twice as long as Bartholomew, and thicker than his wrist.

"Yeoman of the Bowmen," said the King, "shoot off this boy's hat . . . and make it *stay* off!"

Bartholomew was trembling so hard that he could scarcely stand straight. The Yeoman bent back his mighty bow.

G—r—r—zibb! . . . Like a mad giant hornet the arrow tore through the air toward Bartholomew Cubbins.

G—r—r—zapp! . . . The sharp arrow head bit through his hat and carried it off—on and on for a full half mile.

G—r—r—zopp! . . . It plunked to a stop in the heart of an oak tree. Yet there on Bartholomew's head sat another hat.

The face of the Yeoman of the Bowmen went white as the palace walls. "It's black magic!" he shrieked.

"Black magic, that's *just* what it is," sighed the King with relief. "I should have thought of that before. That makes things simple. Back to the Throne Room! Call my magicians!"

In the whole Throne Room there wasn't a sound as loud as a breath. But from the spiral stairs that led down from the southwest tower came the shuffling of slow, padded feet. The magicians were coming! Low and slow, they were chanting words that were strange. . . .

"Dig a hole five furlongs deep,
Down to where the night snakes creep,
Mix and mold the mystic mud,
Malber, Balber, Tidder, Tudd."

In came seven black-gowned magicians, and beside each one stalked a lean black cat. They circled around Bartholomew Cubbins muttering deep and mysterious sounds.

"Stop this useless muttering," ordered the King. "I want a chant that will charm away this boy's hat."

The magicians huddled over Bartholomew and chanted.

"Winkibus
Tinkibus
Fotichee
Klay,
Hat on this demon's head,
Fly far away!
Howl, men, howl away,
Howl away, howl away,
Yowl, cats, yowl away,
Yowl away, yowl away!
Hat on this demon's head,
Seep away, creep away, leap away, gleap away,
Never come back!"

"A mighty good chant," said the King, looking very pleased. "Are you sure it will work?"

All the magicians nodded together.

"But," said the King, looking puzzled, "there still *seems* to be a hat upon his head. How long will it take for the charm to work?"

"Be calm, oh, Sire, and have no fears," chanted the magicians.

"Our charm will work in ten short years."

"*Ten years!*" gasped the King. "Away, fools!" he shouted. "Out of my sight! I can't wait *ten years* to get rid of his hat. Oh, dear, what *can* I do . . . what CAN I do?"

"If I were King," whispered the Grand Duke Wilfred, "I'd chop off his head."

"A dreadful thought," said the King, biting his lip. "But I'm afraid I'll have to."

"Young man," he said to Bartholomew Cubbins, and he pointed to a small door at the end of the room, "march down those steps to the dungeon and tell the executioner to chop off your head."

Bartholomew's heart sank into his boots, but he did as the King commanded. "I *must* take off my hat," he said to himself as he started down the long black stairway. "This is my last chance." One hat after another he tore from his head ". . . 156 . . . 157 . . . 158 . . ." It grew colder and damper. ". . . 217 . . . 218 . . . 219 . . ." Down . . . down . . . down. ". . . 231 . . . 232 . . . 233 . . ." It seemed to Bartholomew he must be in the very heart of the mountain.

"Who's there?" said a voice from the blackness.

Bartholomew turned a corner and stepped into the dungeon.

The executioner was whistling and swinging his axe idly, because at the moment he had nothing to do. In spite of his business, he really seemed to be a very pleasant man.

"The King says you must chop off my head," said Bartholomew.

"Oh, I'd hate to," said the executioner, looking at him with a friendly smile. "You seem like such a nice boy."

"Well . . . the King says you have to," said Bartholomew, "so please get it over with."

"All right," sighed the executioner, "but first you've got to take off your hat."

"Why?" asked Bartholomew.

"I don't know," said the executioner, "but it's one of the rules. I can't execute anyone with his hat on."

"All right," said Bartholomew, "you take it off for me."

The executioner leaned across the chopping block and flipped off Bartholomew's hat.

"What's this?" he gasped, blinking through the holes in his mask, as another hat sat on Bartholomew's head. He flipped this one off . . . then another and another.

"Fiddlesticks!" grunted the executioner, throwing his axe on the floor. "I can't execute you at all." And he shook hands with Bartholomew and sent him back upstairs to the King.

The King had been taking a nap on the throne. "What are you doing back here?" he said to Bartholomew, angry at being awakened.

"I'm sorry, Your Majesty," explained Bartholomew. "My head can't come off with my hat on. . . . It's against the rules."

"So it can't," said the King, leaning back wearily. "Now how many hats does that make altogether?"

"The executioner knocked off 13 . . . and I left 178 more on the dungeon steps," answered Bartholomew.

"Three hundred and forty-six hats," mumbled Sir Alaric from behind his scroll.

"Uncle Derwin," yawned the Grand Duke Wilfred, "I suppose I'll have to do away with him. Send him up to the highest turret and I, in person will push him off."

"Wilfred! I'm surprised at you," said the King. "But I guess it's a good idea."

So the King and the Grand Duke led Bartholomew Cubbins toward the highest turret.

Up and up and up the turret stairs he climbed behind them.

"This is my *last*—my *very last* chance," thought Bartholomew. He snatched off his hat. "Three hundred and forty-seven!" He snatched off another. He pulled and he tore and he flung them behind him. ". . . 398 . . . 399 . . ." His arms ached from pulling off hats. But still the hats came. Bartholomew climbed on.

". . . 448 . . . 449 . . . 450 . . ." counted Sir Alaric, puffing up the stairs behind him.

Suddenly Sir Alaric stopped. He looked. He took off his triangular spectacles and wiped them on his sleeve. And then he looked again. *The hats began to change!* Hat 451 had, not one, but *two* feathers! Hat 452 had three . . . and 453

also had three *and a little red jewel!* Each new hat was fancier than the hat just before.

"Your Majesty! Your Majesty!" cried out Sir Alaric.

But the King and the Grand Duke were 'way up where they couldn't hear. They had already reached the top of the highest turret. Bartholomew was following just behind.

"Step right out here and get out on that wall," snapped the Grand Duke Wilfred. "I can't wait to push you off."

But when Bartholomew stepped up on the wall they gasped in amazement. He was wearing the most beautiful hat that had ever been seen in the Kingdom of Didd. It had a ruby larger than any the King himself had ever owned. It had ostrich plumes, and cockatoo plumes, and mockingbird plumes, and paradise plumes. Beside *such* a hat even the King's Crown seemed like nothing.

The Grand Duke Wilfred took a quick step forward. Bartholomew thought his end had come at last.

"Wait!" shouted the King. He could not take his eyes off the magnificent hat.

"I *won't* wait," the Grand Duke talked back to the King. "I'm going to push him off now! That new big hat makes me madder than ever." And he flung out his arms to push Bartholomew off.

But the King was quicker than Wilfred. He grabbed him by the back of his fine lace collar. "This is to teach you," His Majesty said sternly, "that Grand Dukes *never* talk back to their King." And he turned the Grand Duke Wilfred over his knee and spanked him soundly, right on the seat of his royal silk pants.

"And now," smiled the King, lifting Bartholomew down from the wall, "it would be nice if you'd sell me that wonderful hat!"

". . . 498 . . . 499 . . ." broke in the tired voice of Sir Alaric, who had just arrived at the top of the steps, " and *that* . . ." he pointed to the hat on Bartholomew's head, "makes exactly 500!"

"*Five Hundred!*" exclaimed the King. "Will you sell it for 500 pieces of gold?"

"Anything you say, Sire," answered Bartholomew. "You see . . . I've never sold one before."

The King's hands trembled with joy as he reached for the hat.

Slowly, slowly, Bartholomew felt the weight of the great hat lifting from his head. He held his breath. . . . Then suddenly he felt the cool evening breezes blow through his hair. His face broke into a happy smile. The head of Bartholomew Cubbins was bare!

"Look, Your Majesty! *Look!*" he shouted to the King.

"No! *You* look at *me,*" answered the King. And he put the great hat on right over his crown.

Arm in arm, the King and Bartholomew went down to the counting room to count out the gold. Then the King sent Bartholomew home to his parents . . . no basket on his arm, no hat on his head, but with five hundred pieces of gold in a bag.

And the King commanded that the hat he had bought, and all the other hats, too, be kept forever in a great crystal case by the side of his throne.

But neither Bartholomew Cubbins, nor King Derwin himself, nor anyone else in the Kingdom of Didd could ever explain how the strange thing had happened. They only could say it just "happened to happen" and was not very likely to happen again.

"THAT IS WHY HE WAS ALWAYS CALLED POOH"

A. A. Milne

Younger children like the Pooh books, but sometimes miss part of their humor. In many families parents begin reading Pooh stories to the five- or six-year-olds and are still reading them when the children are ten.

So Winnie-the-Pooh went round to his friend Christopher Robin, who lived behind a green door in another part of the forest.

"Good morning, Christopher Robin," he said.

"Good morning, Winnie-*ther*-Pooh," said you.

"I wonder if you've got such a thing as a balloon about you?"

"*That* Is Why He Was Always Called Pooh." From *Winnie-the-Pooh* by A. A. Milne, published and copyright, 1926, E. P. Dutton & Co., Inc., New York. By permission also of Methuen & Co., Ltd., London

"A balloon?"

"Yes, I just said to myself coming along: 'I wonder if Christopher Robin has such a thing as a balloon about him?' I just said it to myself, thinking of balloons, and wondering."

"What do you want a balloon for?" you said.

Winnie-the-Pooh looked round to see that nobody was listening, put his paw to his mouth, and said in a deep whisper: "*Honey!*"

"But you don't get honey with balloons!"

"*I* do," said Pooh.

Well, it just happened that you had been to a party the day before at the house of your friend Piglet, and you had balloons at the party. You had had a big green balloon; and one of Rabbit's relations had had a big blue one, and had left it behind, being really too young to go to a party at all; and so you had brought the green one *and* the blue one home with you.

"Which one would you like?" you asked Pooh.

He put his head between his paws and thought very carefully.

"It's like this," he said. "When you go after honey with a balloon, the great thing is not to let the bees know you're coming. Now, if you have a green balloon, they might think you were only part of the tree, and not notice you, and if you have a blue balloon, they might think you were only part of the sky, and not notice you, and the question is: Which is most likely?"

"Wouldn't they notice *you* underneath the balloon?" you asked.

"They might or they might not," said Winnie-the-Pooh. "You never can tell with bees." He thought for a moment and said: "I shall try to look like a small black cloud. That will deceive them."

"Then you had better have the blue balloon," you said; and so it was decided.

Well, you both went out with the blue balloon, and you took your gun with you, just in case, as you always did, and Winnie-the-Pooh went to a very muddy place that he knew of, and rolled and rolled until he was black all over; and then, when the balloon was blown up as big as big, and you and Pooh were both holding on to the string, you let go suddenly, and Pooh Bear floated gracefully up into the sky, and stayed there—level with the top of the tree and about twenty feet away from it.

"Hooray!" you shouted.

"Isn't that fine?" shouted Winnie-the-Pooh down to you. "What do I look like?"

"You look like a Bear holding on to a balloon," you said.

"Not," said Pooh anxiously, "—not like a small black cloud in a blue sky?"

"Not very much."

"Ah, well, perhaps from up here it looks different. And, as I say, you never can tell with bees."

There was no wind to blow him nearer to the tree, so there he stayed. He could see the honey, he could smell the honey, but he couldn't quite reach the honey.

After a little while he called down to you.

"Christopher Robin!" he said in a loud whisper.

"Hallo!"

"I think the bees *suspect* something!"

"What sort of thing?"

"I don't know. But something tells me that they're *suspicious!*"

"Perhaps they think that you're after their honey."

"It may be that. You never can tell with bees."

There was another little silence, and then he called down to you again.

"Christopher Robin!"

"Yes?"

"Have you an umbrella in your house?"

"I think so."

"I wish you would bring it out here, and walk up and down with it, and look up at me every now and then, and say 'Tut-tut, it looks like rain.' I think, if you did that, it would help the deception which we are practising on these bees."

Well, you laughed to yourself, "Silly old Bear!" but you didn't say it aloud because you were so fond of him, and you went home for your umbrella.

"Oh, there you are!" called down Winnie-the-Pooh, as soon as you got back to the tree. "I was beginning to get anxious. I have discovered that the bees are now definitely Suspicious."

"Shall I put my umbrella up?" you said.

"Yes, but wait a moment. We must be practical. The important bee to deceive is the Queen Bee. Can you see which is the Queen Bee from down there?"

"No."

"A pity. Well, now, if you walk up and down with your umbrella, saying, 'Tut-tut, it looks like rain,' I shall do what I can by singing a little Cloud Song, such as a cloud might sing. . . . Go!"

So, while you walked up and down and wondered if it would rain, Winnie-the-Pooh sang this song:

How sweet to be a Cloud
　　Floating in the Blue!
Every little cloud
　　Always sing aloud.

"How sweet to be a Cloud
　　Floating in the Blue!"
It makes him very proud
To be a little cloud.

The bees were still buzzing as suspiciously as ever. Some of them, indeed, left their nest and flew all round the cloud as it began the second verse of this song, and one bee sat down on the nose of the cloud for a moment, and then got up again.

"Christopher—*ow!*—Robin," called out the cloud.

"Yes?"

"I have just been thinking, and I have come to a very important decision. *These are the wrong sort of bees.*"

"Are they?"

"Quite the wrong sort. So I should think they would make the wrong sort of honey, shouldn't you?"

"Would they?"

"Yes. So I think I shall come down."

"How?" asked you.

Winnie-the-Pooh hadn't thought about this. If he let go of the string, he would fall—*bump*—and he didn't like the idea of that. So he thought for a long time, and then he said:

"Christopher Robin, you must shoot the balloon with your gun. Have you got your gun?"

"Of course I have," you said. "But if I do that, it will spoil the balloon," you said.

"But if you *don't,*" said Pooh, "I shall have to let go, and that would spoil *me.*"

When he put it like this, you saw how it was, and you aimed very carefully at the balloon, and fired.

"*Ow!*" said Pooh.

"Did I miss?" you asked.

"You didn't exactly *miss,*" said Pooh, "but you missed the *balloon.*"

"I'm so sorry," you said, and you fired again, and this time you hit the balloon, and the air came slowly out, and Winnie-the-Pooh floated down to the ground.

But his arms were so stiff from holding on to the string of the balloon all that time that they stayed up straight in the air for more than a week, and whenever a fly came and settled on his nose he had to blow it off. And I think—but I am not sure—that *that* is why he was always called Pooh.

POOH GOES VISITING AND GETS INTO A TIGHT PLACE

A. A. Milne

Edward Bear, known to his friends as Winnie-the-Pooh, or Pooh for short, was walking through the forest one day, humming proudly to himself. He had made up a little hum that very morning, as he was doing his Stoutness Exercises in front of the glass: *Tra-la-la, tra-la-la,* as he stretched up as high as he could go, and then *Tra-la-la, tra-la —oh, help!—la,* as he tried to reach his toes. After breakfast he had said it over and over to himself until he had learnt it off by heart, and now he was humming it right through, properly. It went like this:

> *Tra-la-la, tra-la-la,*
> *Tra-la-la, tra-la-la,*
> *Rum-tum-tiddle-um-tum.*
> *Tiddle-iddle, tiddle-iddle,*
> *Tiddle-iddle, tiddle-iddle,*
> *Rum-tum-tum-tiddle-um.*

Well, he was humming this hum to himself, and walking along gaily, wondering what everybody else was doing, and what it felt like, being somebody else, when suddenly he came to a sandy bank, and in the bank was a large hole.

"Aha!" said Pooh. (*Rum-tum-tiddle-um-tum.*)

"If I know anything about anything, that hole means Rabbit," he said, "and Rabbit means Company," he said, "and Company means Food and Listening-to-Me-Humming and such like. *Rum-tum-tum-tiddle-um.*"

So he bent down, put his head into the hole, and called out:

"Is anybody at home?"

There was a sudden scuffling noise from inside the hole, and then silence.

"What I said was, 'Is anybody at home?'" called out Pooh very loudly.

"No!" said a voice; and then added, "You needn't shout so loud. I heard you quite well the first time."

"Bother!" said Pooh. "Isn't there anybody here at all?"

"Nobody."

Winnie-the-Pooh took his head out of the hole, and thought for a little, and he thought to himself, "There must be somebody there, because somebody must have *said* 'Nobody.'" So he put his head back in the hole, and said:

"Hallo, Rabbit, isn't that you?"

"No," said Rabbit, in a different sort of voice this time.

"But isn't that Rabbit's voice?"

"I don't *think* so," said Rabbit. "It isn't *meant* to be."

"Oh!" said Pooh.

He took his head out of the hole, and had another think, and then he put it back, and said:

"Well, could you very kindly tell me where Rabbit is?"

"He has gone to see his friend Pooh Bear, who is a great friend of his."

"But this *is* Me!" said Bear, very much surprised.

"What sort of Me?"

"Pooh Bear."

"Are you sure?" said Rabbit, still more surprised.

"Quite, quite sure," said Pooh.

"Oh, well, then, come in."

So Pooh pushed and pushed and pushed his way through the hole, and at last he got in.

"You were quite right," said Rabbit, looking at him all over. "It *is* you. Glad to see you."

"Who did you think it was?"

"Well, I wasn't sure. You know how it is in

the Forest. One can't have *anybody* coming into one's house. One has to be *careful*. What about a mouthful of something?"

Pooh always liked a little something at eleven o'clock in the morning, and he was very glad to see Rabbit getting out the plates and mugs; and when Rabbit said, "Honey or condensed milk with your bread?" he was so excited that he said, "Both," and then, so as not to seem greedy, he added, "But don't bother about the bread, please." And for a long time after that he said nothing . . . until at last, humming to himself in a rather sticky voice, he got up, shook Rabbit lovingly by the paw, and said that he must be going on.

"Must you?" said Rabbit politely.

"Well," said Pooh, "I could stay a little longer if it—if you—" and he tried very hard to look in the direction of the larder.

"As a matter of fact," said Rabbit, "I was going out myself directly."

"Oh, well, then, I'll be going on. Good-bye."

"Well, good-bye, if you're sure you won't have any more."

"*Is* there any more?" asked Pooh quickly.

Rabbit took the covers off the dishes, and said, "No, there wasn't."

"I thought not," said Pooh, nodding to himself. "Well, good-bye. I must be going on."

So he started to climb out of the hole. He pulled with his front paws, and pushed with his back paws, and in a little while his nose was out in the open again . . . and then his ears . . . and then his front paws . . . and then his shoulders . . . and then——

"Oh, help!" said Pooh. "I'd better go back."

"Oh, bother!" said Pooh. "I shall have to go on."

"I can't do either!" said Pooh. "Oh, help *and* bother!"

Now by this time Rabbit wanted to go for a walk too, and finding the front door full, he went out by the back door, and came round to Pooh, and looked at him.

"Hallo, are you stuck?" he asked.

"N-no," said Pooh carelessly. "Just resting and thinking and humming to myself."

"Here, give us a paw."

Pooh Bear stretched out a paw, and Rabbit pulled and pulled and pulled. . . .

"Ow!" cried Pooh. "You're hurting!"

"The fact is," said Rabbit, "you're stuck."

"It all comes," said Pooh crossly, "of not having front doors big enough."

"It all comes," said Rabbit sternly, "of eating too much. I thought at the time," said Rabbit, "only I don't like to say anything," said Rabbit, "that one of us was eating too much," said Rabbit, "and I knew it wasn't *me*," he said. "Well, well, I shall go and fetch Christopher Robin."

Christopher Robin lived at the other end of the Forest, and when he came back with Rabbit, and saw the front half of Pooh, he said, "Silly old Bear," in such a loving voice that everybody felt quite hopeful again.

"I was just beginning to think," said Bear, sniffing slightly, "that Rabbit might never be able to use his front door again. And I should *hate* that," he said.

"So should I," said Rabbit.

"Use his front door again?" said Christopher Robin. "Of course he'll use his front door again."

"Good," said Rabbit.

"If we can't pull you out, Pooh, we might push you back."

Rabbit scratched his whiskers thoughtfully, and pointed out that, when once Pooh was pushed back, he was back, and of course nobody was more glad to see Pooh than *he* was, still there it was, some lived in trees and some lived underground, and——

"You mean I'd *never* get out?" said Pooh.

"I mean," said Rabbit, "that having got *so* far, it seems a pity to waste it."

Christopher Robin nodded.

"Then there's only one thing to be done," he said.

"We shall have to wait for you to get thin again."

"How long does getting thin take?" asked Pooh anxiously.

"About a week, I should think."

"But I can't stay here for a *week!*"

"You can *stay* here all right, silly old Bear. It's getting you out which is so difficult."

"We'll read to you," said Rabbit cheerfully. "And I hope it won't snow," he added. "And I say, old fellow, you're taking up a good deal of room in my house—*do* you mind if I use your back legs as a towel-horse? Because, I mean, there they are—doing nothing—and it would be very convenient just to hang the towels on them."

"A week!" said Pooh gloomily. *What about meals?*

"I'm afraid no meals," said Christopher Robin, "because of getting thin quicker. But we *will* read to you."

Bear began to sigh, and then found he couldn't because he was so tightly stuck; and a tear rolled down his eye, as he said:

"Then would you read a Sustaining Book, such as would help and comfort a Wedged Bear in Great Tightness?"

So for a week Christopher Robin read that sort of book at the North end of Pooh, and Rabbit hung his washing on the South end . . . and in between Bear felt himself getting slenderer and slenderer. And at the end of the week Christopher Robin said, *Now!*

So he took hold of Pooh's front paws and Rabbit took hold of Christopher Robin, and all Rabbit's friends and relations took hold of Rabbit, and they all pulled together. . . .

And for a long time Pooh only said *"Ow!"* . . . And *"Oh!"* . . .

And then, all of a sudden, he said *"Pop!"* just as if a cork were coming out of a bottle.

And Christopher Robin and Rabbit and all Rabbit's friends and relations went head-over-heels backwards . . . and on the top of them came Winnie-the-Pooh—free!

So, with a nod of thanks to his friends, he went on with his walk through the forest, humming proudly to himself. But, Christopher Robin looked after him lovingly, and said to himself, "Silly old Bear!"

THE MAGIC BED-KNOB

Mary Norton

Only Paul knows that Miss Price is studying to become a witch, but when Carey and Charles hear about it, they persuade Miss Price to give them a little magic too.

Afterwards, on the way home, Carey and Charles tackled Paul.

"Paul, why didn't you tell us you'd seen Miss Price on a broomstick?"

"I dunno."

"But, Paul, you ought to have told us. We'd have liked to see it, too. It was very mean of you, Paul."

Paul did not reply.

"When did you see her?"

"In the night."

Paul looked stubborn. He felt as if he might be going to cry. Miss Price always passed so quickly. She would have been gone before he could call anyone (and they would have said at once, "Don't be silly, Paul"). Besides, it had been his secret, his nightly joy. His bed was beside the window and, when the moon was full, it shone on his pillow and wakened him. It had been exciting to lie there, with his eyes fixed on the pale sky beyond the ragged blackness of the cedar boughs. Some nights, he did not wake up. Other nights, he woke up and she did not come. But he saw her often enough and, each time he saw her, she had learned to fly a little better. At first she had wobbled so, balanced sideways on the stick, that he wondered why she did not ride astride. She would grip the broomstick with one hand and try to hold her hat on with the other, and her feet, in their long shoes, looked so odd against the moonlit sky. Once she fell—and the broomstick came down quite slowly, like an umbrella blown inside out, with Miss Price clinging to the handle. Paul had watched her anxiously until she reached the ground. That time, she did not hurt herself.

Partly, he did not tell because he wanted to be proud of Miss Price. He did not want the others to see her until she was really good at it; until, perhaps, she could do tricks on a broomstick and look confident instead of scared. Once, when she had lifted both hands in the air at the same time, Paul nearly clapped. He knew that was hard to do even on a bicycle. He had another worry, too; that the Home Guard might get her. They were out all night patrolling the hills, on the watch for German parachutists. . . .

"You see, Paul," Carey was saying, "it was really very selfish; now Miss Price has hurt her ankle, she won't be flying again for ages. Charles

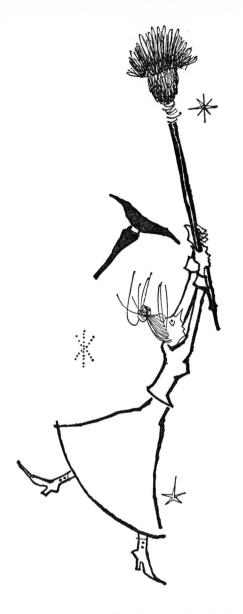

Paul seemed about to burst into speech but was silenced by a kick from Charles; aggrievedly, he swallowed his last mouthful of rice pudding.

"Yes, Aunt Beatrice, we do know where she lives."

It was about four o'clock in the afternoon when the children knocked at Miss Price's neat front door. The path on which they stood was gaily bordered with flowers and, through the half-open windows of the sitting-room, Miss Price's dimity curtains fluttered in the breeze. The door was opened by Agnes, a village girl who served Miss Price for a few hours daily.

As the children entered the little sitting-room for a moment they felt very shy. There lay Miss Price on the sofa, her bandaged foot raised up on pillows. She still looked pale but now her hair was tidy and her white blouse spotlessly neat.

"What lovely peaches! Thank you, my dears, and thank your aunt. Very kind of her, I'm sure. Sit down, sit down."

The children sat down gingerly on the little spindly chairs.

"Agnes is making us some tea. You must stay and keep me company. Carey, can you open that card table?"

The children bustled round and helped to set the room for tea. A little table near Miss Price for the tea-tray and a white cloth on the card table for the scones, the bread and margarine, the quince jelly, and the utility cake.

They enjoyed their tea and, when it was over, they helped Agnes to clear away. Then Miss Price showed Charles and Carey how to play backgammon and loaned Paul a large book full of pictures called "Paradise Lost." Paul liked the book very much. He liked the musty smell of it and the gilt-edged pages.

When they had finished the game of backgammon and it seemed that it must be nearly time to go home, Carey picked up her courage in both hands.

"Miss Price," she said hesitatingly, "If it isn't rude to ask—are you a witch?"

There was silence for a moment and Carey could feel her heart beating. Paul looked up from his book.

Very carefully, Miss Price closed the backgammon board and laid it on the little table

and I may never have the chance of seeing her!"

Later, as they were solemnly eating lunch in the high, dark dining-room, Aunt Beatrice startled them by saying suddenly: "Poor Miss Price!" They all looked up, as if she had read their secret thoughts and were relieved when she went on calmly, "It seems she has fallen off her bicycle and sprained her ankle. So painful, poor soul. I must send her down some peaches."

Paul sat with his spoon halfway to his mouth and his eyes moved round from Charles to Carey.

Carey cleared her throat, "Aunt Beatrice," she said, "could we take the peaches to Miss Price?"

"That's very thoughtful of you, Carey. I don't see why not, if you know where she lives."

beside the sofa. She took up her knitting and unfolded it.

"Well," she said slowly, "I am and I'm not."

Paul sat back on his heels. "You mean, you are sort of," he suggested.

Miss Price threw him a glance. "I mean, Paul," she said quietly, "that I am studying to be a witch." She knitted a few stitches, pursing up her mouth.

"Oh, Miss Price," cried Carey warmly. "How terribly clever of you!"

It was the best thing she could have said. Miss Price flushed but she looked pleased.

"How did you first think of it, Miss Price?"

"Well, ever since I was a girl, I've had a bit of a gift for witchcraft, but somehow—what with piano lessons and looking after my mother—I never seemed to have the time to take it up seriously."

Paul was staring at Miss Price, as if to drink in every detail of her appearance. "I don't think you're a wicked witch," he said at last.

Miss Price dropped her eyes unhappily. "I know, Paul," she admitted in a low voice. "You're quite right. I started too late in life. That's the whole trouble."

"Is being wicked the hardest part?" asked Carey.

"It is for me," Miss Price told her rather sadly. "But there are people who have a natural gift for it."

"Paul has," said Charles.

Paul came nearer and sat down on a chair. He was still staring at Miss Price, as if he longed to ask her something. After a minute, he found courage. "Could you just do a little bit of magic for us now?"

"Oh, Paul!" exclaimed Carey. "Don't worry Miss Price. She can't do magic with a sprained ankle."

"Yes, she could," protested Paul hotly. "She could do it lying down, couldn't you, Miss Price?"

"Well," said Miss Price, "I am a little tired, Paul. But I'll just do a little quick one and then you must all go home. There you are!"

Carey and Charles looked around quickly, following the direction of Miss Price's eyes. Paul's chair was empty. Paul had gone—but where he had been sitting perched a little yellow frog.

Before Carey and Charles had time to exclaim, Paul was back again, still staring expectantly at Miss Price.

"Oh," cried Carey, with a gasp, "That was wonderful, wonderful! How *did* you do it?"

She felt breathless and almost afraid. Magic—a spell—she had seen it with her own eyes.

"I didn't see anything," complained Paul.

Carey looked at him impatiently. "Oh, don't be silly, Paul. You turned into a frog. You must have felt it."

Paul's lips trembled, "I didn't feel anything," he said, in a squeaky little voice. But nobody heard him. Carey was staring at Miss Price with shining eyes."

"Miss Price," she pointed out almost reproachfully, "you could have done that at the Church concert, instead of singing."

Miss Price laid down her knitting. A strange look crept into her face, and she looked hard at Carey as if she were seeing her for the first time. Nervously, Carey drew back in her chair.

"Although you sing so nicely," she added hastily.

But Miss Price did not seem to hear. There was a wild light in her eyes and her lips moved quietly, as if she were reciting. "There must be some way," she was saying slowly. "There-must-be-some-way . . ."

"Some way of what?" asked Charles, after a moment's uncomfortable silence.

Miss Price smiled, showing her long yellow teeth.

"Of keeping your mouths shut," she rapped out.

Carey was shocked. This was far from lady-like. "Oh, Miss Price!" she exclaimed unhappily.

"Of keeping your mouths shut," repeated Miss Price slowly, smiling more unpleasantly than ever.

Paul made a little wriggling movement in his chair. "Now she's getting wicked," he whispered to Carey in a pleased voice.

Carey drew away from him as if she had not heard. She looked worried. "What do you mean, Miss Price? You mean we musn't tell anyone that—" she hesitated.

"That you're a witch?" put in Paul.

But Miss Price was still staring, as if she neither heard nor saw. "In just a minute I'll think of something," she said, as if to herself. "In just a minute—."

Then Carey did something which Charles thought very brave. She got up from her chair and sat down beside Miss Price, on the sofa.

"Listen, Miss Price," she said. "We did try to help you when you hurt your ankle. There isn't any need to use any kind of nasty magic on us. If you want to stop us telling, you could do it in a nice kind of way."

Miss Price looked at her. "How could I do it in a nice kind of way?" she asked, but she sounded more reasonable.

"Well," said Carey, "you could give us something—something magic—and if we told anyone about you, we'd have to forfeit it. You know, like a game. Directly we told, the thing would stop being magic."

"What sort of a thing?" asked Miss Price, but as if the idea held possibilities.

Charles leaned forward. "Yes," he put in, "a ring or something, that we could twist and a slave comes. And, if we told about you, the slave wouldn't come any more. Couldn't you do that?"

Miss Price looked thoughtful. "I couldn't manage a slave," she said after a moment.

"Well, something like that."

Miss Price sat very quiet. She was thinking hard. "I know," she said, after a while. Suddenly, she seemed quite nice and cheerful again. "There's something I've been wanting to try out. Mind you, I'm not sure that it will work. Has anybody got a ring on them?"

Alas, none of them had. Paul felt in his pockets, just in case, but found nothing but the brass knob he had unscrewed from his bed that morning.

"Well, anything. A bracelet would do. It should be something you can twist."

But unfortunately Carey could not produce a bracelet either. "I have one at home," she said, "but I only wear it on Sundays."

"You can twist this," cried Paul suddenly, holding out the bed-knob. "That's just what it does. It twists and it twists and it twists. I twisted it off," he added rather unnecessarily.

Miss Price took the bed-knob and held it thoughtfully between her clean, bony fingers.

"Let me see . . ." she said slowly. Then suddenly she looked up, as if surprised. "Paul I believe this is the best thing you could have given me." (Paul squirmed, pleased but bashful.) "Now, I could do a wonderful spell with this—but I must think it out very carefully. Now, be quiet, children, and let me think—so that I can get this right." Her fingers closed gently round the shining brass. "This should be very good indeed. Now, quiet please!"

The children sat like statues. Even Paul forgot to fidget. A bumblebee came in through the window and buzzed heavily about the room. Except for this, the silence was complete.

After what seemed a long while, Miss Price opened her eyes. And then she sat up, blinking and smiling. "There you are, Paul," she said brightly and handed him back the bed-knob.

He took it reverently. "Is it done?" he asked, in an awe-stricken voice. It looked just the same to him.

"Yes, it's quite done," Miss Price told him. "And it's a very good spell indeed. This is something you'll enjoy. Only don't get yourselves into trouble."

Carey and Charles were looking enviously at Paul.

"What must we do with it?" asked Charles.

"Just take it home and screw it back on the bed. But don't screw it right up. Screw it about half way."

"And then?"

"And then?" Miss Price smiled. "Twist it a little and wish—and the bed will take you to wherever you want to go!"

The children gazed unbelievingly at the gleaming ball in Paul's rather grubby fingers.

"Really?" asked Carey, with a little gasp.

Miss Price was still smiling. She seemed very pleased with herself.

"Well, try it."

"Oh, Miss Price," breathed Carey, still gazing at the knob. "THANK YOU."

"Don't thank me," said Miss Price, taking up her knitting again, "Remember the conditions. One word about me and the spell is broken."

"Oh, Miss Price!" said Carey again. She was quite overcome.

"Well, now off you go. It's getting late. As I say, don't get yourselves into trouble and don't go gallivanting around all night. There's moderation in all things—even in Magic."

SHAWNEEN AND THE GANDER

Richard Bennett

Before you read this story to children, tell them that the leprechaun is an Irish fairy, a fairy shoemaker, in fact. If you can catch one and never take your eye off him, you can make him give you his pot of gold, which he is always guarding. Shawneen knew this, of course, but wait till you hear what happened when he caught a leprechaun.

On the top of a high green hill in Ireland there once lived a little boy and his name was Shawneen.

One bright warm day while his mother was washing out the clothes she said, "The fire is out and there isn't a match in the house. Run down to Mrs. Murphy's shop like a good lad and buy a box. Here is a penny."

Indeed there was no need for a second word about that. Shawneen was always ready to go on errands to Mrs. Murphy's.

"I will to be sure," said he, putting his cap on his head and the penny in his pocket.

Now at the foot of the hill there was a little village with a row of houses and shops up one side of the street and down the other.

Mrs. Murphy's was the prize of the lot. She sold everything.

If you wanted to buy a dress or if you wanted to buy a ham Mrs. Murphy would be sure to have it.

When Shawneen arrived at her shop he was out of breath. He had been running down the hill and it was a good way round when you came by the road.

Before opening the door he stopped for a minute to look in the window.

The first shelf had the usual array of cups and saucers and the second shelf had nothing on it to talk about, but on the third shelf right near the glass Shawneen saw the most beautiful bugle he had ever seen in all his life.

It glistened so brightly in the sun that Shawneen could scarcely look at it.

It was all the color of gold and so shiny he could see himself seven times in it.

When Paddy the postman walked by the window to deliver the letters seven Paddys walked by in the bugle. It was that bright. Oh, I can tell you it was lovely.

Around the middle was tied a blue-and-yellow cord with a silky tassel on each end as big as your hand.

Shawneen went into the shop.

"A box of matches if you please, ma'am," said he to Mrs. Murphy; "and if it wouldn't be asking too much may I have a toot on the bugle?"

"A toot is it?" said Mrs. Murphy. "Indeed you may, my lad, two if you like. There is no harm in a good toot."

So Mrs. Murphy took the bugle out of the window and gave it to Shawneen. The end was cold and smooth and shaped so nicely that it fit snugly over his mouth.

"Now don't be afraid of it, my lad," said Mrs. Murphy. "Give us a good blow."

Shawneen blew very gently at first, then a little louder, and then so loud you could hear it down the street and over the hill and down by the sea.

Shawneen had never heard anything so fine in all his life.

"Ah, it's grand entirely," said he, stroking the tassels. "How much is it?"

"Ah, that's a very fine bugle," said Mrs. Murphy, "I couldn't let you have it for less than ten shillings and sixpence."

Shawneen blew on the bugle again but not so loud this time, then put it back on the counter.

Ten shillings and sixpence was a lot of money. Indeed a pair of shoes would cost as much as that.

Shawneen gave Mrs. Murphy the penny and put the box of matches in his coat pocket.

He walked slowly out the door and down the street.

He was thinking very hard to himself. How could he get ten shillings and sixpence to buy the bugle in Mrs. Murphy's shop window?

There was no money at home to be spent for bugles. Indeed he was well sure of that. Didn't his mother need a new shawl and the donkey a new harness and the window a new pane of glass? Wasn't his mother's teapot badly cracked and she often saying she wished she had the price of a new one? Weren't the soles of his own shoes so thin he decided to take a short cut across the fields as the gravel on the road hurt his feet?

"No, indeed," said Shawneen to himself, "It will be no use asking for ten shillings and sixpence to buy a bugle."

He jumped over the ditch and began to climb the hedge.

The heather and moss at the top felt nice and soft so he sat down for a bit to think the matter over.

He was no sooner nicely settled when all of a sudden he saw a strange little man dressed all in green asleep under a furze bush only a few feet away. He was no more than a foot long and his suit was so much the color of the grass about him that indeed Shawneen had to look sharp to make him out at all.

"It's a Leprechaun surely," whispered Shawneen to himself, "and the very lad who can tell me how I can get ten shillings and sixpence to buy the bugle."

Before you could say two two's Shawneen had the little fellow about the waist.

Now you may be sure it isn't every day you see a Leprechaun and when you do you have to keep your eyes on him or it's off he is in no time at all.

Shawneen lifted the little maneen out from under the bush. The Leprechaun awoke with a great start and let such a yell out of him you wouldn't think he was equal to it. It was that loud.

"Ah, let me down now like a good lad," said the little fellow, kicking this way and that. "This is no way to be treating a gentleman."

"I will, faith," said Shawneen, "but first you must tell me how I can get ten shillings and sixpence to buy the bugle in Mrs. Murphy's shop window."

"Ah, that's easy enough," said the Leprechaun, "but you are hurting me now. Take your thumb off my stomach like a good lad."

Shawneen lifted his thumb a bit and then the Leprechaun began to stretch his arms and stretch his legs and rub his eyes at a great rate.

"This warm weather makes one very sleepy," said he.

"Never mind that now," said Shawneen; "how can I get ten shillings and sixpence to buy the bugle?"

"Ah, you are a very determined lad," said the Leprechaun. "Why, earn it, of course. You can't expect to get something for nothing."

"I know that well enough," said Shawneen, "but how can I earn all that money?"

The Leprechaun put one of his long bony fingers to the side of his nose and leaning forward whispered very mysteriously, "Not a word to a soul now," said he, "hatch the egg and sell the gander."

"What egg?" said Shawneen, squeezing the little fellow tighter than ever.

The Leprechaun didn't say another word but pointed to the earth.

Before Shawneen stopped to think he glanced down and there by the side of the ditch was the biggest goose egg he had ever seen in all his life.

I needn't tell you the Leprechaun was gone in a flash.

"Well, the egg is real enough, faith," said Shawneen, picking it up and putting it in his cap to keep it from breaking.

"An egg the size of this should make a big gander and a big gander should bring a good price at the Fair. I should have enough money in all to buy my mother a new shawl and a new dress and a silver teapot and have still enough left over to buy a bugle."

He was so excited he could hardly wait to get home.

The sooner the hatching began the better.

Over the fields he went, leaping the ditches and climbing the hedges. That the egg wasn't broken was nothing less than a miracle.

When he reached home his mother was hanging out the clothes.

"What have you there, my lad?" said she.

"A goose egg," said Shawneen.

"A goose egg, is it?" said his mother. "I have seen big eggs in my day but nothing the likes of that. Where did you find it?"

Now Shawneen remembered what the Leprechaun had said about keeping quiet.

"I was coming across the field," said he, "and there it was all by itself in the shelter of the ditch."

"And what will you do with an egg like that?" said his mother.

"Hatch it," said Shawneen. "Is there a hen setting?"

"There is, to be sure," said his mother. "Bring it into the shed."

She opened the hen-house door and pointed to a big brown hen nesting in one corner.

"I am afraid she will find it a bit uncomfortable," said Shawneen, pushing the hen aside a bit.

"Oh, in a few days she will be so used to it she will never know it was there at all," said his mother.

Now goodness knows the egg did make the poor hen sit a bit crooked to be sure. But she was a quiet, obliging bird and went on sitting as if nothing had happened.

There she sat with one side up and one side down for days and days, a very mountain of patience.

Every morning Shawneen took a little peek under her wing to make sure all was going well and every now and then he went to have a look at the bugle in Mrs. Murphy's shop window. The bugle seemed to grow more beautiful every day and when Mrs. Murphy let him have a little toot on it now and then it sounded richer and sweeter as the days went by.

Well, the time passed as time will and soon the eggs were hatched—twelve yellow chicks and one yellow gosling. The chicks were fluffy and pretty as you may expect, but the gosling was a sight.

I don't think you could have found an uglier bird in the length and breadth of all Ireland.

His pin feathers stuck out of him like the bristles of an old pig and his feet were so big and red and awkward he was forever stepping on his own toes.

His head was as big as a gosling twice his size and his poor little neck so thin and scrawny that it looked for all the world like a cabbage on the end of a broomstick.

"Ah, he is beautiful," said Shawneen to his mother; "may I raise him myself?"

"Indeed you may," said she. "I am sure I will have nothing to do with him. I have raised ducks and geese in my day but I have never seen anything come out of an egg the likes of that. Goodness knows what kind of a gander he will make. He has altogether too knowing a look in his eye to my notion. Faith, he looks at you as if he knew what you are thinking. Take my word the sooner

you fatten him up and send him off to the Fair the better."

Shawneen thought this was a good idea. The sooner he had the money in his pocket the sooner he could buy his bugle.

So every day he fed his gander the best of this and the best of that. Shawneen thought nothing was too good for him. In no time at all the gander was as big as the hens and as big as the turkeys and soon as big as the geese themselves.

Indeed he grew so fast he became the talk of all the neighbors for lands around.

"That's no common gander," everyone began to say. "He comes from no common stock, I can tell you. Look at the way he carries himself! You would think he owned the world and all!"

Now all this talk and all this attention made the gander very proud. Oh, you have no idea. In fact, he was so carried away with himself that he would have nothing to do with the other birds of the barnyard. With the air of a king he walked before them.

The ducks thought he was very funny and laughed at him.

The hens had never seen his like before and were a bit afraid of him.

But the geese were so put about with his fine airs they couldn't stand the sight of him.

Now with the animals it was a different story.

"Oh, he is only a gander," said they, and went on about their business. They wouldn't even look in his direction.

This didn't please the gander, you may be sure of that. Since they gave him no attention he took great delight in teasing them every chance he could get.

Pulling the pigs' tails while they were eating their supper was one of his favorite tricks.

"Faith, I will wring his neck if he goes on with any more of that," said Shawneen's father.

"Maybe he doesn't like curly tails," said Shawneen; "he was just trying to straighten them out a bit."

"Straighten them out, indeed," said his father. "I'll straighten him out in short order if he goes on with any more of that nonsense."

One day the gander made faces at the donkey and the poor little fellow was so frightened he backed the cart wheel over a boulder and upset two churns of milk and two fine baskets of eggs.

Another day he chased the goats over the young cabbages and the one little patch of potatoes. You can imagine the state of the garden.

One day Shawneen's mother decided to clean out the house. She washed the windows and swept the floor and polished the pots and pans. When everything was nice and neat she went out to get a pail of water.

Meanwhile it started to rain. Over the half door flew the gander as easy as you please and made himself at home in front of the fireplace. He shook the rain off his feathers and flapped his wings, blowing the ashes and cinders all over the house.

"Oh, glory," said Shawneen's mother when she opened the door, "that bird will drive us out of house and home. I think the safest place for him is in the pot."

"Oh, no," said Shawneen, "he was just trying to be helpful and blow up the fire a bit. He is a very thoughtful gander."

"Thoughtful, indeed," said his mother. "It's a nice job he has given me with his thoughtfulness. Another trick like that and into the pot he goes."

I needn't tell you Shawneen was beginning to get worried when he heard this. The gander was acting very strange, to be sure. He would never get to the Fair at the rate he was going. But never a fear had the gander.

He made friends with all the hungry crows of the neighborhood and one evening invited them all in for supper. They ate up the grain in no time at all and the poor hens had to go to bed hungry. Oh, he was a holy terror.

There was no holding him.

Another day Shawneen's mother made some bread. She mixed the dough in a large pan and put it on the table near the fire while she hung out the clothes.

It was a warm afternoon and the gander was feeling a bit drowsy. He jumped over the half door again as familiar as you please and settled himself for a nice comfortable nap in the very middle of the pan.

"Oh, glory," said Shawneen's mother when she opened the door. "This is too much. Tomorrow is Fair day. That gander goes with your father. Whatever price he will bring he will have to go. We can't put up with him a minute longer. There is something very strange about that bird.

Heaven knows what he may do to us all if he takes the notion."

"Sh, sh, sh, sh," said the gander, jumping out of the pan and leaping over the half door. He stood outside for a minute with his ear to the crack and heard the whole story. He knew very well that when ganders or geese went to the Fair they never came back. Oh, he was no fool.

That night he never slept a wink. He stood on one foot and then on the other. When the cock began to crow his mind was made up. He would hide outside the garden wall until Shawneen's father was well out of sight.

Now as luck would have it, who should be sleeping outside the garden wall that very minute but Ned the Napper—the foxiest rogue in all Ireland. He was forever sneaking up and down the countryside stealing everything he could lay his hands on.

Over the wall came the gander and landed squarely on top of his head. Feathers went flying, I can tell you. Such kicking and biting you never saw. For a while in the dim light you couldn't tell which was Ned and which was the gander. But I am sorry to say foxy Ned soon had the upper hand. He tucked the gander safely in his bag, tossed it over his shoulder and made off east the road.

That morning when Shawneen's father had hitched the donkey to the cart and was ready to be off no gander could be found. They all looked high and they all looked low but no gander could they see. They looked behind this and they looked behind that, but not a feather of him was in sight.

"Well, gander or no gander," said Shawneen's father, "I can't wait any longer." So he slapped the lines over the donkey's back and set off to the Fair.

Shawneen watched the donkey cart rattling down the lane and through the gate. Soon it turned a bend of the road and was out of sight. He stood in the middle of the road wondering what to do next. He had waited so long for the egg to hatch and for the gander to grow a bit. Indeed it was a trial keeping him out of the pot with all his strange actions. Now when he was ready for the Fair he was nowhere to be found. Shawneen couldn't help but think of the bugle in Mrs. Murphy's shop window. It was likely to stay just where it was. Shining away for itself on the top shelf.

Shawneen ate his breakfast very slowly, thinking very hard to himself.

"Perhaps he has gone for a walk," said he to his mother.

"Very likely, indeed," said she. "Faith, he was liable to do most anything."

Shawneen decided to take a walk east the road. The gander might have gone in that direction.

Now Shawneen hadn't gone very far when he met two women gathering their washing off the hedges where it had been put out to dry.

"Did you see a big gander pass by here by any chance?" said Shawneen.

"A gander, is it?" said one of the women very crossly. "No, indeed, but I would like to get a glimpse of the rogue that made off with my husband's new Sunday shirt and my two fine linen aprons."

Shawneen went on a little further until he came to a little cottage. Outside the door was an old woman spinning.

"Did you see a big gander pass by here by any chance?" said Shawneen.

"A gander, is it?" said the old woman. "No, my child, but I would like to get a glimpse of my little teapot I put out to dry on the window-sill. A fine, shiny little teapot it was. The fairies must have had their eyes on it."

Shawneen went on his way. Around another bend of the road he met two men cutting turf.

"Did you see a big gander pass by here by any chance?" said Shawneen.

"A gander, is it?" said one of the men very crossly. "Indeed I didn't, but I would like to lay my hands on the rogue that made off with our coats and dinner pail when our backs were turned."

A little way further Shawneen came to a tinkers' van that was standing by the side of the road. Three of the tinkers were talking together in a very wild manner.

"Did you see a big gander pass by here by any chance?" asked Shawneen.

"A gander, is it?" said one of the tinkers very crossly. "No, I didn't, but I would like to lay my hands on the rogue that made off with our finest pots and pans."

Now a little way further Shawneen came to a crossroads where some young people were dancing on a large flat stone by the side of the ditch.

"Did you see a big gander pass by here by any chance?" cried Shawneen.

The young people were so busy laughing and dancing and the fiddler so busy playing and calling out the sets that no one paid any attention.

Shawneen said no more but walked slowly along the little road that ran up the side of a hill.

"A flock of ganders could pass by that crowd and I am sure they would be none the wiser," said Shawneen to himself. "It's too busy dancing they are."

Now he hadn't gone many steps when he met two guards.

"Did you see a big gander pass by here by any chance?" said Shawneen.

"A gander, is it?" said one of the guards. "No, my lad, but we would like to lay our hands on Ned the Napper. We heard he was around these parts."

Shawneen sat on a stone near by and wondered what to do next. His hopes of finding the gander seemed less than ever.

Now during all this time great clouds had been rolling across the sky and soon big raindrops began to fall.

"I'll be drenched surely," said Shawneen, looking about for a bit of shelter. An old ruined castle at the top of a near-by hill was the only thing in sight. He climbed over the hedge and ran up the hill. He walked quickly across the yard and through the castle door.

It was dark and gloomy among the old walls and the ivy rustled and whispered in the wind. In the far corner of the first room Shawneen found a spot that was fairly dry in spite of the wind and rain.

Now he was no sooner nicely settled when all of a sudden he heard a strange noise in the next room.

"Sh, sh, sh, sh," it went very softly.

"Sh, sh, sh, sh," it went again a little louder than before.

"Rain or no rain, I'll stay here no longer," said Shawneen, starting for the door.

"Sh, sh, sh, sh," came the noise again, a little louder this time.

Shawneen stopped a bit. He had heard that sound before.

He tiptoed gently to the door of the next room and peeked in. You can well imagine his surprise. There on the floor was a fierce-looking man fast asleep. By his side was a big bag—and what in the world should be sticking out of the side of it but the gander's head.

The man stirred in his sleep. He began to rub his nose. He was going to wake up, there was no doubt about that. Shawneen held his breath.

Just then the gander leaned over and said "Sh, sh," so softly in his ear the man went on sleeping as sound as ever.

Then the gander began to tear the sack very slowly with his strong bill.

As the hole became bigger and bigger Shawneen suddenly remembered what the guards had said about Ned the Napper. Beyond a doubt this was the very lad the guards were after.

Without a word Shawneen tiptoed across the room. He ran out the door and down the hill.

His feet splashed in all the pools and the rain blinded him so badly he could hardly see. As luck would have it the guards hadn't gone very far. Shawneen came running up puffing and blowing. He was so excited he could hardly speak.

"Up there, up there!" shouted Shawneen, pointing to the castle.

"What's up there, my lad?" said one of the guards.

"Ned the Napper, I think, sir," said Shawneen.

Without another word they all ran up the hill. Before you could say two two's the guards had the fierce-looking man safely between them.

With a few good bites the gander stepped out of the bag and gave himself a good shake. He was as cross as two sticks. And indeed it's well he may be. To be tossed into a bag like an old cabbage head would be hard on anyone's dignity.

"This is a lucky day for you, my lad," said one of the guards to Shawneen. "It will be well worth your while to come down to the barracks with us. This is Ned the Napper all right, all right. It's a long chase he has given us. We will leave his bag here and take care of that later. It will be quite safe in this deserted place."

So down the hill they went—foxy Ned with a guard on each arm and Shawneen and the gander out before.

A few minutes later Shawneen and one of the guards walked out of the barracks door. Shawneen was carrying a little leather sack in one hand. In it was enough money to buy teapots and shoes and dresses and shawls. And bugles!

"Well indeed, my lad," said the guard; "you well deserve this reward for telling us about Ned the Napper. Now that the rain is over let us go back to the castle and see what we can find in the bag."

So up the hill they went. When they reached the castle the guard turned the bag upside down.

Coats and shirts and pots and pans came tumbling out on the floor.

"Why, this must be the old lady's teapot," said Shawneen, "all wrapped up in the turfcutter's coat, and here are the women's aprons and the tinkers' pots and pans."

"Do you know who all these things belong to?" said the guard, scratching his head.

"Indeed I do," said Shawneen, rattling the money in the little sack. "It's scattered west the road they are—tinkers and turfcutters, old ones and young ones. Have a little patience now, your honor. I'll bring them all flying in short order."

Without another word he was down the hill and into Mrs. Murphy's shop. Before you could

say two two's he was out again and up the hill blowing the fine shiny bugle for all he was worth. Ah, indeed, it's fine and clear it sounded ringing out through all the countryside. Through all the lands around its like was never heard before. All who heard it came running up the hill. The tinkers, the women, the turfcutters, the dancers —even the old woman left her spinning wheel and came as far as she could to see what was making such a sweet sound. Soon they all arrived. Shawneen lined them up before the castle door. When each received his bit Shawneen blew a fine lively toot on the bugle. Then there was merry talk, you may be sure. A few minutes later they all went down the hill and west the road. The fiddler played and the young people sang and the gander strutted out before as if he owned the world and all.

"Oh, he is no common gander," everyone said. "It's easy to see that. There isn't a finer bird in the length and breadth of all Ireland."

THE ELEPHANT'S CHILD

Rudyard Kipling

The hilarious Just So Stories *are drolls but may also have been the beginning of science fiction. Probably only adults will fully appreciate Kipling's amusing parodies on processes of evolution, but children enjoy them as fantastic and funny stories. The example chosen for this book is the favorite with children, doubtless because many a child has yearned for the day when he could safely spank his relatives.*

In the high and Far-Off times the Elephant, O Best Beloved, had no trunk. He had only a blackish, bulgy nose, as big as a boot, that he could wriggle about from side to side; but he couldn't pick up things with it. But there was one Elephant—a new Elephant—an Elephant's Child— who was full of 'satiable curtiosity, and that means he asked ever so many questions. *And* he lived in Africa, and he filled all Africa with his

"The Elephant's Child." From *Just So Stories* by Rudyard Kipling. Copyright 1900 by Rudyard Kipling, reprinted by permission of Mrs. George Bambridge, Doubleday & Company, Inc., and The Macmillan Company of Canada Ltd.

'satiable curtiosities. He asked his tall aunt, the Ostrich, why her tail-feathers grew just so, and his tall aunt the Ostrich spanked him with her hard, hard claw. He asked his tall uncle, the Giraffe, what made his skin spotty, and his tall uncle, the Giraffe, spanked him with his hard, hard hoof. And still he was full of 'satiable curtiosity! He asked his broad aunt, the Hippopotamus, why her eyes were red, and his broad aunt, the Hippopotamus, spanked him with her broad, broad hoof; and he asked his hairy uncle, the Baboon, why melons tasted just so, and his hairy uncle, the Baboon, spanked him with his hairy, hairy paw. And *still* he was full of 'satiable curtiosity! He asked questions about everything that he saw, or heard, or felt, or smelt, or touched, and all his uncles and his aunts spanked him. And still he was full of 'satiable curtiosity!

One fine morning in the middle of the Precession of the Equinoxes this 'satiable Elephant's Child asked a new fine question that he had never asked before. He asked, "What does the Crocodile have for dinner?" Then everybody said, "Hush!" in a loud and dretful tone, and they spanked him immediately and directly, without stopping for a long time.

By and by, when that was finished, he came upon Kolokolo Bird sitting in the middle of a wait-a-bit thorn-bush, and he said, "My father has spanked me, and my mother has spanked me; all my aunts and uncles have spanked me for my 'satiable curtiosity; and *still* I want to know what the Crocodile has for dinner!"

Then Kolokolo Bird said, with a mournful cry, "Go to the banks of the great grey-green, greasy Limpopo River, all set about with fever-trees, and find out."

That very next morning, when there was nothing left of the Equinoxes, because the Precession had preceded according to precedent this 'satiable Elephant's Child took a hundred pounds of bananas (the little short red kind), and a hundred pounds of sugarcane (the long purple kind), and seventeen melons (the greeny-crackly kind), and said to all his dear families, "Good-bye. I am going to the great grey-green, greasy Limpopo River, all set about with fever-trees, to find out what the Crocodile has for dinner." And they all spanked him once more for luck, though he asked them most politely to stop.

Then he went away, a little warm, but not at all astonished, eating melons, and throwing the rind about, because he could not pick it up.

He went from Graham's Town to Kimberley, and from Kimberley to Khama's Country, and from Khama's Country he went east and north, eating melons all the time, till he at last came to the banks of the great grey-green, greasy Limpopo River, all set about with fever-trees, precisely as Kolokolo Bird had said.

Now you must know and understand, O Best Beloved, that till that very week, and day, and hour, and minute, this 'satiable Elephant's Child had never seen a Crocodile, and did not know what one was like. It was all his 'satiable curtiosity.

The first thing that he found was a Bi-Coloured-Python-Rock-Snake curled round a rock.

" 'Scuse me," said the Elephant's Child most politely, "but have you seen such a thing as a Crocodile in these promiscuous parts?"

"Have I seen a Crocodile?" said the Bi-Coloured-Python-Rock-Snake, in a voice of dretful scorn. "What will you ask me next?"

" 'Scuse me," said the Elephant's Child, "but could you kindly tell me what he has for dinner?"

Then the Bi-Coloured-Python-Rock-Snake uncoiled himself very quickly from the rock, and spanked the Elephant's Child with his scalesome, flailsome tail.

"That is odd," said the Elephant's Child, "because my father and my mother, and my uncle and my aunt, not to mention my other aunt, the Hippopotamus, and my other uncle, the Baboon, have all spanked me for my 'satiable curtiosity—and I suppose this is the same thing."

So he said good-bye very politely to the Bi-Coloured-Python-Rock-Snake, and helped to coil him up on the rock again, and went on, a little warm, but not at all astonished, eating melons, and throwing the rind about because he could not pick it up, till he trod on what he thought was a log of wood at the very edge of the great grey-green, greasy Limpopo River, all set about with fever-trees.

But it was really the Crocodile, O Best Beloved, and the Crocodile winked one eye—like this!

" 'Scuse me," said the Elephant's Child most politely, "but do you happen to have seen a Crocodile in these promiscuous parts?"

Then the Crocodile winked the other eye, and lifted half his tail out of the mud; and the Elephant's Child stepped back most politely, because he did not wish to be spanked again.

"Come hither, Little One," said the Crocodile. "Why do you ask such things?"

" 'Scuse me," said the Elephant's Child most politely, "but my father has spanked me, my mother has spanked me, not to mention my tall aunt, the Ostrich, and my tall uncle, the Giraffe, who can kick ever so hard, as well as my broad aunt, the Hippopotamus, and my hairy uncle, the Baboon, *and* including the Bi-Coloured-Python-Rock-Snake, with the scalesome, flailsome tail, just up the bank, who spanks harder than any of them; and *so,* if it's quite all the same to you, I don't want to be spanked any more."

"Come hither, Little One," said the Crocodile, "for I am the Crocodile," and he wept crocodile-tears to show it was quite true.

Then the Elephant's Child grew all breathless, and panted, and kneeled down on the bank and said, "You are the very person I have been looking for all these long days. Will you please tell me what you have for dinner?"

"Come hither, Little One," said the Crocodile, "and I'll whisper."

Then the Elephant's Child put his head down close to the Crocodile's musky, tusky mouth, and the Crocodile caught him by his little nose, which up to that very week, day, hour, and minute, had been no bigger than a boot, though much more useful.

"I think," said the Crocodile—and he said it between his teeth, like this—"I think today I will begin with Elephant's Child!"

At this, O Best Beloved, the Elephant's Child was much annoyed, and he said, speaking through his nose, like this, "Led go! You are hurtig be!"

Then the Bi-Coloured-Python-Rock-Snake scuffled down from the bank and said, "My young friend, if you do not now, immediately and instantly, pull as hard as ever you can, it is my opinion that your acquaintance in the large-pattern leather ulster" (and by this he meant the Crocodile) "will jerk you into yonder limpid stream before you can say Jack Robinson."

This is the way Bi-Coloured-Python-Rock-Snakes always talk.

Then the Elephant's Child sat back on his little haunches, and pulled, and pulled, and pulled, and his nose began to stretch. And the Crocodile floundered into the water, making it all creamy with great sweeps of his tail, and *he* pulled, and pulled, and pulled.

And the Elephant's Child's nose kept on stretching; and the Elephant's Child spread all his little four legs and pulled, and pulled, and

pulled, and his nose kept on stretching; and the Crocodile threshed his tail like an oar, and *he* pulled, and pulled, and pulled, and at each pull the Elephant's Child's nose grew longer and longer—and it hurt him hijjus!

Then the Elephant's Child felt his legs slipping, and he said through his nose, which was now nearly five feet long, "This is too butch for be!"

Then the Bi-Coloured-Python-Rock-Snake came down from the bank, and knotted himself in a double-clove-hitch round the Elephant's Child's hind legs, and said, "Rash and inexperienced traveller, we will now seriously devote ourselves to a little high tension, because if we do not, it is my impression that yonder self-propelling man-of-war with the armour-plated upper deck" (and by this, O Best Beloved, he meant the Crocodile), "will permanently vitiate your future career."

That is the way all Bi-Coloured-Python-Rock-Snakes always talk.

So he pulled, and the Elephant's Child pulled, and the Crocodile pulled; but the Elephant's Child and the Bi-Coloured-Python-Rock-Snake pulled hardest; and at last the Crocodile let go of the Elephant's Child's nose with a plop that you could hear all up and down the Limpopo.

Then the Elephant's Child sat down most hard and sudden; but first he was careful to say "Thank you" to the Bi-Coloured-Python-Rock-Snake; and next he was kind to his poor pulled nose, and wrapped it all up in cool banana leaves, and hung it in the great grey-green, greasy Limpopo to cool.

"What are you doing that for?" said the Bi-Coloured-Python-Rock-Snake.

"'Scuse me," said the Elephant's Child, "but my nose is badly out of shape, and I am waiting for it to shrink."

"Then you will have to wait a long time," said the Bi-Coloured-Python-Rock-Snake. "Some people do not know what is good for them."

The Elephant's Child sat there for three days

waiting for his nose to shrink. But it never grew any shorter, and besides, it made him squint. For, O Best Beloved, you will see and understand that the Crocodile had pulled it out into a really truly trunk same as all Elephants have to-day.

At the end of the third day a fly came and stung him on the shoulder, and before he knew what he was doing he lifted up his trunk and hit that fly dead with the end of it.

" 'Vantage number one!" said the Bi-Coloured-Python-Rock-Snake. "You couldn't have done that with a mere-smear nose. Try and eat a little now."

Before he thought what he was doing the Elephant's Child put out his trunk and plucked a large bundle of grass, dusted it clean against his forelegs, and stuffed it into his own mouth.

" 'Vantage number two!" said the Bi-Coloured-Python-Rock-Snake. "You couldn't have done that with a mere-smear nose. Don't you think the sun is very hot here?"

"It is," said the Elephant's Child, and before he thought what he was doing he schlooped up a schloop of mud from the banks of the great grey-green, greasy Limpopo, and slapped it on his head, where it made a cool schloopy-sloshy mud-cap all trickly behind his ears.

" 'Vantage number three!" said the Bi-Coloured-Python-Rock-Snake. "You couldn't have done that with a mere-smear nose. Now how do you feel about being spanked again?"

" 'Scuse me," said the Elephant's Child, "but I should not like it at all."

"How would you like to spank somebody?" said the Bi-Coloured-Python-Rock-Snake.

"I should like it very much indeed," said the Elephant's Child.

"Well," said the Bi-Coloured-Python-Rock-Snake, "you will find that new nose of yours very useful to spank people with."

"Thank you," said the Elephant's Child, "I'll remember that; and now I think I'll go home to all my dear families and try."

So the Elephant's Child went home across Africa frisking and whisking his trunk. When he wanted fruit to eat he pulled fruit down from a tree, instead of waiting for it to fall as he used to do. When he wanted grass he plucked grass up from the ground, instead of going on his knees as he used to do. When the flies bit him he

broke off the branch of a tree and used it as a fly-whisk; and he made himself a new, cool, slushy-squshy mud-cap whenever the sun was hot. When he felt lonely walking through Africa he sang to himself down his trunk, and the noise was louder than several brass bands. He went especially out of his way to find a broad Hippopotamus (she was no relation of his), and he spanked her very hard, to make sure that the Bi-Coloured-Python-Rock-Snake had spoken the truth about his new trunk. The rest of the time he picked up the melon rinds that he had dropped on his way to the Limpopo—for he was a Tidy Pachyderm.

One dark evening he came back to all his dear families, and he coiled up his trunk and said, "How do you do?" They were very glad to see him, and immediately said, "Come here and be spanked for your 'satiable curtiosity."

"Pooh," said the Elephant's Child. "I don't think you peoples know anything about spanking; but *I* do, and I'll show you."

Then he uncurled his trunk and knocked two of his dear brothers head over heels.

"O Bananas!" said they, "where did you learn that trick, and what have you done to your nose?"

"I got a new one from the Crocodile on the banks of the great grey-green, greasy Limpopo River," said the Elephant's Child. "I asked him what he had for dinner, and he gave me this to keep."

"It looks very ugly," said his hairy uncle, the Baboon.

"It does," said the Elephant's Child. "But it's very useful," and he picked up his hairy uncle, the Baboon, by one hairy leg, and hove him into a hornet's nest.

Then that bad Elephant's Child spanked all his dear families for a long time, till they were very warm and greatly astonished. He pulled out his tall Ostrich aunt's tail-feathers; and he caught his tall uncle, the Giraffe, by the hindleg, and dragged him through a thorn-bush; and he shouted at his broad aunt, the Hippopotamus, and blew bubbles into her ear when she was sleeping in the water after meals; but he never let any one touch Kolokolo Bird.

At last things grew so exciting that his dear families went off one by one in a hurry to the banks of the great grey-green, greasy Limpopo River, all set about with fever-trees, to borrow new noses from the Crocodile. When they came back nobody spanked anybody any more; and ever since that day, O Best Beloved, all the Elephants you will ever see, besides all those that you won't, have trunks precisely like the trunk of the 'satiable Elephant's Child.

CAPTAIN COOK

Richard and Florence Atwater

When Mr. Popper received the gift of a penguin, the family little knew what that Antarctic bird would do to their lives. Making his home in the refrigerator is only the beginning.

"Call who Captain Cook?" asked Mrs. Popper, who had come in so quietly that none of them had heard her.

"Why, the penguin," said Mr. Popper. "I was just saying," he went on, as Mrs. Popper sat down suddenly on the floor to recover from her surprise, "that we'd name him after Captain Cook. He was a famous English explorer who lived about the time of the American Revolution. He sailed all over where no one had ever been before. He didn't actually get to the South Pole, of course, but he made a lot of important scientific discoveries about the Antarctic regions. He was a brave man and a kind leader. So I think Captain Cook would be a very suitable name for our penguin here."

"Well, I never!" said Mrs. Popper.

"*Gork!*" said Captain Cook, suddenly getting lively again. With a flap of his flippers he jumped from the tub to the washstand, and stood there for a minute surveying the floor. Then he jumped down, walked over to Mrs. Popper, and began to peck her ankle.

"Stop him, Papa!" screamed Mrs. Popper, retreating into the hallway with Captain Cook after her, and Mr. Popper and the children fol-

"Captain Cook." From *Mr. Popper's Penguins* by Richard and Florence Atwater, by permission of Little, Brown & Co. Copyright 1938 by Richard and Florence Atwater

lowing. In the living room she paused. So did Captain Cook, for he was delighted with the room.

Now a penguin may look very strange in a living room, but a living room looks very strange to a penguin. Even Mrs. Popper had to smile as they watched Captain Cook, with the light of curiosity in his excited circular eyes, and his black tailcoat dragging pompously behind his little pinkish feet, strut from one upholstered chair to another, pecking at each to see what it was made of. Then he turned suddenly and marched out to the kitchen.

"Maybe he's hungry," said Janie.

Captain Cook immediately marched up to the refrigerator.

"*Gork?*" he inquired, turning to slant his head wisely at Mrs. Popper, and looking at her pleadingly with his right eye.

"He certainly is cute," she said. "I guess I'll have to forgive him for biting my ankle. He probably only did it out of curiosity. Anyway, he's a nice clean-looking bird."

"*Ork?*" repeated the penguin, nibbling at the metal handle of the refrigerator door with his upstretched beak.

Mr. Popper opened the door for him, and Captain Cook stood very high and leaned his sleek black head back so that he could see inside. Now that Mr. Popper's work was over for the winter, the icebox was not quite so full as usual, but the penguin did not know that.

"What do you suppose he likes to eat?" asked Mrs. Popper.

"Let's see," said Mr. Popper, as he removed all the food and set it on the kitchen table. "Now then, Captain Cook, take a look."

The penguin jumped up onto a chair and from there onto the edge of the table, flapping his flippers again to recover his balance. Then he walked solemnly around the table, and between the dishes of food, inspecting everything with the greatest interest, though he touched nothing. Finally he stood still, very erect, raised his beak to point at the ceiling, and make a loud, almost purring sound. "*O-r-r-r-h, o-r-r-r-h,*" he trilled.

"That's a penguin's way of saying how pleased it is," said Mr. Popper, who had read about it in his Antarctic books.

Apparently, however, what Captain Cook wanted to show was that he was pleased with their kindness, rather than with their food. For now, to their surprise, he jumped down and walked into the dining room.

"I know," said Mr. Popper. "We ought to have some seafood for him, canned shrimps or something. Or maybe he isn't hungry yet. I've read that penguins can go for a month without food."

"Mamma! Papa!" called Bill. "Come see what Captain Cook has done."

Captain Cook had done it all right. He had discovered the bowl of goldfish on the dining-room window sill. By the time Mrs. Popper reached over to lift him away, he had already swallowed the last of the goldfish.

"Bad, bad penguin!" reproved Mrs. Popper, glaring down at Captain Cook.

Captain Cook squatted guiltily on the carpet and tried to make himself look small.

"He knows he's done wrong," said Mr. Popper. "Isn't he smart?"

"Maybe we can train him," said Mrs. Popper. "Bad, naughty Captain," she said to the penguin in a loud voice. "Bad, to eat the goldfish." And she spanked him on his round black head.

Before she could do that again, Captain Cook hastily waddled out to the kitchen.

There the Poppers found him trying to hide in the still opened refrigerator. He was squatting under the ice-cube coils, under which he could barely squeeze, sitting down. His round, white-circled eyes looked out at them mysteriously from the dimness of the inside of the box.

"I think that's about the right temperature for him, at that," said Mr. Popper. "We could let him sleep there, at night."

"But where will I put the food?" asked Mrs. Popper.

"Oh, I guess we can get another icebox for the food," said Mr. Popper.

"Look," said Janie. "He's gone to sleep."

Mr. Popper turned the cold control switch to its coldest so that Captain Cook could sleep more comfortably. Then he left the door ajar so that the penguin would have plenty of fresh air to breathe.

"Tomorrow I will have the icebox service department send a man out to bore some holes in the door, for air," he said, "and then he can put a handle on the inside of the door so that Captain Cook can go in and out of his refrigerator, as he pleases."

"Well, dear me, I never thought we would have a penguin for a pet," said Mrs. Popper. "Still, he behaves pretty well, on the whole, and he is so nice and clean that perhaps he will be a good example to you and the children. And now, I declare, we must get busy. We haven't done anything but watch that bird. Papa, will you just help me to set the beans on the table, please?"

"Just a minute," answered Mr. Popper. "I just happened to think that Captain Cook will not feel right on the floor of that icebox. Penguins make their nests of pebbles and stones. So I will just take some ice cubes out of the tray and put them under him. That way he will be more comfortable."

TROUBLES WITH A PENGUIN

Richard and Florence Atwater

The next day was quite eventful at 432 Proudfoot Avenue. First there was the service man and then the policeman and then the trouble about the license.

Captain Cook was in the children's room, watching Janie and Bill put together a jigsaw puzzle on the floor. He was very good about not disturbing the pieces after Bill had spanked him for eating one. He did not hear the refrigerator service man come to the back door.

Mrs. Popper had gone marketing for canned shrimps for the penguin, so that Mr. Popper was alone in the kitchen to explain to the service man what he wanted done to the refrigerator.

The service man put his tool bag down on the kitchen floor, looked at the refrigerator, and then at Mr. Popper, who, to tell the truth, had not shaved yet and was not very tidy.

"Mister," he said, "you don't need no ventilating holes in that there door."

"It's my icebox, and I want some holes bored in the door," said Mr. Popper.

They argued about it for quite a while. Mr. Popper knew that to get the service man to do what he wanted, all he had to do was to explain that he was going to keep a live penguin in the icebox, and that he wanted his pet to have plenty of fresh air, even though the door was closed all night. He felt a little stubborn about explaining, however. He didn't want to discuss Captain Cook with this unsympathetic service man, who was already staring at Mr. Popper as if he thought Mr. Popper was not quite right in his head.

"Come on, do what I said," said Mr. Popper. "I'm paying you for it."

"With what?" asked the service man.

Mr. Popper gave him a five-dollar bill. It made him a little sad to think how many beans it would have bought for Mrs. Popper and the children.

The service man examined the bill carefully as if he didn't trust Mr. Popper too much. But at last he put it in his pocket, took a drill from his tool bag, and made five small holes in a neat pattern on the refrigerator door.

"Now," said Mr. Popper, "don't get up. Wait a minute. There is one more thing."

"Now what?" said the service man. "I suppose now you want me to take the door off its hinges to let in a little more air. Or do you want me to make a radio set out of your icebox?"

"Don't get funny," said Mr. Popper indignantly. "That is no way to talk. Believe it or not, I know what I'm doing. I mean, having you do. I want you to fix an extra handle on the inside of that box so it can be opened from the inside of the box."

"That," said the service man, "is a fine idea. You want an extra handle on the inside. Sure, sure." He picked up his tool bag.

"Aren't you going to do it for me?" asked Mr. Popper.

"Oh, sure, sure," said the service man, edging toward the back door.

Mr. Popper saw that for all his words of agreement, the service man had no intention of putting on an inside handle.

"I thought you were a service man," he said.

"I am. That's the first sensible thing you've said yet."

"You're a fine kind of service man if you don't even know how to put an extra handle on the inside of an icebox door."

"Oh, I don't, don't I? Don't think I don't know how. As far as that goes, I've even got a spare handle in my tool bag, and plenty of screws. You needn't think I don't know how to do it, if I wanted to."

Mr. Popper silently reached into his pocket and gave the service man his last five-dollar bill. He was pretty sure that Mrs. Popper would be annoyed at him for spending all that money, but it could not be helped.

"Mister," said the service man, "you win. I'll fix your extra handle. And while I am doing it, you sit down on that chair over there facing me, where I can keep an eye on you."

"Fair enough," said Mr. Popper, sitting down.

The service man was still on the floor, putting in the final screws that held the new handle in place, when the penguin came out to the kitchen on his silent pink feet.

Surprised at seeing a strange man sitting on the floor, Captain Cook quietly walked over and began to peck him curiously. But the service man was even more surprised than Captain Cook.

"Ork," said the penguin. Or perhaps it was the service man. Mr. Popper was not sure just what had happened when he picked up himself and his chair a moment later. There had been a shower of flying tools, a violent slamming of the door, and the service man was gone.

These sudden noises, of course, brought the children running. Mr. Popper showed them how the refrigerator was now all remodeled for the penguin. He showed Captain Cook, too, by shutting him inside it. The penguin at once noticed the shiny new inside handle and bit it with his usual curiosity. The door opened, and Captain Cook jumped out.

Mr. Popper promptly put Captain Cook back inside and shut the door again, to be sure that the penguin learned his lesson. Before long, Captain Cook became quite skillful at getting out and was ready to be taught how to get inside when the door was shut.

By the time the policeman came to the back door, Captain Cook was going in and out the refrigerator as easily as if he had lived in one all his life.

THE THIRTEENTH FLOOR

Joan Howard

A black cat that answers to no name but Merlin is bound to start things. This four-footed Merlin, by putting out his paw and pressing an unseen spring that leads to a nonexistent 13th floor, proves that magic can be as modern as it is powerful. Use this excerpt to lead the children to the book.

It was still raining, and there did not seem much to do now that they had named their cat, and the cat had made it quite clear he had had enough of sitting on laps for a while and was bored with patting at a spool on a string.

Finding the name for the little black cat had been a peculiar business altogether, and Ronnie and Jill had discovered there was a lot more to it than they would ever have guessed.

They had tried all the names they could think of, like Tommie and Tibbie and Toby; like Jerry and Jumper and James; like Blackie and Bobbie and Bill; and ever so many more. Not by the twitch of a whisker would the black cat show an interest in any of them.

"Butch," suggested Ronnie.

"Oh, no! Not for *this* cat," Jill said, and the little cat walked off in offended dignity, switching his tail.

"Well, I'm sorry then," Ronnie apologized.

"Nightshade might be nice, he's so black," Jill ventured. The cat seemed to prick up an ear to listen.

"It won't do, though," Ronnie decided. "There is really something called nightshade—I'm not sure what it is, but the word deadly goes with it. Deadly Nightshade would be a horrid name for a nice cat. Besides, think of trying to call him. . . . 'Here, Nightshade! Here, Nightshade!'"

Jill gave in to such a convincing argument. She could not think of a single other name, so she began trying to talk like a cat.

"*Meee-*ow!" she said. "*Meee-ow!*"

"That's terrible!"

It was quite clear that the cat thought so too.

"Wait a minute," Jill said. "I think I've just about got it."

She began to practice under her breath. Murrauw! No, not quite right yet.

"Mer . . ." she began. She meant to say, "Merrower," but what came out was "MERLIN!"

She said it again. "Why, that is our cat's name. I'm as sure as sure . . . Merlin!"

Merlin came to his name as if he had been waiting for it and thought they were never going to get it right.

"I read about somebody called Merlin in the *Story of King Arthur and His Knights*," Ronnie said. "He was a magician back in those olden times."

"Our Merlin is magical, too." Jill was certain of that.

Merlin purred softly, but his yellow eyes looked slantwise and mysterious.

After Merlin had got tired of sitting around on laps and bored with patting the spool on a string, he settled himself on the window sill between Jill and Ronnie and watched the rain.

Ronnie and Jill began to play an old game of theirs, racing raindrops down the pane, but that soon grew rather monotonous. Especially since today neither of them ever won with their drops. It was always Merlin who put a sure paw on the right one, a far-behind one that would develop an unaccountable burst of speed at that touch through the glass.

Ronnie finally dug some chalk out of his tool chest and began to draw idly on the black linoleum floor.

"What is it?" asked Jill.

"Just a box, I guess."

"It looks more like a door to me."

"All right. That's what it is then—a trapdoor." Ronnie added a couple of hinges at one side and a sort of latch on the other.

Merlin had been regarding the drawing with critical attention. He put out a soft paw, and the latch unfastened at his touch.

Jill stared at it with wide eyes, and Ronnie began to tug.

The trapdoor lifted quite easily, and Ronnie and Jill followed the sedate Merlin down the steps to the thirteenth floor.

At first glance, the thirteenth floor did not

seem so very different from the fourteenth or the seventh or the second, or any other the Saunders children had inspected. Of course, the doors of the various apartments stood open as they never did either upstairs or down; and the hallway was papered in a rather unusual and complicated all-over pattern of bats and owls and triangles and pentacles and broomsticks and large black cauldrons. Round the borders ran the words of old charms and enchantments. Jill and Ronnie thought it the most attractive wallpaper they had ever seen, and they spent quite a time studying it.

"You know," Ronnie declared, "this would be a fine place for magicians to live, especially absent-minded magicians. If they forgot their spells, all they would have to do is read them off the wall."

"I don't think magicians come absent-minded, do they?" Jill objected. "I've never heard of one."

"Except right when they are doing the magic, maybe they are the same as anybody else. We can't be sure, because we have never known any magicians."

Ronnie noticed that Merlin was staring at him, with his yellow eyes particularly slanted and mysterious.

"I wonder . . ." he began.

There was a tiny flurry of grey skittering across the floor, and Merlin was off after it. The mouse reached the wall and vanished with a flicker through a hole in one corner. With his whiskers bristling, Merlin sat down to wait, looking no more than a darker shadow in the dim corner.

"I'm glad he didn't catch the poor little mouse," Jill said with a shiver.

Merlin ignored her words as any sensible cat would. His attention was entirely upon the mousehole, so Ronnie and Jill began to explore on their own.

In any other part of the building they would never have gone into a strange apartment, even if the door did stand open. Having their share of curiosity, they might have peeked, of course, but that would have been all. But somehow none of the ordinary rules seemed to apply to the thirteenth floor.

They watched an old man sitting at a desk. His long thin fingers kept picking up bright round discs that gleamed like gold and stacking them in several different piles. Presently Jill and Ronnie edged through the door and into the room, inch by inch, their footsteps silent on the thick rug.

Quiet as they were, the old man heard them and looked up, not at all startled.

"I am a numismatist!" he stated, without bothering about greetings.

Ronnie took a few quick steps backward toward the door. And Jill, who had a very sympathetic nature, said, "That's too bad. I'm terribly sorry."

Behind them in the hall they heard a hoarse chuckle.

"There's no call for you to feel sorry for *him*, my dear. He means that he's a coin collector."

The man who had spoken did not wait for an answer. He rolled on down the hall as if he were balancing himself on a pitching deck in the teeth of a gale; and he wore so many sweaters under his pea jacket that he looked as fat as Humpty Dumpty.

"He must be a sailor," Ronnie said.

"So he is," the coin collector agreed, with the

air of a man who resigns himself to a visitation from uninvited children and prepares to make the best of it. "I'm pretty busy today, what with it being the thirteenth and all, but I'll show you a few pieces of my fairy gold here and then you can run along."

Ronnie and Jill examined gleaming coins that were handed them one by one. Each had a different design on its face: owl and bat and toad; a black cock and a black cat; a hemlock branch and a hazel rod and a sprig of a plant the collector said was enchanter's nightshade; a wishbone and a rabbit's foot and a pretty design of crossed broomsticks. There were people, too: a tiny man with long whiskers and pointed ears and an elderly lady with a tall hat of a design commonly seen only on Hallowe'en. They were all quite different from Abraham Lincoln and President Jefferson and Miss Liberty.

The money did not feel exactly like the dimes and nickels and pennies they were used to handling, either. It was softer and it shimmered in their fingers.

"Just what is this fairy gold, anyway?" Ronnie hoped that the amiable coin collector would not think him rude for asking.

"It would take me much too long to explain it to you. In these days gold is not as easily come by as it used to be, even for us numismatists, and you have to take what you can get."

"I think it is much more interesting than ordinary money," Jill said politely.

"So do I," the old man agreed. "I would like to give you some lucky pieces, but perhaps I had better not. You'd find them hard to account for and there'd be no guarantee that they would stay by you."

"That's perfectly all right; thank you just the same." The children tried hard to keep the disappointment out of their voices.

"Come to think of it, though, I do have a few trifles here that you might have fun playing with some day." The collector rummaged round on his littered desk and brushed a lot of bright copper Indian head pennies into a paper sack that had dark shiny spots on it. "I'm sorry it's a little greasy," he apologized. "I brought a ham sandwich home in it from the delicatessen for my lunch."

"That doesn't matter—not a bit," Jill said.

"All right, then, you run along. I have to get back to my work."

Merlin was still sitting at his mousehole and he refused to pay the slightest attention to the children.

They hesitated at another doorway to watch a little man rushing round frantically with brooms and brushes and the kind of squee-gee the window-cleaner uses. His clothes were all covered with a shiny dust and he waved a polishing cloth at them.

"Too busy to talk," he panted. "Come some other day. I've got to go right to work. They've gone and discovered a new star and it's *never* been cleaned."

"Yes, we're too busy," said another voice. It came from a chair by the table but neither Ronnie nor Jill could see anybody there. "Let's see now." The invisible voice sounded cross. "Three warps and five woofs—or is it three woofs and five warps? I simply can't concentrate with people watching me."

"Excuse us," said Jill and Ronnie and they tiptoed away from that door.

Their exploration took them next into an apartment that was just like a ship, except that every part of it—bridge and cabin and deck, and even the engine room and hold—was all jumbled together in one big room that managed to stay shipshape in spite of it all.

And where a regular boat like the one that took them out to the Statue of Liberty last Fourth of July had only one wheel, this had seventeen—and no end of compasses and binnacles and such-like.

The wallpaper was a design in green and white of waves that rolled and swirled and broke into whitecaps till Jill felt quite dizzy. She had never seen water look so real, and while Ronnie was examining some bright brass machinery, she tiptoed over to the wall and touched it. Her finger came away wet.

"Well . . ." she said doubtfully. Somehow she could not think of any words that exactly suited the situation.

They did not find the seafaring gentleman who had spoken to them at the coin collector's door and they decided he must have gone out again. Of course it was possible he was hiding somewhere among a lot of furled sails and canvas-covered lifeboats. But if he was, they thought he couldn't be very anxious to have visitors, and maybe they had better leave.

Their last call was something of a social triumph, for here they found a tenant who was obviously delighted to welcome them.

"Come right in, my dears. It is good of you to find time to visit an old fellow."

He was as thin and grey as fog, and his hair curled round his high domed head like wisps of feathery cloud.

"Weatherbee is the name," he went on, and his voice sounded like a soft wind whistling round the corner of the building. "Elemanzer Pyerocket Weatherbee—and you will be the young Saunderses that my friend Merlin has lately adopted."

"Yes, we are, Mr. Weatherbee."

Ronnie shook a hand that was as brittle as a bundle of twigs, and Jill dropped the curtsy that Mrs. Saunders had tried in vain to have her daughter display when guests came to tea. They both wondered how he knew Merlin's name, and why he thought it was Merlin who had adopted *them* when really they had taken the little black cat home themselves. Somehow, though, they did not like to ask; with Mr. Weatherbee, it did not seem polite to begin right off asking questions and they were very anxious that their manners should match his own.

"We are very happy to find you home," they said. "We have wanted to meet you for a long time, Mr. Weatherbee."

That was not strictly accurate, since they had never heard of Mr. Weatherbee before, but it sounded perfectly true to them when they said it. They had wanted to meet somebody like Mr. Weatherbee for a long time, even if they had not known it till they saw him.

Their new friend seemed to understand all this without any more words. His was a homelike apartment, even if it was such a home as they had never encountered, and his voice that rustled and whispered and whistled softly was a happy, restful sound.

The table was spread with every kind of cake that Ronnie and Jill liked best—angel food and devil's food, jelly roll and Lady Baltimore—and there happened to be exactly the right number of forks and napkins laid out. Mr. Weatherbee

drank tea and the children had raspberry soda that tasted of the ripe, freshly gathered fruit, and afterward they sat in front of a fire that glowed with magical colors while the old gentleman told them about his career in the Weather Bureau.

"I am retired now, of course," he said rather wistfully. "They consider me an old fogy, what with all their brand new instruments and their charts for mapping low pressure areas and high pressure areas, and I don't know what all."

"Well, I'll bet the Weather Bureau was better when you ran it than it is now," Ronnie declared loyally. "They are wrong an awful lot of the time."

"Yes, prophecy is not what it used to be," Mr. Weatherbee admitted. "Times have changed."

"How did you used to tell what the weather was going to be like?" Jill asked, all her shyness about asking questions long since forgotten.

"The way any natural man should be able to tell it. There are signs always—the clouds and the wind, and the way the leaves twist on the trees and the birds twitter in the branches. You knew it was going to be a hard winter when the animals grew heavy coats and there was a plentiful supply of berries and nuts for them to eat and store away. When the groundhog came out to look for his shadow on Candlemas Day, you could be sure of six weeks more snow and ice if he found it. If the blackbird did not sing before seven, it would rain by nightfall. There was red sky at night for a fair day, and red sky at morning for a storm; there were rainbows and rings round the moon and the stars shining with an extra twinkling. A natural man could always tell."

"They ought to have had sense enough to let a natural man go on doing it, then," Ronnie said.

"Not they—they began calling themselves meteorologists and got all tangled up in their fancy apparatus. As Ronnie here mentioned a few minutes ago, they are wrong an awful lot of the time."

The room was growing dimmer in the twilight and Mr. Weatherbee more shadowy. Ronnie and Jill said they had better be getting home before their mother began to worry. There was a special reason why they did not want her to be cross with them tonight.

"That will be Merlin, of course," said Mr. Weatherbee. "But it will come out all right—you can trust Merlin."

The long fingers of shadow that moved steadily across the room toward the fire reminded Jill of one more thing she wanted to know.

"Did you take care of the daylight saving, too, when you managed the Weather Bureau?"

"Daylight saving was something I *did* understand, if I do say it myself," Mr. Weatherbee declared with new animation. "The Bureau of Standards and the Interstate Commerce Commission have taken it over now and a fine mess they have made of it between them. Daylight saving, they still call it, but what does it *mean?* What do they do with this daylight; does anyone know? Now, I really *saved* it—why, I've still got rooms full of it here, and every minute a nice bright yellow as new as today. If you children will wait just an instant more, I would like to make you a small present of daylight."

Jill and Ronnie stood in the owl light and watched Mr. Weatherbee open a door just a bright crack and slip through into a clear yellow room. When he came out again, he handed Ronnie a little carved box with a gold padlock on it. The tiny gold key on a chain he hung around Jill's neck.

"You take care of this," he said. "Boys are apt to lose keys."

"I will never, never lose it," Jill promised.

"That's right, my dear. And mind, when you need it, just use one pinch of daylight. A little goes a long way."

"We'll remember," Ronnie declared.

"Thank you for a lovely party, Mr. Weatherbee." Jill curtseyed again.

"And thank you for coming," said Mr. Weatherbee with a courtly bow. "It has been a lovely party for me, too—an old fellow gets lonesome now and then. I see our friend Merlin is waiting for you."

Merlin led the way back up the stairs without a single mew or purr, so Ronnie and Jill were sure the mouse was still safe.

In their playroom, Ronnie shut down the trapdoor. Merlin erased the drawing with his tail and then settled to work washing the chalk off.

From the living room came voices, Mr. Saunders' saying "NO!" very firmly. They could not catch Mrs. Saunders' answer, but Mr. Saunders' next "No!" was not so firm, and after a while they heard him say, "All right, all right. What chance have I got?"

So Ronnie and Jill knew it was safe to take Merlin in and introduce him to their father.

Merlin behaved with the most commendable tact in permitting a little gentle scratching of his ears, and the day was won.

"Where did you get that pretty key and chain?" Mrs. Saunders asked Jill a few minutes later.

"Mr. Weatherbee gave it to me. He gave Ronnie the box that it opens. He told us how the Weather Bureau works and how it used to work better, and all about daylight saving."

"He sounds like an interesting man," said Mr. Saunders. "I've often wondered myself just what goes on down at that Weather Bureau."

"I suppose it is all right for you to keep the presents the gentleman gave you." Mrs. Saunders still sounded a trifle doubtful. "But after this don't accept anything from people unless Daddy and I know them too."

"Yes, Mummie."

"Does Mr. Weatherbee live here in the building?" Mr. Saunders asked Ronnie.

"Yes, sir, down on the thirteenth floor."

"There is no thirteenth floor in this building."

"Oh, but there is—only you can't visit it except on the thirteenth of the month and if a black cat takes you." Jill sounded very sure of the rules she had learned today.

"Now listen to me, you two. I won't have you growing up superstitious. You are not to believe in any such nonsense as a thirteenth floor."

"But Daddy, don't you see? It is the people who *don't* believe in the thirteenth floor who are superstitious," Ronnie explained earnestly.

Mr. Sidney P. Saunders opened his mouth to utter a few carefully chosen arguments. Then he shut it again before they got out. He seemed to be trying to work out something in his head. He gave it up.

"Do you realize what time it is?" he asked, quite crossly. "Go eat your supper quickly and get right to bed."

"We're not hungry, thank you," Ronnie said.

"We had supper down on the thirteenth floor with Mr. Weatherbee," his sister added.

MRS. WALLABY JONES

Joan Howard

Nearly every day, even in weather that was not fit for ducks, Jill and Ronnie played in the park. But this December afternoon, with the sun shimmering on the first light snowfall of the season, was the only time they had met Mrs. Wallaby-Jones there.

They were used to nice old ladies stopping them to talk and to ask questions, so they chattered with that mixture of open friendliness and polite caution that all sensible children maintain till they are sure of a stranger.

"Are you English?" Jill asked politely.

The lady's speech was rather different from their own, and Jill had heard her mother say once that the English went in for hyphenated names. Mrs. Wallaby-Jones had mentioned *her* hyphen when she introduced herself, as if she considered it a mark of distinction.

"No, not English, my dear," Mrs. Wallaby-Jones replied, "though belonging to the British Empire, of course. We Wallaby-Joneses—with the hyphen—are from Australia. New South Wales, to be more precise. We are a cadet branch of the Macropus family. Surely, even in New York, you have heard of the Macropuses? Australia could hardly be said to have a history at all without the Macropuses—or the Wallabies, if it comes to that. Why, we—"

Ronnie and Jill sighed deeply and wondered if they had not better be going now. Even the nicest grown-ups were bores when they got started on the subject of Family. Their own mother—and she *was* the nicest—went on and on sometimes about her family who had come over from England on a boat called the "Mayflower," and then kept on getting into one bit after another of American history.

"I'm pretty good at the standing broad jump," Ronnie said. He was not so much boasting as trying to change the subject tactfully. "I can do five-feet-ten-and-a-half-inches. Jill can't come anywhere near that, but then girls are never much good at that sort of thing."

"Mrs. Wallaby Jones." From *The 13th Is Magic* by Joan Howard, copyright, 1950, Lothrop, Lee and Shepard Co., Inc.

"Are they not?" asked Mrs. Wallaby-Jones.

She sounded distinctly huffy, and as they watched she seemed to grow about two feet taller. Maybe she was swelling with rage about something—they had heard about that, though they had never seen it happen. They wondered anxiously what could have upset her. She surely could not be angry about jumping, since jumping was something ladies never went in for, so it must be because they had interrupted her story about the Macropuses and the Wallaby-Joneses.

Suddenly, without any warning at all, she flew through the air in the most spectacular broad jump either of the young Saunderses had ever witnessed. She cleared two park benches, three laurels and two bayberry bushes, and the bridle path; and then there she stood waiting, as primly respectable as ever, but a good twenty-five feet away from them.

"That was a beaut!" Ronnie yelled excitedly.

"You are perfectly wonderful!" his sister called, and both of them ran to catch up to her.

A grown-up who did not let dignity stand in the way of a broad jump like that was a real friend to cultivate. But they were soon reminded not to let her get back to the subject of Family.

"If you think that was good," she said smugly, with her pointed little nose high in the air, "you should have seen my Uncle Hubert Macropus in his younger days. For thirteen years straight he won first prize for the broad jump in the Caledonian Games they hold in Australia on Robert Burns's birthday. He was made an honorary Scot to be eligible and his name was printed in the program as Hubert *Mac*Ropus—to go with MacDuff and MacGregor and MacDonald and all the rest of the Macs, you see."

Jill and Ronnie did not see, quite, and fascinating as broad jumps are when you are making them yourself or even watching them, the illustrious history of Mr. Hubert Macropus, or *Mac*Ropus, did not hold their interest very long.

"Shall we go over to the lake and feed the ducks?" Jill suggested. "I have a bun in my pocket we can crumble up for them."

"A splendid idea, my dear," agreed Mrs. Wallaby-Jones with enthusiasm. "Rules or no rules, I like to see children remember their furred and feathered friends. For myself, I always fancy a nice bit of greens, but I have heard that ducks relish crumbs. There is no accounting for tastes, I always say."

The children were puzzled. "There isn't any rule against feeding the ducks," Ronnie said.

"Is there not? Well, I do call that unfair when there are stupid notices posted on the cages of all the quadrupeds."

Mrs. Wallaby-Jones sounded highly indignant and off she went in another great leap.

"I wish I could do that," Ronnie said wistfully when they had almost caught up with her again.

"Maybe having big feet is a help," his sister suggested, and she pointed to Mrs. Wallaby-Jones's footprints in the light snow. They certainly were enormous for a lady. "I never saw any like that before, and her hands are smaller than mine."

Mrs. Wallaby-Jones was waiting for them, with her tiny gloved hands demurely folded, so Ronnie could see that Jill was quite right.

Just then he caught sight of a policeman friend of theirs. "Hi, Mr. Harrigan," he called. "Do you want to see something that really *is* something? This lady here can do a broad jump that—"

"Hush now, children, don't talk such nonsense," said Mrs. Wallaby-Jones.

She was in a great hurry suddenly, and she had leaped almost out of sight before Ronnie could finish his sentence.

Mr. Harrigan blinked twice and swallowed hard. He pushed his cap back on his head. "Holy Moses, what is your friend, a kangaroo?" he demanded.

"Well, I told you she was a wonderful broad jumper," Ronnie reminded him.

"She's all of that," agreed the policeman. He looked as if he were thinking up some more questions to ask, but Jill and Ronnie had to leave him to catch up with Mrs. Wallaby-Jones.

Their trip across the park was really wonderful, with their new and already dear friend walking in a series of wild leaps, clearing drinking fountains and perambulators and startling some elderly gentlemen who were sunning themselves on the benches. It was such fun that the children hoped they might meet the lady every day after this.

"Look!" Ronnie called. "There are still boats out. Will you come for a row on the lake with us? Our treat!"

"Thank you, I should love to. We Wallaby-Joneses are very fond of water sports. Why, my Great-Aunt Emmeline was the talk of New South Wales when she paddled her own canoe. That was when she was quite a young girl and people had old-fashioned notions about what was ladylike and what was not."

"We'll have to hurry," Jill broke in quickly. "There is Mr. Murphy bringing in his rowboats."

During the summer the children were always coaxing some grown-up or other to take them rowing on the lake. They did the rowing themselves, rather badly, but they had to have an older person with them or they were not allowed out in a boat. There was a printed notice about that rule tacked up on the side of the boathouse where Mr. Murphy took the money.

Mr. Murphy was unusually late storing his boats for the winter this year. Indian summer had continued all through November, and then he had decided to paint up some of them ready for next season. The snow had reminded him that it was near the middle of December, though, so he was working hard today getting them out of the water and stowing them away in a shed. He was closing up shop till next spring.

It took considerable coaxing before he agreed to let them take out a boat for one last hour, but since the lady was with them . . . Jill and Ronnie pooled their allowances to pay the thirty-five cents and two pennies tax.

In the rowboat, Jill and Ronnie sat side by side, each with an oar, while Mrs. Wallaby-Jones settled herself in the stern, an entirely dignified passenger.

Mr. Murphy shoved them off and they started out all right, but as soon as they got really out in the lake their rowing was the kind that always made their father laugh at them. Because Ronnie pulled on his oar so much harder than his sister could, they had a way of going round and round in circles—on their good days in quite large circles, but more often as if they were caught in a small whirlpool.

This promised to be one of their worst days and they were pretty embarrassed about it all until they suddenly straightened out and cut across the ripples in as clean a line as you please.

"Hey!" Ronnie shouted. "Look at us!"

But Jill could not stop to look at them. She was far too intent upon looking at something else. She nudged her brother to watch too. Their eyes got bigger and bigger as they stared at the queerest thing they had ever seen in all their lives.

There was Mrs. Wallaby-Jones, sitting as prim as ever in her sleek fur coat and her fur hat and tippet, her gloved hands folded in her lap. But she had pulled up her skirt just a trifle, probably to keep it dry. And underneath, hanging over the back of the little rowboat and acting as a rudder, was something—something—Jill and Ronnie were not sure *what* it was, but it certainly did look like the tip of a kangaroo's tail.

They were so astonished they could not say a single word. Not even when, encouraged by their fixed attention, Mrs. Wallaby-Jones told them practically *all* about her family. Not until she got to second-cousins-once-removed did Jill find her voice.

"We have a cat," she announced. "A black cat."

"I am not surprised to hear it, my dear,"

Mrs. Wallaby-Jones said amiably. "That would be Merlin, would it not?"

Jill's mouth dropped open and Ronnie's oar hung dripping in midair. But there was no time for questions. Mr. Murphy was waving his arms at them from the shore to signal that their hour was up, so they had to row back quickly.

Ronnie helped their guest out of the rowboat like a perfect gentleman. He could not see anything peculiar about her then, though his sister noticed that Mrs. Wallaby-Jones wore her skirts just a shade longer than was the fashion this year.

"I must get back now, dears," Mrs. Wallaby-Jones said politely. "It has been a most enjoyable outing."

"When can we see you again?" both children wanted to know. "Can we meet you tomorrow? Or next day? Please . . ."

They had never met a grown-up they were more anxious to see again, as much and as often as possible. They were even willing now to let her talk Family in order that they might enjoy her other charms.

"Well, I cannot be sure just when I shall be free again," Mrs. Wallaby-Jones answered. "I would not want to make a promise and not be able to keep it. It is not always easy to get away, and you never know ahead of time when there is going to be a large audience—it depends upon the weather and so forth. I must not disappoint my public, you know, but one of these days we shall meet again."

It was not till they got home and found Merlin waiting for them to give him his catnip mouse from the toy cupboard that either Jill or Ronnie remembered that this was the thirteenth of the month.

At dinner they could talk of nothing but their new friend. They tried to keep their account as matter-of-fact as possible, knowing from past experiences that anything unusual was apt to be regarded with suspicion, if not actually disbelieved. Sometimes grown-up skepticism is really discouraging.

"When she walked, it was sort of in hops," Ronnie said. He remembered just in time not to mention the length of those hops.

"She had a pointed face and bright brown eyes," Jill put in eagerly. "Her clothes were a little bit old-fashioned but they exactly suited her."

"What do you suppose she meant about not disappointing her public?" Ronnie asked.

"Why, it sounds as though she might be an actress," their mother decided.

It was when Mr. Saunders wanted to know if their rowing had improved that Ronnie forgot to be careful.

"I don't know that we're so much better alone," he confessed, "but we're fine when Mrs. Wallaby-Jones is with us. She sort of steers for us. With her tail."

Mr. Saunders choked on a bread crumb and hastily gulped a whole glass of water. Mrs. Saunders was very much upset.

"It is all very well," she said sternly, "to make up stories now and again. I hope I enjoy a bit of fantasy as well as the next person. But it is *not* nice to be rude when the lady was so kind to you. . . ."

The lecture went on all through the chocolate pudding dessert and for quite a long time afterward, with many remarks of a to-think-that-any-child-of-mine nature. Mr. Saunders got tired of listening and left the table to read his evening paper. He finished the front page and the sports page and then turned back to page two. Presently he looked up from it and changed the subject.

"You children didn't happen to meet a kangaroo in the park today, I suppose? It seems one got loose from the menagerie. Just listen to this. . . ." He began to read and the whole family listened.

REMARKABLE OCCURRENCE IN CENTRAL PARK ZOO

The strange disappearance of a large female wallaby (macropus giganteus) more commonly known as a kangaroo, for two hours today caused considerable excitement at the local menagerie. The animal, who is known to be very friendly and who answers to the name of Jones when called by her keeper, was missing from her cage for that period. At time of going to press, it had not been determined how she got away, nor when and how she was returned. Until her reappearance, her grieving keeper was certain that she had been abducted by a kidnapper disguised as a Miss Smithers, assistant to the curator of the zoo. Their theory was strengthened by the fact that Miss Smithers, an elderly woman, had reported the theft of her outdoor garments—a fur coat, fur hat and tippet—from the closet adjacent to her office. The clothing later reappeared as mysteriously as the missing wallaby, but it was some time before the excitement died down in the zoo.

There was silence for a moment when Mr. Saunders finished reading this extraordinary news item. Then Jill forgot all discretion and burst out in an excited burble of words.

"Why, our Mrs. Wallaby-Jones wore a fur coat and a fur hat an—"

She was stopped short by Ronnie's sharp elbow in her ribs. She yelped, and then the children looked at each other. They both remembered other times when silence had been considerably better than speech.

"Well, I've got some arithmetic homework to do," Ronnie said carelessly. "I expect I'd better get at it. You coming, Jill?"

Jill and Ronnie went off to their own room, followed by a sedate Merlin and the incredulous stares of their parents. Perhaps it was only because it had never before occurred to Ronnie to do his arithmetic homework without being reminded at least three times. Or perhaps . . .

"*What* did they say that woman's name was?" Mrs. Sidney P. Saunders demanded abruptly. "I thought—"

"So did I," admitted her husband. "But it could *not* be that."

ELECTRICITY

Robert Lawson

Children who chuckle over this ridiculous biography of Benjamin Franklin, purportedly written by a mouse, should be urged to read a genuine biography of our "first civilized American." If they are nine or ten, give them Ingri and Edgar d'Aulaire's Ben Franklin. *If they are twelve, give them Enid Meadowcroft's* Benjamin Franklin.

Ben never thereafter mentioned my little adventure in printing, so I tried to be somewhat more lenient about his maxims.

Trying though they were, however, they were nothing compared to an enthusiasm which beset him about this time. This was the study of what he called "Electricity."

It all started with some glass tubes and a book of instructions sent him by a London friend. These tubes he would rub with a piece of silk or fur, thereby producing many strange and, to me, unpleasant effects. When a tube was sufficiently rubbed, small bits of paper would spring from the table and cling to it, or crackling sparks leap from it to the finger of anyone foolish enough to approach.

Ben derived great amusement from rubbing a tube and touching it to the tip of my tail. Thereupon a terrible shock would run through my body, every hair and whisker would stand on end and a convulsive contraction of all my muscles would throw me several inches in the air.

This was bad enough, but my final rebellion did not come until he, in his enthusiasm, used the fur cap to rub the tube. And *I* was in the cap.

"Ben," said I, "this has gone far enough. From now on, kindly omit me from these experiments. To me they seem a perfectly senseless waste of time, but if they amuse you, all right, go ahead with them. Just leave me out."

"I fear that you are not a person of vision, Amos," said he. "You fail to grasp the world-wide, the epoch-making importance of these experiments. You do not realize the force—"

"Oh don't I?" I replied. "My tail is still tingling."

"I shall tear the lightning from the skies," he went on, "and harness it to do the bidding of man."

"Personally," said I, "I think the sky's an excellent place for it."

Nothing I could say, though, served to dampen Ben's enthusiasm.

Soon he received an elaborate machine that could produce much greater currents than the glass tubes. It was worked by a crank which he ground at happily for hours. Our room became cumbered with rods, wires, tubes, copper plates and glass jars filled with evil-smelling liquids. It was difficult to move about without touching something likely to produce one of those hair-stiffening shocks.

Ben even went so far as to organize a group of similarly obsessed people, calling it "the Philosophical Society." They gathered once a week, armed with their glass tubes, bits of silk and wires. They spent whole evenings fiddling with these things or listening to long speeches about the wonders of "electricity," mostly by Ben. I napped.

After he had played with the new apparatus for a few weeks and had it working well, Ben decided to give an exhibition of his achievements in this field.

A large hall having been secured for the occasion by the Philosophical Society, Ben spent several busy days arranging and testing his apparatus, planning various experiments, writing a speech and inviting prominent people.

Frankly, I was bored by the whole affair, but since Ben seemed rather hurt by my attitude I tried to take a little interest. I read his speech and the descriptions of all the various experiments. By noon I understood everything quite thoroughly.

While we ate a light lunch of bread and cheese I told Ben of my studies. He was delighted and quite touched by my interest.

In the afternoon he went to have his hair curled, leaving me in the hall, where I went on with my research. Determined that no errors should mar this performance, since it meant so much to Ben, I carefully went over each wire and piece of apparatus, comparing them with his diagrams and descriptions.

I discovered that he had apparently made several grave mistakes, for not a few of the wires were connected in a manner that seemed to me obviously incorrect. There were so many of these errors to rectify that I was kept quite busy all afternoon. My corrected arrangements seemed to leave several loose wires and copper plates with no place to go, so I just left them in one of the chairs on the stage. I was barely able to finish before Ben arrived from the hairdresser's.

As we hurried home for supper, he was so filled with pride and excitement that I had no opportunity to tell him how narrowly he had escaped ruining the exhibition by his carelessness.

When we arrived back at the hall in the evening the brilliantly lit auditorium was crowded.

Seated in chairs on the stage were the Governor and his Lady; the Mayor; several of the clergy; and the Chief of the Volunteer Fire Brigade holding his silver trumpet.

Ben made his speech, and performed several simple experiments with the glass tubes. They were watched with great interest by the audience and generously applauded.

He then stepped to the new apparatus and signaled to a young apprentice from the print shop who was stationed at the crank. The lad turned with a will, and a loud humming sound came from the whirling wheel while blue sparks cracked about it.

"And now, my friends," said Ben proudly, "when I turn this knob you shall see, if my calculations are correct, a manifestation of electrical force never before witnessed on this continent."

They did.

As Ben turned the knob the Governor rose straight in the air in much the same manner that I used to when Ben applied the spark to my tail. His hair stood out just as my fur did. His second leap was higher and his hair even straighter. There was a noticeable odor of burning cloth.

On his third rising the copper plate flew from the chair, landing, unfortunately, in his Lady's lap. Her shriek, while slightly muffled by her wig, was, nevertheless, noteworthy.

The Fire Chief, gallantly advancing to their aid, inadvertently touched one of the wires with his silver trumpet. This at once became enveloped in a most unusual blue flame and gave off a strange clanging sound.

Ben leaped toward them, but I clamped on his ear. I had felt those shocks before.

"The boy—" I hissed. "Stop the machine!"

He sprang at the apprentice, who was still grinding merrily. The lad, not an admirer of the Governor, ceased his efforts with some reluctance.

The Governor was stiff and white in his chair, his Lady moaned faintly under her wig, the Fire Chief stared dazedly at his tarnished trumpet, and the audience was in an uproar.

"Never mind, Ben," I consoled as we walked home, "I feel certain that we'll succeed next time."

"Succeed!" shouted Ben. "SUCCEED! Why, Amos, don't you realize that I have just made the most successful, the most momentous experiment of the century? I have discovered the effects produced by applying strong electric shocks to human beings."

"Granted the Governor *is* one," I said, "we surely did."

THE STEADFAST TIN SOLDIER

Hans Christian Andersen

Andersen seems to have especially enjoyed writing tales endowing inanimate objects with life. These personifications probably grew out of his lonely childhood and his life-long delight in puppets. See The Shoemaker's Son.

There were once five and twenty tin soldiers, all brothers, for they were the offspring of the same old tin spoon. Each man shouldered his gun, kept his eyes well to the front, and wore the smartest red and blue uniform imaginable. The first thing they heard in their new world, when the lid was taken off the box, was a little boy clapping his hands and crying, "Soldiers, soldiers!" It was his birthday and they had just been given to him; so he lost no time in setting them up on the table. All the soldiers were exactly alike with one exception, and he differed from the rest in having only one leg. For he was made last, and there was not quite enough tin left to finish him. However, he stood just as well on his one leg, as the others on two, in fact he is the very one who is to become famous. On the table where they were being set up, were many other toys; but the chief thing which caught the eye was a delightful paper castle. You could see through the tiny windows, right into the rooms. Outside there were some little trees surrounding a small mirror, representing a lake, whose surface reflected the waxen swans which were swimming about on it. It was altogether charming, but the prettiest thing of all was a little maiden standing at the open door of the castle. She, too,

"The Steadfast Tin Soldier." From *Fairy Tales* by Hans Christian Andersen, translated by Mrs. Edgar Lucas, Everyman's Library, E. P. Dutton & Co., Inc., New York. By permission also of J. M. Dent & Sons, Ltd., London

was cut out of paper, but she wore a dress of the lightest gauze, with a dainty little blue ribbon over her shoulders, by way of a scarf, set off by a brilliant spangle, as big as her whole face. The little maid was stretching out both arms, for she was a dancer, and in the dance, one of her legs was raised so high into the air that the tin soldier could see absolutely nothing of it, and supposed that she, like himself, had but one leg.

"That would be the very wife for me!" he thought; "but she is much too grand; she lives in a palace, while I only have a box, and then there are five and twenty of us to share it. No, that would be no place for her! but I must try to make her acquaintance!" Then he lay down full length behind a snuff box, which stood on the table. From that point he could have a good look at the little lady, who continued to stand on one leg without losing her balance.

Late in the evening the other soldiers were put into their box, and the people of the house went to bed. Now was the time for the toys to play; they amused themselves with paying visits, fighting battles, and giving balls. The tin soldiers rustled about in their box, for they wanted to join the games, but they could not get the lid off. The nutcrackers turned somersaults, and the pencil scribbled nonsense on the slate. There was such a noise that the canary woke up and joined in, but his remarks were in verse. The only two who did not move were the tin soldier and the little dancer. She stood as stiff as ever on tip-toe, with her arms spread out; he was equally firm on his one leg, and he did not take his eyes off her for a moment.

Then the clock struck twelve, when pop! up flew the lid of the snuff box, but there was no snuff in it, no! There was a little black goblin, a sort of Jack-in-the-box.

"Tin soldier!" said the goblin, "have the goodness to keep your eyes to yourself."

But the tin soldier feigned not to hear.

"Ah! you just wait till to-morrow," said the goblin.

In the morning when the children got up they put the tin soldier on the window frame, and, whether it was caused by the goblin or by a puff of wind, I do not know, but all at once the window burst open, and the soldier fell headforemost from the third story.

It was a terrific descent, and he landed at last, with his leg in the air, and rested on his cap, with his bayonet fixed between two paving stones. The maid-servant and the little boy ran down at once to look for him; but although they almost trod on him, they could not see him. Had the soldier only called out, "Here I am," they would easily have found him, but he did not think it proper to shout when he was in uniform.

Presently it began to rain, and the drops fell faster and faster, till there was a regular torrent. When it was over two street boys came along.

"Look out!" said one; "there is a tin soldier! He shall go for a sail."

So they made a boat out of a newspaper and put the soldier into the middle of it, and he sailed away down the gutter; both boys ran alongside clapping their hands. Good heavens! what waves there were in the gutter, and what a current, but then it certainly had rained cats and dogs. The paper boat danced up and down, and now and then whirled round and round. A shudder ran through the tin soldier, but he remained undaunted, and did not move a muscle, only looked straight before him with his gun shouldered. All at once the boat drifted under a long wooden tunnel, and it became as dark as it was in his box.

"Where on earth am I going to now!" thought he. "Well, well, it is all the fault of that goblin! Oh, if only the little maiden were with me in the boat it might be twice as dark for all I should care!"

At this moment a big water rat, who lived in the tunnel, came up.

"Have you a pass?" asked the rat. "Hand up your pass!"

The tin soldier did not speak, but clung still tighter to his gun. The boat rushed on, the rat close behind. Phew, how he gnashed his teeth and shouted to the bits of stick and straw.

"Stop him, stop him, he hasn't paid the toll! he hasn't shown his pass!"

But the current grew stronger and stronger, the tin soldier could already see daylight before him at the end of the tunnel; but he also heard a roaring sound, fit to strike terror to the bravest heart. Just imagine! Where the tunnel ended the stream rushed straight into the big canal. That would be just as dangerous for him as it would be for us to shoot a great rapid.

He was so near the end now that it was impossible to stop. The boat dashed out; the poor tin soldier held himself as stiff as he could; no one should say of him that he even winced.

The boat swirled round three or four times, and filled with water to the edge; it must sink. The tin soldier stood up to his neck in water, and the boat sank deeper and deeper. The paper became limper and limper, and at last the water went over his head—then he thought of the pretty little dancer, whom he was never to see again, and this refrain rang in his ears:

"Onward! Onward! Soldier!
For death thou canst not shun."

At last the paper gave way entirely and the soldier fell through—but at the same moment he was swallowed by a big fish.

Oh! how dark it was inside the fish, it was worse than being in the tunnel even; and then it was so narrow! But the tin soldier was as dauntless as ever, and lay full length, shouldering his gun.

The fish rushed about and made the most frantic movements. At last it became quite quiet, and after a time, a flash like lightning pierced it. The soldier was once more in the broad daylight, and some one called out loudly, "A tin soldier!" The fish had been caught, taken to market, sold, and brought into the kitchen, where the cook cut it open with a large knife. She took the soldier up by the waist, with two fingers, and carried him into the parlour, where everyone wanted to see the wonderful man, who

had travelled about in the stomach of a fish; but the tin soldier was not at all proud. They set him up on the table, and, wonder of wonders! he found himself in the very same room that he had been in before. He saw the very same children, and the toys were still standing on the table, as well as the beautiful castle with the pretty little dancer.

She still stood on one leg, and held the other up in the air. You see she also was unbending. The soldier was so much moved that he was ready to shed tears of tin, but that would not have been fitting. He looked at her, and she looked at him, but they said never a word. At this moment one of the little boys took up the tin soldier, and without rhyme or reason, threw him into the fire. No doubt the little goblin in the snuff box was to blame for that. The tin soldier stood there, lighted up by the flame, and in the most horrible heat; but whether it was the heat of the real fire, or the warmth of his feelings, he did not know. He had lost all his gay color; it might have been from his perilous journey, or it might have been from grief, who can tell?

He looked at the little maiden, and she looked at him; and he felt that he was melting away, but he still managed to keep himself erect, shouldering his gun bravely.

A door was suddenly opened, the draught caught the little dancer and she fluttered like a sylph, straight into the fire, to the soldier, blazed up and was gone!

By this time the soldier was reduced to a mere lump, and when the maid took away the ashes next morning she found him, in the shape of a small tin heart. All that was left of the dancer was her spangle, and that was burnt as black as coal.

THE WILD SWANS

Hans Christian Andersen

Andersen has retold this folk tale with beautiful little touches of his own, such as the swans with golden crowns.

"The Wild Swans." From *Fairy Tales* by Hans Christian Andersen, translated by Mrs. Edgar Lucas, Everyman's Library, E. P. Dutton & Co., Inc., New York. By permission also of J. M. Dent & Sons, Ltd., London

Far away, where the swallows take refuge in winter, lived a king who had eleven sons and one daughter, Elise. The eleven brothers—they were all princes—used to go to school with stars on their breasts and swords at their sides. They wrote upon golden slates with diamond pencils, and could read just as well without a book as with one, so there was no mistake about their being real princes. Their sister Elise sat upon a little footstool of looking-glass, and she had a picture-book which had cost the half of a kingdom. Oh, these children were very happy; but it was not to last thus for ever.

Their father, who was king over all the land, married a wicked queen who was not at all kind to the poor children; they found that out on the first day. All was festive at the castle, but when the children wanted to play at having company, instead of having as many cakes and baked apples as ever they wanted, she would only let them have some sand in a teacup, and said they must make-believe.

In the following week she sent little Elise into the country to board with some peasants, and it did not take her long to make the king believe so many bad things about the boys, that he cared no more about them.

"Fly out into the world and look after yourselves," said the wicked queen; "you shall fly about like birds without voices."

But she could not make things as bad for them as she would have liked; they turned into eleven beautiful wild swans. They flew out of the palace window with a weird scream, right across the park and the woods.

It was very early in the morning when they came to the place where their sister Elise was sleeping in the peasant's house. They hovered over the roof of the house, turning and twisting their long necks, and flapping their wings; but no one either heard or saw them. They had to fly away again, and they soared up toward the clouds, far out into the wide world, and they settled in a big, dark wood, which stretched down to the shore.

Poor little Elise stood in the peasant's room, playing with a green leaf, for she had no other toys. She made a little hole in it, which she looked through at the sun, and it seemed to her as if she saw her brothers' bright eyes. Every time the warm sunbeams shone upon her cheek, it reminded her of their kisses. One day passed just like another. When the wind whistled through the rose-hedges outside the house, it whispered to the roses, "Who can be prettier than you are?" But the roses shook their heads and answered, "Elise!" And when the old woman sat in the doorway reading her Psalms, the wind turned over the leaves and said to the book, "Who can be more pious than you?" "Elise!" answered the book. Both the roses and the book of Psalms only spoke the truth.

She was to go home when she was fifteen, but when the queen saw how pretty she was, she got very angry, and her heart was filled with hatred. She would willingly have turned her into a wild swan too, like her brothers, but she did not dare to do it at once, for the king wanted to see his daughter. The queen always went to the bath in the early morning. It was built of marble and adorned with soft cushions and beautiful carpets.

She took three toads, kissed them, and said to the first, "Sit upon Elise's head when she comes to the bath, so that she may become sluggish like yourself. Sit upon her forehead," she said to the second, "that she may become ugly like you, and then her father won't know her! Rest upon her heart," she whispered to the third. "Let an evil spirit come over her, which may be a burden to her." Then she put the toads into the clean water, and a green tinge immediately came over it. She called Elise, undressed her, and made her go into the bath; when she ducked under the water, one of the toads got among her hair, the other got on to her forehead, and the third on to her bosom. But when she stood up three scarlet poppies floated on the water; had not the creatures been poisonous, and kissed by the sorceress, they would have been changed into crimson roses, but yet they became flowers from merely having rested a moment on her head and her heart. She was far too good and innocent for the sorcery to have any power over her. When the wicked Queen saw this, she rubbed her over with walnut juice, and smeared her face with some evil-smelling salve. She also matted up her beautiful hair; it would have been impossible to recognize pretty Elise. When her father saw her, he was quite horrified and said that she could not be his daughter. Nobody would have anything to say to her, except the yard dog, and the swallows, and they were only poor dumb animals whose opinion went for nothing.

Poor Elise wept, and thought of her eleven brothers who were all lost. She crept sadly out of the palace and wandered about all day, over meadows and marshes, and into a big forest. She did not know in the least where she wanted to go, but she felt very sad, and longed for her brothers, who, no doubt, like herself had been driven out of the palace. She made up her mind to go and look for them, but she had only been in the wood for a short time when night fell. She had quite lost her way, so she lay down upon the soft moss, said her evening prayer, and rested her head on a little hillock. It was very still and the air was mild, hundreds of glowworms shone around her on the grass and in the marsh like green fire. When she gently moved one of the branches over her head, the little shining insects fell over her like a shower of stars. She dreamt about her brothers all night long. Again they were children playing together: they wrote upon the golden slates with their diamond pencils, and she looked at the picture-book which had cost half a kingdom. But they no longer wrote strokes and noughts upon their slates as they used to do; no, they wrote down all their boldest exploits, and everything that they had seen and experienced. Everything in the picture book was alive, the birds sang, and the people walked out of the book, and spoke to Elise and her brothers. When she turned over a page, they skipped back into their places again, so that there should be no confusion among the pictures.

When she woke the sun was already high; it is true she could not see it very well through the thick branches of the lofty forest trees, but the sunbeams cast a golden shimmer round beyond the forest. There was a fresh delicious scent of grass and herbs in the air, and the birds were almost ready to perch upon her shoulders. She could hear the splashing of water, for there were many springs around, which all flowed into a pond with a lovely sandy bottom. It was surrounded with thick bushes, but there was one place which the stags had trampled down and Elise passed through the opening to the water side. It was so transparent, that had not the branches been moved by the breeze, she must

have thought that they were painted on the bottom, so plainly was every leaf reflected, both those on which the sun played, and those which were in shade.

When she saw her own face she was quite frightened, it was so brown and ugly, but when she wet her little hand and rubbed her eyes and forehead, her white skin shone through again. Then she took off all her clothes and went into the fresh water. A more beautiful royal child than she, could not be found in all the world.

When she had put on her clothes again, and plaited her long hair, she went to a sparkling spring and drank some of the water out of the hollow of her hand. Then she wandered farther into the wood, though where she was going she had not the least idea. She thought of her brothers, and she thought of a merciful God who would not forsake her. He let the wild crab-apples grow to feed the hungry. He showed her a tree, the branches of which were bending beneath their weight of fruit. Here she made her midday meal, and, having put props under the branches, she walked on into the thickest part of the forest. It was so quiet that she heard her own footsteps, she heard every little withered leaf which bent under her feet. Not a bird was to be seen, not a ray of sunlight pierced the leafy branches, and the tall trunks were so close together that when she looked before her it seemed as if a thick fence of heavy beams hemmed her in on every side. The solitude was such as she had never known before.

It was a very dark night, not a single glowworm sparkled in the marsh; sadly she lay down to sleep, and it seemed to her as if the branches above her parted asunder, and the Saviour looked down upon her with His loving eyes, and little angels' heads peeped out above His head and under His arms.

When she woke in the morning she was not sure if she had dreamt this, or whether it was really true.

She walked a little farther, when she met an old woman with a basket full of berries, of which she gave her some. Elise asked if she had seen eleven princes ride through the wood. "No," said the old woman, "but yesterday I saw eleven swans, with golden crowns upon their heads, swimming in the stream close by here."

She led Elise a little farther to a slope, at the foot of which the stream meandered. The trees on either bank stretched out their rich leafy branches toward each other, and where, from their natural growth, they could not reach each other, they had torn their roots out of the ground, and leant over the water so as to interlace their branches.

Elise said good-by to the old woman, and walked along by the river till it flowed out into the great open sea.

The beautiful open sea lay before the maiden, but not a sail was to be seen on it, not a single boat. How was she ever to get any further? She looked at the numberless little pebbles on the beach; they were all worn quite round by the water. Glass, iron, stone, whatever was washed up, had taken their shapes from the water, which yet was much softer than her little hand. "With all its rolling, it is untiring, and everything hard is smoothed down. I will be just as untiring! Thank you for your lesson, you clear rolling waves! Some time, so my heart tells me, you will bear me to my beloved brothers!"

Eleven white swans' feathers were lying on the sea-weed; she picked them up and made a bunch of them. There were still drops of water on them. Whether these were dew or tears no one could tell. It was very lonely there by the shore, but she did not feel it, for the sea was ever-changing. There were more changes on it in the course of a few hours than could be seen on an inland fresh-water lake in a year. If a big black cloud arose, it was just as if the sea wanted to say, "I can look black too," and then the wind blew up and the waves showed their white crests. But if the clouds were red and the wind dropped, the sea looked like a rose leaf, now white, now green. But, however still it was, there was always a little gentle motion just by the shore, the water rose and fell softly like the bosom of a sleeping child.

When the sun was just about to go down, Elise saw eleven wild swans with golden crowns upon their heads flying toward the shore. They flew in a swaying line, one behind the other, like a white ribbon streamer. Elise climbed up on to the bank and hid behind a bush; the swans settled close by her and flapped their great white wings.

As soon as the sun had sunk beneath the water, the swans shed their feathers and became eleven handsome princes; they were Elise's brothers. Although they had altered a good deal, she knew them at once; she felt that they must be her brothers and she sprang into their arms, calling them by name. They were delighted when they recognized their little sister who had grown so big and beautiful. They laughed and cried, and told each other how wickedly their stepmother had treated them all.

"We brothers," said the eldest, "have to fly about in the guise of swans, as long as the sun is above the horizon. When it goes down we regain our human shapes. So we always have to look out for a resting place near sunset, for should we happen to be flying up among the clouds when the sun goes down, we should be hurled to the depths below. We do not live here; there is another land, just as beautiful as this, beyond the sea; but the way to it is very long and we have to cross the mighty ocean to get to it. There is not a single island on the way where we can spend the night, only one solitary little rock juts up above the water midway. It is only just big enough for us to stand upon close together, and if there is a heavy sea the water splashes over us, yet we thank our God for it. We stay there over night in our human forms, and without it we could never revisit our beloved Fatherland, for our flight takes two of the longest days in the year. We are only permitted to visit the home of our fathers once a year, and we dare only stay for eleven days. We hover over this big forest from whence we catch a glimpse of the palace where we were born, and where our father lives; beyond it we can see the high church towers where our mother is buried. We fancy that the trees and bushes here are related to us; and the wild horses gallop over the moors, as we used to see them in our childhood. The charcoal burners still sing the old songs we used to dance to when we were children. This is our Fatherland, we are drawn toward it, and here we have found you again, dear little sister! We may stay here two days longer, and then we must fly away again across the ocean, to a lovely country indeed, but it is not our own dear Fatherland! How shall we ever take you with us, we have neither ship nor boat!"

"How can I deliver you?" said their sister, and they went on talking to each other, nearly all night, they only dozed for a few hours.

Elise was awakened in the morning by the rustling of the swan's wings above her; her brothers were again transformed and were wheeling round in great circles, till she lost sight of them in the distance. One of them, the youngest, stayed behind. He laid his head against her bosom, and she caressed it with her fingers. They remained together all day; toward evening the others came back, and as soon as the sun went down they took their natural forms.

"Tomorrow we must fly away, and we dare not come back for a whole year, but we can't leave you like this! Have you courage to go with us? My arm is strong enough to carry you over the forest, so surely our united strength ought to be sufficient to bear you across the ocean."

"Oh yes! take me with you," said Elise.

They spent the whole night in weaving a kind of net of the elastic bark of the willow bound together with tough rushes; they made it both large and strong. Elise lay down upon it, and when the sun rose and the brothers became swans again, they took up the net in their bills and flew high up among the clouds with their precious sister, who was fast asleep. The sunbeams fell straight on to her face, so one of the swans flew over her head so that its broad wings should shade her.

They were far from land when Elise woke; she thought she must still be dreaming, it seemed so strange to be carried through the air so high up above the sea. By her side lay a branch of beautiful ripe berries, and a bundle of savory roots, which her youngest brother had collected for her, and for which she gave him a grateful smile. She knew it was he who flew above her head shading her from the sun. They were so high up that the first ship they saw looked like a gull floating on the water. A great cloud came up behind them like a mountain, and Elise saw the shadow of herself on it, and those of the eleven swans looking like giants. It was a more beautiful picture than any she had ever seen before, but as the sun rose higher, the cloud fell behind, and the shadow picture disappeared.

They flew on and on all day like an arrow whizzing through the air, but they went slower than usual, for now they had their sister to carry. A storm came up, and night was drawing on; Elise saw the sun sinking with terror in her heart, for the solitary rock was nowhere to be seen. The swans seemed to be taking stronger strokes than ever; alas! she was the cause of their not being able to get on faster; as soon as the sun went down they would become men, and they would all be hurled into the sea and drowned. She prayed to God from the bottom of her heart, but still no rock was to be seen! Black clouds gathered, and strong gusts of wind announced a storm; the clouds looked like a great threatening leaden wave, and the flashes of lightning followed each other rapidly.

The sun was now at the edge of the sea. Elise's heart quaked, when suddenly the swans shot downwards so suddenly, that she thought they were falling, then they hovered again. Half of the sun was below the horizon, and there for the first time she saw the little rock below, which did not look bigger than the head of a seal above the water. The sun sank very quickly, it was no bigger than a star, but her foot touched solid earth. The sun went out like the last sparks of a bit of burning paper; she saw her brothers stand arm in arm around her, but there was only just room enough for them. The waves beat upon the rock and washed over them like drenching rain. The heavens shone with continuous fire, and the thunder rolled, peal upon peal. But the sister and brothers held each other's hands and sang a psalm which gave them comfort and courage.

The air was pure and still at dawn. As soon as the sun rose the swans flew off with Elise, away from the islet. The sea still ran high, it looked from where they were as if the white foam on the dark green water were millions of swans floating on the waves.

When the sun rose higher, Elise saw before her half floating in the air great masses of ice, with shining glaciers on the heights. A palace was perched midway a mile in length, with one bold colonnade built above another. Beneath them swayed palm trees and gorgeous blossoms as big as mill wheels. She asked if this was the land to which she was going, but the swans shook their heads, because what she saw was a mirage; the beautiful and ever-changing palace of Fata Morgana. No mortal dared enter it. Elise gazed at it, but as she gazed the palace, gardens and mountains melted away, and in their place stood twenty proud churches with their high towers and pointed windows. She seemed to hear the notes of the organ, but it was the sea she heard. When she got close to the seeming churches, they changed to a great navy sailing beneath her; but it was only a sea mist floating over the waters. Yes, she saw constant changes passing before her eyes, and now she saw the real land she was bound to. Beautiful blue mountains rose before her with their cedar woods and palaces. Long before the sun went down, she sat among the hills in front of a big cave covered with delicate green creepers. It looked like a piece of embroidery.

"Now we shall see what you will dream here tonight," said the youngest brother, as he showed her where she was to sleep.

"If only I might dream how I could deliver you," she said, and this thought filled her mind entirely. She prayed earnestly to God for His help, and even in her sleep she continued her prayer. It seemed to her that she was flying up to Fata Morgana in her castle in the air. The fairy came toward her, she was charming and brilliant, and yet she was very like the old woman who gave her the berries in the wood, and told her about the swans with the golden crowns.

"Your brothers can be delivered," she said, "but have you courage and endurance enough for it? The sea is indeed softer than your hands, and it molds the hardest stones, but it does not feel the pain your fingers will feel. It has no heart, and does not suffer the pain and anguish you must feel. Do you see this stinging nettle I hold in my hand? Many of this kind grow round the cave where you sleep; only these and the ones which grow in the churchyards may be used. Mark that! Those you may pluck although they will burn and blister your hands. Crush the nettles with your feet and you will have flax, and of this you must weave eleven coats of mail with long sleeves. Throw these over the eleven wild swans and the charm is broken! But remember that from the moment you begin this work, till it is finished, even if it takes years, you must not utter a word! The first word you say will fall like a murderer's dagger into the hearts of your brothers. Their lives hang on your tongue. Mark this well!"

She touched her hand at the same moment, it was like burning fire, and woke Elise. It was bright daylight, and close to where she slept lay a nettle like those in her dream. She fell upon her knees with thanks to God and left the cave to begin her work.

She seized the horrid nettles with her delicate hands, and they burnt like fire; great blisters rose on her hands and arms, but she suffered it willingly if only it would deliver her beloved brothers. She crushed every nettle with her bare feet, and twisted it into green flax.

When the sun went down and the brothers came back, they were alarmed at finding her mute; they thought it was some new witchcraft exercised by their wicked stepmother. But when they saw her hands, they understood that it was for their sakes; the youngest brother wept, and wherever his tears fell, she felt no more pain, and the blisters disappeared.

She spent the whole night at her work, for she could not rest till she had delivered her dear brothers. All the following day while her brothers were away she sat solitary, but never had the time flown so fast. One coat of mail was finished and she began the next. Then a hunting-horn sounded among the mountains; she was much frightened, the sound came nearer, and she heard dogs barking. In terror she rushed into the cave and tied the nettles she had collected and woven into a bundle upon which she sat.

At this moment a big dog bounded forward from the thicket, and another and another, they barked loudly and ran backwards and forwards. In a few minutes all the huntsmen were standing outside the cave, and the handsomest of them was the king of the country. He stepped up to Elise: never had he seen so lovely a girl.

"How came you here, beautiful child?" he said.

Elise shook her head; she dared not speak; the salvation and the lives of her brothers depended upon her silence. She hid her hands under her apron, so that the king should not see what she suffered.

"Come with me!" he said; "you cannot stay here. If you are as good as you are beautiful, I will dress you in silks and velvets, put a golden crown upon your head, and you shall live with me and have your home in my richest palace!" Then he lifted her upon his horse, she wept and wrung her hands, but the king said, "I only think of your happiness; you will thank me one day for what I am doing!" Then he darted off across the mountains, holding her before him on his horse, and the huntsmen followed.

When the sun went down, the royal city with churches and cupolas lay before them, and the king led her into the palace, where great fountains played in the marble halls, and where walls and ceilings were adorned with paintings, but she had no eyes for them, she only wept and sorrowed; passively she allowed the women to dress her in royal robes, to twist pearls into her hair, and to draw gloves on to her blistered hands.

She was dazzlingly lovely as she stood there in all her magnificence; the courtiers bent low before her, and the king wooed her as his bride, although the archbishop shook his head, and whispered that he feared the beautiful wood maiden was a witch, who had dazzled their eyes and infatuated the king.

The king refused to listen to him, he ordered the music to play, the richest food to be brought, and the loveliest girls to dance before her. She was led through scented gardens into gorgeous apartments, but nothing brought a smile to her lips, or into her eyes, sorrow sat there like a heritage and a possession for all time. Last of all, the king opened the door of a little chamber close by the room where she was to sleep. It was adorned with costly green carpets, and made to exactly resemble the cave where he found her. On the floor lay the bundle of flax she had spun from the nettles, and from the ceiling hung the shirt of mail which was already finished. One of the huntsmen had brought all these things away as curiosities.

"Here you may dream that you are back in your former home!" said the king. "Here is the work upon which you were engaged; in the midst of your splendor, it may amuse you to think of those times."

When Elise saw all these things so dear to her heart, a smile for the first time played about her lips, and the blood rushed back to her cheeks.

She thought of the deliverance of her brothers, and she kissed the king's hand; he pressed her to his heart, and ordered all the church bells to ring marriage peals. The lovely dumb girl from the woods was to be queen of the country.

The archbishop whispered evil words into the ear of the king, but they did not reach his heart. The wedding was to take place, and the archbishop himself had to put the crown upon her head. In his anger he pressed the golden circlet so tightly upon her head as to give her pain. But a heavier circlet pressed upon her heart, her grief for her brothers, so she thought nothing of the bodily pain. Her lips were sealed, a single word from her mouth would cost her brothers their lives, but her eyes were full of love for the good and handsome king, who did everything he could to please her. Every day she grew more and more attached to him, and longed to confide in him, tell him her sufferings; but dumb she must remain, and in silence must bring her labor to completion. Therefore at night she stole away from his side into her secret chamber, which was decorated like a cave, and here she knitted one shirt after another. When she came to the seventh, all her flax was worked up; she knew that these nettles which she was to use grew in the churchyard, but she had to pluck them herself. How was she to get there? "Oh, what is the pain of my fingers compared with the anguish of my heart," she thought. "I must venture out, the good God will not desert me!" With as much terror in her heart as if she were doing some evil deed, she stole down one night into the moonlit garden, and through the long alleys out into the silent streets to the churchyard. There she saw, sitting on a gravestone, a group of hideous ghouls, who took off their tattered garments, as if they were about to bathe, and then they dug down into the freshly-made graves with their skinny fingers, and tore the flesh from the bodies and devoured it. Elise had to pass close by them, and they fixed their evil eyes upon her, but she said a prayer as she passed, picked the stinging nettles and hurried back to the palace with them.

Only one person saw her, but that was the archbishop, who watched while others slept. Surely now all his bad opinions of the queen were justified; all was not as it should be with her, she must be a witch, and therefore she had bewitched the king and all the people.

He told the king in the confessional what he had seen and what he feared. When those bad words passed his lips, the pictures of the saints shook their heads as if to say: it is not so, Elise is innocent. The archbishop, however, took it differently, and thought that they were bearing witness against her, and shaking their heads at her sin. Two big tears rolled down the king's cheeks, and he went home with doubt in his heart. He pretended to sleep at night, but no quiet sleep came to his eyes. He perceived how Elise got up and went to her private closet. Day by day his face grew darker, Elise saw it but could not imagine what was the cause of it. It alarmed her, and what was she not already suffering in her heart because of her brothers? Her salt tears ran down upon the royal purple velvet, they lay upon it like sparkling diamonds, and all who saw their splendor wished to be queen.

She had, however, almost reached the end of her labors, only one shirt of mail was wanting, but again she had no more flax and not a single nettle was left. Once more, for the last time, she must go to the churchyard to pluck a few handfuls. She thought with dread of the solitary walk and the horrible ghouls; but her will was as strong as her trust in God.

Elise went, but the king and the archbishop followed her, they saw her disappear within the gateway of the churchyard. When they followed they saw the ghouls sitting on the gravestone as Elise had seen them before; and the king turned away his head because he thought she was among them, she, whose head this very evening had rested on his breast.

"The people must judge her," he groaned, and the people judged. "Let her be consumed in the glowing flames!"

She was led away from her beautiful royal apartments to a dark damp dungeon, where the wind whistled through the grated window. Instead of velvet and silk they gave her the bundle of nettles she had gathered to lay her head upon. The hard burning shirts of mail were to be her covering, but they could have given her nothing more precious.

She set to work again with many prayers to God. Outside her prison the street boys sang derisive songs about her, and not a soul comforted her with a kind word.

Toward evening she heard the rustle of swans' wings close to her window; it was her youngest brother, at last he had found her. He sobbed aloud with joy although he knew that the coming night might be her last, but then her work was almost done and her brothers were there.

The archbishop came to spend her last hours with her as he had promised the king. She shook her head at him, and by looks and gestures begged him to leave her. She had only this night in which to finish her work, or else all would be wasted, all—her pain, tears and sleepless nights. The archbishop went away with bitter words against her, but poor Elise knew that she was innocent, and she went on with her work.

The little mice ran about the floor bringing nettles to her feet, so as to give what help they could, and a thrush sat on the grating of the window where he sang all night, as merrily as he could to keep up her courage.

It was still only dawn, and the sun would not rise for an hour when the eleven brothers stood at the gate of the palace, begging to be taken to the king. This could not be done, was the answer, for it was still night; the king was asleep and no one dared wake him. All their entreaties and threats were useless, the watch turned out and even the king himself came to see what was the matter; but just then the sun rose, and no more brothers were to be seen, only eleven wild swans hovering over the palace.

The whole populace streamed out of the town gates, they were all anxious to see the witch burnt. A miserable horse drew the cart in which Elise was seated. They had put upon her a smock of green sacking, and all her beautiful long hair hung loose from the lovely head. Her cheeks were deathly pale, and her lips moved softly, while her fingers unceasingly twisted the green yarn. Even on the way to her death she could not abandon her unfinished work. Ten shirts lay completed at her feet—she labored away at the eleventh, amid the scoffing insults of the populace.

"Look at the witch how she mutters. She has never a book of psalms in her hands, no, there she sits with her loathsome sorcery. Tear it away from her, into a thousand bits!"

The crowd pressed around her to destroy her work, but just then eleven white swans flew down and perched upon the cart flapping their wings. The crowd gave way before them in terror.

"It is a sign from Heaven! She is innocent!" they whispered, but they dared not say it aloud.

The executioner seized her by the hand, but she hastily threw the eleven shirts over the swans, who were immediately transformed to eleven handsome princes; but the youngest had a swan's wing in place of an arm, for one sleeve was wanting to his shirt of mail, she had not been able to finish it.

"Now I may speak! I am innocent."

The populace who saw what had happened bowed down before her as if she had been a saint, but she sank lifeless in her brother's arms; so great had been the strain, the terror and the suffering she had endured.

"Yes, innocent she is indeed," said the eldest brother, and he told them all that had happened.

Whilst he spoke a wonderful fragrance spread around, as of millions of roses. Every faggot in the pile had taken root and shot out branches, and a great high hedge of red roses had arisen. At the very top was one pure white blossom, it shone like a star, and the king broke it off and laid it on Elise's bosom, and she woke with joy and peace in her heart.

All the church bells began to ring of their own accord, and the singing birds flocked around them. Surely such a bridal procession went back to the palace as no king had ever seen before!

THE SWINEHERD

Hans Christian Andersen

In folk tale style, a droll but also a satire, this amusing story is for older children. They will catch the silliness of a princess who prefers the artificial to the real, and they will understand that such folly is not limited to princesses.

There was once a poor Prince; he had only quite a tiny kingdom, but it was big enough to allow him to marry, and he was bent upon marrying.

Now, it certainly was rather bold of him to say to the Emperor's daughter, "Will you have me?" He did, however, venture to say so, for his name was known far and wide; and there were hundreds of Princesses who would have said "Yes," and "Thank you, kindly," but see if *she* would!

Just let us hear about it.

A rose tree grew on the grave of the prince's father, it was such a beautiful rose tree; it only bloomed every fifth year, and then only bore one blossom; but what a rose that was! By merely smelling it one forgot all one's cares and sorrows.

Then he had a nightingale which sang as if every lovely melody in the world dwelt in her little throat. This rose and this nightingale were to be given to the Princess, so they were put into great silver caskets and sent to her.

The Emperor had them carried before him into the great Hall where the Princess was playing at "visiting" with her ladies-in-waiting; they had nothing else to do. When she saw the caskets with the gifts she clapped her hands with delight!

"If only it were a little pussy cat!" said she,— but there was the lovely rose.

"Oh, how exquisitely it is made!" said all the ladies-in-waiting.

"It is more than beautiful," said the Emperor; "it is neat."

But the Princess touched it, and then she was ready to cry.

"Fie, Papa!" she said; "it is not made, it is a real one!"

"Fie," said all the ladies-in-waiting; "it is a real one!"

"Well, let us see what there is in the other casket, before we get angry," said the Emperor, and out came the nightingale. It sang so beautifully that at first no one could find anything to say against it.

"*Superbe! charmant!*" said the ladies-in-waiting, for they all had a smattering of French, one spoke it worse than the other.

"The Swineherd." From *Fairy Tales* by Hans Christian Andersen, translated by Mrs. Edgar Lucas, Everyman's Library, E. P. Dutton & Co., Inc., New York. By permission also of J. M. Dent & Sons, Ltd., London

"How that bird reminds me of our lamented Empress's musical box," said an old courtier. "Ah, yes, they are the same tunes, and the same beautiful execution."

"So they are," said the Emperor, and he cried like a little child.

"I should hardly think it could be a real one," said the Princess.

"Yes, it is a real one," said those who had brought it.

"Oh, let that bird fly away then," said the Princess, and she would not hear of allowing the Prince to come. But he was not to be crushed; he stained his face brown and black, and, pressing his cap over his eyes, he knocked at the door.

"Good morning, Emperor," said he; "can I be taken into service in the palace?"

"Well, there are so many wishing to do that," said the Emperor; "but let me see!—yes, I need somebody to look after the pigs, for we have so many of them."

So the Prince was made imperial swineherd. A horrid little room was given him near the pig-sties, and here he had to live. He sat busily at work all day, and by the evening he had made a beautiful little cooking pot; it had bells all round it and when the pot boiled they tinkled delightfully and played the old tune:

"Ach du lieber Augustin,
Alles ist weg, weg, weg!"

Alas! dear Augustin,
All is lost, lost, lost!

But the greatest charm of all about it was, that by holding one's finger in the steam one could immediately smell all the dinners that were being cooked at every stove in the town. Now this was a very different matter from a rose.

The Princess came walking along with all her ladies-in-waiting, and when she heard the tune she stopped and looked pleased, for she could play "Ach du lieber Augustin" herself; it was her only tune, and she could only play it with one finger.

"Why, that is my tune," she said; "this must be a cultivated swineherd. Go and ask him what the instrument costs."

So one of the ladies-in-waiting had to go into his room, but she put pattens on first.

"How much do you want for the pot?" she asked.

"I must have ten kisses from the Princess," said the swineherd.

"Heaven preserve us!" said the lady.

"I won't take less," said the swineherd.

"Well, what does he say?" asked the Princess.

"I really cannot tell you," said the lady-in-waiting, "it is so shocking."

"Then you must whisper it." And she whispered it.

"He is a wretch!" said the Princess, and went away at once. But she had only gone a little way when she heard the bells tinkling beautifully:

"Ach du lieber Augustin."

"Go and ask him if he will take ten kisses from the ladies-in-waiting."

"No, thank you," said the swineherd; "ten kisses from the Princess, or I keep my pot."

"How tiresome it is," said the Princess. "Then you will have to stand round me, so that no one may see."

So the ladies-in-waiting stood round her and spread out their skirts while the swineherd took his ten kisses, and then the pot was hers.

What a delight it was to them! The pot was kept on the boil day and night. They knew what was cooking on every stove in the town, from the chamberlain's to the shoemaker's. The ladies-in-waiting danced about and clapped their hands.

"We know who has sweet soup and pancakes for dinner, and who has cutlets; how amusing it is."

"Highly interesting," said the mistress of the robes.

"Yes, but hold your tongues, for I am the Emperor's daughter."

"Heaven preserve us!" they all said.

The swineherd—that is to say, the Prince, only nobody knew that he was not a real swineherd—did not let the day pass in idleness, and he now constructed a rattle. When it was swung round it played all the waltzes, galops and jig tunes which have ever been heard since the creation of the world.

"But this is *superbe!*" said the Princess, as she walked by. "I have never heard finer compositions. Go and ask him what the instrument costs, but let us have no more kissing."

"He wants a hundred kisses from the Princess!" said the lady-in-waiting.

"I think he is mad!" said the Princess, and she went away, but she had not gone far when she stopped.

"One must encourage art," she said; "I am the Emperor's daughter. Tell him he can have ten kisses, the same as yesterday, and he can take the others from the ladies-in-waiting."

"But we don't like that at all," said the ladies.

"Oh, nonsense! If I can kiss him you can do

see!" So he pulled up the heels of his slippers for they were shoes which he had trodden down.

Bless us, what a hurry he was in! When he got into the yard, he walked very softly and the ladies were so busy counting the kisses, so that there should be fair play, and neither too few nor too many kisses, that they never heard the Emperor. He stood on tiptoe.

"What is all this?" he said when he saw what was going on, and he hit them on the head with his slipper just as the swineherd was taking the eighty-sixth kiss.

"Out you go!" said the Emperor, for he was

the same. Remember that I pay your wages as well as give you board and lodging." So the lady-in-waiting had to go again.

"A hundred kisses from the Princess, or let each keep his own."

"Stand in front of me," said she, and all the ladies stood round, while he kissed her.

"Whatever is the meaning of that crowd round the pig-sties?" said the Emperor as he stepped out on to the verandah; he rubbed his eyes and put on his spectacles. "Why, it is the ladies-in-waiting, what game are they up to? I must go and

furious, and both the Princess and the Prince were put out of his realm.

There she stood crying, and the swineherd scolded, and the rain poured down in torrents.

"Oh, miserable creature that I am! if only I had accepted the handsome Prince. Oh, how unhappy I am!"

The swineherd went behind a tree, wiped the black and brown stain from his face, and threw away his ugly clothes. Then he stepped out dressed as a Prince, he was so handsome that the Princess could not help curtseying to him.

"I am come to despise thee," he said. "Thou wouldst not have an honourable Prince, thou couldst not prize the rose or the nightingale, but thou wouldst kiss the swineherd for a trumpery musical box! As thou hast made thy bed, so must thou lie upon it!"

Then he went back into his own little kingdom and shut and locked the door. So she had to stand outside and sing in earnest—

"Ach du lieber Augustin
Alles ist weg, weg, weg!"

PINOCCHIO

Carlo Lorenzini

Carlo Collodi was the pen name of a witty Italian by the name of Carlo Lorenzini. Italians and Sicilians have always loved puppets so it is not surprising that Lorenzini should write a story about a puppet that comes to life. Anyone who has ever made puppets or played with them has experienced the uncanny feeling that the creatures really do have a life of their own and may take to their heels any minute. This episode finds Pinocchio in a terrible fix. He has run away from school, failed to keep his promises, and is now so conspicuously punished for his sins that he is repenting for dear life.

Every one, at one time or another, has found some surprise awaiting him. Of the kind which Pinocchio had on that eventful morning of his life, there are but few.

What was it? I will tell you, my dear little readers. On awakening, Pinocchio put his hand up to his head and there he found—

Guess!

He found that, during the night, his ears had grown at least ten full inches!

You must know that the Marionette, even from his birth, had very small ears, so small indeed that to the naked eye they could hardly

be seen. Fancy how he felt when he noticed that overnight those two dainty organs had become as long as shoe brushes!

He went in search of a mirror, but not finding any, he just filled a basin with water and looked at himself. There he saw what he never could have wished to see. His manly figure was adorned and enriched by a beautiful pair of donkey's ears.

I leave you to think of the terrible grief, the shame, the despair of the poor Marionette.

He began to cry, to scream, to knock his head against the wall, but the more he shrieked, the longer and the more hairy grew his ears.

At those piercing shrieks, a Dormouse came into the room, a fat little Dormouse, who lived upstairs. Seeing Pinocchio so grief-stricken, she asked him anxiously:

"What is the matter, dear little neighbor?"

"I am sick, my little Dormouse, very, very sick—and from an illness which frightens me! Do you understand how to feel the pulse?"

"A little."

"Feel mine then and tell me if I have a fever."

The Dormouse took Pinocchio's wrist between her paws and, after a few minutes, looked up at him sorrowfully and said:

"My friend, I am sorry, but I must give you some very sad news."

"What is it?"

"You have a very bad fever."

"But what fever is it?"

"The donkey fever."

"I don't know anything about that fever," answered the Marionette, beginning to understand even too well what was happening to him.

"Then I will tell you all about it," said the Dormouse. "Know then that, within two or three hours, you will no longer be a Marionette, nor a boy."

"What shall I be?"

"Within two or three hours you will become a real donkey, just like the ones that pull the fruit carts to market."

"Oh, what have I done? What have I done?" cried Pinocchio, grasping his two long ears in his hands and pulling and tugging at them angrily, just as if they belonged to another.

"My dear boy," answered the Dormouse to cheer him up a bit, "why worry now? What is done cannot be undone, you know. Fate has decreed that all lazy boys who come to hate books and schools and teachers and spend all their days with toys and games must sooner or later turn into donkeys."

"But is it really so?" asked the Marionette, sobbing bitterly.

"I am sorry to say it is. And tears now are useless. You should have thought of all this before."

"But the fault is not mine. Believe me, little Dormouse, the fault is all Lamp-Wick's."

"And who is this Lamp-Wick?"

"A classmate of mine. I wanted to return home. I wanted to be obedient. I wanted to study and to succeed in school, but Lamp-Wick said to me, 'Why do you want to waste your time studying? Why do you want to go to school? Come with me to the Land of Toys. There we'll never study again. There we can enjoy ourselves and be happy from morn till night.'"

"And why did you follow the advice of that false friend?"

"Why? Because, my dear little Dormouse, I am a heedless Marionette—heedless and heartless. Oh! If I had only had a bit of heart, I should never have abandoned that good Fairy, who loved me so well and who has been so kind to me! And by this time, I should no longer be a Marionette. I should have become a real boy, like all these friends of mine! Oh, if I meet Lamp-Wick I am going to tell him what I think of him—and more too!"

After this long speech, Pinocchio walked to the door of the room. But when he reached it, remembering his donkey ears, he felt ashamed to show them to the public and turned back. He took a large cotton bag from a shelf, put it on his head, and pulled it far down to his very nose.

Thus adorned, he went out. He looked for Lamp-Wick everywhere, along the streets, in the squares, inside the theaters, everywhere; but he was not to be found. He asked every one whom he met about him, but no one had seen him.

In desperation, he returned home and knocked at the door.

"Who is it?" asked Lamp-Wick from within.

"It is I!" answered the Marionette.

"Wait a minute."

After a full half hour the door opened. Another surprise awaited Pinocchio! There in the room stood his friend, with a large cotton bag on his head, pulled far down to his very nose.

At the sight of that bag, Pinocchio felt slightly happier and thought to himself:

"My friend must be suffering from the same sickness that I am! I wonder if he, too, has donkey fever?"

But pretending he had seen nothing, he asked with a smile:

"How are you, my dear Lamp-Wick?"

"Very well. Like a mouse in a Parmesan cheese."

"Is that really true?"

"Why should I lie to you?"

"I beg your pardon, my friend, but why then are you wearing that cotton bag over your ears?"

"The doctor has ordered it because one of my knees hurts. And you, dear Marionette, why are you wearing that cotton bag down to your nose?"

"The doctor has ordered it, because I have bruised my foot."

"Oh, my poor Pinocchio!"

"Oh, my poor Lamp-Wick!"

An embarrassingly long silence followed these words, during which time the two friends looked at each other in a mocking way.

Finally the Marionette, in a voice sweet as honey and soft as a flute, said to his companion:

"Tell me, Lamp-Wick, dear friend, have you ever suffered from an earache?"

"Never! And you?"

"Never! Still, since this morning my ear has been torturing me."

"So has mine."

"Yours, too? And which ear is it?"

"Both of them. And yours?"

"Both of them, too. I wonder if it could be the same sickness."

"I'm afraid it is."

"Will you do me a favor, Lamp-Wick?"

"Gladly! With my whole heart."

"Will you let me see your ears?"

"Why not? But before I show you mine. I want to see yours, dear Pinocchio."

"No. You must show yours first."

"No, my dear! Yours first, then mine."

"Well, then," said the Marionette, "let us make a contract."

"Let's hear the contract!"

"Let us take off our caps together. All right?"

"All right."

"Ready then!"

Pinocchio began to count, "One! Two! Three!"

At the word "Three!" the two boys pulled off their caps and threw them high in air.

And then a scene took place which is hard to believe, but it is all too true. The Marionette and his friend, Lamp-Wick, when they saw each other both stricken by the same misfortune, instead of feeling sorrowful and ashamed, began to poke fun at each other, and after much nonsense, they ended by bursting out into hearty laughter.

They laughed and laughed, and laughed again—laughed till they ached—laughed till they cried.

But all of a sudden Lamp-Wick stopped laughing. He tottered and almost fell. Pale as a ghost, he turned to Pinocchio and said:

"Help, help, Pinocchio!"

"What is the matter?"

"Oh, help me! I can no longer stand up."

"I can't either," cried Pinocchio; and his laughter turned to tears as he stumbled about helplessly.

They had hardly finished speaking, when both of them fell on all fours and began running and jumping around the room. As they ran, their arms turned into legs, their faces lengthened into snouts, and their backs became covered with long gray hairs.

This was humiliation enough, but the most horrible moment was the one in which the two poor creatures felt their tails appear. Overcome with shame and grief, they tried to cry and bemoan their fate.

But what is done can't be undone! Instead of moans and cries, they burst forth into loud donkey brays, which sounded very much like, "Haw! Haw! Haw!"

At that moment, a loud knocking was heard at the door and a voice called to them:

"Open! I am the Little Man, the driver of the wagon which brought you here. Open, I say, or beware!"

THE EMPEROR'S NEW CLOTHES

Hans Christian Andersen

This amusing tale is an allegory and a droll. It sounds much like a folk tale, but no folk tale ever had its wit and its tongue-in-the-cheek attitude towards the pompous incompetents of the world. Andersen in this story takes his revenge on the stupid people who made him suffer.

Many years ago there was an Emperor who was so excessively fond of new clothes that he spent all his money on them. He cared nothing about his soldiers, nor for the theatre, nor for driving in the woods except for the sake of show-

ing off his new clothes. He had a costume for every hour in the day, and instead of saying as one does about any other King or Emperor, "He is in his council chamber," here one always said, "The Emperor is in his dressing-room."

"The Emperor's New Clothes." From *Fairy Tales* by Hans Christian Andersen, translated by Mrs. Edgar Lucas, Everyman's Library, E. P. Dutton & Co., Inc., New York. By permission also of J. M. Dent & Sons, Ltd., London

Life was very gay in the great town where he lived; hosts of strangers came to visit it every day, and among them one day two swindlers. They gave themselves out as weavers, and said that they knew how to weave the most beautiful stuffs imaginable. Not only were the colours and patterns unusually fine, but the clothes that were made of these stuffs had the peculiar quality of becoming invisible to every person who was not fit for the office he held, or if he was impossibly dull.

"Those must be splendid clothes," thought the Emperor. "By wearing them I should be able to discover which men in my kingdom are unfitted for their posts. I shall distinguish the wise men from the fools. Yes, I certainly must order some of that stuff to be woven for me."

He paid the two swindlers a lot of money in advance so that they might begin their work at once.

They did put up two looms and pretended to weave, but they had nothing whatever upon their shuttles. At the outset they asked for a quantity of the finest silk and the purest gold thread, all of which they put into their own bags while they worked away at the empty looms far into the night.

"I should like to know how those weavers are getting on with the stuff," thought the Emperor; but he felt a little queer when he reflected that anyone who was stupid or unfit for his post would not be able to see it. He certainly thought that he need have no fears for himself, but still he thought he would send somebody else first to see how it was getting on. Everybody in the town knew what wonderful power the stuff possessed, and everyone was anxious to see how stupid his neighbor was.

"I will send my faithful old minister to the weavers," thought the Emperor. "He will be best able to see how the stuff looks, for he is a clever man and no one fulfils his duties better than he does!"

So the good old minister went into the room where the two swindlers sat working at the empty loom.

"Heaven preserve us!" thought the old minister, opening his eyes very wide. "Why, I can't see a thing!" But he took care not to say so.

Both the swindlers begged him to be good enough to step a little nearer, and asked if he did not think it a good pattern and beautiful colouring. They pointed to the empty loom, and the poor old minister stared as hard as he could but he could not see anything, for of course there was nothing to see.

"Good heavens!" thought he, "is it possible that I am a fool? I have never thought so and nobody must know it. Am I not fit for my post? It will never do to say that I cannot see the stuffs."

"Well, sir, you don't say anything about the stuff," said the one who was pretending to weave.

"Oh, it is beautiful! quite charming!" said the old minister looking through his spectacles; "this pattern and these colors! I will certainly tell the Emperor that the stuff pleases me very much."

"We are delighted to hear you say so," said the swindlers, and then they named all the colours and described the peculiar pattern. The old minister paid great attention to what they said, so as to be able to repeat it when he got home to the Emperor.

Then the swindlers went on to demand more money, more silk, and more gold, to be able to proceed with the weaving; but they put it all into their own pockets—not a single strand was ever put into the loom, but they went on as before weaving at the empty loom.

The Emperor soon sent another faithful official to see how the stuff was getting on, and if it would soon be ready. The same thing happened to him as to the minister; he looked and looked, but as there was only the empty loom, he could see nothing at all.

"Is not this a beautiful piece of stuff?" said both the swindlers, showing and explaining the beautiful pattern and colours which were not there to be seen.

"I know I am not a fool!" thought the man, "so it must be that I am unfit for my good post! It is very strange though! however, one must not let it appear!" So he praised the stuff he did not see, and assured them of his delight in the beautiful colours and the originality of the design. "It is absolutely charming!" he said to the Emperor. Everybody in the town was talking about this splendid stuff.

Now the Emperor thought he would like to see

it while it was still on the loom. So, accompanied by a number of selected courtiers, among whom were the two faithful officials who had already seen the imaginary stuff, he went to visit the crafty impostors, who were working away as hard as ever they could at the empty loom.

"It is magnificent!" said both the honest officials. "Only see, Your Majesty, what a design! What colours!" And they pointed to the empty loom, for they thought no doubt the others could see the stuff.

"What!" thought the Emperor; "I see nothing at all! This is terrible! Am I a fool? Am I not fit to be Emperor? Why, nothing worse could happen to me!"

"Oh, it is beautiful!" said the Emperor. "It has my highest approval!" and he nodded his satisfaction as he gazed at the empty loom. Nothing would induce him to say that he could not see anything.

The whole suite gazed and gazed, but saw nothing more than all the others. However, they all exclaimed with His Majesty, "It is very beautiful!" and they advised him to wear a suit made of this wonderful cloth on the occasion of a great procession which was just about to take place. "It is magnificent! gorgeous! excellent!" went from mouth to mouth; they were all equally delighted with it. The Emperor gave each of the rogues an order of knighthood to be worn in their buttonholes and the title of "Gentlemen Weavers."

The swindlers sat up the whole night, before the day on which the procession was to take place, burning sixteen candles, so that people might see how anxious they were to get the Emperor's new clothes ready. They pretended to take the stuff off the loom. They cut it out in the air with a huge pair of scissors, and they stitched away with needles without any thread in them. At last they said, "Now the Emperor's new clothes are ready!"

The Emperor, with his grandest courtiers, went to them himself, and both the swindlers raised one arm in the air, as if they were holding something, and said, "See, these are the trousers, this is the coat, here is the mantle!" and so on. "It is as light as a spider's web. One might think one had nothing on, but that is the very beauty of it!"

"Yes!" said all the courtiers, but they could not see anything, for there was nothing to see.

"Will Your Imperial Majesty be graciously pleased to take off your clothes," said the imposters, "so that we may put on the new ones, along here before the great mirror."

The Emperor took off all his clothes, and the impostors pretended to give him one article of dress after the other, of the new ones which they had pretended to make. They pretended to fasten something round his waist and to tie on something; this was the train, and the Emperor turned round and round in front of the mirror.

"How well His Majesty looks in the new clothes! How becoming they are!" cried all the people round. "What a design, and what colours! They are most gorgeous robes!"

"The canopy is waiting outside which is to be carried over Your Majesty in the procession," said the master of the ceremonies.

"Well, I am quite ready," said the Emperor. "Don't the clothes fit well?" and then he turned round again in front of the mirror, so that he should seem to be looking at his grand things.

The chamberlains who were to carry the train stooped and pretended to lift it from the ground with both hands, and they walked along with their hands in the air. They dared not let it appear that they could not see anything.

Then the Emperor walked along in the procession under the gorgeous canopy, and everybody in the streets and at the windows exclaimed, "How beautiful the Emperor's new clothes are! What a splendid train! And they fit to perfection!" Nobody would let it appear that he could see nothing, for then he would not be fit for his post, or else he was a fool.

None of the Emperor's clothes had been so successful before.

"But he has got nothing on," said a little child.

"Oh, listen to the innocent," said its father; and one person whispered to the other what the child had said. "He has nothing on; a child says he has nothing on!"

"But he has nothing on!" at last cried all the people.

The Emperor writhed, for he knew it was true, but he thought "the procession must go on now," so he held himself stiffer than ever, and the chamberlains held up the invisible train.

THE OPEN ROAD

Kenneth Grahame

Kenneth Grahame started telling the stories about Ratty, Mole, and all the other denizens of the river bank to his small son at bedtime. When the child did not want to go to the seashore without his father, Grahame promised to send him stories. A careful nurse who read the installments of The Wind in the Willows *to the boy, recognized their worth and saved the letters. From them, the book grew and was finally put together for publication. It remains one of the great juvenile classics in the English language. This does not mean that every child is going to like it, but children should be exposed to its beauty and humor in the hope that the contagion will "take."*

"Ratty," said the Mole suddenly, one bright summer morning, "if you please, I want to ask you a favour."

The Rat was sitting on the river bank, singing a little song. He had just composed it himself, so he was very taken up with it, and would not pay proper attention to Mole or anything else. Since early morning he had been swimming in the river in company with his friends the ducks. And when the ducks stood on their heads suddenly, as ducks will, he would dive down and tickle their necks just under where their chins would be if ducks had chins, till they were forced to come to the surface again in a hurry, spluttering and angry and shaking their feathers at him, for it is impossible to say quite *all* you feel when your head is under water. At last they implored him to go away and attend to his own affairs and leave them to mind theirs. So the Rat went away, and sat on the river bank in the sun, and made up a song about them, which he called

DUCKS' DITTY

All along the backwater,
Through the rushes tall,
Ducks are a-dabbling,
Up tails all!

Ducks' tails, drakes' tails,
Yellow feet a-quiver,
Yellow bills all out of sight
Busy in the river!

Slushy green undergrowth
Where the roach swim—
Here we keep our larder,
Cool and full and dim.

Every one for what he likes!
We like to be
Heads down, tails up,
Dabbling free!

High in the blue above
Swifts whirl and call—
We are down a-dabbling
Up tails all!

"I don't know that I think so *very* much of that little song, Rat," observed the Mole cautiously. He was no poet himself and didn't care who knew it; and he had a candid nature.

"Nor don't the ducks neither," replied the Rat cheerfully. "They say, '*Why* can't fellows be allowed to do what they like *when* they like and *as* they like, instead of other fellows sitting on banks and watching them all the time and making remarks, and poetry and things about them? What *nonsense* it all is!' That's what the ducks say."

"So it is, so it is," said the Mole, with great heartiness.

"No, it isn't!" cried the Rat indignantly.

"Well then, it isn't, it isn't," replied the Mole soothingly. "But what I wanted to ask you was, won't you take me to call on Mr. Toad? I've heard so much about him, and I do so want to make his acquaintance."

"Why, certainly," said the good-natured Rat, jumping to his feet and dismissing poetry from his mind for the day. "Get the boat out, and we'll paddle up there at once. It's never the wrong time to call on Toad. Early or late he's always the same fellow. Always good-tempered, always glad to see you, always sorry when you go!"

"He must be a very nice animal," observed the Mole, as he got into the boat and took the sculls, while the Rat settled himself comfortably in the stern.

"He is indeed the best of animals," replied Rat. "So simple, so good-natured, and so affectionate. Perhaps he's not very clever—we can't all be geniuses; and it may be that he is both boastful and conceited. But he has got some great qualities, has Toady." Rounding a bend in the river, they came in sight of a handsome, dignified old house of mellowed red brick, with well-kept lawns reaching down to the water's edge.

"There's Toad Hall," said the Rat; "and that creek on the left, where the notice-board says, 'Private. No landing allowed,' leads to his boat-house, where we'll leave the boat. The stables are over there to the right. That's the banqueting-hall you're looking at now—very old, that is. Toad is rather rich, you know, and this is really one of the nicest houses in these parts, though we never admit as much to Toad."

They glided up the creek, and the Mole shipped his sculls as they passed into the shadow of a large boat-house. Here they saw many handsome boats, slung from the cross-beams or hauled up on a slip, but none in the water; and the place had an unused and deserted air.

The Rat looked around him. "I understand," said he. "Boating is played out. He's tired of it, and done with it. I wonder what new fad he has taken up now? Come along and let's look him up. We shall hear all about it quite soon enough."

They disembarked, and strolled across the gay flower-decked lawns in search of Toad, whom they presently happened upon resting in a wicker garden-chair, with a preoccupied expression of face, and a large map spread out on his knees.

"Hooray!" he cried, jumping up on seeing them, "this is splendid!" He shook the paws of both of them warmly, never waiting for an introduction to the Mole. "How *kind* of you!" he went on, dancing round them. "I was just going to send a boat down the river for you, Ratty, with strict orders that you were to be fetched up here at once, whatever you were doing. I want you badly—both of you. Now what will you take? Come inside and have something! You don't know how lucky it is, your turning up just now!"

"Let's sit quiet a bit, Toady!" said the Rat, throwing himself into an easy chair, while the Mole took another by the side of him and made some civil remark about Toad's "delightful residence."

"Finest house on the whole river," cried Toad boisterously. "Or anywhere else, for that matter," he could not help adding.

Here the Rat nudged the Mole. Unfortunately the Toad saw him do it, and turned very red. There was a moment's painful silence. Then Toad burst out laughing. "All right, Ratty," he said. "It's only my way, you know. And it's not such a very bad house, is it? You know you rather like it yourself. Now, look here. Let's be sensible. You are the very animals I wanted. You've got to help me. It's most important!"

"It's about your rowing, I suppose," said the Rat, with an innocent air. "You're getting on fairly well, though you splash a good bit still. With a great deal of patience, and any quantity of coaching, you may—"

"O, pooh! boating!" interrupted the Toad, in great disgust. "Silly boyish amusement. I've given that up *long* ago. Sheer waste of time, that's what it is. It makes me downright sorry to see you fellows, who ought to know better, spending all your energies in that aimless manner. No, I've discovered the real thing, the only genuine occupation for a lifetime. I propose to devote the remainder of mine to it, and can only regret the wasted years that lie behind me, squandered in trivialities. Come with me, dear Ratty, and your amiable friend also, if he will be so very good, just as far as the stable-yard, and you shall see what you shall see!"

He led the way to the stable-yard accordingly, the Rat following with a most mistrustful expression; and there, drawn out of the coach-house into the open, they saw a gipsy caravan, shining with newness, painted a canary-yellow picked out with green, and red wheels.

"There you are!" cried the Toad, straddling and expanding himself. "There's real life for you, embodied in that little cart. The open road, the dusty highway, the heath, the common, the hedgerows, the rolling downs! Camps, villages, towns, cities! Here to-day, up and off to somewhere else to-morrow! Travel, change, interest, excitement! The whole world before you, and a horizon that's always changing! And mind, this is the very finest cart of its sort that was ever built, without any exception. Come inside and look at the arrangements. Planned 'em all myself, I did!"

The Mole was tremendously interested and excited, and followed him eagerly up the steps and into the interior of the caravan. The Rat only snorted and thrust his hands deep into his pockets, remaining where he was.

It was indeed very compact and comfortable. Little sleeping-bunks—a little table that folded up against the wall—a cooking-stove, lockers, bookshelves, a bird-cage with a bird in it; and pots, pans, jugs and kettles of every size and variety.

"All complete!" said the Toad triumphantly, pulling open a locker. "You see—biscuits, potted lobster, sardines—everything you can possibly want. Soda-water here—baccy there—letter-paper, bacon, jam, cards and dominoes—you'll find," he continued, as they descended the steps again, "you'll find that nothing whatever has been forgotten, when we make our start this afternoon."

"I beg your pardon," said the Rat slowly, as he chewed a straw, "but did I overhear you say something about 'we' and 'start' and 'this *afternoon*'?"

"Now, you dear good old Ratty," said Toad imploringly, "don't begin talking in that stiff and sniffy sort of way, because you know you've *got* to come. I can't possibly manage without you, so please consider it settled, and don't argue—it's the one thing I can't stand. You surely don't mean to stick to your dull fusty old river all your life, and just live in a hole in a bank, and *boat*? I want to show you the world! I'm going to make an *animal* of you, my boy!"

"I don't care," said the Rat doggedly. "I'm not coming, and that's flat. And I *am* going to stick to my old river, *and* live in a hole, *and* boat, as I've always done. And what's more, Mole's going to stick to me and do as I do, aren't you, Mole?"

"Of course I am," said the Mole loyally. "I'll always stick to you, Rat, and what you say is to be—has got to be. All the same, it sounds as if it might have been—well, rather fun, you know!" he added wistfully. Poor Mole! The Life Adventurous was so new a thing to him, and so thrill-

ing; and this fresh aspect of it was so tempting; and he had fallen in love at first sight with the canary-coloured cart and all its little fitments.

The Rat saw what was passing in his mind, and wavered. He hated disappointing people, and he was fond of the Mole, and would do almost anything to oblige him. Toad was watching both of them closely.

"Come along in and have some lunch," he said diplomatically, "and we'll talk it over. We needn't decide anything in a hurry. Of course, *I* don't really care. I only want to give pleasure to you fellows. 'Live for others!' That's my motto in life."

During luncheon—which was excellent, of course, as everything at Toad Hall always was—the Toad simply let himself go. Disregarding the Rat, he proceeded to play upon the inexperienced Mole as on a harp. Naturally a voluble animal, and always mastered by his imagination, he painted the prospects of the trip and the joys of the open life and the roadside in such glowing colours that the Mole could hardly sit in his chair for excitement. Somehow it soon seemed taken for granted by all three that the trip was a settled thing; and the Rat, though still unconvinced in his mind, allowed his good-nature to override his personal objections. He could not bear to disappoint his two friends, who were already deep in schemes and anticipations, planning out each day's separate occupation for several weeks ahead.

When they were quite ready, the now triumphant Toad led his companions to the paddock and set them to capture the old grey horse, who, without having been consulted, and to his own extreme annoyance, had been told off by Toad for the dustiest job in this dusty expedition. He frankly preferred the paddock, and took a deal of catching. Meantime Toad packed the lockers still tighter with necessaries, and hung nose-bags, nets of onions, bundles of hay, and baskets from the bottom of the cart. At last the horse was caught and harnessed, and they set off, all talking at once, each animal either trudging by the side of the cart or sitting on the shaft, as the humour took him. It was a golden afternoon. The smell of the dust they kicked up was rich and satisfying; out of thick orchards on either side the road, birds called and whistled to them cheerily; good-natured wayfarers, passing them, gave them "Good day," or stopped to say nice things about their beautiful cart; and rabbits, sitting at their front doors in the hedgerows, held up their fore paws, and said, "O my! O my! O my!"

Late in the evening, tired and happy and miles from home, they drew up on a remote common far from habitations, turned the horse loose to graze, and ate their simple supper sitting on the grass by the side of the cart. Toad talked big about all he was going to do in the days to come, while stars grew fuller and larger all around them, and a yellow moon, appearing suddenly and silently from nowhere in particular, came to keep them company and listen to their talk. At last they turned into their little bunks in the cart; and Toad, kicking out his legs, sleepily said, "Well, good night, you fellows! This is the real life for a gentleman! Talk about your old river!"

"I *don't* talk about my river," replied the patient Rat. "You *know* I don't, Toad. But I *think* about it," he added pathetically, in a lower tone: "I think about it—all the time!"

The Mole reached out from under his blanket, felt for the Rat's paw in the darkness, and gave it a squeeze. "I'll do whatever you like, Ratty," he whispered. "Shall we run away to-morrow morning, quite early—*very* early—and go back to our dear old hole on the river?"

"No, no, we'll see it out," whispered back the Rat. "Thanks awfully, but I ought to stick by Toad till this trip is ended. It wouldn't be safe for him to be left to himself. It won't take very long. His fads never do. Good night!"

The end was indeed nearer than even the Rat suspected.

After so much open air and excitement the Toad slept very soundly, and no amount of shaking could rouse him out of bed next morning. So the Mole and Rat turned to, quietly and manfully, and while the Rat saw to the horse, and lit a fire, and cleaned last night's cups and platters and got things ready for breakfast, the Mole trudged off to the nearest village, a long way off, for milk and eggs and various necessaries the Toad had, of course, forgotten to provide. The hard work had all been done, and the two animals were resting, thoroughly exhausted, by the time Toad appeared on the scene, fresh and gay, remarking what a pleasant easy life it was they were all leading now, after the cares and worries and fatigues of housekeeping at home.

They had a pleasant ramble that day over grassy downs and along narrow by-lanes, and camped, as before, on a common, only this time the two guests took care that Toad should do his fair share of work. In consequence, when the time came for starting next morning, Toad was by no means so rapturous about the simplicity of the primitive life, and indeed attempted to resume his place in his bunk, whence he was hauled by force. Their way lay, as before, across country by narrow lanes, and it was not till the afternoon that they came out on the high road, their first high road; and there disaster, fleet and unforeseen, sprang out on them—disaster momentous indeed to their expedition, but simply overwhelming in its effect on the after-career of Toad.

They were strolling along the high road easily, the Mole by the horse's head, talking to him, since the horse had complained that he was being frightfully left out of it, and nobody considered him in the least; the Toad and the Water Rat walking behind the cart talking together—at least Toad was talking, and Rat was saying at intervals, "Yes, precisely; and what did *you* say to *him?*"—and thinking all the time of something very different, when far behind them they heard a faint warning hum, like the drone of a distant bee. Glancing back, they saw a small cloud of dust, with a dark centre of energy, advancing on them at incredible speed, while from out the dust a faint "Poop-poop!" wailed like an uneasy animal in pain. Hardly regarding it, they turned to resume their conversation, when in an instant (as it seemed) the peaceful scene was changed, and with a blast of wind and a whirl of sound that made them jump for the nearest ditch, it was on them! The "Poop-poop" rang with a brazen shout in their ears, they had a moment's glimpse of an interior of glittering plate-glass and rich morocco, and the magnificent motor-car, immense, breath-snatching, passionate, with its pilot tense and hugging his wheel, possessed all earth and air for the fraction of a second, flung an enveloping cloud of dust that blinded and enwrapped them utterly, and then dwindled to a speck in the far distance, changed back into a droning bee once more.

The old grey horse, dreaming, as he plodded along, of his quiet paddock, in a new raw situation such as this simply abandoned himself to his natural emotions. Rearing, plunging, backing steadily, in spite of all the Mole's efforts at his head, and all the Mole's lively language directed at his better feelings, he drove the cart backwards towards the deep ditch at the side of the road. It wavered an instant—then there was a heart-rending crash—and the canary-coloured cart, their pride and their joy, lay on its side in the ditch, an irredeemable wreck.

The Rat danced up and down in the road, simply transported with passion. "You villains!" he shouted, shaking both fists. "You scoundrels, you highwaymen, you—you—road-hogs! —I'll have the law of you! I'll report you! I'll take you through all the Courts!" His home-sickness had quite slipped away from him, and for the moment he was the skipper of the canary-coloured vessel driven on a shoal by the reckless jockeying of rival mariners, and he was trying to recollect all the fine and biting things he used to say to masters of steam-launches when their wash, as they drove too near the bank, used to flood his parlour carpet at home.

Toad sat straight down in the middle of the dusty road, his legs stretched out before him, and stared fixedly in the direction of the disappearing motor-car. He breathed short, his face wore a placid, satisfied expression, and at intervals he faintly murmured "Poop-poop!"

The Mole was busy trying to quiet the horse, which he succeeded in doing after a time. Then he went to look at the cart, on its side in the ditch. It was indeed a sorry sight. Panels and windows smashed, axles hopelessly bent, one wheel off, sardine-tins scattered over the wide world, and the bird in the bird-cage sobbing pitifully and calling to be let out.

The Rat came to help him, but their united efforts were not sufficient to right the cart. "Hi! Toad!" they cried. "Come and bear a hand, can't you!"

The Toad never answered a word, or budged from his seat in the road; so they went to see what was the matter with him. They found him in a sort of trance, a happy smile on his face, his eyes still fixed on the dusty wake of their destroyer. At intervals he was still heard to murmur "Poop-poop!"

The Rat shook him by the shoulder. "Are you coming to help us, Toad?" he demanded sternly.

"Glorious, stirring sight!" murmured Toad, never offering to move. "The poetry of motion! The *real* way to travel! The *only* way to travel! Here to-day—in next week to-morrow! Villages skipped, towns and cities jumped—always somebody else's horizon! O bliss! O poop-poop! O my! O my!"

"O *stop* being an ass, Toad!" cried the Mole despairingly.

"And to think I never *knew!*" went on the Toad in a dreamy monotone. "All those wasted years that lie behind me, I never knew, never even *dreamt!* But *now*—but now that I know, now that I fully realize! O what a flowery track lies spread before me, henceforth! What dust-clouds shall spring up behind me as I speed on my reckless way! What carts I shall fling carelessly into the ditch in the wake of my magnificent onset! Horrid little carts—common carts—canary-coloured carts!"

"What are we to do with him?" asked the Mole of the Water Rat.

"Nothing at all," replied the Rat firmly. "Because there is really nothing to be done. You see, I know him from of old. He is now possessed. He has got a new craze, and it always takes him that way, in its first stage. He'll continue like that for days now, like an animal walking in a happy dream, quite useless for all practical purposes. Never mind him. Let's go and see what there is to be done about the cart."

A careful inspection showed them that, even if they succeeded in righting it by themselves, the cart would travel no longer. The axles were in a hopeless state, and the missing wheel was shattered into pieces.

The Rat knotted the horse's reins over his back and took him by the head, carrying the bird-cage and its hysterical occupant in the other hand. "Come on!" he said grimly to the Mole. "It's five or six miles to the nearest town, and we shall just have to walk it. The sooner we make a start the better."

"But what about Toad?" asked the Mole anxiously, as they set off together. "We can't leave him here, sitting in the middle of the road by himself, in the distracted state he's in! It's not safe. Supposing another Thing were to come along?"

"O, bother Toad," said the Rat savagely; "I've done with him!"

They had not proceeded very far on their way, however, when there was a pattering of feet behind them, and Toad caught them up and thrust a paw inside the elbow of each of them; still breathing short and staring into vacancy.

"Now, look here, Toad!" said the Rat sharply; "as soon as we get to the town, you'll have to go straight to the police-station, and see if they know anything about that motor-car and who it belongs to, and lodge a complaint against it. And then you'll have to go to a blacksmith's or wheelwright's and arrange for the cart to be fetched and mended and put to rights. It'll take time, but it's not quite a hopeless smash. Meanwhile, the Mole and I will go to an Inn and find comfortable rooms where we can stay till the cart's ready, and till your nerves have recovered from their shock."

"Police-station! Complaint!" murmured Toad dreamily. "Me complain of that beautiful, that heavenly vision that has been vouchsafed me! Mend the cart! I've done with carts forever. I never want to see the cart, or to hear of it, again. O, Ratty! You can't think how obliged I am to you for consenting to come on this trip! I wouldn't have gone without you, and then I might never have seen that—that swan, that sunbeam, that thunderbolt! I might never have heard that entrancing sound, or smelt that bewitching smell! I owe it all to you, my best of friends!"

The Rat turned from him in despair. "You see what it is?" he said to the Mole, addressing him across Toad's head: "He's quite hopeless. I give it up—when we get to the town we'll go to the railway-station, and with luck we may pick up a train there that'll get us back to River Bank to-night. And if ever you catch me going a-pleasuring with this provoking animal again!" —He snorted, and during the rest of that weary trudge addressed his remarks exclusively to Mole.

On reaching the town they went straight to the station and deposited Toad in the second-class waiting-room, giving a porter twopence to keep a strict eye on him. They then left the horse at an inn stable, and gave what directions they could about the cart and its contents. Eventually, a slow train having landed them at a station not very far from Toad Hall, they escorted the spell-bound, sleep-walking Toad to his door, put him inside it, and instructed his housekeeper to feed him, undress him, and put him to bed. Then they got out their boat from the boat-house, sculled down the river home, and at a very late hour sat down to supper in their own cosy riverside parlour, to the Rat's great joy and contentment.

The following evening the Mole, who had risen late and taken things very easy all day, was sitting on the bank fishing, when the Rat, who had been looking up his friends and gossiping, came strolling along to find him. "Heard the news?" he said. "There's nothing else being talked about, all along the river bank. Toad went up to Town by an early train this morning. And he has ordered a large and very expensive motor-car."

THE LADY
WHO PUT SALT IN HER COFFEE

Lucretia Hale

One account of the beginnings of these tales is that "Aunt Lucretia," on the spur of the moment, told the story about salt in the coffee for a sick child. Another account insists that the episode of the lady who wished to go for a drive really happened and gave the author the idea for these tales. However they began, Lucretia, the gifted sister of Edward Everett Hale, learned to pick up every silly mistake which she or any of her friends blundered into, and turn it into a problem for the "lady from Philadelphia."

"The Lady Who Put Salt in Her Coffee." From *The Peterkin Papers* by Lucretia P. Hale, Houghton Mifflin Company

This was Mrs. Peterkin. It was a mistake. She had poured out a delicious cup of coffee, and, just as she was helping herself to cream, she found she had put in salt instead of sugar! It tasted bad. What should she do? Of course she couldn't drink the coffee; so she called in the family, for she was sitting at a late breakfast all alone. The family came in; they all tasted, and looked, and wondered what should be done, and all sat down to think.

At last Agamemnon, who had been to college, said, "Why don't we go over and ask the advice of the chemist?" (For the chemist lived over the way, and was a very wise man.)

Mrs. Peterkin said, "Yes," and Mr. Peterkin said, "Very well," and all the children said they would go too. So the little boys put on their india-rubber boots, and over they went.

Now the chemist was just trying to find out something which should turn everything it touched into gold; and he had a large glass bottle into which he put all kinds of gold and silver, and many other valuable things, and melted them all up over the fire, till he had almost found what he wanted. He could turn things into almost gold. But just now he had used up all the gold that he had round the house, and gold was high. He had used up his wife's gold thimble and his great-grandfather's gold-bowed spectacles; and he had melted up the gold head of his great-great-grandfather's cane; and, just as the Peterkin family came in, he was down on his knees before his wife, asking her to let him have her wedding-ring to melt up with all the rest, because this time he knew he should succeed, and should be able to turn everything into gold; and then she could have a new wedding-ring of diamonds, all set in emeralds and rubies and topazes, and all the furniture could be turned into the finest of gold.

Now his wife was just consenting when the Peterkin family burst in. You can imagine how mad the chemist was! He came near throwing his crucible—that was the name of his melting-pot—at their heads. But he didn't. He listened as calmly as he could to the story of how Mrs. Peterkin had put salt in her coffee.

At first he said he couldn't do anything about it; but when Agamemnon said they would pay in gold if he would only go, he packed up his bottles in a leather case, and went back with them all. First he looked at the coffee, and then stirred it. Then he put in a little chlorate of potassium, and the family tried it all round; but it tasted no better. Then he stirred in a little bichlorate of magnesia. But Mrs. Peterkin didn't like that. Then he added some tartaric acid and some hypersulphate of lime. But no; it was no better. "I have it!" exclaimed the chemist—"a little ammonia is just the thing!" No, it wasn't the thing at all.

Then he tried, each in turn, some oxalic, cyanic, acetic, phosphoric, chloric, hyperchloric, sulphuric, boracic, silicic, nitric, formic, nitrous nitric, and carbonic acids. Mrs. Peterkin tasted each and said the flavor was pleasant, but not precisely that of coffee. So then he tried a little calcium, aluminum, barium, and strontium, a little clear bitumen, and a half of a third of a sixteenth of a grain of arsenic. This gave rather a pretty color; but still Mrs. Peterkin ungratefully said it tasted of anything but coffee. The chemist was not discouraged. He put in a little belladonna and atropine, some granulated hydrogen, some potash, and a very little antimony, finishing off with a little pure carbon. But still Mrs. Peterkin was not satisfied.

The chemist said that all he had done ought to have taken out the salt. The theory remained the same, although the experiment had failed. Perhaps a little starch would have some effect. If not, that was all the time he could give. He should like to be paid, and go. They were all much obliged to him, and willing to give him $1.37½ in gold. Gold was now 2.69¾, so Mr. Peterkin found in the newspaper. This gave Agamemnon a pretty little sum. He sat himself down to do it. But there was the coffee! All sat and thought awhile, till Elizabeth Eliza said, "Why don't we go to the herb-woman?" Elizabeth Eliza was the only daughter. She was named after her two aunts,—Elizabeth, from the sister of her father; Eliza, from her mother's sister. Now, the herb-woman was an old woman who came round to sell herbs, and knew a great deal. They all shouted with joy at the idea of asking her, and Solomon John and the younger children agreed to go and find her too. The herb-woman lived down at the very end of the street; so the boys put on their india-rubber boots again, and they set off. It was a long walk through the village, but they came at last to the herb-woman's house, at the foot of a high hill. They went through her little garden. Here she had marigolds and hollyhocks, and old maids and tall sunflowers, and all kinds of sweet-smelling herbs, so that the air was full of tansy-tea and elder-blow. Over the porch grew a hop-vine, and a brandy-cherry tree shaded the door, and a luxuriant cranberry-vine flung its delicious fruit across the window. They went into a small parlor, which smelt very spicy. All around hung little bags full of catnip, and peppermint, and all kinds of herbs; and dried stalks hung from the ceiling; and on the shelves were jars of rhubarb, senna, manna, and the like.

But there was no little old woman. She had gone up into the woods to get some more wild herbs, so they all thought they would follow her —Elizabeth Eliza, Solomon John, and the little boys. They had to climb up over high rocks, and in among huckleberry-bushes and blackberry-vines. But the little boys had their india-rubber boots. At last they discovered the little old woman. They knew her by her hat. It was steeple-crowned, without any vane. They saw her digging with her trowel round a sassafras bush. They told her their story—how their mother had put salt in her coffee, and how the chemist had made it worse instead of better, and how their mother couldn't drink it, and wouldn't she come and see what she could do? And she said she would, and took up her little old apron, with pockets all round, all filled with everlasting and pennyroyal, and went back to her house.

There she stopped, and stuffed her huge pockets with some of all the kinds of herbs. She took some tansy and peppermint, and caraway-seed and dill, spearmint and cloves, pennyroyal and sweet marjoram, basil and rosemary, wild thyme and some of the other time—such as you have in clocks,—sappermint and oppermint, catnip, valerian, and hop; indeed, there isn't a kind of herb you can think of that the little old woman didn't have done up in her little paper bags, that had all been dried in her little Dutch-oven. She packed these all up, and then went back with the children, taking her stick.

Meanwhile Mrs. Peterkin was getting quite impatient for her coffee.

As soon as the little old woman came she had it set over the fire, and began to stir in the different herbs. First she put in a little hop for the bitter. Mrs. Peterkin said it tasted like hop-tea, and not at all like coffee. Then she tried a little flagroot and snakeroot, then some spruce gum, and some caraway and some dill, some rue and rosemary, some sweet marjoram and sour, some oppermint and sappermint, a little spearmint and peppermint, some wild thyme, and some of the other tame time, some tansy and basil, and catnip and valerian, and sassafras, ginger, and pennyroyal. The children tasted after each mixture, but made up dreadful faces. Mrs. Peterkin tasted, and did the same. The more the old woman stirred, and the more she put in, the worse it all seemed to taste.

So the old woman shook her head, and muttered a few words, and said she must go. She believed the coffee was bewitched. She bundled up her packets of herbs, and took her trowel, and her basket, and her stick, and went back to her root of sassafras, that she had left half in the air and half out. And all she would take for pay was five cents in currency.

Then the family were in despair, and all sat and thought a great while. It was growing late in the day, and Mrs. Peterkin hadn't had her cup of coffee. At last Elizabeth Eliza said, "They say that the lady from Philadelphia, who is staying in town, is very wise. Suppose I go and ask her what is best to be done." To this they all agreed, it was a great thought, and off Elizabeth Eliza went.

She told the lady from Philadelphia the whole story,—how her mother had put salt in the coffee; how the chemist had been called in; how he tried everything but could make it no better; and how they went for the little old herb-woman, and how she had tried in vain, for her mother couldn't drink the coffee. The lady from Philadelphia listened very attentively, and then said, "Why doesn't your mother make a fresh cup of coffee?" Elizabeth Eliza started with surprise. Solomon John shouted with joy; so did Agamemnon, who had just finished his sum; so did the little boys who had followed on. "Why didn't we think of that?" said Elizabeth Eliza; and they all went back to their mother, and she had her cup of coffee.

MRS. PETERKIN

WISHES TO GO TO DRIVE

Lucretia Hale

One morning Mrs. Peterkin was feeling very tired, as she had been having a great many things to think of, and she said to Mr. Peterkin, "I believe I shall take a ride this morning!"

And the little boys cried out, "Oh, may we go too?"

Mrs. Peterkin said that Elizabeth Eliza and the little boys might go.

So Mr. Peterkin had the horse put into the carryall, and he and Agamemnon went off to their business, and Solomon John to school; and Mrs. Peterkin began to get ready for her ride.

She had some currants she wanted to carry to old Mrs. Twomly, and some gooseberries for somebody else, and Elizabeth Eliza wanted to pick some flowers to take to the minister's wife; so it took them a long time to prepare.

The little boys went out to pick the currants and the gooseberries, and Elizabeth Eliza went out for her flowers, and Mrs. Peterkin put on her cape-bonnet, and in time they were all ready. The little boys were in their india-rubber boots, and they got into the carriage.

Elizabeth Eliza was to drive; so she sat on the front seat, and took up the reins, and the horse started off merrily, and then suddenly stopped, and would not go any farther.

Elizabeth Eliza shook the reins, and pulled them, and then she clucked to the horse; and Mrs. Peterkin clucked; and the little boys whistled and shouted; but still the horse would not go.

"We shall have to whip him," said Elizabeth Eliza.

Now Mrs. Peterkin never liked to use the whip; but, as the horse would not go, she said she would get out and turn his head the other way, while Elizabeth Eliza whipped the horse, and when he began to go she would hurry and get in.

So they tried this, but the horse would not stir.

"Perhaps we have too heavy a load," said Mrs. Peterkin, as she got in.

So they took out the currants and the gooseberries and the flowers, but still the horse would not go.

One of the neighbors, from the opposite house, looking out just then, called out to them to try the whip. There was a high wind, and they could not hear exactly what she said.

"I have tried the whip," said Elizabeth Eliza.

"She says 'whips,' such as you eat," said one of the little boys.

"We might make those," said Mrs. Peterkin, thoughtfully.

"We have got plenty of cream," said Elizabeth Eliza.

"Yes, let us have some whips," cried the little boys, getting out.

And the opposite neighbor cried out something about whips; and the wind was very high.

So they went into the kitchen, and whipped up the cream, and made some very delicious whips; and the little boys tasted all round, and they all thought they were very nice.

They carried some out to the horse, who swallowed it down very quickly.

"That is just what he wanted," said Mrs. Peterkin; "now he will certainly go!"

So they all got into the carriage again, and put in the currants, and the gooseberries, and the flowers; and Elizabeth Eliza shook the reins, and they all clucked; but still the horse would not go!

"We must either give up our ride," said Mrs. Peterkin, mournfully, "or else send over to the lady from Philadelphia, and see what she will say."

The little boys jumped out as quickly as they could; they were eager to go and ask the lady from Philadelphia. Elizabeth Eliza went with them, while her mother took the reins.

They found that the lady from Philadelphia was very ill that day, and was in her bed. But when she was told what the trouble was she very kindly said they might draw up the curtain from the window at the foot of the bed, and open the blinds, and she would see. Then she asked for her opera-glass, and looked through it, across the way, up the street, to Mrs. Peterkin's door.

After she had looked through the glass she laid it down, leaned her head back against the

"Mrs. Peterkin Wishes to Go to Drive." From *The Peterkin Papers* by Lucretia P. Hale

pillow, for she was very tired, and then said, "Why don't you unchain the horse from the horse-post?"

Elizabeth Eliza and the little boys looked at one another, and then hurried back to the house and told their mother. The horse was untied, and they all went to ride.

ABOUT ELIZABETH ELIZA'S PIANO

Lucretia Hale

Elizabeth Eliza had a present of a piano, and she was to take lessons of the postmaster's daughter.

They decided to have the piano set across the window in the parlor, and the carters brought it in, and went away.

After they had gone the family all came in to look at the piano; but they found the carters had placed it with its back turned towards the middle of the room, standing close against the window.

How could Elizabeth Eliza open it? How could she reach the keys to play upon it?

Solomon John proposed that they should open the window, which Agamemnon could do with his long arms. Then Elizabeth Eliza should go round upon the piazza, and open the piano. Then she could have her music-stool on the piazza, and play upon the piano there.

So they tried this; and they all thought it was a very pretty sight to see Elizabeth Eliza playing on the piano, while she sat on the piazza, with the honeysuckle vines behind her.

It was very pleasant, too, moonlight evenings. Mr. Peterkin liked to take a doze on his sofa in the room; but the rest of the family liked to sit on the piazza. So did Elizabeth Eliza, only she had to have her back to the moon.

All this did very well through the summer; but, when the fall came, Mr. Peterkin thought the air was too cold from the open window, and the family did not want to sit out on the piazza. Elizabeth Eliza practised in the mornings with

"About Elizabeth Eliza's Piano." From *The Peterkin Papers* by Lucretia P. Hale

her cloak on; but she was obliged to give up her music in the evenings the family shivered so.

One day, when she was talking with the lady from Philadelphia, she spoke of this trouble.

The lady from Philadelphia looked surprised, and then said, "But why don't you turn the piano round?"

One of the little boys pertly said, "It is a square piano."

But Elizabeth Eliza went home directly, and, with the help of Agamemnon and Solomon John, turned the piano round.

"Why did we not think of that before?" said Mrs. Peterkin. "What shall we do when the lady from Philadelphia goes home again?"

THE NIGHT OF THE BIG WIND

Arthur Mason

Some of the Irish folk have a seeing eye for the fairies that other people lack. Danny O'Fay was such a one. He thought kindly of the Wee Men even when he himself was in trouble. And surely the Big Wind was trouble enough for men, beasts, and fairies.

"The Night of the Big Wind," Chapters I and II. From *The Wee Men of Ballywooden* by Arthur Mason. Used with the kind permission of Arthur Mason

Old Danny O'Fay and his donkey lived in a hut by the sea, and Danny sold fish through the country. People wondered how he got his fish. He was never known to buy from fishermen, nor did he ever fish himself. But before he went to bed, he put the wee saddle on his donkey. Another thing he did, and he never missed a night. He would fill his clay pipe, and light it and puff on it for a bit. Then he'd open the door and lay the smoking pipe on the doorstep, saying as he yawned, "A fine night it is, with the sea talking and the corncrake singing. Well, have your smoke and take your donkey ride. You'll not be forgetting my fish for the morning. Good-night to yez all." Then he'd close and bar the door and lie down on his bed of straw and sleep until Jerry, his donkey, hee-hawed him awake. Then up he'd get and open the door and out to his two-wheel cart he'd go, to look at his fish. There they'd be, fresh from the sea, every one of them. Old Danny would smile the gouged wrinkles from his face. "Ah, and it's the fine catch they had last night," he'd say.

This had been going on for quite a while, and old Danny and his donkey thrived fairly well. He had his bowl of red tea, and potatoes and cabbage, and once in a while the leg of a duck. Old Danny was happy as he drove through the country shouting his song, "Fresh fish! Fresh fish! Fresh fish!"

Then came a day when old Danny's customers questioned his honesty.

"Say, Danny O'Fay," they asked, "where do you get your fish? You never buy from fishermen, nor do you ever fish yourself."

"Is it stealing fish you're thinking I am?"

"Oh, the Lord forbid," said Mrs. Blaney, "and us eating every morsel of them! It isn't that at all, at all, Danny O'Fay, but worse. Our eyes we've been keeping on you lately, and it's said by word of mouth, that in the dark of the moon, wee lights are seen dancing around your hut. Now, Danny O'Fay, if it's harboring Willie the Wisp you are, and all of his clan, not a fish will we buy from you."

"Tut, tut," said Danny, "You're all astray in your mind. It's eating too much oatmeal you are, and not enough fish out of the sea."

"Away with you, Danny O'Fay," they scolded.

"Look at the saddle marks on your donkey! How do you explain that?"

"I do a bit of riding in my sleep," answered Danny. "And as for the wee lights you do be seeing in the dark of the moon, sure it may be the flicker of your own candle lights that you haven't blinked out of your eyes."

"Oh, no, Danny O'Fay, it's pious men have seen the lights, and they have warned us to buy no more of your fish. Away with you, now!"

"Get up!" said Danny to his donkey. "It's terrible times we do be having, with people not believing, not buying my fish. Well, well, what will become of us anyway?"

All day long he drove through the country but not a fish could he sell. Nor would the farmers speak to him when he passed. They looked the other way. So heartsore and weary, he turned his donkey homeward, and by the time he reached the four roads, a mile or more from his hut, a wall of clouds banked the setting sun.

Old Danny looked up at the cloud-growing sky. Said he to himself, "I hear the crows scolding on the wing to their nests, but not a sight of one do I see. Put longer strides into your steps!" he shouted to his donkey. "Is it blind you are, that you can't see the clouds falling? Don't be listening to the frogs croaking or the crickets a-singing. Can't you hear the wind starting a fight in the whins? On with you, I say, before the pitch of the night swallows us up!" And Danny trudged on behind his donkey cart, thinking the while of the wind, and the power of it, and of the morrow with the fish in his cart left to rot.

The road now ribboned itself along the strand, and Danny looked out at the sea. "The Wee Men will be doing no fishing to-night," said he to himself, "not with the waves coughing the hearts out of themselves the way they are. Ah, and sure I'll have to be telling them to put their wee nets away. I can't sell a fish. There's a blight upon me. But they'll have their smoke and their donkey ride just the same."

Night came in like a crow lighting on a nest of eggs. Danny was home, unhitching his donkey.

"Ah, what a night! What a night!" he was saying. But he couldn't hear himself talk, for the wind stole the words out of his mouth as fast as his tongue could twist them. "Ah, there'll be a world of trouble to-night. I, with my five and seventy winters, have never listened to the lung-moanings of the wind like this before." He fumbled for the buckle on the donkey's collar. "Keep your ears away from my hands, bad cess to you, and me trying to get you out of the wind."

He opened the door of his hut. There was a wee turf fire burning in the grate. "Good-evening to yez all," he said. "My eyes don't see one of you, but sure that's nothing at all, with a night of nights outside. Come in, Jerry," he said to the donkey, "and be thankful you have a roof over your head." At that moment, the wind lifted a blanket of thatch off the roof. "I may have spoken a bit too quick; anyway, there's a fire in the grate, and your stall is over yonder."

Danny closed and barred the door. The wind tumbled through the hole in the roof and filled the hut. He tried to light a candle but the wind wouldn't let him. He pulled off his cap, scratched a wisp of hair over his ear, and looked up at the roof.

"Where's the moon to-night? Bad luck to her, the hag that she is. You never can see her when you want her. Oh, it's not angry I am at all. It's feeding the donkey I'll be doing." He felt his way to the stall. There stood the donkey eating oats. "What!" exclaimed old Danny. "Did they feed you before they left? Well, well, God bless every one of them! May the roots of the trees take a good grip of the ground while the Wee Men hold onto them, for it's something firm they'll be needing to-night. Ah, why don't they have houses like human beings? But it's not for me to tamper with things that are and things that are not. Anyway, they'll have their smoke, even if the wind lifts the world on its wings."

Danny sat down by the fire and filled his pipe and lit it. He smoked for a bit, then he got up and opened the door to lay his pipe down on the doorstep. The storm, like a byre full of bullocks chased by bumblebees, knocked the pipe out of his hand, and the mouth of the wind gulped its sparks.

"You gluttonous villain!" shouted old Danny. "May the sparks burn a hole in your thrapple!" He placed his back against the door and with his sharp shoulder blades he closed it. "Sure," said he, "it feels as if the tops of the mountains were playing hop, skip, and jump. Oh, what a night

for my wee friends to be out in. No shelter, no smoke, and the world rolling under them."

As old Danny hobbled over to the fire the only window in the hut blew in and crashed around his feet. A roar ran up the chimney and the wee fire chased after it. And to make matters worse, the thatched roof was stripped entirely. Danny was blown against the door, and he stood there, rubbing his hands.

"Is it afraid I am?" he cried. "Tut, tut, Danny O'Fay, put that thought out of your head. It's not the wind you're listening to, at all. It's the music from the big tumbling waves you're hearing." He got down on his hands and knees, and crawled to the donkey stall. "Get over there, Jerry. It's Danny that's talking. Don't you hear me? Get over, I say. Shake the roar out of your ears. There isn't an eye-cup of sleep in the world to-night, but it's alongside of you I'll be doing. If the wild mane of the blow leaves the walls standing, we'll both be here in the morning. Whist! Is that whispering I'm hearing, or is it the wind counting the spokes in the wheels of my cart?"

Old Danny lay down under the Manger, talking to himself, and closed his eyes.

CHAPTER II

The big wind wrought havoc through the country that night. Nothing escaped. Cattle sheds were up-ended. Chimneys tumbled down. Sheets of bog water went flying through the air. The four roads were choked with haystack tops and jaunting cars. Thorns and whin bushes were plucked out by the roots. Hedgehogs, wheelbarrows—all sorts of things were loose and on the run.

Blaney's rooster, that weighed a stone and could crow louder than any rooster in the parish, got stuck in the garden gate. The wind nibbled him naked. The old windmill on Murry's Brae, that hadn't run for years, was spinning to-night, and the squeaks from it sounded louder than a drove of hungry pigs.

The oak tree in the lonely lane had been the talk of generations. It was whispered in the ears of young and old that the Wee Men spent some of their nights in the lonely lane and played around the oak tree. And there wasn't a man in the parish who would pass it after dark. Anyway, the wind hurled against it and it came crashing to the ground. There was no shelter anywhere.

The cow paths looked twisted, and the stepping stiles were open gaps. Even the rushes in the meadow lay like combed hair.

Down by the sea, where a mossy rock lipped over a cove, swarms of Wee Men were hanging, clinging to the moss. The chief of the clan—the Paver-of-Caves—was renowned among the Wee Men for his ability to bend moonflakes with white heather for the flooring of the caves. To-night he was so fearfully frightened that he could hardly make himself heard, even though he spoke in his loudest voice.

"I hope the moss on this rock holds," he cried. "Were there any of you scratched when the oak tree fell?"

"No, no," came wee whines, "but we're all warped and twisted. Our eyes are webbed with eyebrows, and our beards are whistling tunes such as we never heard before!"

"That's to be expected," answered the Paver. "Keep your heads! Don't let the belching waves or the sky wheezings upset you. If the moss holds, well and good. If it doesn't, keep together, whatever happens!"

A wail of a voice reached the Paver's ears. "The moss on this rock is as straggly as the down on a young linnet's breast!"

"Who is that I hear?" asked the Paver.

"The Midsummer Mower," came back the answer.

"I thought as much," cried the Paver. "You're always complaining of a poor harvest. Now then, weigh down your minds," commanded the Paver. "Weigh them down well, with the work you've left undone—and trust to that to hold you to the rock!"

The Wee Men had no difficulty weighing down their minds, but even that weight was no match for the night. All of a sudden, without the yelp of a warning, the arms of the wind began wrestling with the rock.

"Let go," roared the Paver, "before we're tossed into the cove! There's slugging behind us, but nowheres ahead of us. Unballast your minds! Take hold of each other!"

A buzzing of wee voices hummed through the blackness.

"Oh, where are we going?"

"That," shouted the Paver, "is a question I can't answer."

The words were no sooner out of his mouth than the tail of the wind wound itself around the Wee Men and lifted them high in the air.

"We're all right, so far!" the Paver cried out. "Stick together! Don't let go of each other! If I had an eyeful of moonlight, I could tell you which way we're going."

"The sea is under us!" screamed the Crane Chaser.

The Midsummer Mower, who had hold of the Paver's hand, cried out in a tremble, "Have you no power at all?"

"Power?" shrieked back the Paver. "With my feet off the ground? Why, man, what are you thinking about? Power? I'd have you all know that, with the stars mired, and the moon choked, I can do nothing but blow away with the rest of you."

The gale was sweeping them out over the sea. The wee Cradle Rocker began to cry. "I'm getting dizzy from whirling and circling," he whined.

"Stop your crying!" commanded the Paver. "There's noise enough in the world to-night."

"If only I had a light," called out the Cradle Rocker, "I could find myself."

"Hold on," shouted the Paver, "there may be a remedy after all. Is Willie the Wisp among you?"

"That I am," piped up Willie, "but I haven't a spare breath to blow my light lit."

"Where do you think we are now?" spoke the Stooker-of-Wheat-Sheaves.

Grunty, the fisherman, answered, "Over Dundrum Bay."

"If the clouds should let go of us," shouted the Wee Weaver, "I won't have to do any more weaving!"

"Stop your complaining," ordered the Paver. "I'll need a suit the minute we alight."

"How about me?" It was the Quarryman's voice. "My schisty shirt is slit up the back. My cap is gone and my pulse heaters, too. How are we going to get back? Can you answer me that, Paver-of-Caves?"

"We're speeding so fast," answered the Paver, "that my mind can't keep up with me."

There was silence among the Wee Men for a long time, for they had little breath to waste in words. They held tight to each other's hands, while the Big Wind made serpentine curves out of them, as on it swept over the sea, driving them ahead of it. But after a while the Counter-of-Lark-Eggs spoke. Said he, "I smell the morn, and it's fighting its way to be seen."

"Good," said the Paver, "I thought we were nearing something, for I just bumped my chilblain on the top of a mountain."

Far, far away, the tired eye of the morn squeezed through the clouds. Ribbons of sunken sunlight fluttered up and into the sky. And then something happened that brought cheer to the Wee Men, for all of a sudden they found themselves astride the arch of a rainbow.

"Let go of hands," commanded the Paver, "and every man of you slide down the rainbow legs to the ground! But mind and keep your heads, for we don't know what's waiting below."

The Wee Men began to argue about what colors they would choose to slide down.

"Look here," said the Paver, "there are colors enough for all of you. I'm going down on the peacock band."

"I'll follow you on the purple," said the Weaver. "I might even do a bit of weaving on my way down."

"Good!" cried the Paver. "I'm in need of a cloak. Have an eye out for color; it's a green cloak I want."

The Paver looked over his men. "Are you all ready?" he asked.

"We are!"

"Then let us slide down to the ground!"

The Wee Men lay flat on their little bellies, and each one twisted his short legs around the color band he liked best. Then down the rainbow legs they banistered.

The Weaver was the last to land, for he had a large bundle of woven rainbow web under his arm.

THE SKILLFUL HUNTSMAN

Howard Pyle

After Howard Pyle had illustrated his own retelling of the Robin Hood stories, he decided to continue writing the text for his pictures. Pepper and Salt began as a series of humorous verses, but Pyle soon found it easier to write stories than verse. Children and storytellers have been equally delighted with the two collections that resulted.

Once upon a time there was a lad named Jacob Boehm, who was a practical huntsman.

One day Jacob said to his mother, "Mother, I would like to marry Gretchen—the nice, pretty little daughter of the Herr Mayor."

Jacob's mother thought that he was crazy. "Marry the daughter of the Herr Mayor, indeed! You want to marry the daughter of the Herr Mayor? Listen; many a man wants and wants, and nothing comes of it!"

That was what Jacob Boehm's mother said to him.

But Jacob was deaf in that ear; nothing would do but his mother must go to the Herr Mayor, and ask for leave for him to marry Gretchen. And Jacob begged and begged so prettily that at last his mother promised to go and do as he wished. So off she went, though doubt was heavy in her shoes, for she did not know how the Herr Mayor would take it.

"So Jacob wants to marry Gretchen, does he?" said the Herr Mayor.

Yes; that was what Jacob wanted.

"And is he a practical huntsman?" said the Herr Mayor.

Oh yes, he was that.

"So good," said the Herr Mayor. "Then tell Jacob that when he is such a clever huntsman as to be able to shoot the whiskers off from a running hare without touching the skin, then he can have Gretchen."

Then Jacob's mother went back home again. "Now," said she, "Jacob will, at least, be satisfied."

"Yes," said Jacob, when she had told him all that the Herr Mayor had said to her, "that is a hard thing to do; but what one man has done, another man can." So he shouldered his gun, and started away into the world to learn to be as clever a huntsman as the Herr Mayor had said.

He plodded on and on until at last he fell in with a tall stranger dressed all in red.

"The Skillful Huntsman." From *Pepper and Salt* by Howard Pyle, Harper & Brothers

"Where are you going, Jacob?" said the tall stranger, calling him by his name, just as if he had eaten pottage out of the same dish with him.

"I am going," said Jacob, "to learn to be so clever a huntsman that I can shoot the whiskers off from a running hare without touching the skin."

"That is a hard thing to learn," said the tall stranger.

Yes; Jacob knew that it was a hard thing; but what one man had done another man could do.

"What will you give me if I teach you to be as clever a huntsman as that?" said the tall stranger.

"What will you take to teach me?" said Jacob; for he saw that the stranger had a horse's hoof instead of a foot, and he did not like his looks, I can tell you.

"Oh, it is nothing much that I want," said the tall man; "only just sign your name to this paper—that is all."

But what was in the paper? Yes; Jacob had to know what was in the paper before he would set so much as a finger to it.

Oh, there was nothing in the paper, only this: that when the red one should come for Jacob at the end of ten years' time, Jacob should promise to go along with him whithersoever he should take him.

At this Jacob hemmed and hawed and scratched his head, for he did not know about that. "All the same," said he, "I will sign the paper, but on one condition."

At this the red one screwed up his face as though he had sour beer in his mouth, for he did not like the sound of the word "condition." "Well," said he, "what is the condition?"

"It is only this," said Jacob: "that you shall be *my* servant for the ten years, and if, in all that time, I should chance to ask you a question that you cannot answer, then I am to be my own man again."

Oh, if that was all, the red man was quite willing for that.

Then he took Jacob's gun, and blew down into the barrel of it. "Now," said he, "you are as skillful a huntsman as you asked to be."

"That I must try," said Jacob. So Jacob and the red one went around hunting here and hunting there until they scared up a hare. "Shoot!" said the red one; and Jacob shot. Clip! off flew the whiskers of the hare as neatly as one could cut them off with the barber's shears.

"Yes, good!" said Jacob, "now I am a skillful huntsman."

Then the stranger in red gave Jacob a little bone whistle, and told him to blow in it whenever he should want him. After that Jacob signed the paper, and the stranger went one way and he went home again.

Well, Jacob brushed the straws off from his coat, and put a fine shine on his boots, and then he set off to the Herr Mayor's house.

"How do you find yourself, Jacob?" said the Herr Mayor.

"So good," said Jacob.

"And are you a skillful huntsman now?" said the Herr Mayor.

Oh yes, Jacob was a skillful huntsman now.

Yes, good! But the Herr Mayor must have proof of that. Now, could Jacob shoot a feather out of the tail of the magpie flying over the trees yonder?

Oh yes! nothing easier than that. So Jacob raised the gun to his cheek. Bang! went the gun, and down fell a feather from the tail of the magpie. At this the Herr Mayor stared and stared, for he had never seen such shooting.

"And now may I marry Gretchen?" said Jacob.

At this the Herr Mayor scratched his head, and hemmed and hawed. No; Jacob could not marry Gretchen yet, for he had always said and sworn that the man who should marry Gretchen should bring with him a plough that could go of itself, and plough three furrows at once. If Jacob would show him such a plough as that, then he might marry Gretchen and welcome. That was what the Herr Mayor said.

Jacob did not know how about that; perhaps he could get such a plough, perhaps he could not. If such a plough was to be had, though, he would have it. So off he went home again, and the Herr Mayor thought that he was rid of him now for sure and certain.

But when Jacob had come home, he went back of the woodpile and blew a turn or two on the little bone whistle that the red stranger had given him. No sooner had he done this than the other stood before him as suddenly as though he had just stepped out of the door of nowheres.

"What do you want, Jacob?" said he.

"I would like," said Jacob, "to have a plough that can go by itself and plough three furrows at once."

"That you shall have," said the red one. Then he thrust his hand into his breeches pocket, and drew forth the prettiest little plough that you ever saw. He stood it on the ground before Jacob, and it grew very large.

"Plough away," said he, and then he went back again whither he had come.

So Jacob laid his hands to the plough and—whisk!—away it went like John Stormwetter's colt, with Jacob behind it. Out of the farm-yard they went, and down the road, and so to the Herr Mayor's house, and behind them lay three fine brown furrows, smoking in the sun.

When the Herr Mayor saw them coming he opened his eyes, you may be sure, for he had never seen such a plough as that in all his life before.

"And now," said Jacob, "I should like to marry Gretchen, if you please."

At this the Herr Mayor hemmed and hawed and scratched his head again. No; Jacob could not marry Gretchen yet, for the Herr Mayor had always said and sworn that the man who married Gretchen should bring with him a purse that always had two pennies in it and could never be emptied, no matter how much was taken out of it.

Jacob did not know how about that; perhaps he could get it and perhaps he could not. If such a thing was to be had, though, he would have it, as sure as the Mecklenburg folks brew sour beer. So off he went home again, and the Herr Mayor thought that now he was rid of him for certain.

But Jacob went back of the woodpile and blew on his bone whistle again, and once more the red one came at his bidding.

"What will you have now?" said he to Jacob.

"I should like," said Jacob, "to have a purse which shall always have two pennies in it, no matter how much I take out of it."

"That you shall have," said the red one; whereupon he thrust his hand into his pocket, and fetched out a beautiful silken purse with two pennies in it. He gave the purse to Jacob, and then he went away again as quickly as he had come.

After he had gone, Jacob began taking pennies

out of his purse and pennies out of his purse, until he had more than a hatful—hui! I would like to have such a purse as that.

Then he marched off to the Herr Mayor's house with his chin up, for he might hold his head as high as any, now that he had such a purse as that in his pocket. As for the Herr Mayor, he thought that it was a nice, pretty little purse; but could it do this and that as he had said?

Jacob would show him that; so he began taking pennies and pennies out of it, until he had filled all the pots and pans in the house with them. And now might he marry Gretchen?

Yes; that he might! So said the Herr Mayor; for who would not like to have a lad for a son-in-law who always had two pennies more in his purse than he could spend.

So Jacob married his Gretchen, and, between his plough and his purse, he was busy enough, I can tell you.

So the days went on and on and on until the ten years had gone by and the time had come for the red one to fetch Jacob away with him. As for Jacob, he was in a sorry state of dumps, as you may well believe.

At last Gretchen spoke to him. "See, Jacob," said she, "what makes you so down in the mouth?"

"Oh! nothing at all," said Jacob.

But this did not satisfy Gretchen, for she could see that there was more to be told than Jacob had spoken. So she teased and teased, until at last Jacob told her all, and that the red one was to come the next day and take him off as his servant, unless he could ask him a question which he could not answer.

"Prut!" said Gretchen, "and is that all? Then there is no stuffing to that sausage, for I can help you out of your trouble easily enough." Then she told Jacob that when the next day should come he should do thus and so, and she would do this and that, and between them they might cheat the red one after all.

So, when the next day came, Gretchen went into the pantry and smeared herself all over with honey. Then she ripped open a bed and rolled herself in the feathers.

By-and-by came the red one. Rap! tap! tap! he knocked at the door.

"Are you ready to go with me now, Jacob?" said he.

Yes; Jacob was quite ready to go, only he would like to have one favor granted him first.

"What is it that you want?" said the red one.

"Only this," said Jacob: "I would like to shoot one more shot out of my old gun before I go with you."

Oh, if that was all, he might do that and welcome. So Jacob took down his gun, and he and the red one went out together, walking side by side, for all the world as though they were born brothers.

By-and-by they saw a wren. "Shoot at that," said the red one.

"Oh no," said Jacob, "that is too small."

So they went on a little farther.

By-and-by they saw a raven. "Shoot at that, then," said the red one.

"Oh no," said Jacob, "that is too black."

So they went on a little farther.

By-and-by they came to a ploughed field, and there was something skipping over the furrows that looked for all the world like a great bird. That was Gretchen; for the feathers stuck to the honey and all over her, so that she looked just like a great bird.

"Shoot at that! shoot at that!" said the red one, clapping his hands together.

"Oh yes," said Jacob, "I will shoot at that." So he raised his gun and took aim. Then he lowered his gun again. "But what is it?" said he.

At this the red one screwed up his eyes, and looked and looked, but for the life of him he could not tell what it was.

"No matter what it is," said he, "only shoot and be done with it, for I must be going."

"Yes, good! But what *is* it?" said Jacob.

Then the red one looked and looked again, but he could tell no better this time than he could before. "It may be this and it may be that," said he. "Only shoot and be done with it, for they are waiting for me at home."

"Yes, my friend," said Jacob, "that is all very good; only tell me what it is and I will shoot."

"Thunder and lightning!" bawled the red one, *"I do not know what it is!"*

"Then be off with you!" said Jacob, "for, since you cannot answer my question, all is over between us two."

At this the red one had to leave Jacob, so he fled away over hill and dale, bellowing like a bull.

As for Jacob and Gretchen, they went back home together, very well pleased with each other and themselves.

And the meaning of all this is, that many another man beside Jacob Boehm would find himself in a pretty scrape only for his wife.

THE KING
OF THE GOLDEN RIVER,
OR THE BLACK BROTHERS

John Ruskin

This long, rather somber tale in folk style by an art critic and author of many adult books is so dramatic that children do not forget it.

Chapter I: How the Agricultural System of the Black Brothers was interfered with by South-West Wind, Esquire.

In a secluded and mountainous part of Stiria, there was, in old time, a valley of the most surprising and luxuriant fertility. It was surrounded, on all sides, by steep and rocky mountains, rising into peaks, which were always covered with snow, and from which a number of torrents descended in constant cataracts. One of these fell westward, over the face of a crag so high, that, when the sun had set to everything else, and all below was darkness, his beams still shone full upon this waterfall, so that it looked like a shower of gold. It was, therefore, called by the people of the neighborhood the Golden River. It was strange that none of these streams fell into the valley itself. They all descended on the other side of the mountains, and wound away through broad plains and by populous cities. But the clouds were drawn so constantly to the snowy hills, and rested so softly in the circular hollow, that, in time of drought and heat, when all the country round was burnt up, there was still rain in the little valley; and its crops were so heavy, and its hay so high, and its apples so red, and its grapes so blue, and its wine so rich, and its honey so sweet, that it was a marvel to every one who beheld it, and was commonly called the Treasure Valley.

The whole of this little valley belonged to three brothers, called Schwartz, Hans, and Gluck. Schwartz and Hans, the two elder brothers, were very ugly men, with overhanging eyebrows and small, dull eyes, which were always half shut, so that you couldn't see into *them,* and always fancied they saw very far into *you.* They lived by farming the Treasure Valley, and very good farmers they were. They killed everything that did not pay for its eating. They shot the blackbirds, because they pecked the fruit; and killed the hedgehogs, lest they should suck the cows; they poisoned the crickets for eating the crumbs in the kitchen; and smothered the cicadas, which used to sing all summer in the lime trees. They worked their servants without any wages, till they would not work any more, and then quarrelled with them, and turned them out of doors without paying them. It would have been very odd, if, with such a farm, and such a system of farming, they hadn't got very rich; and very rich they *did* get. They generally contrived to keep their corn by them till it was very dear, and then sell it for twice its value; they had heaps of gold lying about on their floors, yet it was never known that they had given so much as a penny or a crust in charity; they never went to mass; grumbled perpetually at paying tithes; and were, in a word, of so cruel and grinding a temper, as to receive from all those with whom they had any dealings, the nickname of the "Black Brothers."

The youngest brother, Gluck, was as completely opposed, in both appearance and character, to his seniors as could possibly be imagined or desired. He was not above twelve years old, fair, blue-eyed, and kind in temper to every living thing. He did not, of course, agree particularly well with his brothers, or rather, they did not agree with *him.* He was usually appointed to the honorable office of turnspit, when there was anything to roast, which was not often; for, to do the brothers justice, they were hardly less sparing upon themselves than upon other people. At other times he used to clean the shoes, floors, and sometimes the plates, occasionally getting what was left on them, by way of encourage-

ment, and a wholesome quantity of dry blows, by way of education.

Things went on in this manner for a long time. At last came a very wet summer, and everything went wrong in the country round. The hay had hardly been got in, when the haystacks were floated bodily down to the sea by an inundation; the vines were cut to pieces with the hail; the corn was all killed by a black blight; only in the Treasure Valley, as usual, all was safe. As it had rain when there was rain nowhere else, so it had sun when there was sun nowhere else. Everybody came to buy corn at the farm, and went away pouring maledictions on the Black Brothers. They asked what they liked, and got it, except from the poor people, who could only beg, and several of whom were starved at their very door, without the slightest regard or notice.

It was drawing towards winter, and very cold weather, when one day the two elder brothers had gone out, with their usual warning to little Gluck, who was left to mind the roast, that he was to let nobody in, and give nothing out. Gluck sat down quite close to the fire, for it was raining very hard, and the kitchen walls were by no means dry or comfortable looking. He turned and turned, and the roast got nice and brown. "What a pity," thought Gluck, "my brothers never ask anybody to dinner. I'm sure, when they've got such a nice piece of mutton as this, and nobody else has got so much as a piece of dry bread, it would do their hearts good to have somebody to eat it with them."

Just as he spoke, there came a double knock at the house door, yet heavy and dull, as though the knocker had been tied up,—more like a puff than a knock.

"It must be the wind," said Gluck; "nobody else would venture to knock double knocks at our door."

No; it wasn't the wind; there it came again very hard, and what was particularly astounding, the knocker seemed to be in a hurry, and not to be in the least afraid of the consequences. Gluck went to the window, opened it, and put his head out to see who it was.

It was the most extraordinary looking little gentleman he had ever seen in his life. He had a very large nose, slightly brass-colored; his cheeks were very round, and very red, and might have warranted a supposition that he had been blowing a refractory fire for the last eight-and-forty hours; his eyes twinkled merrily through long silky eyelashes, his moustaches curled twice round like a corkscrew on each side of his mouth, and his hair, of a curious mixed pepper-and-salt color, descended far over his shoulders. He was about four feet six in height, and wore a conical pointed cap of nearly the same altitude, decorated with a black feather some three feet long. His doublet was prolonged behind into something resembling a violent exaggeration of what is now termed a "swallow-tail," but was much obscured by the swelling folds of an enormous black, glossy-looking cloak, which must have been very much too long in calm weather, as the wind, whistling round the old house, carried it clear out from the wearer's shoulders to about four times his own length.

Gluck was so perfectly paralyzed by the singular appearance of his visitor, that he remained fixed without uttering a word, until the old gentleman, having performed another, and a more energetic concerto on the knocker, turned round to look after his fly-away cloak. In so doing he caught sight of Gluck's little yellow head jammed in the window, with its mouth and eyes very wide open indeed.

"Hollo!" said the little gentleman, "that's not the way to answer the door; I'm wet, let me in."

To do the little gentleman justice, he *was* wet. His feather hung down between his legs like a beaten puppy's tail, dripping like an umbrella; and from the ends of his moustaches the water was running into his waistcoat pockets, and out again like a mill stream.

"I beg pardon, sir," said Gluck, "I'm very sorry, but I really can't."

"Can't what?" said the old gentleman.

"I can't let you in, sir,—I can't indeed; my brothers would beat me to death, sir, if I thought of such a thing. What do you want, sir?"

"Want?" said the old gentleman petulantly, "I want fire and shelter; and there's your great fire there blazing, crackling, and dancing on the walls, with nobody to feel it. Let me in, I say; I only want to warm myself."

Gluck had had his head, by this time, so long out of the window, that he began to feel it was really unpleasantly cold, and when he turned, and saw the beautiful fire rustling and roaring, and throwing long bright tongues up the chimney, as if it were licking its chops at the savory smell of the leg of mutton, his heart melted within him that it should be burning away for nothing. "He does look *very* wet," said little Gluck; "I'll just let him in for a quarter of an hour." Round he went to the door, and opened it; and as the little gentleman walked in, there came a gust of wind through the house, that made the old chimneys totter.

"That's a good boy," said the little gentleman. "Never mind your brothers. I'll talk to them."

"Pray, sir, don't do any such thing," said Gluck. "I can't let you stay till they come; they'd be the death of me."

"Dear me," said the old gentleman, "I'm very sorry to hear that. How long may I stay?"

"Only till the mutton's done, sir," replied Gluck, "and it's very brown."

Then the old gentleman walked into the kitchen, and sat himself down on the hob, with the top of his cap accommodated up the chimney, for it was a great deal too high for the roof.

"You'll soon dry there, sir," said Gluck, and sat down again to turn the mutton. But the old gentleman did *not* dry there, but went on drip, drip, dripping among the cinders, and the fire fizzed, and sputtered, and began to look very black, and uncomfortable; never was such a cloak; every fold in it ran like a gutter.

"I beg pardon, sir," said Gluck at length, after watching the water spreading in long, quicksilver-like streams over the floor for a quarter of an hour; "mayn't I take your cloak?"

"No, thank you," said the old gentleman.

"Your cap, sir?"

"I am all right, thank you," said the old gentleman rather gruffly.

"But,—sir,—I'm very sorry," said Gluck, hesitatingly; "but—really, sir,—you're—putting the fire out."

"It'll take longer to do the mutton then," replied his visitor drily.

Gluck was very much puzzled by the behavior of his guest; it was such a strange mixture of coolness and humility. He turned away at the string meditatively for another five minutes.

"That mutton looks very nice," said the old

gentleman at length. "Can't you give me a little bit?"

"Impossible, sir," said Gluck.

"I'm very hungry," continued the old gentleman; "I've had nothing to eat yesterday, nor today. They surely couldn't miss a bit from the knuckle!"

He spoke in so very melancholy a tone, that it quite melted Gluck's heart. "They promised me one slice to-day, sir," said he; "I can give you that, but not a bit more."

"That's a good boy," said the old gentleman again.

Then Gluck warmed a plate, and sharpened a knife. "I don't care if I do get beaten for it," thought he. Just as he had cut a large slice out of

dle of the kitchen, bowing with the utmost possible velocity.

"Who's that?" said Schwartz, catching up a rolling-pin, and turning to Gluck with a fierce frown.

"I don't know, indeed, brother," said Gluck in great terror.

"How did he get in?" roared Schwartz.

"My dear brother," said Gluck, deprecatingly, "he was so *very* wet!"

The rolling-pin was descending on Gluck's head; but, at the instant, the old gentleman interposed his conical cap, on which it crashed with a shock that shook the water out of it all over the room. What was very odd, the rolling-pin no sooner touched the cap, than it flew out

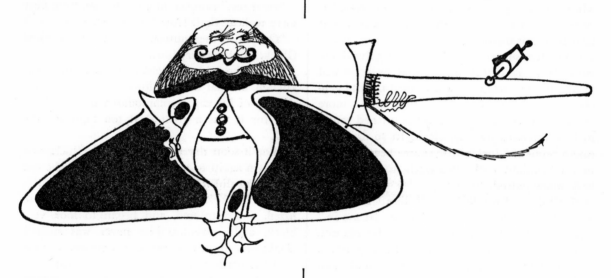

the mutton, there came a tremendous rap at the door. The old gentleman jumped off the hob, as if it had suddenly become inconveniently warm. Gluck fitted the slice into the mutton again, with desperate efforts at exactitude, and ran to open the door.

"What did you keep us waiting in the rain for?" said Schwartz, as he walked in, throwing his umbrella in Gluck's face. "Ay! what for indeed, you little vagabond?" said Hans, administering an educational box on the ear, as he followed his brother into the kitchen.

"Bless my soul!" said Schwartz when he opened the door.

"Amen," said the little gentleman, who had taken his cap off, and was standing in the mid-

of Schwartz's hand, spinning like a straw in a high wind, and fell into the corner at the further end of the room.

"Who are you, sir?" demanded Schwartz, turning upon him.

"What's your business?" snarled Hans.

"I'm a poor old man, sir," the little gentleman began very modestly, "and I saw your fire through the window, and begged shelter for a quarter of an hour."

"Have the goodness to walk out again, then," said Schwartz. "We've quite enough water in our kitchen, without making it a drying house."

"It is a cold day to turn an old man out in, sir; look at my gray hairs." They hung down to his shoulders, as I told you before.

"Ay!" said Hans, "there are enough of them to keep you warm. Walk!"

"I'm very, very hungry, sir; couldn't you spare me a bit of bread before I go?"

"Bread, indeed!" said Schwartz; "do you suppose we've nothing to do with our bread, but to give it to such red-nosed fellows as you?"

"Why don't you sell your feather?" said Hans, sneeringly. "Out with you."

"A little bit," said the old gentleman.

"Be off!" said Schwartz.

"Pray, gentlemen."

"Off, and be hanged!" cried Hans, seizing him by the collar. But he had no sooner touched the old gentleman's collar, than away he went after the rolling-pin, spinning round and round, till he fell into the corner on the top of it. Then Schwartz was very angry, and ran at the old gentleman to turn him out; but he also had hardly touched him, when away he went after Hans and the rolling-pin, and hit his head against the wall as he tumbled into the corner. And so there they lay, all three.

Then the old gentleman spun himself round with velocity in the opposite direction; continued to spin until his long cloak was all wound neatly about him; clapped his cap on his head, very much on one side (for it could not stand upright without going through the ceiling), gave an additional twist to his corkscrew moustaches, and replied with perfect coolness: "Gentlemen, I wish you a very good morning. At twelve o'clock to-night, I'll call again; after such a refusal of hospitality as I have just experienced, you will not be surprised if that visit is the last I ever pay you."

"If ever I catch you here again," muttered Schwartz, coming, half frightened, out of the corner—but, before he could finish his sentence, the old gentleman had shut the house door behind him with a great bang; and there drove past the window, at the same instant, a wreath of ragged cloud, that whirled and rolled away down the valley in all manner of shapes; turning over and over in the air; and melting away at last in a gush of rain.

"A very pretty business, indeed, Mr. Gluck!" said Schwartz. "Dish the mutton, sir. If ever I catch you at such a trick again—bless me, why the mutton's been cut!"

"You promised me one slice, brother, you know," said Gluck.

"Oh! and you were cutting it hot, I suppose, and going to catch all the gravy. It'll be long before I promise you such a thing again. Leave the room, sir; and have the kindness to wait in the coal-cellar till I call you."

Gluck left the room melancholy enough. The brothers ate as much mutton as they could, locked the rest in the cupboard, and proceeded to get very drunk after dinner.

Such a night as it was! Howling wind, and rushing rain, without intermission. The brothers had just sense enough left to put up all the shutters, and double bar the door, before they went to bed. They usually slept in the same room. As the clock struck twelve, they were both awakened by a tremendous crash. Their door burst open with a violence that shook the house from top to bottom.

"What's that?" cried Schwartz, starting up in his bed.

"Only I," said the little gentleman.

The two brothers sat up on their bolster, and stared into the darkness. The room was full of water, and by a misty moonbeam, which found its way through a hole in the shutter, they could see, in the midst of it, an enormous foam globe, spinning round, and bobbing up and down like a cork, on which, as on a most luxurious cushion, reclined the little old gentleman, cap and all. There was plenty of room for it now, for the roof was off.

"Sorry to incommode you," said their visitor, ironically. "I'm afraid your beds are dampish; perhaps you had better go to your brother's room; I've left the ceiling on there."

They required no second admonition, but rushed into Gluck's room, wet through, and in an agony of terror.

"You'll find my card on the kitchen table," the old gentleman called after them. "Remember the *last* visit."

"Pray Heaven it may!" said Schwartz, shuddering. And the foam globe disappeared.

Dawn came at last, and the two brothers looked out of Gluck's little window in the morning. The Treasure Valley was one mass of ruin, and desolation. The inundation had swept away trees, crops, and cattle, and left, in their stead, a waste of red sand, and gray mud. The two brothers crept, shivering and horror-struck into the kitchen. The water had gutted the whole first floor; corn, money, almost every movable thing had been swept away, and there was left only a small white card on the kitchen table. On it, in large, breezy, long-legged letters, were engraved the words:—*South-West Wind, Esquire.*

Chapter II: Of the Proceedings of the Three Brothers after the Visit of South-West Wind, Esquire; and how little Gluck had an Interview with the King of the Golden River.

South-West Wind, Esquire, was as good as his word. After the momentous visit above related, he entered the Treasure Valley no more; and what was worse, he had so much influence with his relations, the West Winds in general, and used it so effectually, that they all adopted a similar line of conduct. So no rain fell in the valley from one year's end to another. Though everything remained green and flourishing in the plains below, the inheritance of the Three Brothers was a desert. What had once been the richest soil in the kingdom, became a shifting heap of red sand; and the brothers, unable longer to contend with the adverse skies, abandoned their valueless patrimony in despair, to seek some means of gaining a livelihood among the cities and people of the plains. All their money was gone, and they had nothing left but some curious old-fashioned pieces of gold plate, the last remnants of their ill-gotten wealth.

"Suppose we turn goldsmiths?" said Schwartz to Hans, as they entered the large city. "It is a good knave's trade; we can put a great deal of copper into the gold, without any one's finding it out."

The thought was agreed to be a very good one; they hired a furnace, and turned goldsmiths. But two slight circumstances affected their trade: the first, that people did not approve of the coppered gold; the second, that the two elder brothers, whenever they had sold anything, used to leave little Gluck to mind the furnace, and go and drink out the money in the ale-house next door. So they melted all their gold, without making money enough to buy more, and were at last reduced to one large drinking-mug, which an uncle of his had given to little Gluck, and which he was very fond of, and would not have parted with for the world; though he never drank anything out of it but milk and water. The mug was a very odd mug to look at. The handle was formed of two wreaths of flowing golden hair, so finely spun that it looked more like silk than metal, and these wreaths descended into, and mixed with, a beard and whiskers, of the same exquisite workmanship, which surrounded and decorated a very fierce little face, of the reddest gold imaginable, right in the front of the mug, with a pair of eyes in it which seemed to command its whole circumference. It was impossible to drink out of the mug without being subjected to an intense gaze out of the side of these eyes; and Schwartz positively averred, that once, after emptying it full of Rhenish seventeen times, he had seen them wink! When it came to the mug's turn to be made into spoons, it half broke poor little Gluck's heart; but the brothers only laughed at him, tossed the mug into the melting-pot, and staggered out to the ale-house; leaving him, as usual, to pour the gold into bars, when it was all ready.

When they were gone, Gluck took a farewell look at his old friend in the melting-pot. The flowing hair was all gone; nothing remained but the red nose, and the sparkling eyes, which looked more malicious than ever. "And no wonder," thought Gluck, "after being treated in that way." He sauntered disconsolately to the window, and sat himself down to catch the fresh evening air, and escape the hot breath of the furnace. Now this window commanded a direct view of the range of mountains, which, as I told you before, overhung the Treasure Valley, and more especially of the peak from which fell the Golden River. It was just at the close of the day, and, when Gluck sat down at the window, he saw the rocks of the mountain tops, all crimson, and purple with the sunset; and there were bright tongues of fiery cloud burning and quivering about them; and the river, brighter than all, fell in a waving column of pure gold, from precipice to precipice, with the double arch of a broad purple rainbow stretched across it, flushing and fading alternately in the wreaths of spray.

"Ah!" said Gluck aloud, after he had looked at it for a little while, "if that river were really all gold, what a nice thing it would be."

"No it wouldn't, Gluck," said a clear metallic voice, close at his ear.

"Bless me, what's that?" exclaimed Gluck, jumping up. There was nobody there. He looked round the room, and under the table, and a great many times behind him, but there was certainly nobody there, and he sat down again at the window. This time he didn't speak, but he couldn't help thinking again that it would be very convenient if the river were really all gold.

"Not at all, my boy," said the same voice, louder than before.

"Bless me!" said Gluck again, "what *is* that?" He looked again into all the corners and cupboards, and then began turning round, and round, as fast as he could, in the middle of the room, thinking there was somebody behind him, when the same voice struck again on his ear. It was singing now very merrily "Lala-lira-la;" no words, only a soft running effervescent melody, something like that of a kettle on the boil. Gluck looked out of the window. No, it was certainly in the house. Up stairs, and down stairs. No, it was certainly in that very room, coming in quicker time, and clearer notes, every moment. "Lala-lira-la." All at once it struck Gluck, that it sounded louder near the furnace. He ran to the opening, and looked in; yes, he saw right, it seemed to be coming, not only out of the furnace, but out of the pot. He uncovered it, and ran back in a great fright, for the pot was certainly singing. He stood in the farthest corner of the room, with his hands up, and his mouth open, for a minute or two, when the singing stopped, and the voice became clear, and pronunciative.

"Hollo!" said the voice.

Gluck made no answer.

"Hollo! Gluck, my boy," said the pot again.

Gluck summoned all his energies, walked straight up to the crucible, drew it out of the furnace, and looked in. The gold was all melted, and its surface as smooth and polished as a river; but instead of reflecting little Gluck's head, as he looked in, he saw meeting his glance, from beneath the gold, the red nose and sharp eyes of his old friend of the mug, a thousand times redder and sharper than ever he had seen them in his life.

"Come, Gluck, my boy," said the voice out of the pot again, "I'm all right; pour me out."

But Gluck was too much astonished to do anything of the kind.

"Pour me out, I say," said the voice rather gruffly.

Still Gluck couldn't move.

"*Will* you pour me out?" said the voice, passionately, "I'm too hot."

By a violent effort, Gluck recovered the use of his limbs, took hold of the crucible, and sloped it, so as to pour out the gold. But instead of a liquid stream, there came out, first, a pair of pretty little yellow legs, then some coat tails, then a pair of arms stuck akimbo, and, finally, the well-known head of his friend the mug; all which articles, uniting as they rolled out, stood up energetically on the floor, in the shape of a little golden dwarf, about a foot and a half high.

"That's right!" said the dwarf, stretching out first his legs, and then his arms, and then shaking his head up and down, and as far round as it would go, for five minutes, without stopping; apparently with the view of ascertaining if he were quite correctly put together, while Gluck stood contemplating him in speechless amazement. He was dressed in a slashed doublet of spun gold, so fine in its texture, that the prismatic colors gleamed over it, as if on a surface of mother-of-pearl; and, over this brilliant doublet, his hair and beard fell full halfway to the ground, in waving curls, so exquisitely delicate, that Gluck could hardly tell where they ended; they seemed to melt into air. The features of the face, however, were by no means finished with the same delicacy; they were rather coarse, slightly inclining to coppery in complexion, and indicative, in expression, of a very pertinacious and intractable disposition in their small proprietor. When the dwarf had finished his self-examination, he turned his small sharp eyes full on Gluck, and stared at him deliberately for a minute or two. "No, it wouldn't, Gluck, my boy," said the little man.

This was certainly rather an abrupt, and unconnected mode of commencing conversation. It might indeed be supposed to refer to the course of Gluck's thoughts, which had first produced the dwarf's observations out of the pot; but whatever it referred to, Gluck had no inclination to dispute the dictum.

"Wouldn't it, sir?" said Gluck, very mildly, and submissively indeed.

"No," said the dwarf, conclusively. "No, it wouldn't." And with that, the dwarf pulled his cap hard over his brows, and took two turns of three feet long, up and down the room, lifting his legs up very high, and setting them down very hard. This pause gave time for Gluck to collect his thoughts a little, and, seeing no great reason to view his diminutive visitor with dread, and feeling his curiosity overcome his amazement, he ventured on a question of peculiar delicacy.

"Pray, sir," said Gluck, rather hesitatingly, "were you my mug?"

On which the little man turned sharp round, walked straight up to Gluck, and drew himself up to his full height. "I," said the little man, "am the King of the Golden River." Whereupon he turned about again, and took two more turns, some six feet long, in order to allow time for the consternation which this announcement produced in his auditor to evaporate. After which, he again walked up to Gluck and stood still, as if expecting some comment on his communication.

Gluck determined to say something at all events. "I hope your Majesty is very well," said Gluck.

"Listen!" said the little man, deigning no reply to this polite inquiry. "I am the King of what you mortals call the Golden River. The shape you saw me in, was owing to the malice of a stronger king, from whose enchantments you have this instant freed me. What I have seen of you, and your conduct to your wicked brothers, renders me willing to serve you; therefore attend to what I tell you. Whoever shall climb to the top of that mountain from which you see the Golden River issue, and shall cast into the stream at its source three drops of holy water, for him, and for him only, the river shall turn to gold. But no one failing in his first, can succeed in a second attempt; and if any one shall cast unholy water into the river, it will overwhelm him, and he will become a black stone." So saying, the King of the Golden River turned

away, and deliberately walked into the centre of the hottest flame of the furnace. His figure became red, white, transparent, dazzling,—a blaze of intense light,—rose, trembled, and disappeared. The King of the Golden River had evaporated.

"Oh!" cried poor Gluck, running to look up the chimney after him; "Oh, dear, dear, dear me! My mug! my mug! my mug!"

Chapter III: How Mr. Hans set off on an Expedition to the Golden River, and how he prospered therein.

The King of the Golden River had hardly made the extraordinary exit related in the last chapter, before Hans and Schwartz came roaring into the house, very savagely drunk. The discovery of the total loss of their last piece of plate had the effect of sobering them just enough to enable them to stand over Gluck, beating him very steadily for a quarter of an hour; at the expiration of which period they dropped into a couple of chairs, and requested to know what he had got to say for himself. Gluck told them his story, of which of course they did not believe a word. They beat him again, till their arms were tired, and staggered to bed. In the morning, however, the steadiness with which he adhered to his story obtained him some degree of credence; the immediate consequence of which was that the two brothers, after wrangling a long time on the knotty question, which of them should try his fortune first, drew their swords, and began fighting. The noise of the fray alarmed the neighbors, who, finding they could not pacify the combatants, sent for the constable.

Hans, on hearing this, contrived to escape, and hid himself; but Schwartz was taken before the magistrate, fined for breaking the peace, and, having drunk out his last penny the evening before, was thrown into prison till he should pay.

When Hans heard this, he was much delighted, and determined to set out immediately for the Golden River. How to get the holy water, was the question. He went to the priest, but the priest could not give any holy water to so abandoned a character. So Hans went to vespers in the evening for the first time in his life, and, under pretence of crossing himself, stole a cupful, and returned home in triumph.

Next morning he got up before the sun rose, put the holy water into a strong flask, and two bottles of wine and some meat in a basket, slung them over his back, took his alpine staff in his hand, and set off for the mountains.

On his way out of the town he had to pass the prison, and as he looked in at the windows, whom should he see but Schwartz himself peeping out of the bars, and looking very disconsolate.

"Good morning, brother," said Hans; "have you any message for the King of the Golden River?"

Schwartz gnashed his teeth with rage, and shook the bars with all his strength; but Hans only laughed at him, and advising him to make himself comfortable till he came back again, shouldered his basket, shook the bottle of holy water in Schwartz's face till it frothed again, and marched off in the highest spirits in the world.

It was, indeed, a morning that might have made any one happy, even with no Golden River to seek for. Level lines of dewy mist lay stretched along the valley, out of which rose the massy mountains,—their lower cliffs in pale gray shadow, hardly distinguishable from the floating vapor, but gradually ascending till they caught the sunlight, which ran in sharp touches of ruddy color along the angular crags, and pierced, in long level rays, through their fringes of spear-like pine. Far above, shot up red splintered masses of castellated rock, jagged and shivered into myriads of fantastic forms, with here and there a streak of sunlit snow, traced down their chasms like a line of forked lightning; and, far beyond, and far above all these, fainter than the morning cloud, but purer and changeless, slept, in the blue sky, the utmost peaks of the eternal snow.

The Golden River, which sprang from one of the lower and snowless elevations, was now nearly in shadow; all but the uppermost jets of spray, which rose like slow smoke above the undulating line of the cataract, and floated away in feeble wreaths upon the morning wind.

On this object, and on this alone, Hans's eyes and thoughts were fixed; forgetting the distance he had to traverse, he set off at an imprudent rate of walking, which greatly exhausted him before he had scaled the first range of the green and low hills. He was, moreover, surprised, on surmounting them, to find that a large glacier, of whose existence, notwithstanding his previous knowledge of the mountains, he had been absolutely ignorant, lay between him and the source of the Golden River. He entered on it with the boldness of a practised mountaineer; yet he thought he had never traversed so strange, or so dangerous a glacier in his life. The ice was excessively slippery, and out of all its chasms came wild sounds of gushing water; not monotonous or low, but changeful and loud, rising occasionally into drifting passages of wild melody, then breaking off into short melancholy tones, or sudden shrieks, resembling those of human voices in distress or pain. The ice was broken into thousands of confused shapes, but none, Hans thought, like the ordinary forms of splintered ice. There seemed a curious *expression* about all their outlines,—a perpetual resemblance to living features, distorted and scornful. Myriads of deceitful shadows, and lurid lights, played and floated about and through the pale blue pinnacles, dazzling and confusing the sight of the traveller; while his ears grew dull and his head giddy with the constant gush and roar of the concealed waters. These painful circumstances increased upon him as he advanced; the ice crashed and yawned into fresh chasms at his feet, tottering spires nodded around him, and fell thundering across his path; and though he had repeatedly faced these dangers on the most terrific glaciers, and in the wildest weather, it was with a new and oppressive feeling of panic terror that he leaped the last chasm, and flung himself, exhausted and shuddering, on the firm turf of the mountain.

He had been compelled to abandon his basket of food, which became a perilous incumbrance on the glacier, and had now no means of refreshing himself but by breaking off and eating some of the pieces of ice. This, however, relieved his thirst; an hour's repose recruited his hardy frame, and with the indomitable spirit of avarice, he resumed his laborious journey.

His way now lay straight up a ridge of bare red rocks, without a blade of grass to ease the foot, or a projecting angle to afford an inch of shade from the south sun. It was past noon, and the rays beat intensely upon the steep path, while the whole atmosphere was motionless, and penetrated with heat. Intense thirst was soon added to the bodily fatigue with which Hans was now afflicted; glance after glance he cast on the flask of water which hung at his belt. "Three drops are enough," at last thought he; "I may, at least, cool my lips with it."

He opened the flask, and was raising it to his lips, when his eye fell on an object lying on the rock beside him; he thought it moved. It was a small dog, apparently in the last agony of death from thirst. Its tongue was out, its jaws dry, its limbs extended lifelessly, and a swarm of black ants were crawling about its lips and throat. Its eye moved to the bottle which Hans held in his hand. He raised it, drank, spurned the animal with his foot, and passed on. And he did not know how it was, but he thought that a strange shadow had suddenly come across the blue sky.

The path became steeper and more rugged every moment; and the high hill air, instead of refreshing him, seemed to throw his blood into a fever. The noise of the hill cataracts sounded like mockery in his ears; they were all distant, and his thirst increased every moment. Another hour passed, and he again looked down to the flask at his side; it was half empty, but there was much more than three drops in it. He stopped to open it, and again, as he did so, something moved in the path above him. It was a fair child, stretched nearly lifeless on the rock, its breast heaving with thirst, its eyes closed, and its lips parched and burning. Hans eyed it deliberately, drank, and passed on. And a dark gray cloud came over the sun, and long, snake-like shadows crept up along the mountain sides. Hans struggled on. The sun was sinking, but its descent seemed to bring no coolness; the leaden weight of the dead air pressed upon his brow and heart, but the goal was near. He saw the cataract of the Golden River springing from the hill-side, scarcely five hundred feet above him. He paused for a moment to breathe, and sprang on to complete his task.

At this instant a faint cry fell on his ear. He turned, and saw a gray-haired old man extended on the rocks. His eyes were sunk, his features deadly pale, and gathered into an expression of despair. "Water!" he stretched his arms to Hans, and cried feebly, "Water! I am dying."

"I have none," replied Hans; "thou hast had thy share of life." He strode over the prostrate body, and darted on. And a flash of blue lightning rose out of the East, shaped like a sword; it shook thrice over the whole heaven, and left it dark with one heavy, impenetrable shade. The sun was setting; it plunged towards the horizon like a red-hot ball.

The roar of the Golden River rose on Hans's ear. He stood at the brink of the chasm through which it ran. Its waves were filled with the red glory of the sunset: they shook their crests like tongues of fire, and flashes of bloody light gleamed along their foam. Their sound came mightier and mightier on his senses; his brain grew giddy with the prolonged thunder. Shuddering, he drew the flask from his girdle, and hurled it into the centre of the torrent. As he did so, an icy chill shot through his limbs; he staggered, shrieked, and fell. The waters closed over his cry. And the moaning of the river rose wildly into the night, as it gushed over THE BLACK STONE.

Chapter IV: How Mr. Schwartz set off on an Expedition to the Golden River, and how he prospered therein.

Poor little Gluck waited very anxiously alone in the house for Hans's return. Finding he did not come back, he was terribly frightened, and went and told Schwartz in the prison all that had happened. Then Schwartz was very much pleased, and said that Hans must certainly have been turned into a black stone, and he should have all the gold to himself. But Gluck was very sorry, and cried all night. When he got up in the morning, there was no bread in the house, nor any money; so Gluck went and hired himself to another goldsmith, and he worked so hard, and so neatly, and so long every day, that he soon got money enough together to pay his brother's fine, and he went, and gave it all to Schwartz, and Schwartz got out of prison. Then Schwartz was quite pleased, and said he should have some of the gold of the river. But Gluck only begged he would go and see what had become of Hans.

Now when Schwartz had heard that Hans had stolen the holy water, he thought to himself that such a proceeding might not be considered altogether correct by the King of the Golden River, and determined to manage matters better. So he took some more of Gluck's money, and went to a bad priest, who gave him some holy water very readily for it. Then Schwartz was sure it was all quite right. So Schwartz got up early in the morning before the sun rose, and took some bread and wine, in a basket, and put his holy water in a flask, and set off for the mountains. Like his brother he was much surprised at the sight of the glacier, and had great difficulty in crossing it, even after leaving his basket behind him. The day was cloudless, but not bright: there was a heavy purple haze hanging over the sky, and the hills looked lowering and gloomy. And as Schwartz climbed the steep rock path, the thirst came upon him, as it had upon his brother, until he lifted his flask to his lips to drink. Then he saw the fair child lying near him on the rocks, and it cried to him, and moaned for water.

"Water indeed," said Schwartz; "I haven't half enough for myself," and passed on. And as he went he thought the sunbeams grew more dim, and he saw a low bank of black cloud rising out of the West; and, when he had climbed for another hour, the thirst overcame him again, and he would have drunk. Then he saw the old man lying before him on the path, and heard him cry out for water. "Water, indeed," said Schwartz, "I haven't half enough for myself," and on he went.

Then again the light seemed to fade from before his eyes, and he looked up, and, behold, a mist, of the color of blood, had come over the sun; and the bank of black cloud had risen very high, and its edges were tossing and tumbling like the waves of the angry sea. And they cast long shadows, which flickered over Schwartz's path.

Then Schwartz climbed for another hour, and again his thirst returned; and as he lifted his flask to his lips, he thought he saw his brother Hans lying exhausted on the path before him, and, as he gazed, the figure stretched its arms to him, and cried for water. "Ha, ha," laughed Schwartz, "are you there? remember the prison bars, my boy. Water, indeed! do you suppose I carried it all the way up here for *you?*" And he strode over the figure; yet, as he passed, he thought he saw a strange expression of mockery about its lips. And when he had gone a few yards farther, he looked back; but the figure was not there.

And a sudden horror came over Schwartz, he knew not why; but the thirst for gold prevailed over his fear, and he rushed on. And the bank of black cloud rose to the zenith, and out of it came bursts of spiry lightning, and waves of darkness seemed to heave and float between their flashes, over the whole heavens. And the sky where the sun was setting was all level, and like a lake of blood; and a strong wind came out of that sky, tearing its crimson clouds into fragments, and scattering them far into the darkness. And when Schwartz stood by the brink of the Golden River, its waves were black, like thunder clouds, but their foam was like fire; and the roar of the waters below, and the thunder above met, as he cast the flask into the stream. And, as he did so, the lightning glared in his eyes, and the earth gave way beneath him, and the waters closed over his cry. And the moaning of the river rose wildly into the night, as it gushed over the TWO BLACK STONES.

Chapter V: How little Gluck set off on an Expedition to the Golden River, and how he prospered therein; with other Matters of Interest.

When Gluck found that Schwartz did not come back, he was very sorry, and did not know what to do. He had no money, and was obliged to go and hire himself again to the goldsmith, who worked him very hard, and gave him very little money. So, after a month, or two, Gluck grew tired, and made up his mind to go and try his fortune with the Golden River. "The little king looked very kind," thought he. "I don't think he will turn me into a black stone." So he went to the priest, and the priest gave him some holy water as soon as he asked for it. Then Gluck took some bread in his basket, and the bottle of water, and set off very early for the mountains.

If the glacier had occasioned a great deal of fatigue to his brothers, it was twenty times worse for him, who was neither so strong nor so practised on the mountains. He had several very bad falls, lost his basket and bread, and was very much frightened at the strange noises under the ice. He lay a long time to rest on the grass, after he had got over, and began to climb the hill just in the hottest part of the day. When he had climbed for an hour, he got dreadfully thirsty, and was going to drink like his brothers, when he saw an old man coming down the path above him, looking very feeble, and leaning on a staff. "My son," said the old man, "I am faint with thirst, give me some of that water." Then Gluck looked at him, and when he saw that he was pale and weary, he gave him the water; "Only pray don't drink it all," said Gluck. But the old man drank a great deal, and gave him back the bottle two-thirds empty. Then he bade him good speed, and Gluck went on again merrily. And the path became easier to his feet, and two or three blades of grass appeared upon it, and some grasshoppers began singing on the bank beside it; and Gluck thought he had never heard such merry singing.

Then he went on for another hour, and the thirst increased on him so that he thought he should be forced to drink. But, as he raised the flask, he saw a little child lying panting by the road-side, and it cried out piteously for water. Then Gluck struggled with himself, and determined to bear the thirst a little longer; and he put the bottle to the child's lips, and it drank it all but a few drops. Then it smiled on him, and got up, and ran down the hill; and Gluck looked after it, till it became as small as a little star, and then turned, and began climbing again. And then there were all kinds of sweet flowers growing on the rocks, bright green moss, with pale pink starry flowers, and soft belled gentians, more blue than the sky at its deepest, and pure white transparent lilies. And crimson and purple butterflies darted hither and thither, and the sky sent down such pure light, that Gluck had never felt so happy in his life.

Yet, when he had climbed for another hour, his thirst became intolerable again; and, when he looked at his bottle, he saw that there were only five or six drops left in it, and he could not

venture to drink. And as he was hanging the flask to his belt again, he saw a little dog lying on the rocks, gasping for breath,—just as Hans had seen it on the day of his ascent. And Gluck stopped and looked at it, and then at the Golden River, not five hundred yards above him; and he thought of the dwarf's words, "that no one could succeed, except in his first attempt;" and he tried to pass the dog, but it whined piteously, and Gluck stopped again. "Poor beastie," said Gluck, "it'll be dead when I come down again, if I don't help it." Then he looked closer and closer at it, and its eye turned on him so mournfully that he could not stand it. "Confound the King and his gold too," said Gluck; and he opened the flask, and poured all the water into the dog's mouth.

The dog sprang up and stood on its hind legs. Its tail disappeared, its ears became long, longer, silky, golden; its nose became very red, its eyes became very twinkling; in three seconds the dog was gone, and before Gluck stood his old acquaintance, the King of the Golden River.

"Thank you," said the monarch; "but don't be frightened, it's all right;" for Gluck showed manifest symptoms of consternation at this unlooked for reply to his last observation. "Why didn't you come before," continued the dwarf, "instead of sending me those rascally brothers of yours, for me to have the trouble of turning into stones? Very hard stones they make too."

"Oh dear me!" said Gluck, "have you really been so cruel?"

"Cruel!" said the dwarf, "they poured unholy water into my stream; do you suppose I'm going to allow that?"

"Why," said Gluck, "I am sure, sir,—your majesty, I mean,—they got the water out of the church font."

"Very probably," replied the dwarf; "but," and his countenance grew stern as he spoke, "the water which has been refused to the cry of the weary and dying, is unholy, though it had been blessed by every saint in heaven; and the water which is found in the vessel of mercy is holy, though it had been defiled with corpses."

So saying, the dwarf stooped and plucked a lily that grew at his feet. On its white leaves there hung three drops of clear dew. And the dwarf shook them into the flask which Gluck held in his hand. "Cast these into the river," he said, "and descend on the other side of the mountains into the Treasure Valley. And so good speed."

As he spoke, the figure of the dwarf became indistinct. The playing colors of his robe formed themselves into a prismatic mist of dewy light; he stood for an instant veiled with them as with the belt of a broad rainbow. The colors grew faint, the mist rose into the air; the monarch had evaporated.

And Gluck climbed to the brink of the Golden River, and its waves were as clear as crystal, and as brilliant as the sun. And when he cast the three drops of dew into the stream, there opened where they fell, a small circular whirlpool, into which the waters descended with a musical noise.

Gluck stood watching it for some time, very much disappointed, because not only the river was not turned into gold, but its waters seemed much diminished in quantity. Yet he obeyed his friend the dwarf, and descended the other side of the mountains, towards the Treasure Valley; and, as he went, he thought he heard the noise of water working its way under the ground. And, when he came in sight of the Treasure Valley, behold, a river, like the Golden River, was springing from a new cleft of the rocks above it, and was flowing in innumerable streams among the dry heaps of red sand.

And as Gluck gazed, fresh grass sprang beside the new streams, and creeping plants grew, and climbed among the moistening soil. Young flowers opened suddenly along the river sides, as stars leap out when twilight is deepening, and thickets of myrtle, and tendrils of vine, cast lengthening shadows over the valley as they grew. And thus the Treasure Valley became a garden again, and the inheritance, which had been lost by cruelty, was regained by love.

And Gluck went, and dwelt in the valley, and the poor were never driven from his door; so that his barns became full of corn, and his house of treasure. And, for him, the river had, according to the dwarf's promise, become a River of Gold.

And, to this day, the inhabitants of the valley point out the place, where the three drops of holy dew were cast into the stream, and trace the course of the Golden River under the ground, until it emerges in the Treasure Valley. And, at the top of the cataract of the Golden River, are still to be seen two BLACK STONES, round which the waters howl mournfully every day at sunset; and these stones are still called by the people of the valley, THE BLACK BROTHERS.

HOW THEY BRING BACK THE VILLAGE OF CREAM PUFFS WHEN THE WIND BLOWS IT AWAY

Carl Sandburg

When a poet turns to nonsense, something unusual is bound to result. Carl Sandburg, poet, newspaperman, and biographer, declared that he was tired of reading his little girls stories about castles and kings. Why not something American, something in a lingo they would understand? With this declaration of independence, he created his Rootabaga Stories. *The fantastic nonsense about a boy who lived in the Village of Liver and Onions or about a Village of Cream Puffs that blew away sent his own three little girls into gales of laughter. Of course, they were luckier than the rest of us because they heard the author of the stories read them in his wonderful voice and manner. But the airy lightness of these tales carries over for any reader. You have to know them well to read them well because they run on like a patter-song with hardly a chance to catch your breath.*

A girl named Wing Tip the Spick came to the Village of Liver-and-Onions to visit her uncle and her uncle's uncle on her mother's side and her uncle and her uncle's uncle on her father's side.

It was the first time the four uncles had a chance to see their little relation, their niece. Each one of the four uncles was proud of the blue eyes of Wing Tip the Spick.

The two uncles on her mother's side took a long deep look into her blue eyes and said, "Her

"How They Bring Back the Village of Cream Puffs When the Wind Blows It Away." From *Rootabaga Stories* by Carl Sandburg, copyright 1922, 1923 by Harcourt, Brace and Company, Inc.; renewed 1950, 1951 by Carl Sandburg. Reprinted by permission of the publishers.

eyes are so blue, such a clear light blue, they are the same as cornflowers with blue raindrops shining and dancing on silver leaves after a sun shower in any of the summer months."

And the two uncles on her father's side, after taking a long deep look into the eyes of Wing Tip the Spick, said, "Her eyes are so blue, such a clear light shining blue, they are the same as cornflowers with blue raindrops shining and dancing on the silver leaves after a sun shower in any of the summer months."

And though Wing Tip the Spick didn't listen and didn't hear what the uncles said about her blue eyes, she did say to herself when they were not listening, "I know these are sweet uncles and I am going to have a sweet time visiting my relations."

The four uncles said to her, "Will you let us ask you two questions, first the first question and second the second question?"

"I will let you ask me fifty questions this morning, fifty questions tomorrow morning, and fifty questions any morning. I like to listen to questions. They slip in one ear and slip out of the other."

Then the uncles asked her the first question first, "Where do you come from?" and the second question second, "Why do you have two freckles on your chin?"

"Answering your first question first," said Wing Tip the Spick, "I come from the Village of Cream Puffs, a little light village on the upland corn prairie. From a long ways off it looks like a little hat you could wear on the end of your thumb to keep the rain off your thumb."

"Tell us more," said one uncle. "Tell us much," said another uncle. "Tell it without stopping," added another uncle. "Interruptions nix nix," murmured the last of the uncles.

"It is a light little village on the upland corn prairie many miles past the sunset in the west," went on Wing Tip the Spick. "It is light the same as a cream puff is light. It sits all by itself on the big long prairie where the prairie goes up in a slope. There on the slope the winds play around the village. They sing it wind songs, summer wind songs in summer, winter wind songs in winter."

"And sometimes like an accident, the wind gets rough. And when the wind gets rough it picks up the little Village of Cream Puffs and blows it away off in the sky—all by itself."

"O-o-h-h," said one uncle. "Um-m-m-m," said the other three uncles.

"Now the people in the village all understand the winds with their wind songs in summer and winter. And they understand the rough wind who comes sometimes and picks up the village and blows it away off high in the sky all by itself.

"If you go to the public square in the middle of the village you will see a big roundhouse. If you take the top off the roundhouse you will see a big spool with a long string winding up around the spool.

"Now whenever the rough wind comes and picks up the village and blows it away off high in the sky all by itself then the string winds loose off the spool, because the village is fastened to the string. So the rough wind blows and blows and the string on the spool winds looser and looser the farther the village goes blowing away off into the sky all by itself.

"Then at last when the rough wind, so forgetful, so careless, has had all the fun it wants, then the people of the village all come together and begin to wind up the spool and bring back the village where it was before."

"O-o-h-h," said one uncle. "Um-m-m-m," said the other three uncles.

"And sometimes when you come to the village to see your little relation, your niece who has four such sweet uncles, maybe she will lead you through the middle of the city to the public square and show you the roundhouse. They call it the Roundhouse of the Big Spool. And they are proud because it was thought up and is there to show when visitors come."

"And now will you answer the second question second—why do you have two freckles on your chin?" interrupted the uncle who had said before, "Interruptions nix nix."

"The freckles are put on," answered Wing Tip the Spick. "When a girl goes away from the Village of Cream Puffs her mother puts on two freckles, on the chin. Each freckle must be the same as a little burnt cream puff kept in the oven too long. After the two freckles looking like two little burnt cream puffs are put on her chin, they remind the girl every morning when she combs her hair and looks in the looking glass. They remind her where she came from and she mustn't stay away too long."

"Oh-h-h-h," said one uncle. "Um-m-m-m," said the other three uncles. And they talked among each other afterward, the four uncles by themselves, saying:

"She has a gift. It is her eyes. They are so blue, such a clear light blue, the same as cornflowers with blue raindrops shining and dancing on silver leaves after a sun shower in any of the summer months."

At the same time Wing Tip the Spick was saying to herself, "I know for sure now these are sweet uncles and I am going to have a sweet time visiting my relations."

A MAD TEA-PARTY

Lewis Carroll

When an astonished England began investigating the author of Alice's Adventures in Wonderland, *it was soon discovered that there was no such person as Lewis Carroll. The name concealed a staid lecturer in mathematics at Oxford, Charles Lutwidge Dodgson. This young man liked children, and on one famous summer afternoon, he rowed three little girls up the River Cherwell. On the river bank, while they were having tea, the children asked for a story, and the young man told them his masterly concoction of sense and nonsense, nightmares and pleasant dreams, the world up-side-down and hind-side-before—fantasia unlimited! If the children enjoy this excerpt, try the whole book.*

There was a table set out under a tree in front of the house, and the March Hare and the Hatter were having tea at it: a Dormouse was sitting between them, fast asleep, and the other two were using it as a cushion, resting their elbows on it, and talking over its head. "Very uncomfortable for the Dormouse," thought Alice; "only, as it's asleep, I suppose it doesn't mind."

The table was a large one, but the three were all crowded together at one corner of it: "No

"A Mad Tea-Party." From *Alice's Adventures in Wonderland* by Lewis Carroll

room! No room!" they cried out when they saw Alice coming. "There's *plenty* of room!" said Alice indignantly, and she sat down in a large arm-chair at one end of the table.

"Have some wine," the March Hare said in an encouraging tone.

Alice looked all round the table, but there was nothing on it but tea. "I don't see any wine," she remarked.

"There isn't any," said the March Hare.

"Then it wasn't very civil of you to offer it," said Alice angrily.

"It wasn't very civil of you to sit down without being invited," said the March Hare.

"I didn't know it was *your* table," said Alice; "it's laid for a great many more than three."

"Your hair wants cutting," said the Hatter. He had been looking at Alice for some time with great curiosity, and this was his first speech.

"You should learn not to make personal remarks," Alice said with some severity: "It's very rude."

The Hatter opened his eyes very wide on hearing this; but all he *said* was, "Why is a raven like a writing-desk?"

"Come, we shall have some fun now!" thought Alice. "I'm glad they've begun asking riddles—I believe I can guess that," she added aloud.

"Do you mean that you think you can find out the answer to it?" said the March Hare.

"Exactly so," said Alice.

"Then you should say what you mean," the March Hare went on.

"I do," Alice hastily replied; "at least—at least I mean what I say—that's the same thing, you know."

"Not the same thing a bit!" said the Hatter. "Why, you might just as well say that 'I see what I eat' is the same thing as 'I eat what I see'!"

"You might just as well say," added the March Hare, "that 'I like what I get' is the same thing as 'I get what I like'!"

"You might just as well say," added the Dormouse, who seemed to be talking in his sleep, "that 'I breathe when I sleep' is the same thing as 'I sleep when I breathe'!"

"It *is* the same thing with you," said the Hatter, and here the conversation dropped, and the party sat silent for a minute, while Alice thought over all she could remember about ravens and writing-desks, which wasn't much.

The Hatter was the first to break the silence. "What day of the month is it?" he said, turning to Alice: he had taken his watch out of his pocket, and was looking at it uneasily, shaking it every now and then, and holding it to his ear.

Alice considered a little, and said, "The fourth."

"Two days wrong!" sighed the Hatter. "I told you butter wouldn't suit the works!" he added, looking angrily at the March Hare.

"It was the *best* butter," the March Hare meekly replied.

"Yes, but some crumbs must have got in as well," the Hatter grumbled: "you shouldn't have put it in with the bread-knife."

The March Hare took the watch and looked at it gloomily: then he dipped it into his cup of tea, and looked at it again: but he could think of nothing better to say than his first remark, "It was the *best* butter, you know."

Alice had been looking over his shoulder with some curiosity. "What a funny watch!" she remarked. "It tells the day of the month, and doesn't tell what o'clock it is!"

"Why should it?" muttered the Hatter. "Does *your* watch tell you what year it is?"

"Of course not," Alice replied very readily: "but that's because it stays the same year for such a long time together."

"Which is just the case with *mine*," said the Hatter.

Alice felt dreadfully puzzled. The Hatter's remark seemed to her to have no sort of meaning in it, and yet it was certainly English. "I don't quite understand you," she said, as politely as she could.

"The Dormouse is asleep again," said the Hatter, and he poured a little hot tea on to its nose.

The Dormouse shook its head impatiently, and said, without opening its eyes, "Of course, of course: just what I was going to remark myself."

"Have you guessed the riddle yet?" the Hatter said, turning to Alice again.

"No, I give it up," Alice replied: "what's the answer?"

"I haven't the slightest idea," said the Hatter.

"Nor I," said the March Hare.

Alice sighed wearily. "I think you might do something better with the time," she said, "than wasting it in asking riddles that have no answers."

"If you knew Time as well as I do," said the Hatter, "you wouldn't talk about wasting *it!* It's *him*."

"I don't know what you mean," said Alice.

"Of course you don't!" the Hatter said, tossing his head contemptuously. "I dare say you never even spoke to Time!"

"Perhaps not," Alice cautiously replied: "but I know I have to beat time when I learn music."

"Ah! That accounts for it," said the Hatter. "He won't stand beating. Now, if you only kept on good terms with him, he'd do almost anything you liked with the clock.

"For instance, suppose it were nine o'clock in the morning, just time to begin lessons: you'd only have to whisper a hint to Time, and round goes the clock in a twinkling! Half-past one, time for dinner!"

("I only wish it was," the March Hare said to itself in a whisper.)

"That would be grand, certainly," said Alice thoughtfully; "but then—I shouldn't be hungry for it, you know."

"Not at first, perhaps," said the Hatter; "but you could keep it to half-past one as long as you liked."

"Is that the way *you* manage?" Alice asked.

The Hatter shook his head mournfully. "Not I!" he replied. "We quarreled last March—just before *he* went mad, you know—" (pointing with his teaspoon at the March Hare,) "—it was at the great concert given by the Queen of Hearts, and I had to sing

'Twinkle, twinkle, little bat!
How I wonder what you're at!'

You know the song, perhaps?"

"I've heard something like it," said Alice.

"It goes on, you know," the Hatter continued, "in this way:—

'Up above the world you fly,
Like a teatray in the sky.
Twinkle, twinkle—' "

Here the Dormouse shook itself, and began singing in its sleep *"Twinkle, twinkle, twinkle, twinkle—"* and went on so long that they had to pinch it to make it stop.

"Well, I'd hardly finished the first verse," said the Hatter, "when the Queen bawled out 'He's murdering the time! Off with his head!' "

"How dreadfully savage!" exclaimed Alice.

"And ever since that," the Hatter went on in a mournful tone, "he won't do a thing I ask! It's always six o'clock now."

A bright idea came into Alice's head. "Is that the reason so many tea-things are put out here?" she asked.

"Yes, that's it," said the Hatter with a sigh: "it's always tea-time, and we've no time to wash the things between whiles."

"Then you keep moving round, I suppose?" said Alice.

"Exactly so," said the Hatter: "as the things get used up."

"But when you come to the beginning again?" Alice ventured to ask.

"Suppose we change the subject," the March Hare interrupted, yawning. "I'm getting tired of this. I vote the young lady tells us a story."

"I'm afraid I don't know one," said Alice, rather alarmed at the proposal.

"Then the Dormouse shall!" they both cried. "Wake up, Dormouse!" And they pinched it on both sides at once.

The Dormouse slowly opened his eyes. "I wasn't asleep," he said in a hoarse, feeble voice: "I heard every word you fellows were saying."

"Tell us a story!" said the March Hare.

"Yes, please do!" pleaded Alice.

"And be quick about it," added the Hatter, "or you'll be asleep again before it's done."

"Once upon a time there were three little sisters," the Dormouse began in a great hurry; "and their names were Elsie, Lacie, and Tillie; and they lived at the bottom of a well—"

"What did they live on?" said Alice, who always took a great interest in questions of eating and drinking.

"They lived on treacle," said the Dormouse, after thinking a minute or two.

"They couldn't have done that, you know," Alice gently remarked. "They'd have been ill."

"So they were," said the Dormouse; *"very* ill."

Alice tried a little to fancy to herself what such an extraordinary way of living would be like, but it puzzled her too much, so she went on: "But why did they live at the bottom of a well?"

"Take some more tea," the March Hare said to Alice, very earnestly.

"I've had nothing yet," Alice replied in an offended tone, "so I can't take more."

"You mean you can't take *less,*" said the Hatter: "it's very easy to take *more* than nothing."

"Nobody asked *your* opinion," said Alice.

"Who's making personal remarks now?" the Hatter asked triumphantly.

Alice did not quite know what to say to this: so she helped herself to some tea and bread-and-butter, and then turned to the Dormouse, and repeated her question. "Why did they live at the bottom of a well?"

The Dormouse again took a minute or two to think about it, and then said, "It was a treacle-well."

"There's no such thing!" Alice was beginning very angrily, but the Hatter and the March Hare went "Sh! Sh!" and the Dormouse sulkily remarked, "If you can't be civil, you'd better finish the story for yourself."

"No, please go on!" Alice said very humbly. "I won't interrupt you again. I dare say there may be *one.*"

"One, indeed!" said the Dormouse indignantly. However, he consented to go on. "And so these three little sisters—they were learning to draw, you know—"

"What did they draw?" said Alice, quite forgetting her promise.

"Treacle," said the Dormouse, without considering at all this time.

"I want a clean cup," interrupted the Hatter: "let's all move one place on."

He moved on as he spoke, and the Dormouse followed him: the March Hare moved into the Dormouse's place, and Alice rather unwillingly took the place of the March Hare. The Hatter was the only one who got any advantage from the change: and Alice was a good deal worse off than before, as the March Hare had just upset the milk-jug into his plate.

Alice did not wish to offend the Dormouse again, so she began very cautiously: "But I don't understand. Where did they draw the treacle from?"

"You can draw water out of a water-well," said the Hatter; "so I should think you could draw treacle out of a treacle-well—eh, stupid?"

"But they were *in* the well," Alice said to the Dormouse, not choosing to notice this last remark.

"Of course they were," said the Dormouse,— "well in."

This answer so confused poor Alice, that she let the Dormouse go on for some time without interrupting it.

"They were learning to draw," the Dormouse went on, yawning and rubbing his eyes, for it was getting very sleepy; "and they drew all manner of things—everything that begins with an M—"

"Why with an M?" said Alice.

"Why not?" said the March Hare.

Alice was silent.

The Dormouse had closed its eyes by this time, and was going off into a doze, but, on being pinched by the Hatter, it woke up again with a little shriek, and went on: "—that begins with an M, such as mousetraps, and the moon, and memory, and muchness—you know you say things are 'much of a muchness'—did you ever see such a thing as a drawing of a muchness?"

"Really, now you ask me," said Alice, very much confused, "I don't think—"

"Then you shouldn't talk," said the Hatter.

This piece of rudeness was more than Alice could bear: she got up in great disgust, and walked off: the Dormouse fell asleep instantly, and neither of the others took the least notice of her going, though she looked back once or twice, half hoping that they would call after her: the last time she saw them, they were trying to put the Dormouse into the teapot.

"At any rate I'll never go *there* again!" said Alice as she picked her way through the wood. "It's the stupidest tea-party I ever was at in all my life!"

Just as she said this, she noticed that one of the trees had a door leading right into it. "That's very curious!" she thought. "But everything's curious today. I think I may as well go in at once." And in she went.

Once more she found herself in the long hall, and close to the little glass table. "Now, I'll manage better this time," she said to herself, and began by taking the little golden key, and unlocking the door that led into the garden. Then she set to work nibbling at the mushroom (she had kept a piece of it in her pocket) till she was about a foot high: then she walked down the little passage: and *then*—she found herself at last in the beautiful garden, among the bright flowerbeds and the cool fountains.

AIRY-GO-ROUND

William Pène du Bois

The "intermission" with which this story begins is in Professor Sherman's lecture on his escape from an island that exploded. In this part of his talk he describes one of his surprising adventures on the Island of Krakatoa.

During the intermission, the mayor and the Chief Surgeon of the San Francisco General Hospital rushed to Professor Sherman's bedside to see if he was all right. "Are you tired?" they asked in one voice. "Would you rather resume tomorrow?" asked the Mayor. "How do you feel?" asked the Chief Surgeon. "Is there anything we can do for you?"

"I feel fine," said Professor Sherman.

"Would you like one of the nurses to change the drinking water in your carafe?" asked the Chief Surgeon.

"I don't care, it tastes all right to me."

"Could I fetch you a little refreshment?" asked the Mayor. "Something to renew your strength?"

"If you insist," said the Professor. The Mayor ran off at a fast puffing trot while the Chief Surgeon busied himself tucking in the comforter on the Professor's bed. It should have been obvious to anyone, even two such important personages as the Mayor and Chief Surgeon, that all Professor Sherman wanted during this intermission he had called was a few minutes of rest.

The Mayor came back with a nip and the Professor swallowed it in one gulp. Then, looking at the Mayor and Surgeon, he said with a smile on his face, "You know, Gentlemen, this to me is very funny. A little over a month ago, I was an insignificant arithmetic teacher who would have found it almost impossible to get to see either one of you. Now you are waiting on me like a pair of well-trained valets. I thank you for your kind attention. It goes to show how wonderful ballooning can be. You never can tell where the winds will blow you, what fantastic good fortune they can lead you to. *Long live balloons!*" he shouted. The Mayor and the Chief Surgeon joined in with a few sheepish giggles, then backed away.

By this time the fifteen minutes were up and Professor Sherman was gratified to see that the people of the audience had quietly returned to their seats and were sitting attentively. The packed auditorium wasn't making a sound. It was waiting anxiously to hear the end of his extraordinary story.

The Chief Surgeon saw, as before, that the Professor was comfortably propped up with pillows, and the Mayor walked over to the Professor's bedside. With one hand resting on the head of the bed, he turned to the audience and said:

"Again it gives me great pleasure to present Professor William Waterman Sherman."

The Professor thanked the Mayor, cleared his throat, and resumed his talk:

Mr. F. led me to the first invention he had promised to show me, the Balloon Merry-Go-Round. On our way I told Mr. F. that the name of the invention suggested something at an amusement park. "Just what is this invention for?"

"It is part of an amusement park," said Mr. F., "which the children of Krakatoa are planning for themselves. You see, our children now are between the ages of ten and fifteen. When we return from our trips to other countries, they help us unload our freighter with great interest. It suddenly dawned on them a year or so ago that it would be an excellent idea if a few boatloads were brought back full of supplies exclusively for them; for after all they do own a share in the mines, too. We agreed to give them two boatloads a year, so all of the children held a meeting to decide how best to fill their freighters.

This amusement park they have started to build is the result of their planning. The Balloon Merry-Go-Round is their own invention, designed with but little help from us."

"Is there any school here?" I asked.

"The children have no formal schooling. We have taught them how to read and write, and we have tried to teach them a little arithmetic. They have all taken part in the building of our international houses—which is most educating in itself. But all in all, a school is sorely needed here. You aren't by any chance a teacher, are you? Just what does the title Professor stand for in your case?"

"Professor of, uh, Aeronautics," I stuttered. "I teach Balloon Theory at, uh, the San Francisco Lighter than Air School." I felt a flush of heat in my cheeks as I waded through this fabulous lie. I had no intention of getting involved again in teaching, the very thing from which this trip of mine was intended to take me.

"How interesting," said Mr. F. "That goes to show how quickly one gets out of touch with one's native city. I can't say that I even recall hearing of such an institution."

"It's one of the latest," I muttered, "practically brand new." Then quickly changing the subject, I asked what other forms of amusement could be found at the park.

"So far, they have just had time to design and build the Merry-Go-Round, but they have a lot more planned. Most of the usual rides found at amusement parks are impractical for Krakatoa because they are higher than the jungle life on the Island and would be visible from the sea. As a matter of fact, we only take rides on the Balloon Merry-Go-Round after thoroughly scanning the horizon for passing ships. We never use it if anything is in sight. Do you see that tall pole in the distance?"

"Yes, I do," I said. The pole was straight and the same width at the bottom as at the top. It was threaded like a gigantic screw and it was about seventy-five feet tall.

"That's part of the Balloon Merry-Go-Round, the axle around which it revolves to give it its spin when it is gaining altitude."

"Can't that be seen from the ocean?"

"Yes, it can. But one lone pole isn't enough to attract much attention from passing ships."

We came to a little forest of palm trees, the same sort of neatly kept little forest I had seen the day before, with freshly cut lawn instead of the usual jungle underbrush. We walked through this forest for a hundred yards or so and then came upon a clearing. In the middle of this clearing was what was apparently the Balloon Merry-Go-Round. There were eight little boats around the base of the pole, all joined together bow to stern. In the place of oarlocks, there were two brass rings on these boats, and through these rings passed poles which all met at the main vertical pole of the Merry-Go-Round where they were screwed into the hub of another large brass ring around the pole, forming spokes of a giant wheel. Each boat was covered with a protective tarpaulin. Mr. F. removed one of the tarpaulins and showed me one. They were nice little centerboard sailboats, sturdy and quite seaworthy. The sails were neatly stowed in trim lockers. I didn't notice any masts, but there was definitely a place for them. Alongside of each of these boats was a large deflated balloon painted a pale sky-blue. Off to one side in the clearing there was a little shack made of bamboo which reminded me very much of my basket house. On its walls outside, eight silk hoses were hanging, neatly coiled up and in line. There was a bell on top of this little shack, which could be reached by climbing a ladder.

Mr. F. walked over to the shack, went inside, and came out again with a spyglass. He climbed up the ladder to the roof of the shack and carefully looked over the horizon around him, apparently for ships. "Would you care to risk a trip in it?" he asked me. "The weather today is ideal."

"As an ardent balloonist, I accept with enthusiasm; but as a sixty-six-year-old man I must confess that I accept with some trepidation. Is it safe?"

"Absolutely," answered Mr. F. "You don't believe that we would allow our children to make ascensions in dangerous contraptions, do you?"

"I guess not," I said, reassured. "I am sure that any invention using balloons and wind as motive power cannot but be enjoyable."

"Very well, then," said Mr. F. He then loudly rang the bell on top of the shack. This sound produced the same reaction, only considerably

happier and more excited, as a school bell back home. We were shortly surrounded by children. These children didn't seem to need to be explained anything either; as soon as they arrived in the clearing they made themselves extremely busy readying the Balloon Merry-Go-Round. They took the tarpaulins off all the boats and rolled them up neatly. Four of the children ran into the shack where they prepared the hydrogen machine and pumps. Another eight each grabbed a silk hose, attached it to the hydrogen machine in the shack on one end, and to one of the balloons on the other. The balloons were all carefully unfolded and laid out flat on the ground, and the nets and ropes which attached them to the boats were carefully placed around and beside them so that they wouldn't get tangled up when the balloons were filled with gas. Slowly the balloons started to fill with hydrogen, the ones nearest the pumps filling faster than the others. They lazily lifted themselves off the ground with the children watching them carefully, constantly straightening the ropes so they wouldn't get tangled. Soon they were all full of hydrogen and straining at the boats which were roped to the ground. All forty children were present, working efficiently on the Merry-Go-Round, although it was apparent that there was only room for fourteen of them on this trip. There was room for two in each boat, making a total of sixteen seats, but Mr. F. and I were going to occupy two of the seats. There was no arguing among the children as to whose turn it was; they must have had some sort of passenger schedule they followed closely. I did notice that neither B-1 nor B-2 were among the children who climbed into the boats when they were ready. I suppose that this was because it was "B" Day of the Month of Lamb and they had plenty of work to do at their British chop house. I sat in a boat with Mr. F's son, F-1, and Mr. F. sat with a child in a boat which was on the opposite side of the big pole from ours. "This will make the Merry-Go-Round balance better," said F-1.

There were two children on the ground near each boat. When we were all aboard, they detached the silk hydrogen hoses and rolled them back up to the shack where they carefully hung them up. They then returned to us and one held a rope at the bow of each boat and the other held a rope at the boat's stern. One of the children passengers had a blank pistol, the sort used for starting races at track meets. He stood up and yelled in a high clear voice, *"Is everybody ready?"*

A shrill and deafening *"yes"* was heard, mixed with the deeper voices of Mr. F. and myself. At this signal, the children standing near the boats all gave their ropes a sharp pull, which seemed to unhook the boats from the ground, and they all ran around the pole in the direction we were heading, giving us a good fast start.

The boats were joined together to form the rim of a wheel. The poles going through the brass oarlocks of the boats formed the spokes of this wheel. The spokes were attached to a big brass ring, or hub of the wheel, and this whole gigantic Merry-Go-Round revolved around the seventy-five-foot pole which was pointing straight up to the sky and was threaded like a screw. The balloons lifted the boats around and around the huge screw up into the air. The Balloon Merry-Go-Round gained speed as it gained altitude. The pole was well greased so that by the time we neared the top we were going very fast. I asked F-1 what happened when we reached the top of the pole. "Do we quickly deflate the balloons and revolve back down to the ground around the pole in the opposite direction?"

"Of course not," said F-1. "We fly right off the pole into the air."

"You'll see," he said.

We soon reached the top and the Merry-Go-Round lunged upward as it lost its grip on the pole. The wind immediately started to carry us off over the Island. We were gaining altitude fast and, of course, still spinning around at great speed. I must admit this was truly a delightful and exciting ride, unlike any other balloon experience I have ever had. I saw now how the boats were kept level. A child in each boat held the ripcord of his boat's balloon. Whenever a boat went a little higher than the others, the ripcord would be pulled releasing a little hydrogen until the boat was again on the same level.

"You must only be able to take short trips," I told F-1, "if you constantly have to release gas to keep the Merry-Go-Round level."

"That's right," he answered. "The length of our trips depends on many things such as the calmness of the weather, how well we distribute the weight in the boats, and how skillfully we control the ripcords. But you understand," he added, "the Balloon Merry-Go-Round wasn't built for travel but rather for short pleasure trips."

"Oh, of course," I said.

The Balloon Merry-Go-Round was heading directly for the mountain. I saw that we were going to fly over it. I asked F-1 if this were not dangerous.

"It isn't dangerous, but it's rather unfortunate because it always means a short trip."

"Why?" I asked.

"Because the huge crater of the volcanic mountain is full of hot air which forms sort of a vacuum. When we fly over the crater, the Merry-Go-Round is sucked downward rather violently and we always use up a lot of gas controlling it and keeping it level."

"Isn't this hazardous?" I asked.

"No," said F-1, "by the time we reach the mountain, we will be high enough to clear it by a great distance. The only danger in taking a ride in this is landing on the ground or on the mountain, or worst of all, in the mountain when the wind is calm. Krakatoa is a small island, and if there is any wind at all, it will carry the Merry-Go-Round out to sea. Once when we first got it, we took a trip on a very calm day. We went straight up, spun around a while, and gradually lost altitude, landing in a forest of palm trees. No one was hurt, but some of the boats were damaged and one of the balloons was torn. Since then, we have only risked trips when there is wind."

We were nearing the mountain and I leaned over the side of my boat to look down at the crater. There was a thick gray smoke crawling around inside. It was like looking into a horrible pit full of elephants. When we were directly over the mountain there was a sickening atmosphere of hot air permeated with sulphurous gases. The Merry-Go-Round started tossing around violently over the pit, and the children with the ripcords kept a careful watch directly across our giant wheel at opposite boats to keep the Merry-Go-Round as steady and level as possible. Hanging on tightly, I leaned over the side of the boat in order to have a direct look into the volcanic

crater itself. In places where the smoke had cleared a bit I could see a lake of thick molten lava boiling and bubbling in slow motion. It was a sickening, frightening sight. As I was leaning over, the Merry-Go-Round suddenly plunged downward, then swayed from side to side as the children steadied it. I must have taken a deep gasp of breath, out of fear, I suppose, and my lungs were suddenly filled with hot sulphurous fumes. The Merry-Go-Round was still spinning fast, as well as pitching and rocking in the air. I hastily drew my head back into the boat, shut my eyes, and lay down on the bottom of the boat. I could hear the rumbling of the mountain beneath me mixed with the hissing noise of hydrogen being released from the balloons. I think I was as close to being sick then as it is possible for anyone to be. We were soon over the mountain, and in fresh, calm air again and I sat up feeling considerably better.

"To tell you the truth, Sir," said F-1, who apparently could well see that I had nearly lost

my British breakfast, "I was nearly sick myself that time. The mountain seems unusually violent this morning. I hope this isn't a bad sign."

I took this to be the remark of a younger balloonist comforting an older one who had nearly made a fool of himself. I told him that my behavior was quite inexcusable.

Flying over water in this spinning airship was completely enjoyable. The magnificent seascape of the Pacific Ocean passed before your eyes half of the time, and Krakatoa in its entirety was beneath you for your careful observation with each turn of the Merry-Go-Round. The Island looked beautiful from the air. Its vegetation was so rich, warm, and soft-looking. The mountain looked so fearful and exciting. The magnificent houses of all nations looked like extraordinary doll's houses on felt lawns, and the Krakatoan crystal house shone like a jewel. The contrast between the trimmed interior and untrimmed ring of jungle around the Island was easy to see from our boats. The Island looked like a formal garden surrounded by a bushy untrimmed hedge.

After a flight lasting approximately thirty-five minutes we were near the surface of the water. The children, controlling their ripcords like experts, lowered the Merry-Go-Round gently and smoothly into the Ocean. We made one complete turn in the water and came slowly to a stop. "Well," I exclaimed, "that was undoubtedly the most thrilling and unusual trip I have ever had the pleasure of taking."

The children in the boats, Mr. F., and I then all leaned back and relaxed a while in the sun, looking up at the balloons which were now half empty and bobbing back and forth with the wind. Suddenly one of the boys, the same one who had fired the starting gun, stood up and said, "All right, everybody, let's go."

At this command, the rest of the children stood up and carefully deflated their balloons and folded them up in their boats without letting any part of them touch water. They folded them lengthwise first, then rolled them from the top toward the bottom where the gas escape was, thus forcing all of the gas out of them and making small neat bundles. They opened the little lockers in the boats, where the sails were, took the sails out, and replaced them with the folded balloons. Each boat had one mainsail.

"How do you sail these boats when they are all attached together like a wheel?" I asked. "And what do you use for masts?" These were foolish questions, I immediately realized, for while I was asking them I managed to figure out these problems for myself.

First of all, the children detached the boats one from the other at their bows and sterns. When this was done, they were still attached to each other by the poles which formed the spokes of the giant wheel. These poles were obviously the masts when the boats were used for sailing. The children, two on each pole, all pushed together toward the center hub until the poles slid out through the brass oarlock rings on their boats. Then, still working two on each pole, they unscrewed the poles from the brass hub in the center. They all unscrewed their poles except one boy, the boy who gave the commands. He pulled his pole in with the hub still attached to it, unscrewed the hub in his boat, and put it away in a separate locker. Now that they each had their masts, it was a simple problem to put them into the mast holes. Mr. F. and I did our best to work as efficiently as any of the other crew members. Soon the mainsail was rigged up and we were ready to sail back to the Island. Only the need for a boom was absent from this compact invention. We lowered centerboards and lined up. It was evidently the custom to race home. The boy who gave the signals took out his gun, fired it, and we were homeward bound as fast as the wind would take us. I am afraid I was more of a hindrance than a capable assistant to young F-1. We finished the race last by about seven minutes. The boats were moored to a dock near the freighter in the hidden inlet and we assembled on shore. F-1 explained to me that the boy who had given the signals was the "Captain of the Day," some sort of honor each child received in turn.

The Captain of the Day told the rest of us that since this was my first trip in the Balloon Merry-Go-Round, the results of the boat race wouldn't count on the Official Scoring Sheet. F-1 let out a whooping cheer at this which made me feel quite badly. The Captain of the Day then took me aside and told me, in a most polite way, that he thought it would be an excellent idea if I learned a bit about sailing since I now found myself to be a citizen of Krakatoa. I assured him that I would.

The Captain of the Day then closed the meeting by saying that the Merry-Go-Round would be reassembled around the flying pole right after supper. "And I want you all to be here and help," he said, looking sternly in my direction.

After forty years of schoolteaching I found myself being ordered about by a child. I couldn't help but find this heretofore impossible turnabout amusing. I was indeed far away from the usual dull school routines I so disliked.

"I'll be there!" I said in a loud voice, as everybody looked at me and laughed.

The whole trip had taken about five hours and we had therefore missed lunch. I devoured an excellent supper at the B.'s chop house, and then Mr. F. and I reported to the flying pole. The Captain of the Day rang the bell on top of the shack assembling all of the children and we were divided into eight groups of five. (B-1 and B-2 were still busy.) With five on each boat, we had the Merry-Go-Round reassembled and ready to go in less than half an hour. I will confess, though, that after this busy second day on the fabulous Island, I was well ready for bed and slept like a top.

from THE CHILDREN OF GREEN KNOWE

Lucy Maria Boston

This book is one of the most unusual and beautiful ghost stories ever written. It is about Toseland (Tolly), a lonely boy, staying with his great-grandmother in a big stone castle. It suggests witches, ghosts, and spells. Tolly encounters all three and comes to love the ghost children from the long, long ago of his own family. Here is the first chapter.

A little boy was sitting in the corner of a railway carriage looking out at the rain, which was splashing against the windows and blotching

From *The Children of Green Knowe*, copyright 1954, © 1955 by L. M. Boston. Reprinted by permission of Harcourt, Brace and Company, Inc., N. Y., and Faber & Faber Ltd., London

downward in an ugly, dirty way. He was not the only person in the carriage, but the others were strangers to him. He was alone as usual. There were two women opposite him, a fat one and a thin one, and they talked without stopping, smacking their lips in between sentences and seeming to enjoy what they said as much as if it were something to eat. They were knitting all the time, and whenever the train stopped the click-clack of their needles was loud and clear like two clocks. It was a stopping train—more stop than go—and it had been crawling along through flat flooded country for a long time. Everywhere there was water—not sea or rivers or lakes, but just senseless flood water with the rain splashing into it. Sometimes the railway lines were covered by it, and then the train-noise was quite different, softer than a boat.

"I wish it was *the* Flood," thought the boy, "and that I was going to the Ark. That would be fun! Like the circus. Perhaps Noah had a whip and made all the animals go round and round for exercise. What a noise there would be, with the lions roaring, elephants trumpeting, pigs squealing, donkeys braying, horses whinnying, bulls bellowing, and cocks and hens always thinking they were going to be trodden on but unable to fly up on to the roof where all the other birds were singing, screaming, twittering, squawking and cooing. What must it have sounded like, coming along on the tide? And did Mrs. Noah just knit, knit and take no notice?"

The two women opposite him were getting ready for the next station. They packed up their knitting and collected their parcels and then sat staring at the little boy. He had a thin face and very large eyes; he looked patient and rather sad. They seemed to notice him for the first time.

"What's your name, son?" asked the fat woman suddenly. "I've never seen you on this train before." This was always a question he dreaded. Was he to say his unexpected real name or his silly pet names?

"Toseland," he said.

"Toseland! That's a real old-fashioned name in these parts. There's Fen Toseland, and Toseland St. Agnes and Toseland Gunning. What's your Christian name?"

"That is it—Toseland."

"Do your mum and dad live round here, son?"

"No, they live in Burma."

"Fancy that now! That's a long way away. Where are you going, then?"

"I don't know. That is, I'm going to my great-grandmother Oldknow at Green Noah. The station in Penny Soaky."

"That's the next station after this. We get out here. Don't forget—the next station. And make sure there's some dry land before you get out of the train. The floods are bad there. Bye-bye, cheerio."

They got out, shouting and joking with the porters and kissing the people who had come to meet them. They started off into the hissing rain as if they loved it. Toseland heard the fat woman's loud voice saying, "Oh, I don't mind this. I like it, it's our home-rain, not like that dirty London water."

The train jogged on again and now Toseland was quite alone. He wished he had a family like other people—brothers and sisters, even if his father were away. His mother was dead. He had a stepmother but he hardly knew her and was miserably shy of her. He had been at a boarding-school, and for the last holidays he had been left behind to stay with the head mistress, Miss Spudd, and her old father. They meant to be kind to him, but they never spoke to him without saying "dear." It was "Finish up your porridge, dear, we don't want you to get thin," or "Put on your coat, dear, we don't want you to catch cold," or "Get ready for church, dear, we don't want you to grow up a heathen." And every day after breakfast, "Run along to your room, dear, we want to read the papers."

But now his great-grandmother Oldknow had written that he was to come and live with her. He had never seen her, but she was his own great-grandmother, and that was something. Of course she would be very old. He thought of some old people he had seen who were so old that it frightened him. He wondered if she would be frighteningly old. He began to feel afraid already, and to shake it off he thought about Green Noah and Penny Soaky. What queer names! Green Noah was pure mystery, but Penny Soaky was friendly like a joke.

Suddenly the train stopped, and the porters were shouting "Penny Soaky! Penny Soaky!" Toseland had no sooner got the door open than a man wearing a taxi-driver's hat came along calling:

"Anybody here for Green Noah? Are you Master Toseland for Green Noah?"

"Oh yes, please. It's me."

"This your luggage? Two more in the van? You stand here out of the rain while I get it."

There were a few houses to be seen on one side of the line, and on the other nothing but flooded fields with hedges standing in the water.

"Come along," said the taxi-man. "I've put all your luggage in the car. It'll be dark before we get there and we've got to go through a lot of water."

"Is it deep?"

"Not so deep, I hope, that we can't get through."

"If it rains forty days and forty nights will it be a real flood?"

"Sure enough it would."

Toseland sat by the driver and they set off. The windscreen wipers made two clear fans on the windscreen through which he could see the road half covered with water, with ditches brimming on either side. When they came near the bridge that crossed the river, the road disappeared under water altogether and they seemed to drive into the side of the river with a great splash that flew up against the windows; but it was only a few inches deep, and then they reached the humpbacked bridge and went up and over it, and down again into deeper water on the other side. This time they drove very carefully like bathers walking out into cold water. The car crept along making wide ripples.

"We don't want to stick here," said the driver, "this car don't float."

They came safely through that side too, and now the headlights were turned on, for it was growing dark, and Toseland could see nothing but rain and dazzle.

"Is it far?" he asked.

"Not very, but we have to go a long way round to get past the floods. Green Noah stands almost in the middle of it now, because the river runs alongside the garden. Once you get

there you won't be able to get out again till the flood goes down."

"How will I get in, then?"

"Can you swim?"

"Yes, I did twenty strokes last summer. Will that be enough?"

"You'll have to do better than that. Perhaps if you felt yourself sinking you could manage a few more?"

"But it's quite dark. How will I know where to swim to?"

The driver laughed. "Don't you worry. Mrs. Oldknow will never let you drown. She'll see you get there all right. Now here we are. At least, I can't go any further." Toseland pushed the car door open and looked out. It had stopped raining. The car was standing in a lane of shallow water that stretched out into the dark in front and behind. The driver was wearing Wellington boots, and he got out and paddled round the car. Toseland was afraid that he would be left now to go on as best he could by himself. He did not like to show that he was afraid, so he tried another way of finding out.

"If I am going to swim," he said, "what will you do with my luggage?"

"You haven't got no gum boots, have you?" said the driver. "Come on, get on my shoulders and we'll have a look round to see if anyone's coming to meet you." Toseland climbed on to his shoulders and they set off, but almost at once they heard the sound of oars, and a lantern came round the corner of the lane rocking on the bows of a rowing boat. A man called out, "Is that Master Toseland?" The driver shouted back, "Is that Mr. Boggis?" but Toseland was speechless with relief and delight.

"Good evening, Master Toseland," said Mr. Boggis, holding up the lantern to look at him, while Toseland looked too, and saw a nice old cherry-red face with bright blue eyes. "Pleased to meet you. I knew your mother when she was your size. I bet you were wondering how you were going to get home?" It was nice to hear somebody talking about "home" in that way. Toseland felt much happier, and now he knew that the driver had been teasing him, so he grinned and said: "I was going to swim."

The boat was moored to somebody's garden

gate while the two men put the trunk and tuck-box into it.

"You'll be all right now," said the taxi-man. "Goodnight to you both."

"Goodnight, and thank you," said Toseland.

Mr. Boggis handed him the lantern and told him to kneel up in the bows with it and shout if they were likely to bump into anything. They rowed round two corners in the road and then in at a big white gate. Toseland waved the lantern about and saw trees and bushes standing in the water, and presently the boat was rocked by quite a strong current and the reflection of the lantern steamed away in elastic jigsaw shapes and made gold rings round the tree trunks. At last they came to a still pool reaching to the steps of the house, and the keel of the boat grated on gravel. The windows were all lit up, but it was too dark to see what kind of a house it was, only that it was high and narrow like a tower.

"Come along in," said Mr. Boggis. "I'll show you in. I'd like to see Mrs. Oldknow's face when she sees you."

The entrance hall was a strange place. As they stepped in, a similar door opened at the far end of the house and another man and boy entered there. Then Toseland saw that it was only themselves in a big mirror. The walls round him were partly rough stone and partly plaster, but hung all over with mirrors and pictures and china. There were three big old mirrors all reflecting each other so that at first Toseland was puzzled to find what was real, and which door one could go through straight, the way one wanted to, not sideways somewhere else. He almost wondered which was really himself.

There were vases everywhere filled with queer flowers—branches of dry winter twigs out of which little tassels and rosettes of flower petals were bursting, some yellow, some white, some purple. They had an exciting smell, almost like something to eat, and they looked as if they had been produced by magic, as if someone had said "Abracadabra! Let these sticks burst into flower." "What if my great-grandmother is a witch!" he thought. Above the vases, wherever there was a beam or an odd corner or a doorpost out of which they could, as it were, grow, there were children carved in dark oak, leaning out over

the flowers. Most of them had wings, one had a real bird's nest on its head, and all of them had such round polished cheeks they seemed to be laughing and welcoming him.

While he was looking round him, Boggis had taken his coat and cap from him and hung them up. "Your great-grandmother will be in here," he said, and led him to a little old stone doorway such as you might find in a belfry. He knocked on the door. "Come in," said a clear voice. Boggis gave Toseland a shove, and he found himself inside.

The room seemed to be the ground floor of a castle, much like the ruined castles that he had explored on school picnics, only this was not a ruin. It looked as if it never possibly could be. Its thick stone walls were strong, warm and lively. It was furnished with comfortable polished old-fashioned things as though living in castles was quite ordinary. Toseland stood just outside the door and felt it must be a dream.

His great-grandmother was sitting by a huge open fireplace where logs and peat were burning. The room smelled of woods and wood-smoke. He forgot about her being frighteningly old. She had short silver curls and her face had so many wrinkles it looked as if someone had been trying to draw her for a very long time and every line put in had made the face more like her. She was wearing a soft dress of folded velvet that was as black as a hole in darkness. The room was full of candles in glass candlesticks, and there was candlelight in her ring when she held out her hand to him.

"So you've come back!" she said, smiling, as he came forward, and he found himself leaning against her shoulder as if he knew her quite well.

"Why do you say 'come back'?" he asked, not at all shy.

"I wondered whose face it would be of all the faces I knew," she said. "They always come back. You are like another Toseland, your grandfather. What a good thing you have the right name, because I should always be calling you Tolly anyway. I used to call him Tolly. Have you got a pet name? I'm sure they don't call you Toseland at school."

"No, I get called Towser."

"And at home?"

"My stepmother calls me Toto, but I hate it. It's worse than Towser."

"I think I agree with you. Here we are all used to Toseland, it's the family name and doesn't seem queer to us. So you shan't be Toto here. Do you mind Tolly?"

"I like it. It's what my mother used to call me. What shall I call you?"

"Granny," she said. "What does one generation more or less matter? I'm glad you have come. It will seem lovely to me."

Tolly watched the flames tugging loose from the logs and leaping up the black chimney. They reminded him of bonfire flames wrestling and tearing and whistling in the sky on the fifth of November. Those had been frightening, but these were wonderful.

"Are these our flames?" he asked. "I mean, are they our own?"

"The blue ones are yours and the orange ones are mine."

"And the candle-flames?"

"All yours."

Tolly hesitated, then asked in a very little voice because he hardly dared, "Is it my house—I mean, partly?"

"Of course it is—partly, as you say. Well, now that you are here what shall we do first? Are you hungry?"

She rose and, standing, looked much older. Her figure was bent and shrunken, her face no higher than Tolly's own. The folds of her dress seemed both to weigh her down and hold her up. She brought a tray that was laid ready for him on the sideboard, and put it on a low table in front of the fire. There were egg sandwiches and chicken sandwiches and iced orange cake and jelly and chocolate finger biscuits. Toseland ate happily and tried not to make crumbs.

"I came in a boat with a lantern," he said. "I played the house was Noah's Ark."

"Oh, the Ark! So you played it was the Ark."

"Yes. Do you think Noah had a whip like a circus man and made the animals run round and round for exercise?"

"Yes. And Ham juggled with clubs and plates to pass the time away, and Shem and Japhet were clowns and tried to make Mrs. Noah laugh. But she never did, because if she had done, all her buttons would have burst off. She was done up very tight."

At that moment the fire went *pop!* and shot a piece of wood out into the room. *Pop!* again.

"Buttons! Who said buttons? Poor Mrs. Noah." Tolly chased the sparks and trod on them to put them out.

"Why do you live in a castle?" he said, looking round.

"Why not? Castles were meant to live in."

"I thought that was only in fairy tales. Is it a real castle?"

"Of course."

"I mean, do things happen in it, like the castles in books?"

"Oh yes, things happen in it."

"What sort of things?"

"Wait and see! I'm waiting too, to see what happens now that you are here. Something will, I'm sure. Tomorrow you can explore the inside of the house up and down, and learn your way about and to feel at home in it, because you won't be able to go outside until the floods go down. And now you must come and see your own room, and you must go to bed early tonight."

She led him up winding stairs and through a high, arched room like a knight's hall, that she called the Music Room, and on up more stairs to the very top of the house. Here there was a room under the roof, with a ceiling the shape of the roof and all the beams showing. It was a long room with a triangle of wall at each end and no walls at the sides, because the sloping ceiling came down to the floor, like a tent. There were windows on three sides, and a little low wooden bed in the middle covered with a patchwork quilt, as unlike a school bed as anything could be. There was a low table, a chest of drawers and lots of smooth, polished, empty floor. At one side there was a beautiful old rocking-horse—not a "safety" rocking horse hanging on iron swings from a centre shaft, but a horse whose legs were stretched to full gallop, fixed to long rockers so that it could, if you rode it violently, both rear and kick. On the other side was a doll's house. By the bed was a wooden box painted vermilion with bright patterns all over it, and next to it all Tolly's luggage piled up, making the room look really his.

A wicker bird-cage hung from one of the beams. On the only side that had no window there hung a big mirror reflecting all the rest—the rafters, the wicker cage, the rocking-horse, the doll's house, the painted box, the bed.

"In this house," said Tolly, "everything is twice!" He tried the lid of the painted box, but could not open it.

"The key is lost," said Mrs. Oldknow. "I don't know what's in it. It used to be the children's toy-box."

He put his hand on the rocking-horse's mane, which was real horse-hair. Its tail was real hair too, black and soft and long. He started it rocking. It made a nice creaky sound, like a rocking-chair. He opened the front of the doll's house. "Why, it's this house!" he said. "Look, here's the knight's hall, and here's the stairs, and here's my room! Here's the rocking-horse and here's the red box, and here's a tiny bird-cage! But it's got four beds in it. Are there sometimes other children here?"

Mrs. Oldknow looked at him as if she would like to know everything about him before she answered.

"Yes," she said, "sometimes."

"Who are they?"

"You'll see when they come, if they come."

from THE BORROWERS

Mary Norton

If you know exactly where you put your favorite pencil, but it is not there when you return for it, then probably your house has THEM *—the* BORROWERS. *They are tiny ingenious folk who live under the floor and who borrow what they need from "human beans"—such as a thimble for a kettle or a stamp for a portrait to hang on their walls. Their greatest danger is being seen by the giant humans. In this chapter, Pod returns from a borrowing expedition, thoroughly frightened—he has been seen!*

Pod came in slowly, his sack on his back; he leaned his hat pin, with its dangling name-tape, against the wall and, on the middle of the kitchen table, he placed a doll's tea cup; it was the size of a mixing bowl.

"Why, Pod—" began Homily.

"Got the saucer too," he said. He swung down the sack and untied the neck. "Here you are," he said, drawing out the saucer. "Matches it."

He had a round, currant-bunny sort of face; tonight it looked flabby.

"Oh, Pod," said Homily, "you do look queer. Are you all right?"

Pod sat down. "I'm fair enough," he said.

"You went up the curtain," said Homily. "Oh, Pod, you shouldn't have. It's shaken you—"

Pod made a strange face, his eyes swiveled round toward Arrietty. Homily stared at him, her mouth open, and then she turned. "Come along, Arrietty," she said briskly, "you pop off to bed, now, like a good girl, and I'll bring you some supper."

"Oh," said Arrietty, "can't I see the rest of the borrowings?"

"Your father's got nothing now. Only food. Off you pop to bed. You've seen the cup and saucer."

Arrietty went into the sitting room to put away her diary, and took some time fixing her candle on the upturned drawing pin which served as a holder.

"Whatever are you doing?" grumbled Homily. "Give it here. There, that's the way. Now off to bed and fold your clothes, mind."

"Good night, Papa," said Arrietty, kissing his flat white cheek.

"Careful of the light," he said mechanically, and watched her with his round eyes until she had closed the door.

"Now, Pod," said Homily, when they were alone, "tell me. What's the matter?"

Pod looked at her blankly. "I been 'seen,'" he said.

Homily put out a groping hand for the edge of the table; she grasped it and lowered herself slowly on to the stool. "Oh, Pod," she said.

There was silence between them. Pod stared at Homily and Homily stared at the table. After a while she raised her white face. "Badly?" she asked.

Pod moved restlessly. "I don't know about badly. I been 'seen.' Ain't that bad enough?"

"No one," said Homily slowly, "hasn't never been 'seen' since Uncle Hendreary and he was the first they say for forty-five years." A thought struck her and she gripped the table. "It's no good, Pod, I won't emigrate!"

"No one's asked you to," said Pod.

"To go and live like Hendreary and Lupy in a badger's set! The other side of the world, that's where they say it is—all among the earthworms."

"It's two fields away, above the spinney," said Pod.

"Nuts, that's what they eat. And berries. I wouldn't wonder if they don't eat mice—"

"You've eaten mice yourself," Pod reminded her.

"All draughts and fresh air and the children growing up wild. Think of Arrietty!" said Homily. "Think of the way she's been brought up. An only child. She'd catch her death. It's different for Hendreary."

"Why?" asked Pod. "He's got four."

"That's why," explained Homily. "When you've got four, they're brought up rough. But never mind that now. . . . Who saw you?"

"A boy," said Pod.

"A what?" exclaimed Homily, staring.

"A boy." Pod sketched out a rough shape in the air with his hands. "You know, a boy."

"But there isn't—I mean, what sort of a boy?"

"I don't know what you mean 'what sort of a boy.' A boy in a night-shirt. A boy. You know what a boy is, don't you?"

"Yes," said Homily, "I know what a boy is. But there hasn't been a boy, not in this house, these twenty years."

"Well," said Pod, "there's one here now."

Homily stared at him in silence, and Pod met her eyes. "Where did he see you?" asked Homily at last.

"In the schoolroom."

"Oh," said Homily, "when you was getting the cup?"

"Yes," said Pod.

"Haven't you got eyes?" asked Homily. "Couldn't you have looked first?"

"There's never nobody in the schoolroom. And what's more," he went on, "there wasn't to-day."

"Then where was he?"

"In bed. In the night-nursery or whatever it's called. That's where he was. Sitting up in bed. With the doors open."

"Well, you could have looked in the nursery."

"How could I—halfway up the curtain!"

"Is that where you was?"

"Yes."

"With the cup?"

"Yes. I couldn't get up or down."

"Oh, Pod," wailed Homily, "I should never have let you go. Not at your age!"

"Now, look here," said Pod, "don't mistake me. I got up all right. Got up like a bird, as you might say, bobbles or no bobbles. But"—he leaned toward her—"afterwards—with the cup in me hand, if you see what I mean. . . ." He picked it up off the table. "You see, it's heavy like. You can hold it by the handle, like this . . . but it drops or droops, as you might say. You should take a cup like this in your two hands. A bit of cheese off a shelf, or an apple—well, I drop that . . . give it a push and it falls and I climbs down in me own time and picks it up. But with a cup—you see what I mean? And coming down, you got to watch your feet. And, as I say, some of the bobbles was missing. You didn't know what you could hold on to, not safely. . . ."

"Oh, Pod," said Homily, her eyes full of tears, "what did you do?"

"Well," said Pod, sitting back again, "he took the cup."

"What do you mean?" exclaimed Homily, aghast.

Pod avoided her eyes. "Well, he'd been sitting up in bed there watching me. I'd been on that curtain a good ten minutes, because the hall clock had just struck the quarter—"

"But how do you mean—'he took the cup'?"

"Well, he'd got out of bed and there he was standing, looking up. 'I'll take the cup,' he said."

"Oh!" gasped Homily, her eyes staring, "and you give it him?"

"He took it," said Pod, "ever so gentle. And then, when I was down, he give it me." Homily put her face in her hands. "Now don't take on," said Pod uneasily.

"He might have caught you," shuddered Homily in a stifled voice.

"Yes," said Pod, "but he just give me the cup. 'Here you are,' he said."

Homily raised her face. "What are we going to do?" she asked.

Pod sighed. "Well, there isn't nothing we can do. Except—"

"Oh, no," exclaimed Homily, "not that. Not emigrate. Not that, Pod, now I've got the house so nice and a clock and all."

"We could take the clock," said Pod.

"And Arrietty? What about her? She's not like those cousins. She can *read*, Pod, and sew a treat—"

"He don't know where we live," said Pod.

"But they look," exclaimed Homily. "Remember Hendreary! They got the cat and—"

"Now, now," said Pod, "don't bring up the past."

"But you've got to think of it! They got the cat and—"

"Yes," said Pod, "but Eggletina was different."

"How different? She was Arrietty's age."

"Well, they hadn't told her, you see. That's where they went wrong. They tried to make her believe that there wasn't nothing but was under the floor. They never told her about Mrs. Driver or Crampfurl. Least of all about cats."

"There wasn't any cat," Homily pointed out, "not till Hendreary was 'seen.' "

"Well, there was, then," said Pod. "You got to tell them, that's what I say, or they try to find out for themselves."

"Pod," said Homily solemnly, "we haven't told Arrietty."

"Oh, she knows," said Pod; he moved uncomfortably. "She's got her grating."

"She doesn't know about Eggletina. She doesn't know about being 'seen.' "

"Well," said Pod, "we'll tell her. We always said we would. There's no hurry."

Homily stood up. "Pod," she said, "we're going to tell her now."

SPACE SHIP *BIFROST*

Robert A. Heinlein

Robert Heinlein's books are usually listed for teen-age reading. They are not easy, but this one sample is included because of the tremendous interest of older boys in the whole idea of space and the mastery of space travel. These books of Mr. Heinlein will interest adults as well as children, and interplanetary travel will begin to seem as possible as an airplane ride from here to England. This episode has to do with the beginning of a journey to Ganymede, where the boy and his family are going to settle.

I woke up hungry but I suddenly remembered that this was it!—my last day on Earth. Then I

"Space Ship *Bifrost*." Reprinted from *Farmer in the Sky* by Robert A. Heinlein; copyright 1950 by Robert A. Heinlein; used by permission of the publishers, Charles Scribner's Sons

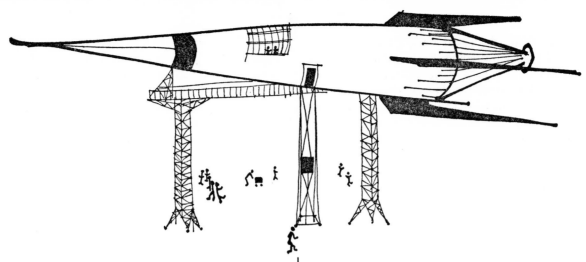

was too excited to be hungry. I got up, put on my Scout uniform and my ship suit over it.

I thought we would go right on board. I was wrong.

First we had to assemble under awnings spread out in front of the hotel near the embarking tubes. It wasn't air conditioned outside, of course, but it was early and the desert wasn't really hot yet. I found the letter "L" and sat down under it, sitting on my baggage. Dad and his new family weren't around yet; I began to wonder if I was going to Ganymede by myself. I didn't much care.

Out past the gates about five miles away, you could see the ships standing on the field, the *Daedalus* and the *Icarus,* pulled off the Earth-Moon run for this one trip, and the old *Bifrost* that had been the shuttle rocket to Supra-New-York space station as far back as I could remember.

The *Daedalus* and the *Icarus* were bigger but I hoped I would get the *Bifrost;* she was the first ship I ever saw blast off.

A family put their baggage down by mine. The mother looked out across the field and said, "Joseph, which one is the *Mayflower?*"

Her husband tried to explain to her, but she still was puzzled. I nearly burst, trying to keep from laughing. Here she was, all set to go to Ganymede and yet she was so dumb she didn't even know that the ship she was going in had been built out in space and couldn't land anywhere.

The place was getting crowded with emigrants and relatives coming to see them off, but I still didn't see anything of Dad. I heard my name called and turned around and there was Duck Miller. "Gee, Bill," he said, "I thought I'd missed you."

"Hi, Duck. No, I'm still here."

"I tried to call you last night but your phone answered 'service discontinued,' so I hooked school and came up."

"Aw, you shouldn't have done that."

"But I wanted to bring you this." He handed me a package, a whole pound of chocolates. I didn't know what to say.

I thanked him and then said, "Duck, I appreciate it, I really do. But I'll have to give them back to you."

"Huh? Why?"

"Weight. Mass, I mean. I can't get by with another ounce."

"You can carry it."

"That won't help. It counts just the same."

He thought about it and said, "Then let's open it."

I said, "Fine," and did so and offered him a piece. I looked at them myself and my stomach was practically sitting up and begging. I don't know when I've been so hungry.

I gave in and ate one. I figured I would sweat it off anyhow; it was getting hot and I had my Scout uniform on under my ship suit—and that's no way to dress for the Mojave Desert in June! Then I was thirstier than ever, of course; one thing leads to another.

I went over to a drinking fountain and took a very small drink. When I came back I closed the candy box and handed it back to Duck and told him to pass it around at next Scout meeting and tell the fellows I wished they were going along. He said he would and added, "You know, Bill, I wish I was going, I really do."

I said I wished he was, too, but when did he change his mind? He looked embarrassed but about then Mr. Kinski showed up and then Dad showed up, with Molly and the brat—Peggy—and Molly's sister, Mrs. van Metre. Everybody shook hands all around and Mrs. van Metre started to cry and the brat wanted to know what made my clothes so bunchy and what was I sweating about?

George was eyeing me, but about then our names were called and we started moving through the gate.

George and Molly and Peggy were weighed through and then it was my turn. My baggage was right on the nose, of course, and then I stepped on the scales. They read one hundred and thirty-one and one tenth pounds—I could have eaten another chocolate.

"Check!" said the weightmaster, then he looked up and said, "What in the world have you got on, son?"

The left sleeve of my uniform had started to unroll and was sticking out below the half sleeve of my ship suit. The merit badges were shining out like signal lights.

I didn't say anything. He started feeling the lumps the uniform sleeves made. "Boy," he said, "you're dressed like an arctic explorer; no wonder you're sweating. Didn't you know you weren't supposed to wear anything but the gear you were listed in?"

Dad came back and asked what the trouble was? I just stood there with my ears burning. The assistant weightmaster got into the huddle and they argued what should be done. The weightmaster phoned somebody and finally he said, "He's inside his weight limit; if he wants to call that monkey suit part of his skin, we'll allow it. Next customer, please!"

I trailed along, feeling foolish. We went down inside and climbed on the slide strip, it was cool down there, thank goodness. A few minutes later we got off at the loading room down under the rocket ship. Sure enough, it was the *Bifrost,* as I found out when the loading elevator poked above ground and stopped at the passenger port. We filed in.

They had it all organized. Our baggage had been taken from us in the loading room; each passenger had a place assigned by his weight. That split us up again; I was on the deck immediately under the control room. I found my place, couch 14-D, then went to a view port where I could see the *Daedalus* and the *Icarus.*

A brisk little stewardess, about knee high to a grasshopper, checked my name off a list and offered me an injection against dropsickness. I said no, thanks.

She said, "You've been out before?"

I admitted I hadn't; she said, "Better take it."

I said I was a licensed air pilot; I wouldn't get sick. I didn't tell her that my license was just for copters. She shrugged and turned away. A loudspeaker said, "The *Daedalus* is cleared for blasting." I moved up to get a good view.

The *Daedalus* was about a quarter of a mile away and stood up higher than we did. She had fine lines and was a mighty pretty sight, gleaming in the morning sunshine. Beyond her and to the right, clear out at the edge of the field, a light shone green at the traffic control blockhouse.

She canted slowly over to the south, just a few degrees.

Fire burst out of her base, orange, and then blinding white. It splashed down into the ground baffles and curled back up through the ground vents. She lifted.

She hung there for a breath and you could see the hills shimmer through her jet. And she was gone.

Just like that—she was gone. She went up out of there like a scared bird, just a pencil of white fire in the sky, and was gone while we could still hear and feel the thunder of her jets inside the compartment.

My ears were ringing. I heard someone behind me say, "But I haven't had breakfast. The Captain will just have to wait. Tell him, Joseph."

It was the woman who hadn't known that the *Mayflower* was a space-to-space ship. Her husband tried to hush her up, but he didn't have any luck. She called over the stewardess. I heard her answer, "But, madam, you can't speak to the Captain now. He's preparing for blast-off."

Apparently that didn't make any difference. The stewardess finally got her quiet by solemnly promising that she could have breakfast after blast-off. I bent my ears at that and I decided to put in a bid for breakfast, too.

The *Icarus* took off twenty minutes later and then the speaker said, "All hands! Acceleration stations—prepare to blast off." I went back to my couch and the stewardess made sure that we were all strapped down. She cautioned us not to unstrap until she said we could. She went down to the deck below.

I felt my ears pop and there was a soft sighing in the ship. I swallowed and kept swallowing. I knew what they were doing: blowing the natural air out and replacing it with the standard helium-oxygen mix at half sea-level pressure. But the woman—the same one—didn't like it. She said, "Joseph, my head aches. Joseph, I can't breathe. Do something!"

Then she clawed at her straps and sat up. Her husband sat up, too, and forced her back down.

The *Bifrost* tilted over a little and the speaker said, "Minus three minutes!"

After a long time it said, "Minus two minutes!"

And then "Minus one minute!" and another voice took up the count:

"Fifty-nine! Fifty-eight! Fifty-seven!"

My heart started to pound so hard I could hardly hear it. But it went on: "—thirty-five! Thirty-four! Thirty-three! Thirty-two! Thirty-one! *Half!* Twenty-nine! Twenty-eight!"

And it got to be: *"Ten!"*

And "Nine!"

"Eight!

"Seven!

"And six!

"And five!

"And four!

"And three!

"And two—"

I never did hear them say "one" or "fire" or whatever they said. About then something fell on me and I thought I was licked. Once, exploring a cave with the fellows, a bank collapsed on me and I had to be dug out. It was like that—but nobody dug me out.

My chest hurt. My ribs seemed about to break. I couldn't lift a finger. I gulped and couldn't get my breath.

I wasn't scared, not really, because I knew we would take off with a high *g*, but I was awfully uncomfortable. I managed to turn my head a little and saw that the sky was already purple. While I watched, it turned black and the stars came out, millions of stars. And yet the Sun was still streaming in through the port.

The roar of the jets was unbelievable but the noise started to die out almost at once and soon you couldn't hear it at all. They say the old ships used to be noisy even after you passed the speed of sound; the *Bifrost* was not. It got as quiet as the inside of a bag of feathers.

There was nothing to do but lie there, stare out at that black sky, try to breathe, and try not to think about the weight sitting on you.

And then, so suddenly that it made your stomach turn flip-flops, you didn't weigh anything at all.

BIBLIOGRAPHY

All 1959–1960 titles, together with their annotations, have been added by the kindness of Miss Ruth Hadlow, Assistant Supervisor of Work with Children, Cleveland Public Library.

COLLECTIONS OF FOLK TALES

African and Ethiopian

AARDEMA, VERNA, *Tales from the Story Hat: African Folk Tales*, ill. by Elton Fax, Coward, 1960. In West Africa the storyteller wears a broad-brimmed hat from which dangle tiny objects representing tales of magic and wonder and fun. 7–11

COURLANDER, HAROLD, and HERZOG, GEORGE, *The Cow-Tail Switch, and Other West African Stories*, ill. by Madge Lee Chastain, Holt, 1947. Seventeen tales of West Africa, told in lively style and revealing much of the customs and life of the people. 10–12

COURLANDER, HAROLD, and LESLAU, WOLF, *The Fire on the Mountain and Other Ethiopian Stories*, ill. by Robert W. Kane, Holt, 1950. Ethiopian folk tales, outstanding in style, illustrations, and content. 10–14

DAVIS, RUSSELL, and ASHABRANNER, BRENT, *The Lion's Whiskers: Tales of High Africa*, ill. by James Teason, Little, 1959. Woven into these forty-one tales from Ethiopia and its borderlands are "a little history, a bit of geography, some personal adventure, and a liberal sprinkling of anthropology." 11–15

RICKERT, EDITH, *The Bojabi Tree*, ill. by Anna Braune, Doubleday, 1958. An old African folk tale about the hungry, forgetful jungle animals who finally earn their dinner. 5–8

SHERLOCK, PHILIP MANDERSON, *Anansi, the Spider Man*, ill. by Marcia Brown, Crowell, 1954. These stories, told by Jamaicans, had their roots in African folklore. 9–12

Arabian

BROWN, MARCIA, *The Flying Carpet*, ill. by author, Scribner's, 1956. 6–10

COLUM, PADRAIC, ed., *The Arabian Nights: Tales of Wonder and Magnificence*, ill. by Lynd Ward, Macmillan, 1953. This new and attractive edition of an outstanding collection will appeal to younger readers. 10–14

WILLIAMS-ELLIS, AMABEL, ed., *The Arabian Nights*, ill. by Pauline Diana Baynes, Criterion, 1957. Jewel-like pictures illustrate these vivid retellings of thirty favorites. 10–14

Chinese

HSI YU CHI, *The Adventures of Monkey*, ill. by Kurt Wiese, adapted from the Chinese by Arthur Waley, Day, 1944. Monkey is the traditional Chinese Mickey Mouse—adventurous, impudent, and curious. His antics and magic are good fun but decidedly intellectual. 12–16

RITCHIE, ALICE, *The Treasure of Li-Po*, ill. by T. Ritchie, Harcourt, 1949. These six Chinese fairy tales have dignity and distinction, wit and wisdom. They are delightful to tell or to read aloud or to be read by imaginative children. 10–14

English, Scottish, and Welsh

JACOBS, JOSEPH, ed., *English Fairy Tales*, Putnam's, n.d. *More English Fairy Tales*, Putnam's, n.d. These are not only reliable sources for the favorite English tales but are also appealing to children in format and illustrations. 9–12

Favorite Fairy Tales Told in England, retold by Virginia Haviland, ill. by Bettina, Little, 1959. An easy-to-read, attractive edition of six familiar English folk tales. Miss Haviland has done a similar piece of work for the tales of Germany and France. 6–11

JONES, GWYN, *Welsh Legends and Folk Tales*, ill. by Joan Kiddell-Monroe, Oxford, 1955. Retellings of ancient sagas as well as folk and fairy tales are included. 11–14

REEVES, JAMES, *English Fables and Fairy Stories*, ill. by Joan Kiddell-Monroe, Oxford, 1954. 10–14

TREGARTHEN, ENYS, *The White Ring*, ed. by Elizabeth Yates, ill. by Nora S. Unwin, Harcourt, 1949. An exquisite Celtic fairy tale about the Cornish fairies. To be read aloud. 7–12

WILSON, BARBARA KER, *Scottish Folk Tales and Legends*, ill. by Joan Kiddell-Monroe, Oxford, 1954. 11–14

YOUNG, BLANCHE C., ed., *How the Manx Cat Lost Its Tail, and Other Manx Folk Stories*, ill. by Nora S. Unwin, McKay, 1959. 7–12

Eskimo

GILLHAM, CHARLES EDWARD, *Beyond the Clapping Mountains: Eskimo Stories from Alaska*, ill. by Chanimum,

Macmillan, 1943. Illustrated by an Eskimo girl, these are unusual and highly imaginative tales. 10–12

Finnish

BOWMAN, JAMES CLOYD, and BIANCO, MARGERY, *Tales from a Finnish Tupa,* from a tr. by Aili Kolehmainen, ill. by Laura Bannon, Whitman, 1936. Here are the everyday folk tales of the Finnish people, not the epic stories. 10–14

French

DOUGLAS, BARBARA, comp., *Favorite French Fairy Tales; Retold from the French of Perrault, Madame D'Aulnoy, and Madame Le Prince de Beaumont,* ill. by R. Cramer, Dodd, 1952. "Beauty and the Beast" and "Prince Darling" by Mme. de Beaumont and "The White Cat" and "Goldenlocks" by Mme. D'Aulnoy are included with the Perrault tales. 9–12

PERRAULT, CHARLES, *Favorite Fairy Tales Told in France,* retold by Virginia Haviland, ill. by Roger Duvoisin, Little, 1959. 7–11
Gustave Doré Album: All the French Fairy Tales, retold by Louis Untermeyer, ill. by Gustave Doré, Didier, 1946. The reproduction of the superb Doré illustrations makes this edition a notable one. 9–12

PICARD, BARBARA, *French Legends, Tales and Fairy Stories: Retold,* ill. by Joan Kiddell-Monroe, Oxford, 1955. A rich source of folklore ranging from epic literature to medieval tales; from legends to fairy tales. 10–14

German

GRIMM, JACOB and WILHELM, *Favorite Fairy Tales Told in Germany,* retold by Virginia Haviland, ill. by Susanne Suba, Little, 1959. 7–11
Grimm's Fairy Tales, tr. by Margaret Hunt, rev. by James Stern, Pantheon, 1944. This is the edition teachers should examine or own, and by which other editions should be checked.
Grimm's Fairy Tales, tr. by Mrs. E. V. Lucas, Lucy Crane, and Marian Edwards, ill. by Fritz Kredel, Grosset, 1945. A recent edition that is thoroughly satisfying to children. 9–12
Grimm's Tales, ill. by Helen Sewell and Madeleine Gekiere, Oxford, 1954. A collection of sixteen tales. 10–12
Household Stories, tr. by Lucy Crane, ill. by Walter Crane, Macmillan, 1923. 10–12
Gone Is Gone, retold and ill. by Wanda Gág, Coward, 1935. 6–8
Tales from Grimm, freely tr. and ill. by Wanda Gág, Coward, 1936. 8–12
Three Gay Tales from Grimm, tr. and ill. by Wanda Gág, Coward, 1943. 8–12
Popular Stories, tr. by Edgar Taylor, ill. by George Cruikshank, a reprint of the first English edition, Clowes, London, 1913. This edition is interesting to adults as a reproduction of the first English translation of the Grimm tales.

Indian

BABBITT, ELLEN C., *The Jataka Tales,* ill. by Ellsworth Young, Appleton, 1912.

More Jataka Tales, ill. by Ellsworth Young, Appleton, 1912.
These fables have more elaborate plots and characterization than Aesop's fables, and are often rather humorous. Large libraries should have these even if they are still out of print. 6–10

TURNBULL, LUCIA, *Fairy Tales of India,* retold and ill. by Hazel Cook, Criterion, 1960. Sixteen tales, many unfamiliar to American children, that are full of Oriental color and wisdom. Published in England under the title *Indian Fairy Tales.* 8–13

Irish

BENNETT, RICHARD, *Little Dermot and the Thirsty Stones, and Other Irish Folk Tales,* ill. by Richard Bennett, Coward, 1953. Eight lively tales for younger readers. 9–12

COLUM, PADRAIC, *The Big Tree of Bunlahy,* ill. by Jack Yeats, Macmillan, 1933. This collection from one of our most successful adapters of myths gives the storytelling background of each tale. 8–12

JACOBS, JOSEPH, ed., *Celtic Fairy Tales,* ill. by John D. Batten, Putnam's, 1893.
More Celtic Fairy Tales, ill. by John D. Batten, Putnam's, n.d.
Jacobs includes Welsh, Scotch, Cornish, and Irish in his two Celtic collections. 9–12

O'FAOLAIN, EILEEN, *Irish Sagas and Folk-Tales,* ill. by Joan Kiddell-Monroe, Oxford, 1954. 10–14

Italian

BOTSFORD, MRS. FLORENCE H., *Picture Tales from the Italian,* ill. by Grace Gilkison, Stokes, 1929. These nineteen tales are amusing and are interspersed with short rhymed riddles. 7–10

VITTORINO, DOMENICO, *Old Italian Tales,* ill. by Kathryn L. Fligg, McKay, 1958. Twenty short tales alive with humor and wisdom. 7–12

Japanese

MCALPINE, HELEN and WILLIAM, *Japanese Tales and Legends,* ill. by Joan Kiddell-Monroe, Walck, 1959. Traditional tales of Japan's legendary past, folk tales, and the epic of the Heike. A volume in the distinguished Oxford series of myths and legends. 10–15

STAMM, CLAUS, *The Very Special Badgers, A Tale of Magic from Japan,* ill. by Kazue Mizumura, Viking, 1960. An old Japanese tale about two tribes of wily badgers, bitter rivals, that set out to prove which is stronger by pitting their best "cheater and changer" against the other. Amusing ink sketches. 6–10

UCHIDA, YOSHIKO, *The Dancing Kettle and Other Japanese Folk Tales;* retold; ill. by Richard C. Jones, Harcourt, 1949. Fourteen Japanese folk tales, well told, moralistic, and full of magic. 9–12
The Magic Listening Cap, More Folk Tales from Japan, ill. by author, Harcourt, 1955. 9–12

Mexican and South American

BRENNER, ANITA, *The Boy Who Could Do Anything, and Other Mexican Folk Tales,* ill. by Jean Charlot, W. R. Scott, 1942. These curious tales have the ring of authenticity. 8–12

HENIUS, FRANK, comp., *Stories from the Americas*, ill. by Leo Politi, Scribner's, 1944. Twenty folk tales or legends which are favorites of the peoples in Mexico, Central and South America. 9–11

STORM, DAN, *Picture Tales from Mexico*, ill. by Mark Storm, Stokes, 1941. Nineteen stories, many of them animal tales involving the lion as well as the native coyotes and rabbits. 8–10

Norwegian

ASBJÖRNSEN, PETER CHRISTIAN, and MOE, JÖRGEN, *East of the Sun and West of the Moon*, ill. by Hedvig Collin, Macmillan, 1953. A new and attractive edition of a title published twenty-five years ago. Based on the Dasent translation. 10–14

JONES, GWYN, *Scandinavian Legends and Folk Tales*, ill. by Joan Kiddell-Monroe, Oxford, 1956. 8–12

Russian

AFANASIEV, ALEXANDER N., *Russian Fairy Tales*, tr. by Norbert Guterman, Pantheon, 1945. Here, at last, is a reliable English source of the Russian tales collected by Afanasiev in the nineteenth century. The fables, talking beast tales, adventure stories, and romances are developed with a prodigal use of magic and much that is gory and terrifying. An adult source.

CARRICK, VALERY, *Picture Tales from the Russian*, tr. by Nevill Forbes, Stokes, 1913. Eleven little animal stories for the five- and six-year-olds. 5–6

RANSOME, ARTHUR, *Old Peter's Russian Tales*, ill. by Dimitri Mitrokhin, Nelson, 1917. This is the teacher's most practical source for the Russian tales. 8–12

Spanish

BOGGS, RALPH STEELE, and DAVIS, MARY GOULD, *The Three Golden Oranges*, ill. by Emma Brock, Longmans, 1936. Romantic and exciting stories for older children. One remarkable ghost story. 10–12

DAVIS, ROBERT, *Padre Porko*, ill. by Fritz Eichenberg, Holiday, 1939. 8–12

SAWYER, RUTH, *Picture Tales from Spain*, ill. by Carlos Sanchez, Stokes, 1936. Eleven little stories for children 7 to 10 years old, with rhymed riddles in between. Miss Sawyer has the ideal storytelling style. 7–10

United States: North American Indian

BELL, CORYDON, *John Rattling-Gourd of Big Cave: A Collection of Cherokee Indian Legends*, ill. by author, Macmillan, 1955. An outstanding collection of twenty-four legends. 10–14

BROUN, EMILY, *A Ball for Little Bear*, ill. by Dick Mackay, Aladdin, 1955. How the world was rescued from darkness after Big Bear took the sun from the sky for Little Bear to play with.
How Rabbit Stole Fire, ill. by Jack Ferguson, Aladdin, 1954. How Rabbit stole sacred fire and gave it to the people. 7–10

MAC FARLAN, ALLAN A., *Indian Adventure Trails; Tales of Trails and Tipis, Ponies and Paddles, Warpaths and Warriors*, ill. by Paulette Jumeau and Bob Hofsinde (Gray Wolf), Dodd, 1953. These stories offer more plot and action than many Indian folk tales. 11–14

MACMILLAN, CYRUS, *Glooskap's Country, and Other Indian Tales*, ill. by John A. Hall, Oxford, 1956. First published in 1918, this is one of the finest collections of Indian stories. 8–12

PENNEY, GRACE, *Tales of the Cheyennes*, ill. by Walter Richard West, Houghton, 1953. Long-ago legends explaining nature and customs, and a group of humorous tales. 10–14

United States: North American Negro

HARRIS, JOEL CHANDLER, *Complete Tales of Uncle Remus*, ed. by Richard Chase, Houghton, 1955.
Uncle Remus, His Songs and Sayings, rev. ed., ill. by A. B. Frost, Appleton, 1947. 8–adult

United States: Tall Tales

BLAIR, WALTER, *Tall Tale America*, ill. by Glen Rounds, Coward, 1944. A legendary history of our humorous heroes. 10–14

BONTEMPS, ARNA, and CONROY, JACK, *Sam Patch, the High, Wide and Handsome Jumper*, ill. by Paul Brown, Houghton, 1951. This tall tale is enhanced with wonderful action pictures of the jumpingest boy in the world. 10–12

BOWMAN, JAMES CLOYD, *Pecos Bill*, ill. by Laura Bannon, Whitman, 1937. 11–14

FELTON, HAROLD, *John Henry and His Hammer*, ill. by Aldren A. Watson, Knopf, 1950. The author has compiled a dramatic and effective account of the Negro superman's whole life, which is a part of our railroad epic. 10–13

MALCOMSON, ANNE, *Yankee Doodle's Cousins*, ill. by Robert McCloskey, Houghton, 1941. This is one of the finest and most satisfying collections of real and mythical heroes from all sections of the United States. 10–14

PECK, LEIGH, *Pecos Bill and Lightning*, ill. by Kurt Wiese, Houghton, 1940. A brief edition with copious illustrations to aid and comfort the slow reader. 8–12

ROUNDS, GLEN, *Ol' Paul the Mighty Logger*, ill. by author, Holiday, 1949. Glen Rounds has retold some of the Paul Bunyan stories with an earthy, exuberant zest that is delightful. 10–adult

SHAPIRO, IRWIN, *How Old Stormalong Captured Mocha Dick*, ill. by Donald McKay, Messner, 1942. Not only Stormalong, but the legendary superwhale, Moby (or Mocha) Dick. A good yarn. 10–14
Yankee Thunder, the Legendary Life of Davy Crockett, ill. by James Daugherty, Messner, 1944. 10–14

SHEPHARD, ESTHER, *Paul Bunyan*, ill. by Rockwell Kent, Harcourt, 1941. This is a good version of the Paul Bunyan epic. 10–14

TURNEY, IDA VIRGINIA, *Paul Bunyan, the Work Giant*, ill. by Norma Madge Lyon and Harold Price, Binfords & Mort, 1941. For slow readers who could never complete the whole epic, this brief text with its enormously funny pictures should make a satisfying substitute. 8–12

Variants of European folk tales in the United States

CHASE, RICHARD, ed., *Grandfather Tales*, ill. by Berkeley Williams, Jr., Houghton, 1948. 9–12
Jack and the Three Sillies, ill. by Joshua Tolford, Houghton, 1950. 7–10

The Jack Tales, ill. by Berkeley Williams, Jr., Houghton, 1943. 9–12

Wicked John and the Devil, ill. by Joshua Tolford, Houghton, 1951. 9–12

The American versions of the old world tales are as vigorous and fresh as the mountain people of the Cumberlands and the Smokies from whom they came.

JAGENDORF, MORITZ ADOLF, *The Marvelous Adventures of Johnny Caesar Cicero Darling,* ill. by Howard Simon, Vanguard, 1949. Johnny Darling is a spinner of superlative yarns. His tall tales are compiled by a notable folklorist and make a welcome addition to American frontier humor. 10–adult

New England Bean-Pot, ill. by Donald McKay, Vanguard, 1948. The dry humor characteristic of the New England people is found in these folk tales from the six states. 10–13

SAWYER, RUTH, *Journey Cake, Ho!,* ill. by Robert McCloskey, Viking, 1953. Mountain folk-tale version of *The Pancake.* Attractive picture book. 6–10

Other Countries

ĆURČIJA-PRODANOVIĆ, NADA, *Yugoslav Folk-Tales,* ill. by Joan Kiddell-Monroe, Walck, 1957. 10–14

DEUTSCH, BABETTE, and YARMOLINSKY, AVRAHM, *Tales of Faraway Folk,* ill. by Irena Lorentowicz, Harper, 1952. A unique collection of tales from Baltic, Russian, and Asiatic lands. Told with simplicity that will have special appeal for young readers. 9–12

FILLMORE, PARKER, *The Shepherd's Nosegay, Stories From Finland and Czechoslovakia,* ed. by Katherine Love, ill. by Enrico Arno, Harcourt, 1958. Eighteen old favorites selected by a children's librarian from three out-of-print books of folk tales retold by Mr. Fillmore. 9–13

JEWETT, ELEANORE MYERS, *Which Was Witch? Tales of Ghosts and Magic from Korea,* ill. by Taro Yashima (pseud. for Jun Iwamatsu), Viking, 1953. Fourteen stories with sparkle and suspense, excellent for storytelling. 9–13

KELSEY, ALICE GEER, *Once the Mullah,* ill. by Kurt Werth, Longmans, 1954. Stories told by the Mullah give insight into Persian life and folklore and are often exceedingly funny. 9–12

MERRILL, JEAN, *Shan's Lucky Knife; A Burmese Folk Tale Retold,* ill. by Ronni Solbert, W. R. Scott, 1960. A Burmese folk tale telling how Shan, a country boy, tricks Ko Tin, a crafty boat-master from Rangoon. Illustrated with black, brown, and orange pictures of life along the Irrawaddy River and of the Burmese street bazaars. 7–11

MÜLLER-GUGGENBÜHL, FRITZ, *Swiss-Alpine Folk-Tales,* tr. by Katharine Potts, ill. by Joan Kiddell-Monroe. Walck, 1958. These tales and *Yugoslav Folk-Tales* are distinguished collections of national folklore in the Oxford series of myths and legends. 10–14

Anthologies of folk tales

BELTING, NATALIA M., *Cat Tales,* ill. by Leo Summers, Holt, 1959. Why does a dog chase a cat? Why does a cat catch mice? Here are sixteen fun-filled cat stories from many lands that answer such wonderings. 8–11

COURLANDER, HAROLD, *The Tiger's Whisker, and Other Tales and Legends from Asia and the Pacific,* ill. by Enrico Arno, Harcourt, 1959. Simple concepts and brevity make these suitable storytelling material for a wide range of children. 7–14

LINES, KATHLEEN, comp. *A Ring of Tales,* ill. by Harold Jones, Watts, 1959. A distinguished treasure trove of stories, old and new, familiar and not-so-familiar. 7–11

MACNEILL, JAMES, *The Sunken City, and Other Tales from Round the World,* ill. by Theo Dimsson, Walck, 1959. A direct, vigorous style marks these twenty folk tales that are just right for the storyteller. 8–12

ROSS, EULALIE S., comp. *The Buried Treasure, and Other Picture Tales,* ill. by Josef Cellini, Lippincott, 1958. Twenty-two favorite fables and folk tales selected from the Picture Tales series. 7–10

Single folk tales in picture book form

CHAUCER, GEOFFREY, *Chanticleer and the Fox,* adapted and ill. by Barbara Cooney, Crowell, 1958. 6–9

GRIMM, JACOB and WILHELM, *Hansel and Gretel,* ill. by Warren Chappell, music by Humperdinck, Knopf, 1944. 8–12

The Shoemaker and the Elves, ill. by Adrienne Adams, Scribner's, 1960. 5–9

The Sleeping Beauty, ill. by Felix Hoffmann, Harcourt, 1960. 6–11

Snow White and the Seven Dwarfs, ill. by Wanda Gág, Coward, 1938.

The Traveling Musicians, ill. by Hans Fischer, Harcourt, 1955. 4–8

The Wolf and the Seven Little Kids, ill. by Felix Hoffmann, Harcourt, 1959. 5–9

PERRAULT, CHARLES, *Cinderella; or The Little Glass Slipper,* ill. by Marcia Brown, Scribner's, 1954. 5–9

Puss in Boots, ill. by Marcia Brown, Scribner's, 1952. 6–9

Puss in Boots, ill. by Hans Fischer, Harcourt, 1959. 5–8

Dick Whittington and His Cat, adapted and ill. by Marcia Brown, Scribner's, 1950. 4–8

The Fast Sooner Hound, adapted from American folklore by Arna Bontemps and Jack Conroy, ill. by Virginia Burton, Houghton, 1942. 8–12

The Five Chinese Brothers, an old tale retold by Claire Huchet Bishop, ill. by Kurt Wiese, Coward, 1938. 5–10

The Old Woman and Her Pig, ill. by Paul Galdone, McGraw (Whittlesey), 1960. 3–6

Stone Soup, an old tale retold and ill. by Marcia Brown, Scribner's, 1947. 7–10

COLLECTIONS OF FABLES

Aesop's fables

JACOBS, JOSEPH, ed., *The Fables of Aesop,* ill. by Kurt Wiese, Macmillan, 1950. This classic edition of the fables includes Jacobs' short history of the fables and is delightfully illustrated by Kurt Wiese. 10–12

TOWNSEND, GEORGE TYLER and JAMES, THOMAS, trs., *Aesop's Fables,* ill. by Glen Rounds, Lippincott, 1950. This translation is simpler than Jacobs' and the humorous illustrations appeal strongly to children. 10–12

French fables

The Fables of La Fontaine, tr. by Margaret Wise Brown, ill. by André Hellé, Harper, 1940. This large picture book with bright colors is designed for children. 8–10

Indian Fables

GAER, JOSEPH, *The Fables of India,* ill. by Randy Monk, Little, 1955. Beast tales from three outstanding collections of Indian fables: the Panchatantra, the Hitopadesa, and the Jatakas. 12–16

The Panchatantra, tr. by Arthur W. Ryder, Univ. of Chicago, 1925. Adult students of the fables will be interested in discovering here the sources of many Aesop and La Fontaine fables.

Modern fables

BRENNER, ANITA, *A Hero by Mistake,* ill. by Jean Charlot, W. R. Scott, 1953. Afraid of his own shadow, this little man accidentally captures some bandits, is hailed as a hero, and learns to behave like one. 6–8

COLLECTIONS
OF MYTHS AND EPICS

English epics

LANIER, SIDNEY, *The Boy's King Arthur,* ill. by N. C. Wyeth, ed. from Sir Thomas Malory's *History of King Arthur and His Knights of the Round Table,* Scribner's, 1942. An authoritative and popular version of this hero cycle; the best one to use for reading or telling. 10–14

MC SPADDEN, J. WALKER, *Robin Hood and His Merry Outlaws,* ill. by Louis Slobodkin, World Pub., 1946. 9–12

PYLE, HOWARD, *The Merry Adventures of Robin Hood of Great Renown in Nottinghamshire,* ill. by author, Scribner's, 1933. This is the great prose edition of the Robin Hood tales, the best source both for reading and telling. This earlier edition is better than the streamlined 1946 edition. 12–14

Some Merry Adventures of Robin Hood, rev. ed., ill. by author, Scribner's, 1954. This book contains a dozen stories adapted from the longer book, and would serve as an introduction for younger readers. 10–13

The Story of King Arthur and His Knights, ill. by author, Scribner's, 1933. 12–14

SANDYS, E. V., *Beowulf,* ill. by Rolf Klep, Crowell, 1941. A recent and satisfying version of *Beowulf,* dramatically illustrated. 12–16

Greek and Roman myths and epics

CHURCH, ALFRED JOHN, *The Odyssey for Boys and Girls,* Macmillan, 1906. An excellent source for children to read or adults to tell. Stories are arranged in chronological order. 10–14

COLUM, PADRAIC, *The Adventures of Odysseus and the Tale of Troy, or The Children's Homer,* ill. by Willy Pogany, Macmillan, 1918. A distinguished version, in cadenced prose. 10–14

The Golden Fleece; and the Heroes Who Lived Before Achilles, ill. by Willy Pogany, Macmillan, 1921. A companion volume to *The Children's Homer.* 10–14

COOLIDGE, OLIVIA E., *Greek Myths,* ill. by Edouard Sandoz, Houghton, 1949. Mrs. Coolidge has retold twenty-seven of the most widely known Greek myths. Here the gods are not idealized—indeed the book opens with an unappealing tale of trickery—but the stories have authenticity. They will appeal to youth rather than children. 10–16

DE SÉLINCOURT, AUBREY, *Odysseus the Wanderer,* ill. by Norman Meredith, Criterion, 1956. A lusty, modern retelling of the Odyssey. 11–adult

HAWTHORNE, NATHANIEL, *A Wonder Book for Girls and Boys,* ill. by Walter Crane, Houghton, 1851.
Tanglewood Tales for Girls and Boys, Houghton, 1853. 10–14

The Golden Touch, ill. by Paul Galdone, McGraw (Whittlesey), 1959. 10–14

HOMER, *The Odyssey,* abridged and tr. by George Kerr, ill. by John Verney, rev. ed. Warne, 1958. 10–14

KINGSLEY, CHARLES, *The Heroes,* ill. by Vera Bock, Macmillan, 1954. Thirty of the tales are beautifully retold and make a fine cycle for the storyteller. 10–14

SEWELL, HELEN, *A Book of Myths,* selections from Bulfinch's *Age of Fable,* ill. by Helen Sewell, Macmillan, 1942. Striking illustrations suggestive of ballet postures and movement distinguish this collection. 10–14

Norse myths and epics

COLUM, PADRAIC, *Children of Odin.* ill. by Willy Pogany, Macmillan, 1920. Norse myths and hero tales retold in a continuous narrative ending with the death of Sigurd. 10–14

SELLEW, CATHARINE, *Adventures with the Heroes,* ill. by Steele Savage, Little, 1954. Retold in simple language are the stories of the Volsungs and Niblungs. 9–12

Other national epics

BALDWIN, JAMES, *The Sampo: A Wonder Tale of the Old North,* ill. in color by N. C. Wyeth, Scribner's, 1912. Hero Tales from the Finnish *Kalevala.* 9–12

DEUTSCH, BABETTE, *Heroes of the Kalevala,* ill. by Fritz Eichenberg, Messner, 1940. This version has not only literary distinction but continuity. Text and illustrations bring out the lusty humor of the tales. 10–14

GAER, JOSEPH, *The Adventures of Rama,* ill. by Randy Monk, Little, 1954. One of the best-loved epics of India. 12–14

MODERN FANCIFUL TALES

ANDERSEN, HANS CHRISTIAN, *Fairy Tales,* 1835.
Ill. by George and Doris Hauman, Macmillan, 1953. 10–14

Ill. by Rex Whistler, Macmillan, 1950. 10–12

The Emperor and the Nightingale, retold and ill. by Bill Sokol, Pantheon, 1959. Retold with sensitive feeling and strikingly illustrated in a modern manner. 9–12

The Emperor's New Clothes, tr. and ill. by Erik Blegvad, Harcourt, 1959. A charming companion to the translator-illustrator's *The Swineherd.* 7–10

The Emperor's New Clothes, ill. by Virginia Lee Burton, Houghton, 1949. An enchanting edition of Andersen's funniest story. Children and adults will find Virginia Burton's pictures as irresistible as the story. 7–10

Seven Tales, tr. and adapted by Eva Le Gallienne, ill. by Maurice Sendak, Harper, 1959. Pleasant, appreciative renderings of some of Andersen's simpler tales with the illustrations done in a medieval manner. Large, clear print and wide margins add to the appeal of this volume. 8–12

The Steadfast Tin Soldier, ill. by Marcia Brown, Scribner's, 1953. Beautiful pastel illustrations. 6–10

The Swineherd, tr. and ill. by Erik Blegvad, Harcourt, 1958.   5–9

AYMÉ, MARCEL, *The Wonderful Farm,* tr. by Norman Denny, ill. by Maurice Sendak, Harper, 1951. The wonderful farm is quite an ordinary French farm except that the animals happen to talk. This is a book both children and adults will enjoy.   7–10

BAILEY, CAROLYN, *Miss Hickory,* ill. by Ruth Gannett, Viking, 1946. (Newbery Medal)

BANNERMAN, HELEN, *Little Black Sambo,* ill. by author, Stokes, 1900.   3–6

BARRIE, SIR JAMES, *Peter Pan,* ill. by Nora Unwin, Scribner's, 1950. Peter Pan, the boy who never grew up, and all his delightful companions are beautifully visualized for the children by Nora Unwin's illustrations for this new edition.   9–12

BATE, NORMAN, *Who Built the Highway? A Picture Story,* ill. by author, Scribner's, 1953. This is the first of several picture books by this author about machines and the workers who use them.   6–9

BECKER, EDNA, *900 Buckets of Paint,* ill. by Margaret Bradfield, Abingdon, 1949. Appealing pictures in full color accompany this amusing story of an old woman moving from house to house trying to satisfy her four fussy pets. The conclusion will bring anticipatory chuckles from astute small fry.   4–7

BELL, THELMA HARRINGTON, *Pawnee,* ill. by Corydon Bell, Viking, 1950. "Pawnee was a buckskin brave. But everyone thought Pawnee was just a doll." This distinction was a source of confusion both to Pawnee and Bobby Spencer's family. Amusing fantasy of a boy's doll.   5–8

BIANCO, MARGERY, *The Little Wooden Doll,* ill. by Pamela Bianco, Macmillan, 1925. A wistful, appealing tale reminiscent of Hans Christian Andersen.   6–10

BOSTON, L. M., *Treasure of Green Knowe,* ill. by Peter Boston, Harcourt, 1958.   11–15

BROOKS, WALTER, *Freddy and the Man from Mars,* Knopf, 1954.
Freddy Goes to Florida, Knopf, 1949.
Between these two books lies a long series of Freddy stories that enjoy enormous popularity. Freddy the pig, Charles the rooster, Jinx the cat, and their friends can be counted on for fun and excitement.   9–12

BROWN, MARGARET WISE, *The Runaway Bunny,* ill. by Clement Hurd, Harper, 1942. A small bunny discovers that he can never run away from his mother's love.   4–7

BRUNOFF, JEAN DE, *The Story of Babar, the Little Elephant,* Random, 1933. A series of these books follows.   5–8

BULLA, CLYDE, *The Poppy Seeds,* ill. by Jean Charlot, Crowell, 1955. A suspicious old man who in an arid land kept his clear spring to himself learns that to share is to be rich.   7–10

BURTON, VIRGINIA, *Choo Choo,* ill. by author, Houghton, 1937.
The Little House, ill. by author, Houghton, 1942.
Katy and the Big Snow, ill. by author, Houghton, 1943.
                                                4–9

CARROLL, LEWIS, *Alice's Adventures in Wonderland* and *Through the Looking Glass* in 1 vol., ill. by John Tenniel, Heritage, 1944. (1865 and 1871)   10–adult

CAMERON, ELEANOR, *The Wonderful Flight to the Mushroom Planet,* ill. by Robert Henneberger, Little, 1954. Two small boys and their inventive neighbor build a space ship and take off to aid the people of a dying planet.   9–11

COBLENTZ, CATHERINE CATE, *The Blue Cat of Castle Town,* ill. by Janice Holland, Longmans, 1949. The blue kitten,

born under a blue moon, learned the river's song, "Enchantment is made of three things—of beauty, peace and content."   12–14

CROWLEY, MAUDE, *Azor,* Oxford, 1948.
Azor and the Haddock, ill. by Helen Sewell, Oxford, 1949.
Azor and the Blue-Eyed Cow, ill. by Helen Sewell, Oxford, 1951.
Azor is a small, everyday sort of boy who happens to understand animals when they talk to him. Their confidences sometimes get him into trouble but his complete honesty and good will invariably save the day.   5–8

DAUGHERTY, JAMES, *Andy and the Lion,* ill. by author. Viking, 1938. Young Andy has read about lions but never expected to meet one. The encounter ends in high adventure for both of them, and for the young reader.   6–8

DAVIS, ALICE, *Timothy Turtle,* ill. by G. B. Wiser, Harcourt, 1940.   4–7

DE LA MARE, WALTER, *The Three Mulla-Mulgars,* ill. by Dorothy Lathrop, Knopf, 1919.   12–16

DE LEEUW, ADELE, *Nobody's Doll,* ill. by Anne Vaughan, Little, 1946. The story of a lost doll and a kindly Scottie, both of whom finally come to the little boy and girl they yearn for. Each adventure is a complete episode. Good to read aloud.   7–10

DOLBIER, MAURICE, *Torten's Christmas Secret,* ill. by Robert Henneberger, Little, 1951. The freshest, gayest, Christmas story in years involves Santa's toy factory, hardworking gnomes, lists of good and bad children and lovely glimpses of Santa's frosty, sparkling Arctic world.
                                                4–8

DRUON, MAURICE, *Tistou of the Green Thumbs,* tr. by Humphrey Hare, ill. by Jacqueline Duhéme, Scribner's, 1958. A unique fantasy, beautifully told, of a small French boy who used his strange gift with flowers to bring happiness and peace to others.   9–13

DU BOIS, WILLIAM PÈNE, *Peter Graves,* ill. by author, Viking, 1950. "The Horrible House of Horton" or "The House of the Horrible Houghton" was known far and wide. Houghton was an inventor who was always having to be rescued by the fire department. A boy, Peter Graves, went to see him with hair-raising results.   10–14

DUVOISIN, ROGER, *Petunia, Beware!* ill. by author, Knopf, 1958. This is one of several amusing books about Petunia, a silly and adventurous goose.   4–8

ELKIN, BENJAMIN, *Six Foolish Fishermen,* ill. by Katherine Evans, Childrens Press, 1957. At the end of their day each of the six fishermen forgot to count himself and was sure one had drowned. A small boy points out their foolish mistake. A perfect read-aloud.   4–7

ETS, MARIE HALL, *Mister Penny,* ill. by author, Viking, 1935. Poor Mr. Penny's good-for-nothing animals did nothing to help themselves or him. But after they ate up old Thunderstorm's garden, they redeemed themselves and saved Mr. Penny from a life of toil. Amusing pictures!   6–8
Mr. T. W. Anthony Woo, ill. by author, Viking, 1951. Mr. Woo, the cobbler, his cat, dog, and mouse live together, but not too happily. When Mr. Woo's meddling sister moves in with the idea of reforming them, they unite against the common enemy and learn to live peacefully. Humorous pictures add to the fun.   4–8

FAIRSTAR, MRS., pseud. for Richard Horne, *Memoirs of a London Doll,* ill. by Emma L. Brock, Macmillan, 1922. A classic doll story of another age.   9–12

FATIO, LOUISE, *The Happy Lion,* ill. by Roger Duvoisin, McGraw (Whittlesey), 1954. An unlocked gate inspires the amiable lion in a little French zoo to return the calls of the villagers with wild results. Roger Duvoisin's drawings in color are humorous and full of atmosphere. This first story about the Happy Lion has been followed by others equally hilarious and popular.   5–8

FIELD, RACHEL, *Hitty, Her First Hundred Years,* ill. by Dorothy P. Lathrop, Macmillan, 1929. Hitty's adventures in her hundred years are varied and satisfying to little girls.   10–13

FRISKEY, MARGARET, *Seven Diving Ducks,* ill. by Lucia Patton, McKay, 1940. One little duck was afraid to dive but finally made it.   4–7

GÁG, WANDA, *Millions of Cats,* ill. by author, Coward, 1928.
Snippy and Snappy, ill. by author, Coward, 1931.
The Funny Thing, ill. by author, Coward, 1929.   4–9

GANNETT, RUTH STILES, *My Father's Dragon,* Random, 1948.
The Dragons of Blueland, ill. by Ruth Chrisman Gannett, Random, 1951.   6–10

GEISEL, THEODORE SEUSS (pseud. Dr. Seuss), *Bartholomew and the Oobleck,* ill. by author, Random, 1949.
And to Think That I Saw It on Mulberry Street, Vanguard, 1937.
Horton Hatches the Egg, Random, 1940.
The King's Stilts, Random, 1939.
McElligot's Pool, Random, 1947.   6–12

GODDEN, RUMER, *Impunity Jane,* ill. by Adrienne Adams, Viking, 1954. An excellent doll story.   8–10
The Mousewife, ill. by William Pène du Bois, Viking, 1951. Expanded into a story from a note in Dorothy Wordsworth's Journal, this is an exquisitely written little fable of the friendship of a mouse and a caged dove. 6–9

GRAHAME, KENNETH, *The Wind in the Willows,* ill. by Ernest Shepard, Scribner's, 1960. The Golden Anniversary Edition of this beloved classic has, in addition to Mr. Shepard's familiar black and white drawings, eight new full-page drawings in color.   10–adult
Ill. by Arthur Rackham, Heritage, 1944.   10–adult

GRAMATKY, HARDIE, *Little Toot,* ill. by author. Putnam's, 1939.
Hercules, ill. by author, Putnam's, 1940.
Loopy, ill. by author, Putnam's, 1941.
A tug boat, an ancient fire engine, and an airplane are amusingly personified in these popular picture-stories.   4–9

HALE, LUCRETIA P., *The Peterkin Papers,* ill. by Harold Brett, Houghton, 1924. (1880)   9–12

HEINLEIN, ROBERT, *Red Planet,* Scribner's, 1949.
Rocket Ship Galileo, Scribner's, 1947.
Space Cadet, Scribner's, 1948.   12–adult

HOLT, ISABELLA, *The Adventures of Rinaldo,* ill. by Erik Blegvad, Little, 1959. How a rather old and worn albeit courageous knight seeks and wins a wife and castle makes a jaunty, whimsical tale in the manner of Don Quixote.   10–13

HOPP, ZINKEN, *The Magic Chalk,* tr. from the Norwegian by Susanne H. Bergendahl, ill. by Malvin Neset, McKay, 1959. Translated into more than eight languages, this delightful tale of fun and fantasy tells of John Albert Brown Sunnyside who found a piece of witch's chalk by which he could draw himself in and out of fabulous adventures.   7–10

JANICE (pseud.), *Little Bear's Sunday Breakfast,* ill. by Mariana, Lothrop, 1958. Little Bear steps right out of the old folk tale and hurries to Goldilocks' house, he is so hungry.   3–6

JOHNSON, CROCKETT (pseud. of David J. Leisk), *Ellen's Lion,* ill. by author, Harper, 1959. Twelve whimsical stories

about Ellen's conversations with her stuffed toy lion— talk, though seemingly absurd, carries bits of wisdom.   6–9

JONES, ELIZABETH ORTON, *Twig,* ill. by author, Macmillan, 1942. Twig was lonely, so she made a tomato can house for a fairy, and sure enough, an elf came to visit her. When Twig finally discovered that everyday life can be magical too, she did not need her elf any more.   9–11

JOSLIN, SESYLE, *What Do You Say, Dear?* ill. by Maurice Sendak, W. R. Scott, 1958. Manners for the youngest in a delightful read-aloud. Simple phrases of courtesy become memorable through the nonsense situations which inspire them.   4–7

KAHL, VIRGINIA, *Away Went Wolfgang!* ill. by author, Scribner's, 1954. Wolfgang was the least useful dog in an Austrian village, until the housewives discovered that when Wolfgang ran, he could churn a whole cartful of milk into butter!   5–8
The Duchess Bakes a Cake, ill. by author, Scribner's, 1955. A humorous, rhymed story of the duchess who was carried skyward atop the light fluffy cake she had baked.   6–10
The Perfect Pancake, ill. by author, Scribner's, 1960. A light-hearted rhymed story about the good wife who limited her "feathery, fluffy, and flavory" pancakes one to a person.   6–10

KENDALL, CAROL, *The Gammage Cup,* ill. by Erik Blegvad, Harcourt, 1959. The self-satisfied, unimaginative Minnipins exile four of their members who are nonconformists. How the exiles warn the villagers of attack by their ancient enemies makes an enthralling fantasy that has originality and charm.   9–12

KIPLING, RUDYARD, *The Jungle Book,* ill. by Kurt Wiese, Doubleday, 1932.   12–14
Just So Stories, Doubleday, 1902. Each story published in a separate volume, ill. by Feodor Rojankovsky, Harper.   8–12

LEWIS, CLIVE STAPLES, *The Lion, the Witch and the Wardrobe,* Macmillan, 1950. The first of a series of books about the imaginary land of Narnia.   10–14

LIPKIND, WILLIAM, and MORDVINOFF, NICOLAS, *Chaga,* Harcourt, 1955. Chaga the elephant was none too kind to creatures smaller than himself. He learns his lesson when he swallows some grass that makes him shrink to a very small size.   5–8
The Two Reds, Harcourt, 1950.
Finders Keepers, Harcourt, 1951. (Caldecott Award) The two Reds are a boy and a cat, who mistrust each other for good reasons. After they escape together from a common peril, they are fast friends ever after. *Finders Keepers,* written in folk-tale style, is the rollicking fable of two dogs who solve the problem of who shall keep the bone, with admirable common sense.   4–8

LOFTING, HUGH, *The Story of Dr. Dolittle,* ill. by author, Stokes, 1920.
The Voyages of Dr. Dolittle, ill. by author, Stokes, 1922. There are seven more books in the Dolittle series, but the first two remain the favorites.   9–12

LORENZINI, CARLO (pseud. Collodi), *The Adventures of Pinocchio,* tr. by Carol Della Chiesa, ill. after Attilio Mussino, Macmillan, 1951. The rascally puppet is at his best in these lively illustrations, which are the nearest to the original Mussino pictures now available.   9–11

MACDONALD, GEORGE, *At the Back of the North Wind,* ill. by George and Doris Hauman, Macmillan, 1950.
The Princess and the Goblin, ill. by Nora S. Unwin, Macmillan, 1951.

Here are new editions of two old favorites, beautifully written but moralistic and limited in their appeal. 9–12

MASON, ARTHUR, *The Wee Men of Ballywooden*, ill. by Robert Lawson, Garden City, 1937. 10–14

MC GINLEY, PHYLLIS, *The Horse Who Lived Upstairs*, Lippincott, 1944.

The Horse Who Had His Picture in the Paper, ill. by Helen Stone, Lippincott, 1951.

In the first book, it takes a trip to the country to teach discontented Joey that he is a true city dweller at heart. The second book finds Joey again restless. This time he yearns for publicity that will silence the policeman's boastful horse. The climax is utterly satisfying. 4–8

MCLEOD, EMILIE, *Clancy's Witch*, ill. by Lisl Weil, Little, 1959. How nine-year-old Clancy helps a witch with seven black pots, seven black cats, and thirteen brooms unhaunt an empty house. 7–10

MILNE, A. A., *The World of Pooh*, ill. by E. H. Shepard, Dutton, 1957. Distinctive color illustrations give a festive air to this new large-print volume, containing *Winnie-the-Pooh* and *The House at Pooh Corner*. 5–10

MINARIK, ELSE H., *Father Bear Comes Home*, ill. by Maurice Sendak, Harper, 1959.

Little Bear, ill. by Maurice Sendak, Harper, 1957. Easy-to-read books for the primary. 4–8

NORTON, MARY, *The Borrowers Afield*, ill. by Beth and Joe Krush, Harcourt, 1955. 9–12

The Borrowers Afloat, ill. by Beth and Joe Krush, Harcourt, 1959. 9–12

PEARCE, A. PHILIPPA, *Tom's Midnight Garden*, ill. by Susan Einzig, Lippincott, 1959. When the ancient grandfather clock struck thirteen, Tom entered into charming and suspenseful adventures in time and eternity. (Winner of the Carnegie Medal as the outstanding English children's book of 1958.) 10–13

PEET, BILL, *Hubert's Hair-Raising Adventure*, ill. by author, Houghton, 1959. Haughty and vain, Hubert the lion learns a lesson in humility when he loses his elegant mane. Clever rhythmic verse makes this just right for reading aloud, and the brightly colored cartoon-like art work makes it fun for looking, too. 6–9

POTTER, BEATRIX, *The Tale of Peter Rabbit*, ill. by author, Warne, 1903. A favorite nursery classic followed by *The Tale of Benjamin Bunny, Jemima Puddleduck,* and many others, all illustrated by the author and published by Warne. 3–8

PROKOFIEFF, SERGE, *Peter and the Wolf*, ill. by Warren Chappell, with a foreword by Serge Koussevitzky, Knopf, 1940. This is a delightful version of the story of how Peter outwits the wolf. It is especially valuable as an introduction to the orchestral recording of the story. 7–12

PYLE, HOWARD, *Wonder Clock*, ill. by author, Harper, 1887.

REY, H. A. *Curious George Gets a Medal*, ill. by author, Houghton, 1957. Curious George, the little monkey hero of many popular tales, daringly rockets into space and wins a medal for his courage. 5–8

RUSKIN, JOHN, *King of the Golden River*, ill. by Fritz Kredel, World Pub., 1946. (1840) 10–14

SAUER, JULIA L., *Fog Magic*, Viking, 1943. Girls enjoy this sensitive and beautifully written story of a little girl who goes back in time to a people and a village which no longer exist. The day comes when she knows that her "fog magic" must end. 10–12

SCHLEIN, MIRIAM, *The Raggle-Taggle Fellow*, ill. by Harvey Weiss, Abelard, 1959. Written in a folk-tale manner, this engaging story of Dick, a wandering musician,

holds wisdom and entertainment for the story hour. 7–10

SEUSS, DR. *See* Theodore Seuss Geisel.

SHARP, MARGERY, *The Rescuers*, ill. by Garth Williams, Little, 1959. A clever fantasy concerning the adventures of three mice who attempt to rescue a Norwegian poet from the dungeon of the Black Castle. Adults will catch the satire. Charming mousey drawings. 9–adult

SHURA, MARY FRANCIS, *Simple Spigott*, ill. by Jacqueline Tomes, Knopf, 1960. A friendly Scottish spook proves a wonderful guide and companion to three American children who visit Scotland. A first-person narrative that happily blends fantasy and realism. 7–10

SLEIGH, BARBARA, *Carbonel: The King of the Cats*, ill. by V. H. Drummond, Bobbs, 1957. Humorous magical tale of two children who rescue the king of cats from the spell of an old witch.

The Kingdom of Carbonel, ill. by D. M. Leonard, Bobbs, 1960. 9–12

SMITH, AGNES, *The Edge of the Forest*, ill. by Roberta Moynihan, Viking, 1959. Poetic, mystical, sensitive, yet starkly realistic at times, this presents the power of love and of death in the relationship of a young black leopardess and an orphaned lamb. 11–15

STEELE, WILLIAM O., *Andy Jackson's Water Well*, ill. by Michael Ramus, Harcourt, 1959. When a terrible drought hit frontier Nashville, Andrew Jackson, attorney-at-law, and his friend, Chief Ticklepitcher, went east to get water. Their hilarious and exaggerated experiences are told with a lively dry humor and perfectly illustrated by Michael Ramus' line drawings. 9–14

SWAYNE, SAMUEL F. and ZOA, *Great-grandfather in the Honey Tree*, ill. by authors, Viking, 1949. Pioneer days in Indiana are the background of this amusing tall tale of Great-grandfather's hunting trip. His fantastic adventures land him up to his neck in honey. The hilarious absurdity of this tale tickles children. 5–12

THURBER, JAMES, *Many Moons*, ill. by Louis Slobodkin, Harcourt, 1943. Told in fairy-tale style, this is the appealing story of a little princess who yearned for the moon but learned to be satisfied with less. 7–10

TITUS, EVE, *Anatole and the Cat*, ill. by Paul Galdone, McGraw (Whittlesey), 1957. An alert little French mouse outwits the cat who interferes with his duties as Cheese Taster in M'sieu Duval's cheese factory. 5–7

Anatole and the Robot, ill. by Paul Galdone, McGraw (Whittlesey), 1960. That French mouse *magnifique*, First Vice-President in Charge of Cheese Tasting, meets the challenge of a cheese-testing machine. 5–7

TRAVERS, P. L. *Mary Poppins*, ill. by Mary Shepard, Harcourt, 1934.

Mary Poppins Comes Back, ill. by Mary Shepard, Harcourt, 1935.

Mary Poppins Opens the Door, ill. by Mary Shepard and Agnes Sims, Harcourt, 1943.

This wind-borne nurse sternly ignores the magic which charms her charges and keeps them hoping for Mary's return. 8–12

UNGERER, TOMI, *Emile*, ill. by author, Harper, 1960. The originator of Crictor and the Mellops now introduces another uncommon picture-book character—an engaging octopus. 5–8

WALDEN, DANIEL, *The Nutcracker*, ill. by Harold Berson, Lippincott, 1959. In contrast to the vigorous Chappell version (Knopf, 1958), this retelling of the familiar Nutcracker ballet is marked by grace and delicacy in both text and pictures. Both versions are welcome. 8–12

WATKINS-PITCHFORD, DENYS J., *The Little Grey Men*, ill. by the author, Scribner, 1949. Rich in woodland atmosphere is this story of the adventures of four little gnomes. First published in England, this book won a Carnegie Medal award (British equivalent of the Newbery Medal).　　　　　　　　　　　　　10–13
Forest of the Railway, ill. by the author, Dodd, 1957.
WHITE, ANNE H., *The Story of Serapina*, ill. by Tony Palazzo, Viking, 1951. Serapina, the cat who could carry in milk bottles with her tail and both discipline and entertain the children, is a modern tall tale or fantasy of great originality. It is also very funny.　　　　　　　8–12
WINTERFELD, HENRY, *Castaways in Lilliput*, tr. from the German by Kyrill Schabert, ill. by William Hutchinson, Harcourt, 1960. Adrift on a rubber raft, three Australian children are cast ashore on a fully modernized Lilliput. A good introduction to the Swift story.　　　　9–13
YOUNG, ELLA, *The Unicorn with the Silver Shoes*, ill. by Robert Lawson, Longmans, 1932. This exquisite Irish fairy lore about Ballor's son and his adventures with a Pooka should be read aloud for its beauty and subtle humor.　　　　　　　　　　　　　　　　10–14

ADULT REFERENCES

ARBUTHNOT, MAY HILL, *Children and Books*, Scott, Foresman and Company, 1957. Folk tales, myths, fables, and modern fanciful tales are discussed fully in Chapters 11–14.
ARBUTHNOT, BRIGGS, CLARK, LONG, and WHITE, *Children's Books Too Good to Miss*, Press of Western Reserve University, Cleveland, 1948. 75c. Here is a list of books, old and new, which children should have a chance to know. The books are grouped in four age-levels—under 6; 6, 7, and 8; 9, 10, 11; 12 and 13. Careful and readable annotations and price lists make this bibliography useful for ordering, either for an individual child or for a school library.
HAZARD, PAUL, *Books, Children and Men*, tr. by Marguerite Mitchell, Horn Book, 1944. A member of the French Academy and professor of comparative literature both in France and in the United States writes engagingly of the great children's books of many countries.
JORDAN, ALICE M., *From Rollo to Tom Sawyer and Other Papers*, decorated by Nora S. Unwin, Boston, Horn Book, 1949.
KIEFER, MONICA, *American Children Through Their Books, 1700–1835*, University of Pennsylvania Press, 1948. This book will be of special value to students interested in the history of American books for children. Miss Kiefer's book is carefully documented and indexed.
MONTGOMERY, ELIZABETH RIDER, *The Story Behind Modern Books*, Dodd, 1949. Every elementary school will wish to add to its library Mrs. Montgomery's book about the modern authors and illustrators of children's books.

SAWYER, RUTH, *The Way of the Storyteller*, Viking, 1942. Informally written in Ruth Sawyer's fine style, this is a contribution both to the art of storytelling and the history of the old tales. It also contains eleven unusual stories.

PUPPETS

FICKLEN, BESSIE, *Handbook of Fist Puppets*, Stokes, 1935. Detailed instructions for making hand puppets and their theater are given along with three plays.　12–adult
HOBEN, ALICE M., *The Beginner's Puppet Book*, Noble, 1938. Covers the simplest kind of puppets, with diagrams and photographs to amplify the text. Contains also a few plays which may be studied by the teacher for suggestions; but children should make their own plays.　　　　　　　　　　　　　　　　　　　10–13
JAGENDORF, MORITZ ADOLF, *Penny Puppets, Penny Theater and Penny Plays*, ill. by Fletcher Clark, Bobbs, 1941. Nine short and humorous plays are given along with directions for making inexpensive puppets, marionettes, and theaters.　　　　　　　　　　　　　10–14
MILLS, WINIFRED H., and DUNN, LOUISE M. *Marionettes, Masks and Shadows*, ill. by Corydon Bell, Doubleday, 1927. A standard book on the history of puppets, their construction, the setting, scenery, lighting, and training of the puppeteers.　　　　　　　　　　　　　　12–14
PELS, GERTRUDE. *Easy Puppets*, ill. by Albert Pels, Crowell, 1951. A unique handbook on how to make puppets from almost anything from potatoes to papier mâché. The book also includes directions for making stages, scenery, curtains, and props. Even young children could follow her step-by-step directions.　　　　　　　7–14
Puppetry, a yearly publication from 1930 to 1940, Paul McPharlin, Puppetry Imprints, Birmingham, Michigan. These copiously illustrated, inexpensive little imprints are invaluable. Photographs, text, and diagrams make every detail clear and are richly suggestive of puppet possibilities.

BIOGRAPHICAL REFERENCES

KUNITZ, STANLEY J., *British Authors of the 19th Century*, Wilson, 1936.
KUNITZ, STANLEY J. and HAYCROFT, HOWARD, *American Authors, 1600–1900*, Wilson, 1938. A biographical dictionary of American literature, complete in one volume.
KUNITZ, STANLEY J. and HAYCROFT, HOWARD, *The Junior Book of Authors*, 2nd ed. revised, Wilson, 1951. Includes biographical or autobiographical sketches of authors of both classic and contemporary juvenile literature.
KUNITZ, STANLEY J. and HAYCROFT, HOWARD, *Twentieth Century Authors*, Wilson, 1942; First Supplement, 1955. A biographical dictionary of modern literature. Gives information about writers of this century of all nations.

INDEX